# STATISTICAL METHODS

# STATISTICAL METHODS

*by*

STEFAN SZULC

*Formerly Professor of Statistics*
*University of Warsaw*

*Translated from the Polish by*
J. STADLER

*Translation edited by*
H. INFELD, C.D.I. FORRESTER

**PERGAMON PRESS**

OXFORD · LONDON · EDINBURGH · NEW YORK
PARIS · FRANKFURT

**PAŃSTWOWE WYDAWNICTWO EKONOMICZNE**
WARSAW

Pergamon Press Ltd., Headington Hill Hall, Oxford
4 & 5 Fitzroy Square, London W.1
Pergamon Press (Scotland) Ltd., 2 & 3 Teviot Place, Edinburgh 1
Pergamon Press Inc., 122 East 55th St., New York 22, N.Y.
Pergamon Press GmbH, Kaiserstrasse 75, Frankfurt-am-Main

Library of Congress Catalog Card No. 64-18438

Printed in Poland

# CONTENTS

# INTRODUCTION

## 1. THE CHIEF TREND OF DEVELOPMENT IN STATISTICS

The presentation of selected problems from the history of statistics is not the main purpose of this book. Rather it is concerned with certain facts, the knowledge of which helps in understanding modern statistics. The presentation of these facts will be neither exhaustive nor systematic: many important facts and the names of some eminent authors will be omitted. On the other hand, certain facts may be mentioned which would rank low in importance in a systematic exposition. Emphasis will be laid on the presentation of facts in such a way as to stress their relevance and meaning.

a. *The collection of numerical data for purpose of government administration.* Even in remote antiquity we can find traces of research that—in accordance with present terminology—could be called statistical research. In Egypt, Babylon, Persia, ancient China and Israel a census of population is known to have been taken.

In Egypt—with her centralized and bureaucratic state organization—the population census was one of the mainstays of public administration. Censuses of population and capital assets, primarily for fiscal purposes, were made, beginning from the time of the 2nd dynasty, that is, at least 3000 years before our era, regularly every two years, and later annually.[1]

In the Bible we find information about several population censuses. Their description is so detailed that we can effectively reconstruct their technique. In the Fourth Book of Moses, "Numbers", there is a description of two censuses of the male population in Israel "from the age of 20 and over, of those who can go to war". These censuses were made in the desert during the migration. In order to make them, special officials were appointed, one for each generation, and these reported the number of persons according to tribes. The censuses did not apply to the Levites, who were counted separately—all males "one month old and over". Besides this, records were made of all the Levites aged 30–50 working on the Ark of the Covenant. On another occasion all firstborn males one month old and over were counted.[2] Numerical results of these censuses were given, but they are not at all reliable.

In the Second Book of Samuel there is a description of a population census which was made at the time of King David. The census applied to "strong, sword-

---

[1] Plinio Fraccaro, *Enciclopedia Italiana*, vol. 9, Milano— Rome 1931, p. 734.
[2] "Numbers", chapters 1, 3, 4, 26.

1

wielding men". On the order of the King it was made by the Military Commander, Joab, who visited all the territories of Israel and Juda. The census lasted for 9 months and 20 days. The Levites and the Benjaminites were excluded from the census.[3]

Apart from these censuses we find numerical records which we would call statistical today. For instance, in the First Book of Esdras, Chapter 2, there are statistics on the repatriation from Babylonian captivity at the time of Cyrus and Artaxerxes. The number of the repatriates in given by tribes, as well as the number of male and female servants, male and female singers and livestock which the repatriates brought with them.

These were not censuses in the modern meaning of this term, but even then the basic features of a census did appear. The objective of this research—and this should be particularly stressed—was the accumulation of factual data necessary for military and fiscal administration purposes, as well as for religious administration —as was the case, for instance, with the Israelites. We therefore come across such research primarily where there is a state organization conscious of its objectives.

The most far-reaching in this respect was the ancient Roman census whose beginnings date back to the epoch of the Kings, and which later extended over the whole period of the Republic and the beginning of the Empire, about five hundred years altogether. The name of census was attached to fairly regular lists—usually prepared at 5-year intervals—with the names of all Roman citizens and the members of their families, both adults and children, and with a detailed description of fixed property and livestock, farm animals and slaves. The objective of the census was not "statistics", i. e. the numerical presentation of socio-economic relations, but the preparation of a list of citizens, persons who had definite rights and obligations (military service, taxes, etc.). The census contained an abundance of material, so diversified, and reaching so deep into the essence of economic relations, that the extent of the information it provided compares favourably with the most exhaustive and comprehensive statistical studies of modern times. Similar censuses were taken in newly conquered provinces, immediately after their annexation.

There is also fairly abundant material of a statistical nature from the Middle Ages. In contrast to the Roman census it pertains more to private economy—in line with the feudal State system. I refer, first of all, to the estate inventories of royal families, of princes, feudal overlords and monasteries: quite a few of these records have been preserved intact.[4]

The detailed description of England in the *Domesday Book*, ordered by William the Conqueror in 1085 and completed in 1086, is an example of a nation-wide

---

[3] The Second Book of Samuel, ch. 24.

[4] Most detailed instructions on keeping such inventories are contained in *Capitulare de Villis* of Carl the Great.

survey. The description comprised the property of the king, the clergy, the church institution, the barons, and so on. It provided an estimate of the value of real estate, the number of plough teams (a team comprised eight oxen), the area of arable land, meadows, woods, pastures, fish ponds and rivers (harnessed by mill dams), water mills and other sources of income, and finally the number of peasants of different categories. For certain areas of England livestock were also included.[5]

This description does not contain the numerical tables characteristic of present-day statistical studies: according to our terminology it is raw statistical material which can be tabulated just as easily as the census material taken in our times. Very early censuses were also taken in Russia, first by the Tartars—several times, starting from the middle of the thirteenth century—and then by the Grand Dukes of Moscow, Dymitri Donskii (1359–89) and Vasyl Dymitrovitch (1389–1425).[6]

Together with the centralized state—whose activities began to affect man's life to an increasing extent toward the end of the fourteenth century—there appeared a greater need for statistical data covering a greater variety of problems.

The beginnings can already be found in the early Italian states, particularly in Venice and Florence. "The governments of Venice and Florence collected detailed data on the balance of trade, the level of production in each industry, the population and its wealth, tax and customs revenues, the tonnage of ships, education, religious relations and social institutions. They did not confine themselves to collecting detailed information on the internal situation of their countries, but also gathered exhaustive statistical data on the situation in the neighbouring states with which they maintained relations or were at war."[7]

Information and statistical material was collected in Spain during the reign of Philip II, in France at the time of Henry IV (under the direction of Sully) and Louis XIV (under Colbert), in Russia during the reign of Peter I, and in Prussia during the reigns of William I and Frederic II. Not all information was numerical: there were verbal descriptions, and so it was not always what are called statistics today. The use of numerical data, however, was on the increase and they were becoming more diversified. At the end of the eighteenth century they pertained to population, professions and trades, agriculture, handicrafts, commerce, taxes, church relations, etc.

The French Revolution and the growth of State organization in the post-revolutionary period intensified the need for numerical data in a growing number of fields. At the beginning of the nineteenth century the first statistical bureau were set up with the special and exclusive task of collecting numerical data on the state and society. Such bureau existed in France, Italy, Spain, in some German

---

[5] *Encyclopaedia Britannica*, vol. VII, 1947, pp. 514–5.

[6] *Bolshaya Sovyetskaya Entseclopedya*, vol. 45, 1940.

[7] S. Inglot, *Historia społeczna i gospodarcza średniowiecza. (Social and Economic History of the Middle Ages)*, 2nd ed. Wrocław, 1949, p. 255.

States (particularly in Bavaria and Prussia), and also in Poland (the Duchy of Warsaw in 1810). Not all of these bureaux survived long in their original form, but a start had been made. During the nineteenth century the activities of government statistical offices increased, and so did the number of statistical publications. At first the information gathered was regarded as a government secret: the government did not feel obliged to publish it. If any statistical information leaked out and became public knowledge, it was through the studies of individual scholars who had permission to use official statistics. In the eighteenth century, and at the beginning of the nineteenth century, there were many such individual studies, some of them very valuable. With the passage of time the views on this matter changed: it was recognized that statistical offices should not only collect and process statistical data, but should also make them available to the public, so as to make possible the formation of independent, individual opinions and scientific research. The publications of statistical offices increased in number and gradually formed whole libraries. For instance, the publications of the Central Statistical Office of the Republic of Poland between 1919 and 1939 exceeded 300 volumes, some of them very large, in spite of rather modest financial means.

In this period of the development of statistics, data were collected for administrative purposes. The scope and nature of information changed in the course of history, depending upon the changes in the scope and nature of government activities, but as a rule the objective was always to satisfy the needs of the administration, particularly those of a military and economic nature.

b. *The "science" of government. The origin of the term "statistics".* The expression "statistics" (German *Statistik)* was first used in print in the middle of the eighteenth century by Gottfried Achenwall, Professor at the University of Marburg and later in Gottingen. However, judging from the way the word "statistics" was referred to, it would appear that it had been in use before. Achenwall speaks, though, of the "so-called statistics", and in his handwritten notes he mentions that this name "bloomed" (*"florebat"*) in the seventeenth century. Also the adjective "statisticus" was already in use in the seventeenth century.

According to Achenwall's definition, statistics is the science of the structure of the state in the broad sense of this word and the structure of the state is defined as "the totality of essential peculiarities of the state" (*"Der Inbegriff der wirklichen Staatsmerkwürdigkeiten eines Reiches oder einer Republik"*). To this belongs everything that is related to the welfare of the country in the positive or negative sense, i. e. physiographical conditions, population, the system of government, the social system, legislature, economy, etc. As we shall see later, the word statistics was used here to denote a subject which is very remote from what we call statistics today.

The subject denoted by this term—the science of "the peculiarities of the State", or the science of the State, or more exactly, the Science of States (*"Staats-*

*kunde"*)—has evolved from the same needs of modern government administration that led to the collection of statistical data. A strong and active State, conscious of its objectives, must know its resources as well as the means and resources of other states. Achenwall was not by any means the first, to make an attempt at a comparative systematization of this kind of information for a number of countries. The beginnings should perhaps be sought in classical antiquity, in the lost work by Aristotle *Politeiai,* which contained a description of the Greek states, in the author's time. As direct antecedents of Achenwall, numerous Italian, French and Dutch authors from the end of the sixteenth century and from the seventeenth century should be mentioned. The more important of them are the Italians Francesco Sansovino (1562) and Giovanni Botero (1589), the Frenchman Pierre d'Avity (1614), the Dutchman Jan de Laet and his coworkers (1624–40),[8] then the German professors whose lectures, partly published, pertained to the same subject; Herman Conring, professor at Helmstadt is considered the most outstanding of them. He was the first—in the seventeenth century—to introduce the science of the State to the university curriculum. The works of these professors were primarily of a descriptive nature. Numerical material was not yet available. Later, the authors used figures to a limited extent. In principle, however, the idea of presenting the phenomena studied in figures had not yet been conceived of at that time. On the other hand, it should be realized that the "Science of the State" was in fact a collection of useful information on different subjects, rather than a science with a defined subject. No wonder, therefore, that with the development of knowledge this science was divided into a number of separate subjects, such as economics, state and administrative law, geography, etc.

After Achenwall, many authors published their works in this field; some of them tried to introduce methodically new points of view (as did Anton Friedrich Büsching and August Ludwig von Schlözer). From the beginning of the nineteenth century one can only talk of epigones. However, even in the middle of the century there still appear quite numerous monographs of a descriptively numerical character, in Polish as well, e.g. "The geographical-statistical outline", or "The historical-statistical outline" of a given country, or of a part of it. Mention should be made here of a small study by Staszic *On Poland's Statistics—a short collection of information needed by those who want to liberate this country and those who want to rule it.* (Warsaw, 1807). In the title itself there is a reference to the "Science of the State" as a collection of information needed by statesmen.

"Statistics" in this sense and under this name survived longest in Austrian school text-books comprising a collection of information on the system of govern-

---

[8] The figures in brackets denote the dates of publication of principal works on the Science of the State by the authors mentioned above.

ment, geography, law, economic, etc. In Austria this subject "statistics" was included in civil service examinations. (Its contents largely correspond to those of
what is called in Poland "The science of Poland and the contemporary world").

On the whole the descriptive "Science of the State" does not actually bring anything essential to the history of statistics, except the very name "statistics". But
just here something strange happened: the branch of science for which this name
had been created disappeared, while the name "statistics" itself remained, to
denote something quite different. Even the old authors, particularly Conring,
emphasized that the information about the state of the country should be concrete.
There are certain problems, however, with regard to which concrete information
can be provided only in figures. The amount of numerical material increased
greatly during the eighteenth century: authors writing on the Science of the State
provided more numerical tables to illustrate their points. There even developed
a special trend among the "Scientists of the State" to limit the description of a state
to the table form. These tables, incidentally, contained not only numbers, but
also—placed in appropriate panels—descriptive information, for example, of the
political system. The originator of this method was the Russian J. K. Kuriłlov
and, perhaps independently, the Dane J. P. Anchersen, the author of *Descriptio
Statuum Cultiorum in Tabulis* (Copenhagen and Leipzig, 1741). Towards the
end of the eighteenth century this method of presenting facts found many imitators,
to the great dismay of the believers in descriptive statistic of the Achenwall
variety, who considered that this soulless method of presentation deprived statistics of important qualities. At the same time, it became fashionable to collect,
for one's own pleasure, numerical data on different subjects and from different
sources. This led to the practice of using the term statistics for the mere collections
of figures. Finally, the name statistics began to be applied to collections of
figures gathered by the government for administrative purposes. In this way the
meaning of the term broadened and almost imperceptibly began to denote
something that was only loosely related to the old meaning of statistics. Nor did
the evolution stop here.

c. *Graunt and the political arithmeticians, Statistical method.* John Graunt's
work was published in London in 1662. Its abbreviated title was  *Natural and
Political Observations Made upon the Bills of Mortality... of the City of London.*
This date can be truly regarded as the date of the birth of statistics in the
modern sense: as a specific method of numerical analysis of a certain type of
phenomena.

Graunt (1620–74) was a merchant; his hobby was collecting; his knowledge
was acquired by self-education. Graunt's *Observations* were presented to the
Society of Philosophers (later the Royal Society), the most important learned
Society in London; this resulted in Graunt's election to membership of the Society.
His activity in the Society, however, was negligible and short-lived. Apart from

the *Observations* and a small essay on the propagation and growth of carp and salmon presented to the Society of Philisophers, no other works by Graunt are known.

The *Observations* are based on records of births and deaths. Records of baptisms and funerals and sometimes also of marriages were kept in various European cities, including London, as early as the sixteenth century. In London they had been published since the beginning of the seventeenth century as a weekly called *Bills of Mortality*. At first only the number of deaths was given (deaths due to the plague were shown separately), but later data were introduced on baptisms, causes of death, sex of the deceased and baptised. Graunt had at his disposal a sizeable collection comprising several dozens of annals and he proved that out of these "meager" Bills, as he called them, varied and very important scientifics conclusions could be drawn.

His conclusions were of different kinds. He determined the population of London, the number of men and women, married persons, fertile women, men capable to bear arms, etc. He was surprised to find out that there was an almost perfect balance between the sexes of new-born babies, with a small surplus of boys over girls (in London 14 : 13 more or less) maintained on the same level in spite of the apparently random nature of this phenomenon. The author arrived at the frequencies of different causes of deaths, and particularly the low probability of deaths from certain diseases particularly feared by the people. Graunt discovered that in London the number of deaths exceeded the number of births, and in spite of that the population of the city increased because of the influx from outside. He described how the plague decimated the population of the city (e.g. in 1625, one of the worst periods, only 6983 baptisms were recorded, as compared with 54,265 deaths, of which 35,417 were caused by the plague).

The population of London was at that time usually estimated as at least one million.

Graunt arrived at a different figure by using the following method:

(1) Assuming that the number of child-bearing women was twice as high as the number of births (i.e. that every married woman bore a child every two years), and knowing that the annual number of births was 12,000 he arrived at the figure of 24,000 child-bearing women and $24,000 \times 2 = 48,000$ families. (The other 24,000 were families in which there were no married women of child-bearing age). Considering a family to consist of 8 persons (the parents, 3 children and 3 servants) he arrived at the figure of 384,000 persons.

(2) According to the data from several parishes there were 3 deaths per 11 families per annum; at the average rate of 13,000 deaths (in the years in which there was no plague) this also gave approximately 48,000 families.

(3) On the basis of the map of the centre of London, Graunt estimates that within the city walls there were 11,880 houses (and as many families). Since the

number of deaths in all London was four times as high as the number of deaths within the city walls, he again arrived at the figure of $11,880 \times 4 = 47,520$ houses (families) which is almost identical with the figures previously arrived at.

The results achieved in this way may not have been, and probably were not very accurate, but the figure 384,000 showed the order of magnitude of the population of the city, whereas the statements of his contemporaries about one or several million were sheer fantasy.

To realise the pioneering importance of Graunt's reasoning it is necessary to recapture the atmosphere of a time when statistical data were met for the first time. The author found "much pleasure in drawing so many profound and unexpected conclusions" from these "meager and despised Bills". He rightly considered it as his merit that he "reduced a great number of complex volumes to a few, clear tables, and formulated in a few, concise paragraphs, without elaborate arguments, the conclusions that naturally follow from them." Graunt showed that a penetrating analysis of figures permits one to discover many essential and important things which are hidden from the eyes of people who do not know how to approach a problem in the right way. His contribution in this respect cannot be denied in spite of the fact that many of his conclusions turned out to be wrong in the light of later studies based on more detailed material. Graunt was also the first to understand that there is a regularity, an "order", in the nature of the laws governing phenomena, that can be discovered if large numbers of them are studied. Thus Graunt laid the foundations for what we call to-day *statistical methods*.

We have mentioned here the works of Graunt but not of William Petty (1623–87)—the most prominent of the political arithmeticians—who, like Graunt, presented social and economic relations on the basis of numerical estrinates, but whose main contribution lies in a different field. Petty was primarily an economist: the first of the scientists to create classical political economy, according to Marx, Petty often used figures to prove his statements, but as far as the depth of *statistical analysis* is concerned, as well as a critical approach to numerical data, he comes second to Graunt.[9]

d. *The theory of probability and statistics.* The theory of probability is a branch of higher mathematics. It was first applied—as early as the seventeenth century—to

---

[9] Extensive information on the history of statistics in earlier times can be found in V. John's *Geschichte der Statistik*, pt. 1, *Von dem Ursprung der Statistik bis auf Quetelet* (1835), Stuttgart 1884, p. 376. (Pt. 2 has never been published), and M. Ptucha *Otcherky po istoree statistikee 17–18 viekov*, Ogiz, 1945, p. 352; the latter also provides information on the development of statistics in Russia up to the end of the eighteenth century. A short chapter on the development of statistics in pre-revolutionary Russia can be found in the textbook by S. S. Ostroumov, entitled: *Soudyebnaya Statistika, Tchast Obshtchaya*, Moscow, 1949, p. 239. The author points out the independent achievements of Russian statistical thought, and the great practical importance of Russian statistics.

the analysis of certain problems in gambling (random events). The splendid growth of the theory of probability is due to the works of the best mathematicians, such as Pascal, Bernoulii, Laplace, Gauss, and in later times the Russian and Soviet mathematicians Tchebyshev, Markov, Bernstein, Kolmogorov, and others.

The theory of probability explains the conditions under which regularities can be observed in mass statistical phenomena, and, in a sense, constitutes a basis for all statistical deduction, and in particular for research by sampling. For this reason the elementary presentation of certain assumptions of the theory of probability is given in the last part of this work.

The renowned Belgian statistician Quetelet (1796–1874) was the first to apply the theory of probability to social statistics. His contribution in this field—as in many other fields—is undoubtedly considerable, although his fatalistic view of social phenomena, formed in consequence of his one-sided understanding of statistical "regularities"—is undoubtedly quite wrong.

e. *Lenin, the real founder of modern Marxian statistics.* The main thought interwoven in all his works is the rigorous linking of statistical method to the subject studied and, more exactly, to the problems of political economy. Lenin also properly posed the problem of classification for computing averages.

As we said before, we shall not follow in detail the development of statistical methods. However, we shall draw the reader's attention to the broadening of the scope of application of statistical methods to many fields not connected with socio-economic relations in human societies. It may be appropriate here to mention Graunt's contribution in his study on the propagation and growth of carp and salmon.[10] And it should suffice to list certain branches of science in which statistical methods are now in general use, such as astronomy and physics.[11] Without statistics modern meteorology and climatology could not exist. The phenomena of living nature could not be studied without the extensive use of statistics, nor would it be possible to appraise the results obtained by experimental methods. Quality control in industry is based on statistical methods. Human societies and the manifestations of their activities could not be studied without statistics—not only socio-economic activities, but also cultural.

Many more examples could be quoted: it should suffice, however, to point out that statistical methods of analysis are used in many different fields. The definition of statistical method has to allow for this fact.

---

[10] The full content of this essay is not known. A summary of it is recorded in the minutes of the Royal Society and was reprinted by Hull in *The Economic Writings of Sir William Petty* (vol. 2, p. 432). From this it can be surmised that the statistical analysis in this essay was as penetrating as in the *Observations,* although the subject matter of the essay pertained to a relatively unimportant question.

[11] J. I. Frenkel recently published a very extensive dissertation entitled *Statisticheskaya physica,* Moscow–Leningrad, 1948, p. 760.

## 2. THE DEFINITION OF STATISTICAL METHOD

The variety of ways in which statistics have developed has led to an under-standable confusion in attempts to define this branch of Science. There are several dozen, if not over a hundred, different definitions. Many of them, however, are only different formulations of the same idea, but the confusion is undeniable. We shall not undertake here the futile job of collecting and classifying or appraising these definitions: instead, we shall try to give a definition of statistical method that corresponds to the present level of science. To do this we make certain assumptions. *Statistical method is a specific method of numerical analysis of special types of populations.*

This does not mean, however, that any *numerical* description of a single object can be called statistics. For instance, we may describe a table in figures: we can give its height, width, the length and thickness of its top, the number of legs; even the colour of the table can be described by giving the wave-length of the corre-sponding light. This, of course, is not statistics.

Not every population lends itself to statistical analysis. If a population consists of identical units, so that by describing one unit we actually describe all, then such a population does not lend itself to statistical analysis, unless it is of a quality control type. For instance artillery shells of a given type, gauge, use, etc., do not constitute a statistical population in the ordinary sense. Were they not identical, they could not serve their purpose. If, however, we measure the diameter of these shells, using high-precision instruments, we find minute differences between partic-ular shells. These differences are due to the imperfection of the instruments and machines used in production, and of the work of the men operating these instru-ments and machines. They are considered permissible if they do not reduce the usefulness to the product, i.e. if the deviations are within the limits of technical tolerance. But these minute deviations from the norm may be a subject of analysis. Such an analysis is important, e.g. from the point of view of production technique: in this case the artillery shells become a statistical population.

In other words, depending upon the point of view, the same population may be a statistical population or may not be one. Generalizing, we can say that it is a statistical population in so far as the units of which it is composed are studied from the point of view of the *differences* that exist between them, and it is not a statistical population if the units comprising it are looked upon from the point of view of *common* characteristics.

The next example will enable us to define more precisely the notion of statistical population, and to determine the basic problems involved in a study of such pop-ulations.

Let us consider man. From the point of view of Nature, man, *homo sapiens,* is a mammal and one of the species of the anthropoidal family, which, in turn, belongs to the order of primates, and so on. To determine what man is we establish the characteristics which are common to all men and which are not possessed by other mammals. primates, or anthropoids. Instead of taking general characteristics of man as a species, we can generalize the characteristics of certain groups of men. From the anthropological point of view we can establish in this way the notion of anthropological types. Man may also be looked upon from the socio-economic point of view by creating such notions as a worker, a peasant, a craftsman, a capitalist and a merchant. These general notions, too, are created by determining for each group those common characteristics which distinguish it from all other groups.

However, instead of creating general notions of "man", or "the *Lapponoidal* type", or "worker", or "merchant" we can describe a specific human being. The description may include its anthropological characteristics (height, shape of skull, etc.), may take into consideration the type of blood and the blood pressure, the functioning of the circulatory system, the digestive system, the eyes, the ears, the characteristics relevant from the point of view of man's belonging to society (education, occupation, etc.); and it may also take into account the psychological characteristics which, so far, have more often been the object of creative artistic presentation than of strictly scientific investigation. All this together gives a picture of a particular, in a sense unique, different and unrepeatable, representative of the species *homo sapiens*.

The subject of statistical research and the procedure accepted in statistical methods are different from the two approaches given in the above examples. This can be explained by the following example. Consider a number of groups of people divided on the basis of some criterion, e.g. territorial division—the populations of different states or different parts of one state (provinces, counties); or on the criterion of socio-economic division (workers, peasants, etc.). Each of these groups differs from the analogous ones first by its size, and then by its structure, considered from different points of view: the anthropological types of which it consists, sex, age, occupation, etc. These are typical examples of stastistical populations. Each of these groups can be described in a similar way as the species of *homo sapiens*: by determining the characteristics common to all members of the group and distinguishing it from all other groups. In the case of territorial division this common and distinguishing characteristic is the fact of living within a certain defined territory, such as a county. In the case of socio-economic division, e.g. workers or peasants, the distinguishing characteristic is the function performed in the socio-economic system.

Since statistical analysis is scientific, not every collection of objects or events may be called a statistical population. We cannot regard as a statistical population a collection of persons or objects which we see on a concert stage: the musicians and the conductor, the musical instruments, the scores, the arms, legs, noses, shoes, jackets, ties, or other details of clothing. This is a collection, not a population. On the other hand, all the objects in a pawn-shop, in spite of their apparently random character, could be treated as a statistical population if we consider that the kind of objects pawned reflects the economic position of the clientele. Thus, we shall use the term statistical population for such a collection of non-identical objects or events, as could logically (and not only formally) be defined and as is possessed of a definable meaning.

In an analysis of a population precision can be achieved only if we use a statistical method. The proper procedure in using a statistical method is as follows:

(1) The precise determination of the population under examination (in the way described above).

(2) The establishing—for each unit in the population—of those characteristics that we consider as relevant to our analysis. With reference to some characteristics (sex, nationality, occupation, etc.) it is suffcient to state whether a given unit is possessed of this characteristic or not; whether it is a man or a woman; a blacksmith or a physician, etc. With regard to other characteristics (height, age, etc.) a description is possible only by measuring them (the height, in centimetres; the age, in years).

(3) The counting of the units possessing particular characteristics: the determination of the number of men and women, the number of blacksmiths and physicians, the number of persons in different height, or age groups, etc.

In this way we obtain statistical raw material which serves as a basis for proper statistical research. The presentation of the methods used for such research is the purpose of this book. As we become acquainted with these methods we shall find out that they are quite different from all other methods of scientific research.

The word statistics has two different meanings. First of all, statistics is a *method of numerical analysis of statistical populations*. Thus, it is a discipline which determines appropriate methods of analysis and the choice of a statistical method. In the general classification of the sciences, statistics—in the above interpretation—is a branch of the general methodology of the sciences—of the science of science.

Secondly, statistics is a *collection of numerical data* which characterize either particular statistical populations, or the many populations relevant to a given problem. In this sense we use the word statistics, e.g. with reference to the statistics on social insurance, education, agriculture, or, more generally, the national statistics of Poland, which is a collection of statistical information pertaining to a variety of fields in the economy. The use of the word statistics in this sense is not contrary to the definition of statistics, but we should remember that this word has two different meanings.

There is another important question that should be raised. The word statistics in the expression "foreign trade statistics" determines the formal side, the way in which information on foreign trade is presented. In a sense, of course, the term "foreign trade statistics" also determines the content of the information: it provides information as to what can be presented numerically in the form of statistical tables. Usually it is information on the size of trade turnover with a break-down by imported and exported commodities, geographical destination, origin, etc. However, no information is given on the organization of foreign trade, or on theoretical problems connected with foreign trade as an economic function. In any case, "foreign trade statistics" is more in the nature of knowledge of foreign trade, than of a branch of statistics. Similarly the statistics on education are part of the knowledge of education, the statistics on agriculture are a part of the knowledge of argiculture, etc. The word statistics defines, as said above, the *form* in which information is given, and only in a certain sense, indirectly, the *content* of this information. We shall return to this matter later, when we deal with the relationship of statistics to other sciences.

## 3. THE RELATIONSHIP BETWEEN STATISTICS AND REALITY

From what was said above important conclusions follow with regard to the relationship between statistics and other sciences.

Since statistics is a *method* of research used in different sciences the *subject* of research is, of course, the concern of the science and not of statistics. Therefore the posing of the problem and the formulation of the questions that have to be answered is the responsibility of this science, and not of statistics. This statement is of utmost importance. Statistics cannot be treated as something independent, unrelated to the subject of analysis. A statistician who deals with financial statistics must also be an economist familiar with finance. If this requirement is disregarded and statistics is treated as something independent and not influenced by the specific needs of the science involved, the result will only be a futile exercise which does not enlarge our knowledge. Such a danger is quite real: we often encounter a more or less clever juggling of figures, or ingenious use of statistical tricks, instead of solid research which has to start from posing a problem; this can only be done from the point of view of a given science. From a statistican we require good knowledge of the problem which is to be the subject of statistical analysis.

This point of view much stressed by Lenin. His great work *The Development of Capitalism in Russia*[12] written in 1896–9 is solidly based on statistical material. But the author characteristically deemed it necessary to provide an extensive introduction which contains an exposition of Marxian economic theory with reference to the problems raised in the book. This introduction provides a proper foundation for statistical reasoning. Lenin states clearly that his study is an economic analysis for which statistics only supplies material. The type of statistical

---

12 W. I. Lenin, *Works*, vol. 3, Warsaw, 1954.

approach depends, therefore, on the economic approach. Statistics is not a purpose unto itself. Both in the study mentioned above and in his other works Lenin often says that it is very dangerous to be carried away by statistical data and to make them an objective in themselves. He ridicules the authors who "were so carried away by a medley of figures [that] they transformed an economic analysis into a statistical exercise". "Instead of studying the types of peasant farms (labourer, medium farmer, entrepreneur) they indulge in an amateurish study of endless columns of figures, as if their purpose was to astound the world with their arithmetical zest."[13] Without a proper economic foundation statistics degenerates into a play with figures, leading nowhere, or, what is worse, leading to wrong conclusions, at odds with economic reality.

What applies here to economic statistics also applies to every other field in which statistical methods are used. Statistics in biology must be based on the premises of biology, statistics in medicine—on the premises of medicine. This applies not only to the general starting point, but also to the posing of particular problems; they must be related to the point of view of the science in question and statistics must be used in such a way as to enable the solving of these problems. The same principle may be formulated in a different way: *the purpose of statistics is always the cognition of a specific reality.* Let us always remember this basic definition and avoid mere "juggling with figures".

To illustrate the point, let us take an example. From a series of positive numbers a mathematician can compute different averages: the arithmetic, geometric, harmonic, and power means. He can say that the geometric mean is greater that the harmonic mean, that the arithmetic mean is greater than the geometric one, etc. A statistician studying a specific reality under given circumstances may usually compute only the average that is appropriate under the given conditions; he must choose whether it will be the arithmetic mean or geometric mean, for instance, and as a rule, he cannot compute one average instead of the other.

The use of statistical formulas or methods without properly considering whether they are appropriate from the point of view of our objective is called statistical formalism. It does not always appear in its extreme form, but the less obvious it is, the greater the danger that the results will be wrong without the error being noticed.

Formalism can be avoided by the strict observance of the principle that the purpose of statistics is the cognition of reality. If this principle is observed the results will be realistic. To achieve this we should not shun the use of even the most complex mathematical methods if they produce the most precise and correct results leading to the solution of the problem under examination.

However, there is also another side to the story. In almost all branches of

---

[13] *Ibid.*

science there are problems that must be studied with the help of statistical methods. Therefore the student of such a problem should possess at least a basic knowledge of statistical methods. This does not mean that every physicist or physician must also be a statistician. Both in physics and in medicine there are many problems that have nothing to do with statistics. However, when a physicist or a physician gets involved in a problem that should be solved by a statistical method, he will not be able to handle it without a knowledge of statistics. The view, unfortunately quite common, that statistics is so simple that it is enough to use common sense to be able to solve the problem with a statistical method, is wrong and dangerous.

This is not to say that common sense is not important. On the contrary, it is a necessary condition for arriving at a sensible conclusion. Experience proves, however, that very often the "statistics" of a domestic variety and based on common sense alone lead to wrong conclusions in cases where even some statistical experience would help in producing correct, and often very important results.

This is true with respect to all branches of science, but primarily to those which one way or another are connected with human society to social sciences in the broad sense of this word. In social sciences there is practically no problem that can be presented and solved without statistics. It is not an exaggeration to say that all who work in the social sciences should have a sound knowledge of statistics if the results of their work are to be true and fruitful. This is necessary, not only for solving the problems posed, but also for posing them. The question must be formulated in an appropriate way if the answer is to be of a statistical kind. The posing of a problem is not by any means a simple matter and often requires a lot of statistical experience and a sound knowledge of statistical methods. Such sound knowledge of these methods, often very complex, cannot always be expected from a specialist in a given field. He can be required, however, to be sufficiently well versed in statistics to realize where the essence of the problem lies from the statistical point of view. Only then will he know when to ask an expert statistician for advice and assistance. On the other hand, an expert statistician cannot be expected to have a full command of the sciences in which statistical methods are used. Before he starts dealing with specific problems, however, he must get acquainted with the field from which these problems have been selected in order to know what questions are to be answered.

In more complex cases the statistician and the expert in the subject may have to cooperate. This kind of cooperation between a specialist from a given field and an expert statistician often produces excellent results providing that each side is sufficiently aware of the requirements of the other; only in this way can a common language be found.

This book is based on the premise that *statistical methods* are essentially the same, no matter in which field they are used. This does not mean, however, that *statistics* are the same. Statistical research in economics is essentially economic research, statistical research in biology, biological research. This means that in each of these fields we *pose the problem* in a specific way dictated by the needs of the given discipline. This also means that in each field the statistical methods chosen may be different, depending upon the objective of the analysis. Thus, in practice the exposition of statistical methods should be adapted to the scope of research as well as to the needs and interests of those to whom it is addressed. This work is written primarily for those who are interested in problems related to human society. This will be reflected in the choice of statistical methods used for a more extensive treatment and the choice of examples to illustrate a theoretical point; however, we shall not avoid giving examples from other fields if they are more suitable.

We consider it very desirable that the research worker using statistical methods in his field be well versed, at least in general terms, in methods worked out in other fields, since it may turn out that some of them could be suitable for solving his problems. For each research worker to discover them anew is socially undesirable. In statistical methods collective efforts are necessary since only in this way is it possible to take full advantage of the experience and achievements of all disciplines.

We shall now discuss briefly what is usually called *branch* statistics, such as statistics of industry, trade, education, etc. The purpose of branch statistics is to develop practical ways of collecting and processing numerical data, to adapt general statistical methods to the objectives in a given field, to find the statistical measures of yardsticks that provide correct solutions in a way best suited to statistical treatment. The last point is of particular importance in branch statistics. For instance, we have to answer the question of what the labour productivity is and how it changes, how the factory is equipped with mechanical power, and the degree of the utilization of power equipment. To translate these questions into figures it is necessary to know the technical and economic side of the problem; it is also necessary, however, to have sufficient theoretical and practical knowledge of statistical methods so that the yard-stick chosen will be correct and easily applicable.

The above considerations may also help in explaining the relationship between statistical methodology and mathematics. Statistics is not mathematics. Whereas mathematics, roughly speaking, deals with formal relationships between magnitudes, in statistics each quantity has a meaning only in so far as it represents a reality, and only from the point of view of this reality are we interested in the relationships between magnitudes.[14]

Since statistics deal with figures they need mathematics as a medium of research. But the real *essence* of the method, as we tried to show above, does not by any means consist in the application of mathematics to an analysis of a population. Nevertheless in more complicated cases, the demands that statistics makes on

---

[14] See above, p. 14.

mathematics are considerable and many a statistical problem still awaits mathematical solution. However, most problems that confront a practising statistician require only a moderate knowledge of mathematics. Nevertheless, every statistician must have a good command of elementary calculus and should be able to think in simple mathematical terms. Without this he will not be able to understand even elementary statistical methods, or to apply them intelligently.

Even in most elementary presentations, it may be desirable to employ more mathematics, even higher mathematics, if the reader can reasonably be expected to possess some elementary knowledge of it. Mathematical proofs are almost always more precise and shorter than those based only on logical reasoning and elementary calculus.

Certain textbooks are called "Mathematical Statistics". This sometimes means that the author uses mathematics extensively in his considerations. Usually, however, this term is understood to cover a set problems based on the mathematical theory of probability. This approach is justified from two points of view. First, many phenomena with which statistical methods have to deal can be analysed only on the basis of probability; these include not only certain problems in theoretical physics, but also many other natural phenomena. Second, the theory of probability is a logical foundation and a technical tool of the sampling method which in most fields outside human society is practically the only method of research, and even in problems related to human society it plays a more and more important role.

This separation of "mathematical" statistics from "ordinary" statistics is, perhaps, not very desirable. It creates a danger of formalism in the treatment of problems based on the theory of probability, a danger of becoming detached from the subject that is to be studied. On the other hand, not every statistician can be expected to possess a sufficiently thorough knowledge of mathematics to enable him to understand a rigorous mathematical exposition. For this reason "mathematical statistics" will in practice still exist—in a sense—as a separate subject.

Of course, in each field of application of statistical methods the approach to the problem differs from those used in other fields. Particularly in socio-economic relations the role of mathematical statistics proper is relatively small—with the exception of the sampling method in which its importance is undeniable.

The exposition of proper statistical methods will be preceded by a discussion of the principles of the organization and technique of statistical research, with the emphasis on its application to the problems in social statistics, particularly those compiled by government agencies. We feel that this is necessary because in social problems the question of the organization and technique of research is most important and because understanding the problems of methodology is easier with some knowledge of the practical problems. It should be added that statistical methods cannot be learned from even a very conscientious study of the text-book. It is necessary to relate theory to practice. This means, first of all, that in addition to reading the text-book it is necessary to peruse the statistical material available in various publications. This also means that it is worth while to study works from different fields, based on the analysis of statistical data, particularly such classics as Lenin's *The Development of Capitalism in Russia*, or *New Data on the Laws of the Development of Capitalism in Agriculture*.

Finally, our advice to those who really want to master the theory of stastistics is to undergo a solid training in a statistical laboratory (e.g. in a data processing department). They should also use the case method and complete, from beginning to end, at least one comprehensive study in which the problems have to be posed by the research worker and an appropriate statistical method has to be selected by him to be applied to the statistical material available in such a way as to arrive at a correct solution. The lack of a direct contact with problems from real life increases the danger of substituting statistical formalism for true and useful statistics.

PART I

# The Organization
# and Technique of Statistical Research

# CHAPTER 1

# THE ORGANIZATION OF STATISTICAL WORK

## 1. THE ROLE AND TASK OF STATISTICS IN ADMINISTRATION

a. *Introduction.* The results of statistical research are presented in the form of tables and graphs. However, in order to prepare a table or a graph concerning a certain population it is necessary to have relevant information concerning every unit it contains. In this chapter we shall discuss how to organize the collection of such information on individual units, mainly as accomplished by government agencies.

In many sciences the research worker himself has to collect numerical data for statistical analysis. His task is to observe facts accurately and to record them. As an example consider an anthropologist who studies the ratio of the length to the width of the skull for a given group of people. The statistical material in this case will be the skull measurements for the group of people. First, the necessary measurements must be taken either by the research worker himself of by his assistants. Sometimes it is possible to use data previously accumulated by others. In this case the anthropologist must take care that the material is suitable to his task: that the measurements used actually pertain to the same group, that the method of taking measurements was the same, and soon. Another example is that of a physician studying the effect of a new drug. He will use observations from his own clinic or private practice. If he uses material from other clinics or the experience of other physicians, he must first be sure that all the observations are correct and can produce comparable results.

The common feature of these and other similar types of statistical research in the natural sciences is that they comprise only a part—and sometimes a very small part—of the population to be studied. On the basis of the part analysed, or the sample, conclusions are drawn with respect to the whole population. The methods used for this type of investigation will be discussed later.

Basically, there is no obstacle to applying the same procedure in collecting statistical data on social problems when the population studied is a human society, or the manifestations of the activities of man as a member of this society. In this field, however, we often encounter very complex populations which require the accumulation of much more extensive statistical material. What is more, it is not always practical to take a sample, and it may even be necessary to record observations on all the units comprising a given population, which in some cases means hundreds of millions of observations. Quite often they are technically more difficult in the social sciences than in the natural sciences.

For this reason in the social sciences we only rarely deal with the material gathered by one researcher. More commonly we have at our disposal questionnaire data accumulated by scientific institutes, or social institutions which engage in studies of socio-economic relations. We often use these data not only because the accumulation of the necessary material is costly and difficult, but also because it would then be superfluous to collect new material.

b. *The role of statistics in administration.* Speaking of the role of statistics in administration we have in mind not only public administration, but administration in general, including the management of large organizations, factories, trade enterprises, etc.

(1) Statistics provide administration with *information concerning the terrain on which a given activity is taking place.* Just as a construction engineer must examine the ground on which he is going to build, so an administrator must become thoroughly acquainted with the field for which he is to issue a set of rules and regulations: otherwise these rules may cause much harm. To plan a school system it is necessary to know the territorial distribution of children in different age groups. It would be unfortunate to have too few or too many schools, or to build them where they are not needed. That is why we have to consider not only the number of children of school age now in different localities, but also the estimated number for future years. We can make such forecasts if we have the appropriate census data for the present and if we know how to calculate from life tables the number of children that will reach school age. To make forecasts for longer periods of time we would also have to know how to estimate the number of births and would become involved in a complex demographic analysis.

Let us suppose that we are planning the development of a new branch of industrial production. The targets are given on the basis of our general objectives, and their realization must be based on solid statistical information. First of all, we have to ascertain whether it is possible to achieve the objectives, i.e. we have to consider whether we have sufficient raw materials, whether we can set up a new factory, obtain the necessary machinery and equipment, whether we have sufficient labour power at our disposal, whether we know the potential demand for the new product, etc. If our preliminary statistical investigation leads to the discovery of certain difficulties, it does not mean that the project has to be abandoned. It does mean that we have to search for ways and means to overcome these difficulties and perhaps to revise our original project, or to extend it in time. It is essential not to embark even upon the most sensible project, from the general point of view, without a previous statistical analysis of the conditions under which it will be implemented.

Thus, to give the administrator the necessary knowledge statistics cannot be confined to simple facts on a given phenomenon, but must penetrate to the essence of the problem.

(2) The importance of statistics to administration is not limited to studying the field of the administrator's activity. Not less important are statistics as *a means of checking the effectiveness of the regulations that have been issued*. If a campaign against illiteracy is embarked upon, statistics will show how many persons took advantage of the facilities provided and the next population census will reveal what improvements have resulted from the campaign. If new traffic regulations are issued to improve safety conditions, then statistics will show whether the objective has been achieved. When new and modern principles are introduced into the penal code revising the conditions under which suspended sentences can be given—then statistics will tell how often a second offence is committed.

We can go further and say that statistics should provide answers not only concerning the effectivenes of new regulations, but also the *general effects,* i.e. not only the intended effects, but also the *side,* or *incidental* effects. We may change the type of road surface in order to save on the maintenance costs, or because we can build the new type of surface faster, or for some other technical or financial reason. But we also want to know, of course, how this change effects safety on the road. Here again appropriate statistical data will provide the ansver.

In some capitalist countries, including pre-war Poland, and, to an even greater extent, in tsarist Russia, government budgets were often balanced by high revenues from government monopolies, especially from liquor monopolies. Let us suppose that the Minister of Finance lowers the price of liquor in the hope that increased consumption will raise the revenues. This sort of attitude—although quite understandable from a purely capitalistic point of view—is socially harmful. Therefore it would be quite appropriate for the Minister of Health to try to find out how increased consumption of alcohol affects public health, and for the Minister of Justice to investigate the effects of increased alcohol consumption on the number and types of offences. Also in this case statistics could provide the answer.

In the People's Poland the price of liquor was raised several times in an effort to reduce consumption. And statistics were expected to show not only whether and to what extent the direct purpose had been achieved, but also what the side effects were. Such secondary effects may be quite far-reaching and appear in the most unexpected places; well planned statistics should help uncover even seemingly wery remote repercussions.

(3) Finally, statistics provide administration with a powerful *means of control of its own activities.* The field for the application of statistics may be very wide in this respect. For instance, statistics on absenteeism amongst the employees provide a warning signal as to when remedial measures should be taken. The

statistics on court activities show whether the number of cases handled corresponds to the number of new cases brought before the courts, and thus whether there are no arrears and whether the system of justice functions efficiently. This kind of statistics will not show the reasons for the deficiencies in the functioning of the courts. There may have been a sudden, unexpectedly large influx of new cases, the court procedure may be too complicated, or the court personnel may not work efficiently. To establish the real cause it may be necessary to engage in additional investigation, statistical or non-statistical. Sometimes, however, properly prepared statistics may provide the answer right away.

The statistics on the teaching staff turnover shows how many teachers, and with what qualifications, have been added to the staff, how many have left, and for what reasons (transfer to another school, change of profession, sickness, death). This sort of statistics shows not only whether new teachers are hired at the proper pace, but also indicates what types of remedies are required.

In any case, properly prepared statistics on all kinds of administrative activities not only shed light on the existing situation, but may often indicate where remedies should be sought.

c. *Statistics in a socialist planned economy* also provide information on the economic activities of the State, make possible an analysis of the effects of new measures and regulations (e.g. the control of the implementation of the plan), and enables the checking and appraisal of the efficiency of the administrative mechanism.

There are, however, essential differences between statistics in a capitalist and in a socialist state.

In a capitalist system the role of statistics is often reduced to the passive recording of facts, or, what is even worse, to providing misleading information.

In a socialist system statistics play an active part—first of all, as *a tool of planning*, an indispensable element in State management. It is a truism to say that no constructive work, no planning on a national scale is possible without a proper recording system; and no recording is possible without statistics.

This is not merely a question of whether, or to what extent, the plan has been carried out. If there are deficiencies in any area then statistics should not only register this fact but should also throw some light on the circumstances under which these deficiencies arose and thus facilitate the search for proper remedies. If the plan is exceeded, this fact should be stated not only to show good results but also to enable others to accomplish similar results by showing how they can be achieved. In this way, a proper reporting system on the implementation of the plan in a socialist economy becomes a powerful weapon in the struggle for a better future and is rightly considered a crucial element in the organization of government statistics. It follows that in a planned economy current statistical reporting must be detailed, comprehensive and penetrating to a degree that is unattainable and perhaps superfluous in other systems.

Owing to the existence of a more comprehensive reporting system it is easier to obtain full statistical information in a planned economy than it is in a capitalist economy. Current reporting, however, is not sufficient and in a socialist economy special attention should be paid not only to the direct results of the measures taken, as reflected in statistical reports, but also to indirect effects, sometimes not intended and seemingly unrelated. For instance, a rise in real wages not only increases consumption, but also changes its structure; this will indirectly affect habits, customs, morals, etc. A higher standard of education will increase cultural needs and will necessitate studying them so that they can be properly satisfied. These indirect effects can usually be traced only by special statistical research. There are areas of life that do not lend themselves to planning and probably will never be planned directly. In these very areas events of utmost importance may occur and some of them may directly affect the areas that are regulated by planning.

In accordance with the law of dialectical materialism, all these matters must be treated as interrelated. Thus we have to conclude that the already very wide scope of current statistical reporting on general statistics and population censuses in the planned, socialist economy, should be further developed and be more far reaching and penetrating than it is in a capitalist economy. If we also remember the importance of the knowledge of ever changing fields of human activities in a planned economy we must conclude that good results can be achieved in a planned economy only by keeping a watchful eye on statistics in *every field*.

d. *Statistics in business administration.* Statistics find a wide field of application in the administration of enterprises, both socialized and private. A statistical department of a large factory faces formidable tasks. First of all, it collects, from all available sources, information required for production and sales planning: on the state of the market, on the sales of the commodities it produces, and particularly on foreign trade, price movements, etc. This information is based mainly on government statistical publications and partly on the factory's own sources of information. Sales statistics do not only reflect the actual state of bussiness by showing, for instance, in which districts the sales organization does not produce sufficiently good results. They also enable the management to evaluate the effectiveness of its sales policy, e.g. with regard to price changes, improvements in the quality and appearance of the product, and other moves designed to attain the ultimate objective—from the point of view of free enterprise—a maximum profit. And finally, statistics are necessary for controlling the functioning of the production, sales and administrative organization. Statistics are also of great importance in testing the quality of the raw materials used in production, in quality control of the goods produced and in the control of the whole production process.

The literature on the application of statistics to business administration in the capitalist countries is considerable. In the socialist countries—in which an enterprise serves the public, and not private interest and in which the operations of an enterprise are constantly controlled both from the legal point of view and from the point of view of the social needs it is intended to satisfy—the role of statistics in business management is much more important. Also it is more effective because company statistics are included in the national system of statistical reporting.

Details of the role and organization of company statistics, however, are not the subject of this work.

e. *What is required from administration statistics?* At the basis of our discussion on the scope and organization of government statistics is the statement that such statistics serve the needs of government administration in the broadest sense of this word.

To fulfill its tasks properly statistics should satisfy certain requirements.

(1) Statistics should serve a definite purpose, i.e. should contain what the government needs. This requirement, seemingly obvious and indisputable, is not always satisfied in practice. In the negative sense it means that administration statistics should not be a collection of numerical information gathered for some vague purposes, or because "it may be useful in the future", or because it is interesting. In the positive sense it means that the needs that administration statistics are to satisfy should always be clearly defined, the questions that it is to answer should always be clearly formulated, and the data collected should be those which are needed for answering the questions. It follows that an administrative statistician should be fully acquainted with the needs and objectives of the administration and should have a good knowledge of the field to which his statistics pertain. For instance, if he works on agricultural production statistics he should be familiar with the natural and economic conditions of this productions, with agricultural technique, with the social conditions under which this production takes place; he should also know the economic objectives of the agricultural production. A statistician working in the field of educational statistics should know the organization of the school system, its current needs and future plans, the objectives of the educational system and the social conditions in which the schools operate. At the same time, we should not go to the other extreme and require that the statistician be an expert on the field in which he collects statistical data, but we must require from him a good working knowledge of the problems involved.

(2) Statistics should be what we may call *of full value*. That is, they should provide a sufficient amount of information and not be confined to supplying elementary information. It is important to give administration sufficient material to arrive at proper decisions in solving the problems with which it may be faced.

*Example.* The measures to be taken in livestock breeding should be decided with a good knowledge of the previous developments. If it is desirable to breed more animals, all signs indicating the danger of a decrease in livestock should cause an immediate issuing of counter measures. It may happen that a decrease in the number of calves less than one year old (a warning signal of an impending decline in cattle population) may be accompanied by an increase in the total number of cattle, if the cattle population increased rapidly in the preceding years and a relatively small number were slaughtered. If the statistics are not broken down by age groups there will be no basis for making the right decision.

It statistics is to be of full value it is necessary that information be given in such a way as to make possible its full use. This requirement applies to both substance and form. The statistical data that provide certain information in a territorial division which differs from the one that is required in the given case, are not of full value. If, for example, the Courts of Appeal districts differ from the administrative, court statistics should be shown according to the former instead of, or in addition to, the latter division. From the formal point of view statistics from which we cannot compute—if such computations are required—the arithmetic mean, the mean deviation, the correlation coefficient, are not statistics that can be regarded as being of full value.

This leads us to the conclusion that the requirements on statistics are quite high and that it takes a fairly good knowledge of statistical methods for a statistician to be able to satisfy them. When these requirements are not met, as often happens even when much valuable material had been collected at considerable expense, the statistical data are published in such a way that do not lend themselves to analysis by correct statistical methods. Hence the coclusion that the practicing statistician engaged in the tabulation of data should posses a sound knowledge of the basic principles of statistical theory.

And finally, statistics are of full value when they are true and honest, i.e. when they provide information that reflects the true state of affairs. Thus, they should be free from errors, within attainable limits. Statistics may be misleading even when the figures are essentially correct but the information supplied does not exactly pertain to the problem mentioned in the title of the analysis or in the heading of the table, so that the reader does not find what he expects; or when the problem is stated in a vague or biased way; or when the information provided throws light only on certain aspects of the problem and neglects other aspects of the true state of affairs. A simple example of such misleading, although not directly forged, statistics is the statement that a plan has generally been fulfilled with surpluses in some lines, without a statement that there were serious shortages in certain products; or the statement that a plan has been exceeded, without stating that this was done at the expense of the quality of the products.

It is obvious that statistics of this kind are without value to an administration that requires exact and comprehensive information. Moreover, the practice of making public only incomplete information not only renders impossible an honest appraisal and self-criticism, but also encourages unfair criticism often made in bad faith.

(3) Statistical activities should be *coordinated* internally and should be synchronized with the activities of other administrative departments. Much of the material on which the statistics are based comes from other departments; this is called secondary statistical material and it is discussed below. The point is to organize the flow of raw data in a way that is the least burdensome to the administration. This means that information should be requested when it is convenient for the normal administrative routine; if one administrative unit acts as a source of information for different branches of statistics, reports should be combined, and as far as possible should be so made out as to eliminate the need for providing essentially the same information several times.

The same requirement applies, of course, to statistical data supplied by sources outside the administration, by individuals or civic institutions. Statistical research conducted by the administration should not place a superfluous burden on the reporting units through a great variety of forms and questionaires replaceable by one comprehensive form. It is also important to make sure that statistical information requested from a unit conforms to the documents at its disposal.

On the other hand, some coordination between the different branches of administrative statistics is also necessary. Where such coordination is lacking certain branches may be better developed than others and some may not be developed at all. It may happen that certain kinds of statistical information are collected and processed by several units. The data on the same subject may even differ in various reports either due to differences in classification, lack of precision in analysis, or as a result of using different sources or posing the problem in different ways. Statistics should be organized so that each branch properly reflects the importance of, and the practical need for, different types of information. As far as possible, each type of information should be dealt with only once, but in a correct and exhaustive manner.

(4) Statistics should be *inexpensive.* This does not mean that the funds earmarked for statistics should be meagre, but an effort should be made to achieve a given result at the lowest possible cost. One of the basic conditions for making statistics inexpensive in this sense is the coordination of statistical activities. Moreover, from several equally good available sources of information on a given problem the one should be chosen that permits the attainment of the same results at the lowest cost. Finally, the inexpensiveness of statistics depends on the technical efficiency of the whole process of research.

In the final analysis administrative statistics should help lower the cost of administration. Statistics should *pay for themselves.* Excessively developed statistics do not pay for themselves. There is no doubt, however, that even large sums of money spent on statistics may reduce total government expenditures if they help improve management and avoid mistakes or an incompetent search for better ways. Unfortunately such savings are not immediately apparent and almost never can be calculated. Hence numerous misunderstandings, erroneous appraisals of the cost of statistics and short-sighted saving campaigns. This is what happened in pre-war Poland when appropriations for statistics were reduced at a time of budget difficulties, when the opposite course of action might have been desirable.

(5) Only *quickly* obtainable results of statistical research enable the administration to reach the right decisions at the right time and to appraise the situation at the time when some remedial action is still possible. The requirement for speed puts great demands on the statistical apparatus. Experience has proved that this requirement can also be met in a capitalist economy. Some complex reports are known to have been prepared and published very quickly. At the same time certain areas have been neglected. Among them, for instance, are vital statistics. The detailed results of population censuses or current vital statistics reports have often been published only after several years. In this way, before the published data could be put to some useful purpose, they were obsolete and thus almost completely deprived of practical value. Nevertheless, they could have constituted a valuable basis for research and, in the long run, could also have been useful for practical administration purposes. In a planned socialist economy the question of speed in preparing statistical reports is of much greater importance.

(6) Finally, statistics should be *easily available*. Public administrative agencies should be in a position to obtain required statistics easily and quickly. This requirement can easily be satisfied if non-confidential statistical reports are printed or mimeographed and delivered to those interested. By printing statistical reports another requirement is also met, that of making statistics available to the general public. Few statistical data are of interest only to the public administration authorities; usually they contain information of great importance to the general public as well.

In the past the attitude toward this problem varied. Only in the 19th century was the practice established of printing and publishing all kinds of statistics, even those of a primarily technical and administrative nature.

There is no doubt that the publishing of statistical data contributed considerably to increase the understanding of socio-economic relations. If statistics were considered as the exclusive concern of the administration, the development of modern political economy, sociology and other humanities would not have been possible.

No less important is the educational value of statistics to the general public and especially to those who should be aware of the current state of affairs and of the transformations that are taking place; this is particularly true with reference to a society developing a socialist system.

f. *Government statistics and science.* We stated above that government statistics serve the needs of public administration, and primarily of its economic agencies. This postulate, however, should not be treated too narrowly. It would not suffice for statistics to meet current and obvious needs. Statistics should provide foundations for basic decisions, should make possible a critical appraisal of any situation, and provide premises for long-term planning. These requirements considerably broaden the scope of statisitcs but only in this way will they come to have full value.

Statistics also supply the necessary and valuable material for research which goes far beyond the direct needs of the administration. The use of government statistics for this purpose is secondary and usually does not interfere with the main programme of statistical reporting geared to satisfy the needs of the government. It may happen, however, that scientific institutes and scientific research workers interested in obtaining certain statistical data may decide that the scope of statistical reporting conducted by the government should be broadened to cover new fields. When they approach appropriate authorities with this kind of request they will very likely get a negative answer or an outright refusal—and perhaps rightly so. If government statistics are to serve the needs of the government administration the broadening of their scope beyond these needs would constitute an unnecessary burden on the governmental budget and on the agencies involved. However, it would be very short-sighted for the government to refuse to cooperate merely to maintain the position that such requests should be refused. It may develop that meeting such requests would also provide the government with better statistics for its own purposes. Indeed, research men should widen the horizon and see relationships hidden from those who concentrate on practical, current tasks. Science probes further into the future. The scientist should have a free hand since it is hard to say when theoretical achievements will have important practical applications or how great they may be. The very task of science in a socialist state is to lead the way into the future. For this reason those responsible for government statistics should be careful about rejecting the requests of scientists especially when such requests can be satisfied without interfering with the main statistical program and without substantial additional costs.

Yet there may be requests from scientists which do go beyond the objectives of government statistics and which cannot be met without serious changes in statistical reporting and without extra cost. Considering that this kind of data for research usually cannot be obtained from other than government sources or that obtaining such statistics in some other way would involve exorbitant costs it would seem appropriate to observe the following rules.

(1) Government statistical agencies can, and under certain circumstances should, have the right to conduct research or prepare additional statistical reports beyond their regular programme at the expense of the scientific and civil organizations con-

cerned, provided this does not interfere with the normal functioning of the government statistical apparatus.

(2) Since scientific and civic organizations do not always have sufficient means at their disposal, provision should be made for such exigencies in the government budget and funds should be provided for statistical research outside the regular program of statistical reporting. Such funds could be included in the budgets of governments statistical agencies or could be provided as special government grants for research. On the other hand it should be remembered that in a socialist system a scientist should not remain in an "ivory tower", and his first task is to supply what is required for current work. This means that he should not only try to solve the problems posed by someone from outside and answer a question encountered in real life, but he himself should also pose such problems which may not yet be manifest but which may have importance for the future. This requirement is not always observed by our scientists, who often work in isolation from the outside world. It should be stressed that the scientist, as prime organizer should have the proper basis to work intelligently.

## 2. ORGANIZATION PROBLEMS

a. *National statistics.* The general outline of the organization of national statistics given here has emphasized the technical aspects. In appraising technical instructions it should be remembered, however, that the organization of national statistics should be directly related to the role, task and organization of the State itself. Statistics in a socialist country should be related to the nature of a planned economy. In particular they should be based on the following premises:

(1) There must be a central authority to control statistics; this is a direct consequence of the organization principles of a socialist State.

(2) The central statistical bureau should work in very close contact with a planning authority since statistics form one of the basic tools of economic planning.

(3) Statistics must be very closely related to the daily activities of the national executive body of the planning authority since they play a very essential part in management. This also applies to government authorities on both national and local levels.

In Poland the central statistical authority is the Central Statistical Office in Warsaw.

An extensive statistical apparatus serving the needs of a modern State should be properly organized. Looking at the problem of organization from a historical perspective we find different stages of its development. The beginnings were usually very modest. As the need arose for certain numerical data appropriate agencies were instructed to collect the information required; they performed task, using their own facilities, in addition to their regular activities. At this stage the preparing of statistics was not yet a separate function divorced from other administrative activities. This state of affairs could not last as the tasks of statistics were becoming more involved and information was needed, not on sporadic occasions, but continuously. Then it became necessary to form a special agency to collect statistical data: thus statistics appeared as a specialized function *separate* from other administrative activities. Special statistical sections were sometimes created in particular offices, or separate bureaux or offices were set up when the scope of their activities warranted it. It is obvious that this kind of statistical organization is better than performing statistical functions on a sporadic basis, or as a sideline. To work even on simpler statistical jobs requires a knowledge of the subject, often a specialized knowledge, and always some experience. The work will be more efficient, more to the point, more exact, quicker and cheaper if it is done by persons specially assigned to this type of job. Of course, this kind of organization is possible only when there is a considerable amount of statistical work and when it is fairly evenly distributed in time. Otherwise the setting up of a special statistical unit is not practical. Such a unit may be composed of several people, or even one person, or it may be a large department or bureau employing hundreds or even thousands of workers and possessing complicated technical equipment.

As a rule, all government statistics are handled by special units or bureaux; this is undoubtedly the right method. It would be erroneous, however, to assume that at the present stage of development of government statistics they must be separated from other administrative functions. As always, the decisive factor should be the purpose served. When statistical reports are few their preparation does not require much time or skill, when this task is directly connected with the performing of specific administrative functions—then of course, these reports can usefully be prepared by an office clerk on the side. For instance, if the statistics on the number of offences handled by the police, and therefore based on police records, are to show only the number of offences dealt with by the police and the section of the code under which the offenders are to be tried, then obviously this kind of statistics can easily be recorded by a police clerk who handles the records. If, however, more complex statistics are required, giving the time and place where an offence was commited, the circumstances of discovering it and personal data concerning the offenders or suspects, then this kind of work would probably be better done by special employee.

The problem of separating statistics from other administrative functions is connected with the problem of the centralization or decentralization of statistical work. Statistics are centralized when all statistical work pertaining to different fields is done in one office. In an extreme case of centralization all statistical functions in a given State are performed by one statistical office. Centralization may affect different fields, or may consist of substituting one central office for district offices. Statistics are decentralized when the statistics on different fields of human activity are divided into separate divisions, or when the responsiblity for the statistics on particular regions is delegated to regional statistical offices.

The science of public administration, even in capitalist states, gives definite preference to fairly far advanced centralization of statistics. The experience of different States has led to many varied solutions. Generally, in countries in which statistics developed early and gradually encompassed new fields, as in England or France, the degree of decentralization is most marked; almost every important government department has its own statistical office. When, in addition to these offices there is a central office for compiling statistics not kept by departmental offices—its scope of activities is very narrow. Thus, in France, up to the Second World War, the *Statistique Generale de la France* in the Ministry of the Interior handled population statistics (population censuses, population movements), price statistics and several less important questions. Besides demographic statistics, perhaps the most important function of the Statistique Générale was the publishing of the Statistical Yearbook for France which carried statistical information on different fields of governmental activity, compiled and submitted in ready form by the appropriate offices. Now statistics in France are the responsibility of the *Institut National de la Statistique et des Études Économiques* (the National Institute of Statistics and Economic Research); its scope of activities is much wider.

The Central Statistical Office in England was not set up until the Second World War. Its task is not so much the coordination of statistical research as the collecting and tabulating of information obtained from different sources in such a way as to facilitate its use. Particular branches of statistics are run, as before, by corresponding governmental departments and offices.

In contrast, in countries where statistical work developed, or was reorganized relatively late, it is highly centralized, sometimes to the point where all statistical work is done in one office—at least in theory, since in practice exceptions often have to be made from a uniformly designed system.

The advantages of centralization are manifold and important. Some of them are of the same kind as result from separating statistics from other administrative functions. The setting up of one large statistical bureau makes it possible to use the available personnel more effectively: in managerial jobs those with better educational qualifications and experience may be employed, in subordinate jobs greater specialization may be developed. Only in a large office it is possible to take full advantage of modern office equipment such as specialized computers which can be profitably employed only for very extensive studies. When studies in different fields are prepared in the same office it is possible to employ the available man hours much more efficiently. Particular studies can be distributed over a period of time in the most convenient way. Not all studies are equally urgent; thus the less urgent ones can be started during slack periods or when the urgent reports are completed. In this way it is possible to satisfy the important condition for efficient work in every institution: the elimination of peak periods and—as far as possible—the steady, uniform, and full utilization of working time and equipment. Another advantage of centralization and of having one office for preparing studies from different fields is the possibility of using the experience gained in one field for studies in other fields. This reduces costs and often produces better results.

Although all these considerations are essential, there is another, the most important advantage of centralization in statistics: only by this means is it possible to coordinate fully the statistical reporting in the country and to arrange it a uniform and consistent system. When work is decentralized certain divisions are always better developed than others, and some may even be neglected. Quite often there is overlapping or duplication in statistical reporting when it is done simultaneously by different institutions. This is not only a waste of means and resources; it is not uncommon to arrive at considerably different results when different methods are employed or insufficient care is taken in the preparation of some studies. When contradictory information is published the confidence in statistics is undermined and the general public is misinformed. In different studies, when different methods are used, the results may be published in different ways. The centralization of all statistical work in one institution removes these shortcomings and produces better results with less effort and minimum cost. It also enables the setting up of a statistical reporting system in which all divisions are developed according to their actual importance and through which we can obtain a complete statistical picture of the state, in line with the requirements of scientific and practical needs.

These advantages of centralization should be set against certain advantages of decentralized statistics assigned to particular divisions of public administration. Decentralized statistics are more closely connected with the field to which they pertain and this enables the statistician to grasp more easily the essence of the problem involved and to better satisfy practical needs. Owing to this close contact it is also easier to control directly the completeness and the exactness of the data collected. And finally—the argument often used by the spokesmen of those government departments which would prefer to retain separate statistical offices—studies prepared in departmental offices are often completed faster than they would by in a central office. Moreover, the latter easily develops an inflexible routine, whereas departmental statistical offices sooner adapt themselves to changing conditions and find new ways when new problems arise. It could also be argued that the employees of a particular department will find the statistics processed by their own bureau closer to their interests and more easily understood. This will produce greater eagerness and confidence than would material from outside sources.

All these arguments have a certain validity but not all the conclusions are correct. From the arguments quoted above only one thing follows—that the requirements placed on centralized statistics should be the greatest since they can and should meet such requirements in order to fulfill their task. The managerial staff must be adequate and properly trained to be capable of tackling particular problems in an appropriate manner. The central bureau should maintain a very close contact with the institutions for which it provides statistical data. In cooperation with the central bureau these institutions *decide* what and to what extent should be covered by statistics, and the central bureau is *obliged* to meet their *legitimate* needs. Not all needs can be satisfied, for non-statisticians sometimes demand things which cannot be done, or are out of line with the whole statistical reporting system. On the other hand the statisticians from the central statistical office may sometimes provide more than is required of them by specialists in different fields of public administration since their statistical skill and experience makes it possible for them to pose particular problems appropriately, to see what information can be derived from the existing statistical material, or—if it is insufficient—how to obtain additional data quickly. Finally, the central statistical office must prepare urgent statistical studies in the shortest possible time. If this requirement is kept in mind then the central office can always provide the required information more quickly than specialized offices could. At the same cost, greater speed in supplying information by specialized offices is almost always achieved by increasing the number of employees engaged in preparing a study or a report.

The most important requirement facing the central statistical office is that its work must be creative and its management should never get into a rut. It should carefully follow new developments and problems, anticipate the requests that may come from outside and never fall behind. The centralization of statistics thus conceived will be a most constructive factor in the development of the country and society. A proper and consistent solution of these problems is possible only in a planned socialist economy.

To avoid any possible misunderstandings a few more remarks are in order.

When we speak of the centralization of statistics we have in mind the gathering in one place of all the functions related primarily to the collecting of statistical data, their processing, tabulation and publication. This kind of centralization, or a monopoly on the collecting and processing of statistical data, however, is not the only method of *coordination* of government statistics. Coordination can also be achieved by the creation of a centre for decision-taking, management and control while retaining a decentralized system of operations. The most frequently chosen is probably the "middle of the road" method of a partial monopoly.

An altogether different problem is the analysis of the collected material and the drawing of conclusions both of a theoretical nature for research and of a practical nature for administrative purposes. This kind of analysis may (but not necessarily) be carried out by the central statistical office. It is imperative, however, not only that the division of the government administration to which the statistics in question pertain should be able to take advantage of the available studies and reports but also that they actually do take advantage of them. In major administrative departments and in dealing with more complex statistical problems, this will necessitate the setting up of special statistical research sections managed by personnel well versed in statistical methods and responsible for the analysis of statistical material from the point of view of the needs of the department concerned. Such sections may employ quite a few people since research frequently requires tedious and time-consuming preparatory work.

The existence of these statistical research sections does not by any means infringe upon the principle of centralization of government statistics. Their setting up is desirable since only in this way is it possible to utilize fully the material supplied by the central statistical office. At the same time the managers of these sections can form an effective liaison between the administrative department of which they are a part and the central statistical office.

Government statistics should be centralized both from the point of view of subject matter and function, and from the point of view of territorial division. The motives are the same: the need for the coordination of statistical work and the striving for greater technical efficiency.

As a rule local administrative units can be entrusted with the collection of statistical data only if it is done according to a unified plan controlled by the central statistical office.

Territorial decentralization can assume various forms. For instance, local authorities may carry out local studies adapted to the specific needs of the locality concerned. Very frequently, however, the same objective can be better achieved within the framework of a national study by introducing appropriate local modifications to the general plan. However, if in exceptional cases local authorities have to engage in statistical enquiries, it is necessary that the content, scope and method of enquiry by worked out in the strictest cooperation with the central statistical office. If local studies are undertaken too frequently the whole statistical apparatus may become completely disorganized. Local needs can be satisfied if, in designing statistical reporting centrally, a sufficiently detailed territorial division is introduced. Where it is not possible to show all the details of territorial division in statistical publications, the required information can be sent to local authorities in non-printed form.

Local authorities may also be entrusted with the processing of the data obtained through an enquiry carried out for the whole country in a centralized manner. This would simplify the organization of work in the central statistical office; in extensive studies it would eliminate the necessity of engaging a host of extra workers, providing accomodation and office equipment for them, organizing their work, etc. Certain savings in budget expenditures may also be achieved if it is possible to add additional statistical work to the normal office routine of local administrative employees. But in this way the social cost—the total amount of work—will almost always be greater than if the work is done in the central statistical office where it is easier to achieve greater efficiency. Under special circumstances this method is acceptable to a certain extent, providing that the scope and procedure are carefully worked out by the central statistical office for all local units participating in the enquiry. On the other hand, it is not only permissible but desirable, in extensive general enquiries, to delegate to the local authorities the responsibility for preparing interim reports that are simple and easy to carry out; this speeds up the collecting of reports from the whole country. We shall return to this matter later on. Local authorities should, of course, submit statistical reports of an established pattern, either to higher units or to the central statistical office.

An important part can also be played by community statistics. Every community, especially urban, has many specific characteristics distinguishing it from other similar units. It possesses information on regular community activities; such information enables us to study various fields of activity by statistical methods. It is then justified to set up separate community statistics pertaining to specific community problems in general and those of a given unit in particular. Since national statistics may deal with these problems only superficially, or not at all, community statistics can be regarded as a valuable supplement. It is obvious that here, too, a proper degree of coordination between government and community statistics is necessary if overlapping or duplication is to be avoided.

Examples of problems in urban statistics can be found in city development or redevelopment projects which are specific to each city or town, housing and health problems, the prices of basic consumer goods, the area from which food supplies are brought to town, etc.

It should be remembered, however, that there is another way to organize community statistics. The central statistical office may, under certain circumstances, undertake special studies for the community authorities, at their expense, either by introducing a more detailed breakdown by territories or, by expanding the scope of its regular reports, or by making new studies on the basis of available data, or by collecting and processing the data of which, as a rule makes no use. In this way it can help the community authorities which thus need not excessively expand their own statistical activities but make use of a superior national statistical organization. Properly coordinated work also results in savings.

b. *Statistics outside government administration*. National statistics in modern societies comprise a large part of what is needed to advance our statistical knowledge of human society and of its activities within national organizations.

However, there are other sources of statistical information on subject—incomparably poorer quantitatively but sometimes very important as to content. Among them are research studies conducted by scientific and social institutes or even by individual scientists. Though usually fragmentary, these studies may go deeper into the essence of the problem. Between the two world wars considerable amount of research was done in Poland by the Institute of Business Cycle and Price Studies;

much valuable statistical material on agriculture was collected by the Department of Agricultural Economics of Small Farms of the Scientific Institute at Puławy: urban and rural socio-economic relations were studied at the Institute of Social Economy; fertility studies were carried on by the Polish Institute of Population Studies. Since such studies usually combine statistical and other methods of research they are as a rule, typical examples of partial statistical studies. Their results are valuable in so far as the requirements of scientific research are observed; this problem will be discussed in the last part of this book.

In capitalist countries a considerable amount of statistical data is provided by private institutions. Particularly, manufacturers' associations of a cartel type often keep detailed statistics on the production and sales of their own products and sometimes publish certain data. In cases when the cartel includes all, or almost all the manufacturers in a given industry such statistics may even replace government statistics, if the latter are not yet sufficiently well organized, or they can supplement government statistics by providing additional data.

c. *International statistics.* The necessity of making international comparisons in statistics is obvious. It is necessary to know what goes on elsewhere and no phenomenon can be properly understood without a basis for comparison. Unfortunately, making comparisons is particularly difficult in international statistics. The approach to the same problem may differ considerably from country to country, and the same terms may have completely different meanings. This often results from various methods used to express certain facts statistically.

Let us take crime statistics as an example:[15] This kind of statistics, if they are to illuminate the state of affairs, should be based on court sentences in criminal cases, for only from court records is it possible to obtain detailed data on the circumstances under which the crime was committed, or information about the offender—in short, everything that enables us to apprehend the crime as a social phenomenon. But then, the number of facts that can be expressed statistically, their interpretation, etc., depend upon the penal code and court procedure in force in a country. The same deed may be considered an offence in one but not in another: or it may be treated as an misdemeanour in one country and a severely punishable crime in another. Thus, the crime ratio understood as a ratio of the offenders sentenced in criminal cases to the total population will have different meanings in different countries. Crime statistics may include sentences in all criminal cases or only sentences in more serious ones. This is another reason why it is difficult to make direct international comparisons.

Let us consider another example—unemployment statistics in capitalist countries. The term unemployment may have many meanings and it is difficult to give its unequivocal definition. Even if we could arrive at a definition valied for all countries we would still have to use the unemployment statistics or current unemployment

---

[15] The examples are taken mainly from the statistics of capitalist countries.

registration records. The number of unemployed may be established either by direct statistical studies (e.g. at the time of collecting data for a population census—but then we get information at long intervals because censuses are usually held every ten years), or by frequent sampling, say, every month or every quarter. Proper statistical sampling produces the best and most comprehensive information on unemployment. Usually, however, unemployment statistics are based on records kept for other purposes. The value of information thus obtained depends upon the purpose of these records and the method of registration. When there is a general unemployment insurance system under which every unemployed person can receive unemployment benefits by registering for them, unemployment statistics may correctly reflect the actual situation. Usually, however, not all categories of workers are covered by unemployment insurance, and not all of those insured are eligible for benefit payments (e.g. unemployment benefits may be available only to those who had been employed for a specified length of time before becoming unemployed).

Even if formal regulations require that everyone who has lost a job be registered, the records may not be complete since only those who are eligible for benefits are interested in registering. In certain countries unemployment statistics are based not on unemployment insurance registration records but on the records of those seeking work through public or private employment agencies. The degree of completeness of statistics in this case depends upon the chance of obtaining employment through such agencies. The unemployed will not seek the agency's help if he can find a job in some other way, or if he appraises the changes of finding employment through the agency as fairly low. In some countries statistics may include only the registered unemployed members of trade unions. Moreover there may be differences in the statistical definition of unemployment, e.g. it may include all the registered unemployed workers, or only those who receive benefit payments.

The *Yearbook of Labour Statistics* provides for its unemployment statistics special explanation notes on the methods of obtaining unemployment data in each country. It shows six different types of sources[16] as well as additional sources for some countries.

Under these circumstances international unemployment data are among the least comparable, both with regard to the number of unemployed an their percentage of the labour force, and with regard to seasonal unemployment fluctuations which may depend upon the source used for their computations. This facilitates all kinds of "dressing up", or "lying with figures", especially since unemployment is one of the most reluctantly admitted economic ills.

Unemployment statistics in the United States are quite extensive. They are based

---

[16] They are: (a) labour force sampling, (b) compulsory unemployment insurance statistics, (c) unemployment benefit payments statistics, (d) Trade Union statistics, (e) employment agencies' statistics based on unemployment registrations and on registration of situations wanted.

on monthly samplings of all population from the age of 14. The population is divided into: (1) labour force: (a) employed, (b) unemployed, and (2) not in labour force, which includes the dependent members of the family and those who do not work for reasons other than unemployment. Unemployment statistics include all those who were unemployed and those who were seeking work (i.e. also those who have not had any paid employment before but are now seeking work). The unemployed are classified according to age and length of unemployment. According to these statistics the number of unemployed in December 1950 was 2,229,000 which amounted to 3·6 per cent of all persons employed and unemployed. But out of 60,308,000 of those classified as "employed" only 48,160,000 wore fully or almost fully employed (35 hours a week or more); 7,506,000 worked 15–34 hours a week and 2,666,000 from 1 to 14 hours a week. When we speak of unemployment we can hardly disregard those who are partially unemployed. Besides, there is a category of those "with a job but not at work". This considerable group (1,976,000) comprises not only those on sick leave or on holidays, but also those temporarily laid off and those not working because of weather conditions, or other reasons; a substantial portion of them receive no remuneration and therefore should also be classified as unemployed.

Thus the actual number of unemployed—working less than 35 hours a week may turn out to be considerably higher than the official statistics show. The true picture may be obtained, however, after a careful analysis of detailed statistics and other available information. The trouble is, though, that such statistics usually appear in publications with a relatively low circulation and access to them may not be very easy. In the more widely known publications—such as those of the United Nations Organization or the International Labour Office—the unemployment figures are given only in the narrow sense of this term, as is the case in all kinds of official utterances or publications which contain information formally correct[17] but, in fact, misleading. True information can usually be obtained by examining the original source and by an appropriate and unbiased interpretation of the available data.

There may be divergences in statistics from different countries in fields where, it would seem, they should not appear. A case in point is foreign trade statistics. It is understandable that the data on the value of goods brought from country A to country B may be different as shown in the statistics of the two countries. The value of the goods may be estimated in different ways, certain additional costs may be or may not be included (e.g. transport, insurance, etc.) It would seem, however, that at least the figures on the amount of goods imported to one country from another

---

[17] Even if the number of fully unemployed is correct, the percentage figure in relation to the total labour force is incorrect, since the latter includes not only the "hired workers" category, from which the unemployed actually come, but also the "self-employed" group. Thus in the calculation of the percentage of unemployed the denominator is artificially inflated, and the percentage figure is diminished and gives a false picture.

should be identical in the statistics of both countries. None the less, there are many cases in which slight differences in quantitative data appear in the statistics of different countries; in some cases these differences may be quite substantial.[18]

Sometimes there are no important differences in the contents of the statistics, but there are differences in the presentation of data which may render impossible all direct comparisons. For instance, let us consider, differences in classification. In population statistics age may be given in various age groups. When it is given for 10-year intervals we have groups from 10 to 20, from 20 to 30, etc. In some Anglo-Saxon countries, however, the 10-year intervals are given in figures ending in five, e.g. 25–35, 35–45, etc. The group from 10 to 20 years usually means from 10 years of age up to, but not including, 20 years of age; this may be written 10–19. In some statistics the intervals may be from 11 to 20, from 21 to 30, etc.; in other words the year ending with zero may either start or end a 10-year group. Differences in classification are even more pronounced when a division into equal groups is impossible because of certain peculiar characteristics of the population structure. In farm statistics the groups for small farms must be smaller than for large ones. Whether farms are divided into classes of up to 2 hectares, 2–5, 5–10, 10–15, 15–50, over 50 hectares, as was the case in the census of occupations in Poland in 1931, or in some other way, will depend on what kind of classification will be considered characteristic from the socio-economic point of view of the country in question. This example shows that an entirely different content may be hidden behind what seems to be the same type of classification.

These examples should suffice to show how difficult it is to make international comparisons of statistics on socio-economic problems. It is important to find a method of making such comparisons since they may be of great importance.

Different ways may lead to a full or partial solution of this problem. To solve the problem completely it would be necessary to introduce uniform statistical methods for each field in all countries. This would be extremely difficult, if not impossible, because differences in statistics stem from deeply rooted differences in the social and economic system. Since these differences are important, the introduction of formal uniformity in statistics—even if it were possible—would be undesirable from the point of view of individual countries, since it might create considerable difficulty in presenting the actual state of affairs in each of them. Finally, custom and statistical tradition have great influence; natural human inertia makes people resist change. Of course there are also more essential, objective reasons. One of the most important is that a change in the manner of dealing with statistics may make it difficult or impossible to keep records or make comparisons in a country. Nevertheless, with a certain amount of good will much could be done to improve the situation in

---

[18] The reasons for the existence of divergences in Polish and foreign statistics on foreign trade are explained in an extensive study published some time ago by the Central Statistical Office of Statistics, Poland, Series C, No. 2, Warsaw 1934.

this respect, especially if a discussion on international forum should conclude that certain changes are desirable.

It may happen that certain statistical tabulations lend themselves to a uniform formula for all the countries required for an international comparison. Quite often, however, the countries concerned keep separate statistics for internal use and employ different methods, more appropriate for their needs. All these questions should be regulated by international agreements which can be reached only after cumbersome machinery has been set in motion. They would also have to be preceded by public discussion and international conferences.

A more modest solution would be to make a comparative analysis of the statistical methods used in particular fields in the different countries with an explanation of the differences so that appropriate transformations the statistics could be used for international comparisons. Where such transformations are not feasible, a comparative analysis will at least clarify the situation in each country and thus inhibit unwarranted conclusions.

These more modest solutions will be appropriate for individual scientists and statistical or scientific institutions in particular countries. Much has already been done in this respect. Central statistical offices in all major countries now publish comparable data in special international sections or at least provide comments which enable the reader to draw his own conclusions and which help him avoid errors.

Work of this type can also be undertaken by international organizations like scientific societies or associations which have more practical objectives. Such international organizations may have the twofold objective of: (1) studying jointly the situation in individual countries, discussing the problems involved and then preparing international statistics, and (2) preparing the basis on which international understanding can be reached, leading to a uniform statistical system in all the countries concerned.

In some cases it is possible that governments or governmental administrative authorities may conclude an international agreement concerning certain specialized branches of statistics.

The first large-scale attempt to reach an international agreement concerning statistics was the International Statistical Congress. It convened for the first time in Brussels in 1853 and between that year and 1876 it was held eight times in different cities; a permanent committee of the Congress operated until 1878. The noted Belgian statistician Quetelet was very active in the organization of the Congress and in its works. His contributions were of great value, both in the theory of statistics and in the more practical field of organizing government statistics. In the works of the Congress perticipated both the representatives of government statistical institutions, research workers and other interested parties. The results of these works were published in the reports of particular sessions and in numerous other publications. They pertained to both theoretical and practical problems of laying the foundations for comparable international statistics. One means to be used was a broadly conceived publication *International Statistics*. Statistical bureaux of individual countries were to prepare the different parts of this publication. The results of their work on some problems were published according to a uniform and detailed plan, but only a small part of the whole programme was completed.

In 1885 the International Statistical Institute was formed. It had a very limited membership; only prominent representatives of public administration and statisticians were selected. Sessions of the Institute were held every two years. The eighteenth session was held in Warsaw in 1929. The twenty-fourth was to be held in Prague in September 12–17, 1939, but was interrupted after two days because of the seriousness of the political situation. The minutes of the meetings and the papers read were published in the *Bulletin de l'Institut International de Statistique*.

The quarterly *Revue de L'Institut International de Statistique* began to appear in 1933; it contains papers on theoretical problems. Moreover comparative international statistics are published in special publications.

However, neither the Congress nor the International Statistical Institute did, nor could impose on individual countries a definite method of conducting statistical work. Indeed, the first attempt to coordinate statistics in different countries, made by the Permanent Committee of the Statistical Congress, ended in breaking up the Congress. Nevertheless, the wide discussion helped to elucidate many problems and resulted in the application of better methods; the detailed analysis of methods used in different countries helped produce better comparisons in many fields than had been possible before.

Between the two world wars, the League of Nations undertook a broad coordination, particularly in economic statistics. Owing to the initiative of the League of Nations the "International Convention Relating to Economic Statistics" was concluded in 1928. It set the frame-work. Particular problems (international trade statistics, occupation statistics) were worked upon by a committee of statistical experts and their recommendations were gradually put into effect. The countries which signed the Convention carried on their statistics as they deemed fit, but were obliged to prepare additional reports of a uniform pattern so that the results could be compared directly and without special reservations.

This was not the first attempt of its kind. Both the International Telegraph Union (founded in 1868) and the International Postal Union (1874) required that the member-countries supply statistical data according to an established formula; these data were published annually in international comparisons. The credit for systematizing agricultural statistics should go primarily to the International Agricultural Institute set up in 1905, with its head office in Rome.

Even when an international organization confines itself to collecting data from different countries and analysing their comparability it indirectly contributes to the better organization and improvement in statistics in those countries, if only by making the statisticians more aware of the problems and the different ways of solving them.

Since World War II considerable efforts to improve the coordination of international statistics have been made by the United Nations Organization and especially by its committees on statistics and population. Special problems are dealt with by a subcommittee on sampling methods. Statistical problems also play an important part in the works of most specialized agencies, like the International Labour Organization, the Food and Agriculture Organization, the World Health Organization, etc.

The United Nations Organization has its own Statistical Office. Its tasks are of a technical nature and include the coordination of statistics of specialized agencies, the collection and publication of statistical data submitted by the member states, by the specialized agencies and by other institutions, etc.

d. *Statistical publications.* The United Nations Organization publishes a considerable number of statistical reports, both numerical (see below) and descriptive. They are primarily technical and pertain to such problems as population censuses, sample surveys, etc.[19]

In using international statistical publications the following should be kept in mind:

(1) These publications, as a rule, provide data officially submitted by statistical offices of individual countries. Thus the responsibility for the figures and the method of handling the problem rests with those countries. Even if it is assumed that the figures are formally correct, the method may, sometimes even purposely, distort reality.

(2) In spite of all the efforts of the Bureau of the United Nations to introduce a certain degree of uniformity into the statistics of different countries, in many cases there are differences in approach which diminish the validity of comparisons, or render them altogether impossible.

(3) The greatest difficulties are encountered in comparing statistical data from the capitalist countries on the one hand, and from the U.S.S.R. and the People's Democracies on the other.

(4) Most important is the fact that in very many cases the figures published are too general and improperly arranged and therefore they are not sufficient for a proper appraisal of the facts by scientific methods. This may be due to the lack of skill in using proper methods but may also be caused by a desire to hide or "beautify" certain inconvenient facts.

In all these cases it may be helpful to refer to the orginal data of the countries concerned. This will not only help in understanding the meaning of the published

---

[19] On the Statistical activities of the United Nations Organization see a paper by J. Fabijański in *Przegląd Statystyczny (Statistical Survey)* No. 1–2, vol. 3, Warsaw, 1949.

statistical data, or in establishing to what extent they are comparable, but may also lead to a new understanding of the real situation in these countries. For this, however, it is necessary to have a really good command of scientific methods.[20]

The results of studies undertaken by government statistical bureaux appear in different publications. Major studies usually appear in special publications or in separate volumes dealing with each major problem individually. Such publications usually appear as a series under a common title, e.g. *Poland's Statistics,* or *Czechoslovak Statistics,* etc. Here would appear both the results of a single special study, or of studies repeated at long intervals, and the results of annual studies *(Yearbook of Education Statistics, Yearbook of Industrial Statistics,* etc.). These studies are intended for specialists; they give very detailed information and should also provide sufficient comments and explanation on the method of analysis, on the significance and exactness of the results, etc., so that the reader can form his own judgment. Sometimes an analysis and appraisal of the numerical data is also included. In Poland altogether 176 volumes of *Poland's Statistics* were published in 1919–39.

In certain fields, where more frequent information is needed, the reports may be published quarterly or monthly; they are also quite detailed and are also intended for specialists. Such pre-war Polish publications as *Foreign Trade Statistics,* a monthly, or *Labour Statistic,* a quarterly, are of this kind.

There is another type of publication addressed to the general public interested in social problems. Important here are statistical yearbooks published in almost all countries possessing organized statistics. Such yearbooks usually comprise all available statistical data regardless whether they come from the central statistical office, or from other government or civic officies, or even from private sources. Information is presented in a concise and accessible form without excessive or too detailed explanations so that it can be used not only by specialists but by anyone interested in a given problem. There are two types of yearbooks: "large" volumes of several hundred large pages, and concise or "small" ones in which only the most important information is given in a condensed form.

Up-to-date information from different fields for the general public is published as it is prepared for different periodicals having different frequencies, some monthly or more often, some every two or three months.

In some of these publications only tables are included (as in the *Statistical Bulletin* published by the Central Statistical Office in Poland), in others also explanatory comments, often illustrated by graphs.

Some government statistical offices also publish periodically extensive analyses of the results of statistical research, papers on the organization and technique of research, or even dissertations on the theory of statistics.

---

[20] The proper direction to be taken here was shown by Lenin in his work: New Data on the Laws of the Development of Capitalism in Agriculture (*Works,* vol. 3, Warsaw, 1954).

Such were the *Statistical Monthly*, and then the *Statistical Quarterly* published in Poland before the war by the Central Statistical Office; after the war *Statistical Studies and Papers* which appeared in 1950–51, and *Statistical News* which has been published since 1956.

There are also various publications that do not fall in any of the above categories, e.g. statistical atlases, lists of towns and villages, auxiliary lists or tables for statistical research (e.g. statistical commodity lists for foreign trade statistics or for industrial production statistics), etc.

It should be added that tables given in general publications of the "Yearbook" or "Statistical News" type may suffice for general information only. For more extensive analysis both of a theoretical, scientific nature and of a more practical kind, it is necessary to refer to more detailed information at source since only in this way one can form an independent opinion.

International comparisons of statistical data are published in most statistical yearbooks either in separate tables in appropriate chapters of the yearbook (as in the Polish pre-war *Concise Statistical Yearbook*), or in separate chapters on international statistics which sometimes are very extensive. (Separate chapters on international statistics are published, for instance, in the Polish *Statistical Yearbook* and in the *Concise Statistical Yearbook*). The most extensive statistics of this kind were previously published in the French *Annuaire Statistique de la France* and in the German *Statistisches Jahrbuch für das Deutsche Reich*.

In addition there are international statistical publications; the most important in the inter-war period was the Statistical Yearbook of the League of Nations which gave particularly extensive information on demographic and economic problems. In additional to general yearbooks there were many special publications such as *Annuaire des Statistique du Travail* published by the International Labour Organization, *Annuaire International de Statistique Agricole* and many others.

These publications have been continued since the war by the United Nations Organization and its specialized agencies. The Statistical Bureau of the United Nations, apart from resuming the publication of the Statistical Yearbook issued by the Leagne of Nations, introduced a special yearbook on population, *Demographic Yearbook*. Certain private publications giving internatonal information also contain statistical data.

Of course, the above review is incomplete, but it should give the reader a rough idea of the subject and help him find other appropriate sources.

CHAPTER 2

# THE FORMATION OF STATISTICAL MATERIAL

## 1. THE NOTION AND KINDS OF STATISTICAL MATERIAL

Statistics present phenomena in the form of tables which show how many times or in what numbers certain phenomena appear in a given population. In order to design a statistical table it is necessary to know the particular units of which the population is composed and to discover for each of them separately those characteristics which are to appear in the table. For instance, to design a statistical table in which the leaves of a birch tree are classified according to length and width, we have to know the length and width of every leaf of the birch.

This individual information we shall call statistical material. It is formed by the gathering of individual data on each unit separately. Cases in which we demand the number of units possessing a particular characteristic are only a seeming departure from this description. For when we ask our informant how many cows of each breed there are in a particular village he has to find out to which breed each particular cow belongs. If, then, he says how many head there are in each breed, this means that apart from *having collected the material* he also has performed the next phase of statistical work primitive *processing* of the material.

In the case of the leaves of a birch the task of those collecting the material consisted in measuring each leaf and writing down the results. The difficulties that may arise  here results from the requirement that the measurements be taken correctly. If this work is done by a single investigator the number of leaves measured must be very limited. The same is true in other fields when the whole material is collected by one or several persons. If it is possible to determine exactly the characteristics for each unit then the difficulties may result only from the great amount of work required to do the job, there being no difficulties with regard to technique or organization. The problem consists in deciding whether it is better to write down all the information concerning each particular unit on a separate sheet of paper, or to make out a form in which to note, one by one, the data on each unit. If we decide in favour of sheets, they have to be conveniently stored, preferably in boxes or drawers with appropriate labels, etc.

On the other hand, when the material comprises many thousands, or even millions of units, as is the case in social statistics, and the amount of information about each unit is considerable and when, moreover, it is often difficult to establish

47

the required characteristics for each unit—then the technical side of organizing the collection of data becomes a very important problem. Upon its successful solution largely depend, the results of the whole statistical enquiry.

It is difficult to formulate systematically all the requirements that have to be met for the result to be satisfactory. Besides, these requirements will differ from case to case. Certain general recommendations can, however, be given.

From the point of view of the origin of the statistical material there are two possible cases. In the one case we collect information on the units studied especially for the purpose of preparing our statistics—then we have *primary statistical material*. In the second case such information already exists in sources accessible to us, so that it is only necessary to extract and write down the required data—and then we have *secondary statistical material*. The latter is particularly common concerning the organization of human society in a country.

From the point of view of the nature of the facts dealt with by statistics there are again two cases. We can study a given population at a certain moment, e.g. the population of a country on the last day of December of the year *t*, or we can analyse the events that occurred during a given period of time, e.g. births and deaths that occured in a given territory during the year *t*, or the amount and type of commodities exported from the country in a given month, etc. An enquiry of the first type depicting the state of the population at a given moment we shall call a *census*, and of the second type we shall call a *registration*. Both a census and a registration may be based on primary or on secondary statistical material; registration, for technical reasons, is often based on secondary material.

## 2. THE CONDITIONS FOR OBTAINING GOOD STATISTICAL MATERIAL

We shall try to state the necessary conditions of collecting material for the results to be as intended. We shall deal primarily with the requirements for a census based on primary material. However, most of these requirements, can be applied directly, or after minor changes, to censuses based on secondary material, and to registrations as well. Certain matters related to secondary material will be discussed separately.

Many of the examples given below are based on statistical experience accumulated in the capitalist countries. In a socialist economy quite a few complications can be considerably simplified. Basically, however, the technical and organization problems remain the same. It should be remembered that in Poland, which is now going through the stage of building socialism, statistical technique must take into consideration the existence of capitalistic elements and small commodity markets.

a. *Exact definition and limitation of the population.* That this be done is a very obvious requirement. Proper enquiry is possible only when we exactly define its subject and instruct each person engaged in collecting data as to which units should be included and which omitted. Practical application of this requirement to statistics is not always simple and when the people conducting a study are not properly trained mistakes are often made. Let us consider a few examples. It may happen that a certain type of information about children in a given district is required, but the age limit is not given. Every person supplying information will have to decide whether a boy 14 years of age is still a child, or not. The material thus obtained will not be uniform and even if, by chance, all the informants decide upon the same age limit it will still not be certain whether the limit chosen by them complies with the intentions of those who originated the enquiry. Another similar example: if the enquiry concerns orphans the question should be settled whether by orphans we mean those who have lost both parents or just one. The upper age limit should also be determined: for instance, it could be, 14, or 16, or 18 years of age.

One more example from the field of demography will show what complications may arise in seemingly simple cases. It would appear that nothing could be simpler than to determine what is meant by the population of a given locality. But demography distinguishes two, or even three categories of population. Thus we have, first, the present, or actual population, i.e. all who at the time of the census happen to be at the locality, regardless what their permanent residence may be. There is also the resident or permanent population which includes all who permanently reside in the locality regardless where they may be at the time of the census. The two categories differ both in size and composition. Sometimes another category of population is distinguished—the legal population, or all who belong to a given community. The legal population may differ considerably in size from the present or permanent population; many persons may be included in it even though they left the community long before and are not present at the time of taking the census.

For instance, according to Polish legislation the population registered as "staying" in a given locality is by no means identical with the resident population, as defined above, because quite a few people may be registered for a temporary stay and, on the other hand, those registered as permanent residents may live elsewhere. This last fact means that the total of those registered for permanent and temporary residence is not identical with the present population. When we start making a census we have to determine clearly which category of population we have in mind and those who collect the data should be instructed accordingly.

An example from a different field: if an enquiry—in a capitalist or small commodity market economy—is to include small peasant farms we have to determine what we consider a peasant farm. The simplest solution is to fix the lower and upper limit of the size of the farm. We may decide to include farms with an area of from 0·5 to 50 hectares, (1·25–125 acres) on the assumption that farms smaller than 0·5 hectares cannot provide independent existence and therefore their owners have to rely on something other than farming as their main source of income, and that farms greater than 50 hectares are estates. But it must be decided whether we have in mind the total area including woods and barren land, or only the cultivated land which comprises arable land, pastures and meadows, orchards and gardens. It is also conceivable to use different farm size limits for different parts of the country, depending upon the local differences in the economy. But the criterion of the size of farm, may be misleading since the area does not always reflect the nature of the farming. On several hectares of land we may have a cattle breeding farm with several dozens of cows fed with purchased fodder, or we may have a large-scale dairy farm. This type of enterprise is not a peasant farm. On several hectares a well-to-do owner may have a park, gardens and a villa in which he spends his summer holidays: this, of course, is not a peasant farm, or for that matter, not a farm at all. For this reason, instead of basing our classification of the size of the farm it may be better to take into consideration all the circumstances under which each farm operates.

Although more correct, this principle is not easily applied in practice. This, incidentally, is a good example of how the solving of the technical statistical aspect is connected with problems from the field of enquiry. What a peasant farm is has to be decided by socio-economic analysis, and only after this question has been answered can we seek a formal criterion as to exactly what population we wish to study. This formal criterion must be as simple as possible and easy to grasp; otherwise, it could not be applied in practice in such an extensive research as a census of peasant farms. The example of peasant farms indicates clearly how difficult it is to reconcile the requirement of exactness with that of simplicity.

For such problems as the one we have just been discussing, as for, indeed, all cases where statistical practice is involved, it is difficult to give a solution that will meet all objections. The examples given above should suffice, to give an idea what questions may arise and how they are solved by statisticians.

In spite of these difficulties the general rules for determining a population can be formulated. In order to define the population that we want to study we have to analyse it from the point of view of the branch of science to which it belongs. Often several solutions may be possible; then, by comparative analysis, we should study their usefulness, their relative advantages and disadvantages. On the other hand, we should consider the practical aspects—the possibilities of applying statistical methods to the problem.

The separation of the units we want to include from the others should be based on easily comprehended and not very complicated criteria. The lack of such criteria makes work difficult and may lead to substantial errors. If the simplicity of the criterion cannot be reconciled with the definition of the population resultant from the analysis of the problem, then a compromise solution should be sought so as to make the statistical task as easy as possible without deviating too much from that definition of the population which we recognize as the best.

b. *The timing of a study.* We shall discuss separately the conditions for making a census which describes the population at a given moment, and the conditions for conducting a registration which records the facts that take place within a certain period of time.

A census may be made once or may be repeated. If it is repeated, it is preferable that it be done periodically, at regular intervals. However this rule cannot always be strictly observed, especially in a capitalist economy. The results of a census of the unemployed may vary considerably depending on the phase of the business cycle at which it is made. If such a census is made, say every five years, and one falls due during a boom and another during a recession, then the results cannot be compared either with regard to the number of unemployed or with regard to the structure of unemployment. In such cases it may be better to adjust the timing of the census to the phase of the business cycle rather than to make it at regular intervals.

If it turns out that it is both possible and advisable to make a census at regular intervals then we should determine the length of the interval. It should be related to the nature of the statistical population. Every statistical population undergoes changes. The size of the population may change as well as the characteristics of its member units, and thus its structure may also change. These changes may be rapid or slow. In natural phenomena they may be so slow, so imperceptible, that for practical purposes the population can be regarded as unchanged; in such cases it may be sufficient to make one census. Populations connected with human society are subject to more or less rapid transformations. Sometimes, however, these transformations are relatively slow and uniform. The population of a country, as approached from a demographic point of view, belongs in this category. For this reasons a population census, under normal conditions, can be made at relatively long intervals. In most countries it is made every ten years, sometimes every five years. On the other hand the statistics on the livestock population cannot rely on  censuses taken every ten or even five years. Changes in the livestock population and its structure are rapid and irregular; in these circumstances censuses should be made every year or even more often.

The census is supposed to reflect the state of the population at a certain moment. Therefore, this moment should be clearly determined. The census cannot be spread over a long period of time since changes occurring in the population would make the results non-uniform and for different parts of the population would pertain to different times in the process of development. It would then be comparable to a photograph out of focus because the object we attempted to photograph had moved. In addition there is a difficulty of a practical nature: when the mobility of the units of which the population is composed is high the spreading of the census over a long period of time may result in counting certain units several times and omitting others altogether.

The requirement that the census should be made at a fixed time is usually interpreted as meaning that it should be completed in one day. This is both too small and too great a requirement. It is not enough to say that the census should be made on a certain day; the time must be more strictly defined. On the other hand, it may be impossible to complete the census within one day for technical reasons.

Modern statistics has a solution to this problem. On the one hand the time of the census is strictly determined, say the midnight between December 31 and January 1. On the other hand, the technical proceedings involved in completing the census are spread over a somewhat longer period say, several days. The material obtained is adjusted to fit the exact time selected for the census by correcting for any changes that may have occurred in the meantime. Such corrections may, of course, be difficult if a long period of time has elapsed.

Thus the length of time required for making the census should be reduced to a minimum. Only in a census of immobile populations can the requirement of a strictly defined time be relaxed. In such cases the census may be spread over a longer time without fear of distortion; we can even disregard the changes that have occurred between the selected and the actual time of making the census.

The next problem is the fixing of the date of the census: the time of the year and the day when the census is to be made. Sometimes it may be a matter of indifference. Then we should be guided by practical considerations such as convenience or the dates of others censuses. Under certain circumstances we may prefer to make several different censuses on the same day for the sake either of the problem studied or the technique and organization. In other cases, for practical reasons we may want to avoid having two censuses made too close to one another. Sometimes it may be worth while to set the date for the census on the same day as censuses in other countries so that we can better compare the results. On the other hand, there are cases where the fixing of the date of the census is of essential importance. This is particularly true with regard to populations in which changes are of a seasonal character, i. e. they are repeated at regular intervals at a certain time of the year. In such cases it is by no means indifferent which season we select for our census, because our choice may affect not only the results, but also their comparative significance. One such populations is livestock. Its size and structure change considerably during the year. In certain periods it may be quite plentiful because of new born animals; at other times its number may drop considerably. There is a great difference in the results of studying livestock at its peak and at its lowest point.

An expert studying the livestock problem from the point of view of breeding technique and from the point of view of economics will decide which of these figures is more suitable in a given case. It is quite possible that he will consider it worth while, or even necessary, to have several censuses at different times of the year.

In this field censuses are, in fact, often taken semi-annually or quarterly.

In more complex cases it may be difficult, or even impossible, to reconcile different types of requirements. For many reasons it is advisable to have a population census in winter time, when people are less mobile and it is easier to avoid errors caused by the difficulty in intercepting those who move. If, however, several countries decide to select the midnight between December 31 and January 1, then practical considerations may be of decisive moment. Many phenomena related to population are registered by statistics as they occur within the calendar year. Such phenomena can be more easily related to the state of the population if censuses are taken at the end of the calendar year. On that date, however, the main advantage of the winter period—the low mobility of the population—is questionable because just at Christmas and New Year time many people leave their permanent residence. With regard to population, there is also a basic difficulty related, not to technical considerations but to an essential feature of the population itself. For population censuses are also censuses of occupations and these cannot be considered as normal in winter.

From this point of view it might be better to select a different time of the year when the highest proportion of people are employed in their regular occupations. Thus, looking at the problem from different point of view we may have conflicting considerations. In such cases, we have to find a compromise depending upon the relative importance of our objectives and upon considerations of a practical nature.

If a population is subject to seasonal variations and censuses are to be repeated they should be made at the same time of the year for the results to be comparable. We cannot compare the livestock census made on July 1 in one year with that made on January 1 in another year.

Major difficulties appear when the cycle of periodic fluctuations is longer, for instance the business cycle in a capitalist country which affects all sectors of the economy. We may choose the period of the year for the population census, but it is difficult to take into consideration the phase of the business cycle in selecting the date. If we decide to make censuses at 10-year intervals, one of them may occur during a boom and another during a depression. Changes in business conditions definitely affect different population phenomena, primarily those of an occupational and employment nature. During a depression there are more unemployed, fewer employed, and there are shifts in the occupation structure. But business conditions may also exert a considerable influence in other fields. During prosperity the process of urbanization and a shift from agricultural to industrial and commercial occupations may be speeded up; during recessions these processes are slowed down and sometimes even reversed. Strictly speaking, the results of the censuses made at different phases of the business cycle are not comparable. So far, little attention has been paid to this fact. Among other reasons, this has been due to the fact that long-term population trends are of over-riding intensity in comparison with population changes due to business cycles. A census made ten years after the preceding one will almost always show an increase in the urbanization process, a relative increase in industrial and commercial occupations, even if the first census was made during a boom, and the second during a depression. In such cases, however, on the basis of available data we can judge the long-run trend correctly only in general terms, but we cannot draw immediate conclusions concerning the rate of change.

Since the dates of censuses are not adjusted to the phase of the business cycle we have to allow for business fluctuations in analysing the results of the census, and particularly in comparing the results of different censuses. This more sophisticated type of analysis is possible after we learn about the relations between the business cycle and the demographic phenomena. These considerations should be taken into account in analysing the results of censuses in capitalist countries which are subject to business fluctuations.

The problem is different when the element of time concerns, not a census but a registration in which we want to record facts that occurred within a certain period of time. This type of study is of a continuous nature and the problem to be settled is the frequency with which we want to receive reports on what has taken place. In some cases we receive information on each event separately as soon as it has occurred. The physician reports each case of contagious diseases that he encounters in his practice. More often, however, reports are submitted at certain intervals—once a year, once a month, or even weekly or daily, depending upon the importance of the information being up-to-date. It is also possible to design annual reports in such a way as to show information for each month separately. Reports may also give information about each event separately. For instance, in quarterly vital statistical reports the data on children born and persons deceased may be recorded separately.

Regardless of the frequency of the reports it is important that they be submitted as soon as possible after the end of the reporting period. This speeds up the processing, facilitates control and expedites the work of those reporting. It should be remembered, however, that the deadlines must be realistic and must take into consideration the date when the reporter receives information himself and the length of time needed by him to make the necessary tabulations.

c. *The scope of the study*. After defining the population that we want to analyse we have to decide which characteristics of its units have to be taken into consideration. Sometimes we may confine ourselves to a few very simple characteristics and their choice presents no difficulties. If the object of our study is to establish some main index, e.g. the ratio of the length to the width of the skull, and nothing else, the material to be collected will always contain only two measurements: the length and the width. In most cases, however, the matter is not quite so simple. We may know which population we have to analyse but the scope of analysis may be broad or narrow. In studying farms we may confine ourselves to giving their size and area according to the type of cultivation (arable land, meadows, pastures, etc.); or we may also consider the type of crop (the area under wheat, rye, potatoes and other crops), agricultural machinery used for cultivation and harvesting, the number and type of farm workers, and many other characteristics.

Generally speaking, the number and type of questions are related to the purpose of the study, and for this reason both the immediate object of analysis and the number of characteristics to be taken into account should be considered jointly. Even if the purpose of the study is precisely stated, the problem of what questions should be asked is not always automatically solved. The questions may be limited to the most necessary characteristics, or we may want to take advantage of the fact that the study has been embarked upon and ask questions only loosely connected with the actual study. In principle, such a broadening of the scope of analysis beyond its actual objective is not advisable since if defies the principle of the economy of effort. A tendency in this direction, however, is understandable since it may lead to a better knowledge of the problem. Moreover it is so troublesome to organize the collection of material that we may be tempted to extend the scope of analysis—even so as to include quite new problems—merely because the additional cost of obtaining new information not originally required is quite negligible.

In order to maintain a sense of perspective, we have to consider several aspects of the matter. The original task of the study is basic, and anything that might interfere with it should be rejected *a priori*. Additional questions make the questionnaire form more complicated and the work of all those involved in the study more difficult. This applies both to those who answer the questions and to those who direct and control the job of collecting the material. Too many complications may induce reluctance and carelessness in the people involved and thus spoil the results. On the other hand, the desire to make an analysis more penetrating is undoubtedly legitimate even when it is not absolutely necessary for the immediate purpose of the study. In such cases there may be a conflict between the requirements of statistical technique, narrowly interpreted, and the broader scientific objectives, both theoretical and practical. Very often, both research workers and those responsible for realizing the scientific conclusions demand the inclusion of additional questions because there is an opportunity to do so. The statistical technician opposes such a broadening of the scope of the enquiry. It should not be difficult to reach a compromise if both sides show moderation: those who want to extend the scope of the study should understand the priority of the current needs it is to satisfy, and the statistical technicians should realize the scientific and practical importance of making a study more far-reaching. In the final analysis, the technical possibilities and the amount of available resources may turn out to be decisive. In solving the conflict the experience of the practicing statistician will be helpful since he should know best what can be achieved under the circumstances.

The same considerations will apply to studies of a purely scientific nature, without any immediate practical implications. In these cases too, we must be guided by the means and resources available, which must suffice both for collecting the material and for its subsequent tabulation and processing.

Related to the question just discussed is the problem of the advisability and feasibility of combining several statistical enquiries into one large statistical operation. This is often possible and, under certain circumstances, may produce considerable savings in cost in comparison with the total joint cost of such studies undertaken separately. Savings are primarily due to the possibility of using one organizational set-up—which is always expensive—for several enquiries. The combining of several enquiries on problems that are different but related to each other will undoubtedly contribute to a better understanding of reality. On the other hand, all the reservations concerning unnecessary complications, too many questions, etc., remain valid and should be kept in mind.

In general, the greater the material resources at our disposal, the more intelligent and better trained the staff employed and the more accustomed to statistical enquiries the population to which the questions are addressed, the easier it is to extend the scope of enquiry.

d. *Proper formulation of questions.* The results of an enquiry depend, to a large extent, upon whether the questions that have to be answered have been properly formulated. They should be simple, clear, and easy to answer. However, in this respect many statistical enquiries show considerable deficiencies which may render questionable the results obtained and thus the usefulness of the whole enquiry. A proper formulation of questions in statistical enquiries is difficult and requires a lot of care, skill and experience. Questions should be as short as possible, both to save space and to make it easy for those questioned. At the same time questions should be clear, unambiguous and easily understandable. Any experienced statistician can amuse us with stories of misunderstandings met in answering seemingly simple questions. Such misunderstandings are more likely to occur during questionnaire surveys in large countries with different ethnic groups. The same word may have different meanings in different parts of the country or in different population groups. Sometimes the name of a profession or trade may have different meanings, or the same occupation may be known under different names in different parts of the country.

Statistical experience suggests certain rules in formulating questions to help secure the correct answers. The questions should be clear and precise so as to induce brief and precise answers. It is often possible to formulate a question so that it is answerable by a simple "yes" or "no", or by writing only one word or one number. Sometimes it is helpful to list all possible answers. For instance, on statistical forms for industrial establishments there may be the question: "Does the establishment possess a motor?" The answer can be suggested: "Yes or no". The next question: "If so, how many?" has a number for answer. The next question may be: "Type of motor?". In order to facilitate the answer and avoid possible misunderstandings we may list the types ("Answer whether steam turbine or steam engine or hydro-turbine, etc."). Thus the answer is reduced to a simple underlining of an appropriate word or to crossing out the unnecessary words. Listing the answers also serves to eliminate possible misundertandings and make the answer easier—when it is *exhaustive,* i.e. when *all* possible answers are given. In our example this would amount to listing all possible types of motors. It is possible to list only the more important answers, adding at the end: "etc", or better: "or others (name the type)". In such cases, however, the person asked may try to force his answer into one of the listed categories thus giving misleading information.

It is obvious that we should avoid asking *unnecessary* questions, i.e. the questions that we shall not work upon. However, we may include additional *control* questions which are of no basic importance by themselves but may help in checking whether the main question had been properly understood and whether the answers are correct. Such control questions may play an important part in obtaining reliable statistical material.

The proper formulation of questions also depends on the design of the questionnaire form.

e. *Design of questionnaire. Explanations. Instructions.* There are two main types of statistical questionnaire: an individual form and a list. In the first case, each unit in the population has a separate sheet of form on which we put all the required information pertaining to this particular unit. The questions are placed on the sheet so that the answers can be written next to the appropriate questions. The list type is designed so that it can contain information on more than one unit—several or even several dozen units. Usually the questions are placed at the top of the list and the answers are given in appropriate columns; for each unit we can allow one or several lines, according to need. Less frequently the questions are placed in lines on the left-hand side of the sheet. Information on each separate unit will then be found in one particular column.

Both types—the individual form and the list—have certain advantages. On an individual form we have more room, we can place the questions more conveniently, formulate them with less brevity and provide all the necessary explanations. We can also leave more space for the answers which can thus be written more legibly— an important consideration, particularly when our informants are not used to writing. On individual forms it is also easier to use various special methods to facilitate answers. On the other hand, it is easier to give answers on a list, and the whole picture is clearer and more lucid, which is important from the point of view of checking the results. It is also easier to store such material and to check its completeness. Thus we have to decide in each case which type of questionnaire is preferable and which we should select. Quite often our choice may be influenced by the method of tabulation, which we shall discuss later. If we decide in favour of the *filing card system* then we should probably select an individual form type of questionnaire; for other methods of processing statistical material a list is usually more convenient. Sometimes, however, the confidential nature of the statistical material may make the list type of questionnaire undesirable, because those who fill in the form may see what has been written by others and thus violate the principle of secrecy. Even if a list is filled in by a special employee, those who are interested may steal a glance at previous entries. This consideration has to be taken into account in choosing the type of questionnaire

A list may be designed to contain information only about a defined group of units, e.g. in population censuses all persons belonging to one family or living in one apartment; or a list may be designed so that no particular groups are singled out, but entries are made as information is obtained. In the first case, after obtaining the data on all the units belonging to a given group we take a new form, and if the number of units in the group is greater than the number of lines or columns on the list we have to fill in an additional list, supplementary to the first. Such lists for definite groups of units are less economical since on each sheet there is almost always quite a lot of space left, but they are very useful when we are concerned not only with particular units of which the population is composed, but also with a certain group of those units—in our example, the families or groups of people living in one apartment. By using a separate sheet for each group we have the group separated and the task of checking and processing the material is made easier. This type of consideration does not enter into the picture when we list consecutively events that are not related to each other, e.g. the persons deceased during a certain period listed in the chronological order of the date of death.

In considering the design of the questionnaire we also have to take into account such matters as explanations of the meaning of particular questions, the way they should be answered, other comments on filling in the questionnaire, the checking of entries and further processing of filled-in questionnaires.

Explanations and instructions can be roughly divided into two categories. To the first belong those directly related to filling in the questionnaire. Here we would have all the explanations concerning the meaning of particular questions, the form in which answers should be given, etc. Explanations of this kind should be as close to the question as possible (e.g. directly under the question) and, in any case, they should be on the questionnaire form. If explanations are not given with the question they should be placed in a conspicuous place, preferably at the top or at the bottom of the sheet. General comments should be separated from explanations concerning particular questions. Such explanations can also be given in the reference form at the bottom of the sheet with reference marks placed at appropriate questions.

On the other hand, it may be necessary to give more detailed instructions on filling in the questionnaire and the procedure to be observed in the whole enquiry. Such instructions may also be printed on the questionnaire form if there is enough room; or they can be given separately, particularly when they are addressed not to those who give the answers but to the employees who collect the material. In the latter case instructions and explanation should be more detailed, and should take into account rare and special cases in which certain difficulties may arise. However, these instructions should also be relatively short since experience shows that long instructions are read reluctantly and carelessly.

The questions should be so arranged on the questionnaire form as to facilitate the answer, e.g. questions on related subjects should be close to each other. Sometimes the design of the questionnaire depends upon technical considerations connected with the intended method of tabulating the collected material.

The above remarks on the design of the questionnaire are purposely (and of necessity) presented in a somewhat misleading manner. It is impossible to give rigid rules for a good design of a questionnaire since it is impossible to include all the great variety of different conditions that are encountered in statistical practice. Each particular case should be planned on the basis of a thorough knowledge of all the circumstances in which the enquiry is undertaken, its purpose, the sources on which the answers should be based, the intellectual level and the experience in giving answers on the part of the persons to whom the questions are addressed, the number and quality of the auxiliary statistical personnel, the means at our disposal, etc. Besides meeting the considerations enumerated above, each case should be based on statistical experience gained in preparing similar studies.

We can in conclusion that to design a questionnaire is a difficult task which requires much time and effort even when done by experienced statisticians. A thoughtless design may cause difficulty in filling in the questionnaire and may result in errors which considerably lower the value of the study or even render it worthless.

f. *The organization of the study.* In order to understand how complicated and responsible is the organization of an extensive statistical enquiry, it should suffice to comprehend the magnitude of such a venture. A large census comprises millions or tens of millions of units. The number of questionnaires required goes into the millions; they must be supplied in time and properly distributed to be available at the right time and in the required amount. It is necessary to organize the whole procedure involved in filling them in, checking, collecting and handing them over to the institution concerned. Up to hundreds of thousands of people may be directly employed in collecting information for the census. They have to be properly selected and trained since for most of them the job will be new and unfamiliar.

It may be possible to take advantage of the existing administrative apparatus (e.g. local government) in making a census; this considerably facilitates the work and reduces the cost. The matter should be handled with great care, however. On the one hand, it is not advisable to overburden the administrative personnel with additional work because this may adversely affect their regular routine work. On the other hand, if the statistical material is collected by the administrative personnel the people questioned may react unfavourably. If, for instance, the employees of the treasury department take part in the enquiry, and if this enquiry touches upon the financial position of the population, a suspicion may easily arise that the enquiry is really intended for tax purposes and the resultant fear may prompt people to give false information. Nevertheless, the participation of the administrative authorities is permissible, and may be very valuable when they can facilitate the checking of the answers.

In every extensive statistical enquiry a considerable number of specially trained employees must be engaged. Those employed for collecting data for the census are usually called census enumerators. Their tasks may differ, depending upon who is supposed to fill in the questionnaire. Sometimes this is done by the person queried; in population censuses it will be the head of the house, in agricultural censuses, it will be the person managing the farm, etc. In these cases the role of the census enumerator is relatively simple: his main job is to see to it that the questionnaires are delivered in time to all those concerned and returned before the deadline. In cases of smaller enquiries this task can be assigned to the employees of the central statistical office or of the local administrative authorities. For large inquiries (e.g. in general population censuses) it is necessary to engage special census personnel even when the people are to fill in the questionnaires themselves, since the job of checking involves millions of questionnaires.

To assign the task of filling in the questionnaires to the persons queried is possible only under especially favourable circumstances. They must be fairly well educated, and they should be somewhat familiar with statistics so that they can understand the questions and answer them correctly. This can be expected from the managers of large industrial or commercial establishments who have at their disposal adequate and properly trained administrative staff. On the other hand the majority of the peasant population will not be able to fill in a questionnaire correctly, especially when the questionnaire is fairly complicated. Even the filling in of a relatively simple one may be too difficult a task for many a peasant. In all such cases the census enumerators will not only have to distribute and collect the questionnaires, but also to fill them in. Thus their job becomes much more responsible and burdensome and their number must be increased accordingly.

Different countries approach this problem in various ways. Some try to have the questionnaires filled in by the person queried in as many statistical enquiries as possible. This lowers the cost of the enquiry and simplifies the problem of organization. However, it can be done only when the conditions discussed above are satisfied. Besides, this method is possible only in relatively simple statistical investigations. For these reasons many statisticians working in the field feel that, as a rule, it is better to conduct an enquiry with the help of especially hired personnel who not only collect the questionnaires, but also fill them in. This guarantees that they are properly completed and enables the initiators of the enquiry to pose the problems in a more appropriate way since they do not have to worry about making the questionnaire complicated or long if necessary. The choice of this method depends, however, upon the chances of finding enough people with sufficient qualifications and upon the financial means available.

The staff hired for conducting a census must be properly selected and trained for this responsible job. In countries where the educational level is relatively low, it may be very difficult to find a sufficiently large number of literate and bright people who have enough time to undertake the job. It is often necessary to ask certain types of civil servants, such as teachers, for cooperation. If this is the case they should be relieved, at least partially, of their regular duties while they work on the census; advantage may be taken of holidays or vacation periods. University and high school students may also be hired for this kind of work.

In simpler cases personnel training can be limited to supplying printed instructions. In more complex enquiries special courses can be arranged together with practical demonstrations, possibly followed by an examination. Such courses should not be too burdensome for the participants although a certain minimum standard of training should be ensured. After training the census personnel are usually supplied with appropriate identity cards and during the census act, in a sense, as civil servants. This gives them certain rights with respect to those who are to be querried. For example, they can demand answers to the questions, require the presentation of certain documents, etc. But this also imposes upon them certain obligations, such as the completion of the tasks assigned, not withdrawing from them in such a way as to endanger the whole enquiry and performing their functions conscientiously and promptly. Finally, the census enumerators are obliged to treat the information obtained as confidential and not to impair the principle of the secrecy of statistical information if this principle is involved in the investigation. Both the rights and the obligations of the census enumerators should be clearly stated in appropriate regulatioms.

A great deal is expected of the census enumerator, and his work is often burdensome, always responsible, and sometimes very hard and long. The census may last for a week or longer. In principle this type of work should be properly paid. Considering the great number of enumerators engaged in the census work the total cost is very high even when the rate of pay is relatively low. For this reason the government may sometimes try to obtain enumerators without pay by appealing to their civic sense of duty or by imposing additional duties on the civil service staff. This sort of practice must sometimes be tolerated since the reason for it is a desire to reduce the cost, but, in principle, it should be regarded as unjustified.

g. *The attitude of the population toward statistical enquiry.* The results of a statistical enquiry depend, to a large extent, upon the attitude of the people who answer the questions. If they are unwilling, and particularly when they are afraid that the census may have unpleasant consequences for them (e.g. new taxes), the results of the statistical enquiry must be adversely affected. The persons from whom one wishes to obtain information will then try to avoid giving answers, or will give inaccurate, if not altogether false information. Even the mere reluctance toward the enquiry, not complicated by any particular fears, and stemming simply from the lack of understanding of its purpose or from excessive questioning, or even from the coincidence of too frequent enquiries, may have undesirable effects. A skillful propaganda campaign may somewhat counteract this sort of negative attitude. The type of propaganda will depend upon the type of person to whom it is directed. In special enquires pertaining only to well-educated people, it may suffice to state briefly the objective of the enquiry. Sometimes a propaganda campaign may have to be carefully prepared. A popular explanation of the purpose of the investigation may have to be given in such a way as to make clear its administrative and scientific objectives and to get people interested in the results—in short, in such a way as to change an indifferent or even hostile attitude into an actively friendly one.

One of the basic conditions of achieving this aim is the conviction of the queried that the census will harm nobody and therefore correct and true answers should be given. Such a conviction will be widespread only when it is generally known that the information obtained for statistical purposes will be made public only in a statistical form, or in other words that the principle of the secrecy of statistics will be preserved. This principle is usually expressed by stating clearly that information obtained in the course of the statistical enquiry may be used exclusively for statistical purposes, i.e. can be made public only in the form of tables so designed as to make it impossible to derive information concerning particular units. The census authorities or the census enumerators have no right to disclose individual statistical information to anybody, be it a private individual or an institution. In this way, for instance, information on the financial situation of any person obtained in the course of a statistical enquiry cannot be passed on to the treasury authorities for tax purposes. Similarly, no personal information can get into the hands of unauthorized persons lest some publicity harmful to the queried result. The prime condition for the success of the enquiry is the trust of the population. To gain this trust it might be worth while to state clearly the confidential nature of the enquiry in some conspicuous place on the questionnaire.

This consideration ceases to play a part in a socialist economy when the reporting unit is a socialized enterprise. However, in a socialist economy, especially during the period of transition to socialism, the observance of the principle of the secrecy of statistics in certain fields is very useful, it not necessary, from the point of view of the results of the enquiry.

The principle of statistical secrecy facilitates the tasks of the propaganda campaign for the census by removing a very important source of fear. It is necessary, of course, to convince the population that the principle of secrecy will actually be observed. Besides, the right kind of propaganda campaign should not only prove that the census will not bring harm to anybody but also that it is necessary, useful and even interesting. Only then will the answers be given willingly and in good faith.

Where the pre-census propaganda fails the rest should be accomplished by the census enumerator directly involved in the enquiry. His function is to convince directly those who give the answers. However, it may happen that some people will refuse to answer questions or will give obviously false information. The legislation or regulations concerning statistics usually provide for a special procedure in such cases. It may be stated in the regulations that every person queried in the course of a statistical enquiry is obliged to give true answers to the questions and that a refusal to answer or giving false answer is punishable. The statistician does not like to resort to this kind of regulation or to impose penalties, rightly considering that the best answers are those which are given voluntarily and willingly. In some cases, however, when it is impossible to obtain true answers on the basis of good will the existence of such regulations may be very useful. Sometimes the enumerator is authorized to check certain documents and this should also be clearly stated in the appropriate acts or regulations.

In the final analysis, however, much depends upon the skill of approach, tact and inventiveness, of the enumerator collecting the information. For this reason the proper selection of the personnel is of great importance.

h. *The completeness and correctness of statistical material.* The whole organization of a statistical enquiry should be geared to the most important objective—the ensuring of the completeness of the statistical data. This is the aim of all the measures discussed above. It should be added that the organization of a census should be precise enough to prevent the omission of any unit belonging to the population analysed. This requires special measures. The point is to make sure that every person in the population from whom we want to obtain information gets the questionnaire, and that all the questionnaires are properly completed and returned to the institution responsible for the processing of the material. The difficulty with this requirement lies chiefly in the first part—to reach every unit of the population. The second part—the control over the collecting of filled-in questionnaires—is relatively simple since it is fairly easy to lay down rules concerning the flow of completed questionnaires that will ensure their speedy and complete delivery to the central statistical office. With regard to the first part, we can resort to different measures depending upon the circumstances. The most important one is the preparation of a list of all the units included in the investigation. Sometimes this does not involve any major difficulty. If the census concerns, major industrial establishments, appropriate lists may be obtained from the administrative authorities (the treasury or industrial division). Sometimes, however it is impossible to prepare a list before embarking upon a statistical enquiry. Let us take a population census as an example. One of its objectives is to establish the number of people, so we are obviously in no position to know beforehand all the inhabitants and their addresses. But it is possible to make a list of all inhabited localities. With the help of this list the census authorities may check that no locality had been omitted. It is also possible and advisable to give the census enumerator a list of real estate in his area. This helps to control the completeness, and makes it easier to reach every home or apartment. There remains the very important question of making sure that all the people living in every a flat are taken into account. This depends, to a very large extent, upon the conscientiousness and skill of the census enumerator. It is difficult, however, to have complete certainty, especially when the attitude of the population toward the census is negative. In some cases the census enumerator can check on the spot the actual state of affairs, e.g. the number and kind of animals in stables, cow barns and at pasture (providing the people do not try to hide some of their livestock).

The problem is much more difficult when we are making not a census, but a registration of certain events that have occurred within a certain period of time. Only in exceptional cases is it possible to establish how many events of interest to us have actually occurred, unless a registration of them has been carried on for some other, non-statistical reason. Therefore a registration as a purely statistical function is resorted to only very rarely. Most commonly, secondary statistical material is used for this purpose, or a statistical investigation based on non-statistical activities of the administrative authorities.

The safeguards that should be used in order to obtain correct answers have already been discussed. The census enumerator usually makes an initial check of these safeguards. He may confine himself to ascertaining that all the blank spaces of the questionnaire have been filled in; he may have to make a rough check of the answers. A further and more exact control usually starts later, in the course of processing the collected material. This subject, together with the methods of control, will be discussed later. We shall then raise another important matter—errors in statistics which cannot be completely eliminated and which have to be dealt with somehow.

## 3. SECONDARY STATISTICAL MATERIAL. THE COMBINING OF STATISTICAL RESEARCH WITH ADMINISTRATIVE FUNCTIONS

In the course of regular administrative work many facts come to light and are recorded. Their statistical interpretation is important not only from the administrative point of view, but also from the general point of view of learning about the phenomena that take place in human society. For instance, railway ticket offices have to keep records of railway tickets sold; this is necessary for the purpose of accounting and current job control. Statistics based on such current records enable the management to control the production of tickets and their distribution in appropriate numbers to particular wickets. Statistics broken down by routes and classes give the management an idea about the traffic on particular routes, and this enables them to regulate the frequency of trains, the number of cars, etc. However, the same statistics are also important outside railway companies since they throw some light on population movements, their direction and intensity, and so on.

Statistical material from non-statistical sources, and based on records used in the regular course of administrative activities, we call *secondary statistical material*.

Statistical interpretation of this kind of non-statistical administrative documents is relatively simple and inexpensive and definitely much less costly than a similar investigation especially embarked upon. In most cases it will not be necessary to employ additional personnel for collecting material for further statistical processing.[21]

Statistics based on secondary material may be either of a census or a registration type. On the basis of residence registrations we may obtain tables giving us the population figure at a certain date: from the point of view of statistics this will be a census. We can also get birth statistics for a given year from the birth registration records for this year: this will be a registration from the statistical point of view. In the last case secondary material is particularly valuable, since in the statistical recording of facts occurring within a certain period we encounter the greatest difficulties.

The use of secondary statistical material has many advantages in comparison

---

[21] We have in mind here the use of documents, possessed by the administrative authorities, for general statistical purposes. Naturally, these documents are an important source of information for evaluating the work of the administration and they should be—although not always are—used primarily for this purpose.

with the direct collecting of information. In this way we avoid a major part of the expense and trouble connected with the collecting of information. The facts are established and registered, and it suffices to make appropriate notes for further statistical processing. Since such facts are often documented there is no problem of checking their authenticity. Thus the whole study may be not only less expensive but also more reliable.

Attention should be drawn, however, to certain qualities of secondary material which may lower its value for statistical purposes. First of all, the conditions that we recognized as being of particular importance with reference to secondary material are not always satisfied: the data are not always precise and exhaustive. The reason may be a faulty functioning of the administrative machinery in a given sector. It is obvious that in such cases both the administrator and the statistician are interested in removing the source of trouble. However, this is not always easily done, particularly when the facts of special interest to the statistician are less important from the administrative point of view and the introduction of additional control would be troublesome. It may also happen that administrative registration does not take into account all the facts in a given category, but only some of them—e.g. not all the industrial establishments in a certain industry, but only those which pay a certain type of tax. In this case, a registration of all establishments is clearly unfeasible from an administrative point of view, and if we still wish to use the material we must take this shortcoming into account.

Similar conflicts between the requirements of statistics and the objectives of the administration may arise with regard to the question of a greater or smaller amount of information on the registered facts. More detailed information may be needed for statistical than for administrative purposes (e.g. a more exhaustive description of industrial establishments). In such cases the two types of requirements can seldom be reconciled since only in very few cases can the administrative authorities introduce additional information into their records just because it is needed by the statistician.

The greatest and the most important difficulty from the point of view of statistics is the fact that the administrative records of their very nature reflect a certain legal situation which does not always fit the situation of interest to the statistician. For instance, treasury records show the number of farms and the area of taxable land. This material is of great importance for students of agrarian relations and on its basis exact and comprehensive statistics on farming can be prepared. It is necessary to know, however, whether a taxable unit is identical with the notion of a farm in agricultural economics. Quite often a taxable unit means, in fact, something quite different, since for tax purposes particular parcels of land acquired by one person in different ways are treated as separate taxable units; and under the term farm we understand all land used and administered by one centre of decision. Thus the number of taxable units will be greater than the number of farms, and the size of the former will be smaller, so that the economist who drew his conclusions on the agrarian structure from such statistics would be quite wrong. It may also happen that the treasury records do not show the total area of the farm, but only the taxable area. The non-taxable area may vary depending upon tax regulations and its size may depend upon non-economic considerations. Statistics based on such data will depict the situation correctly from the fiscal point of view, but may be quite misleading from the economic point of view.

Let us take another example. The income tax records are an excellent and often unique source of information on the distribution of income in society. It may be questionable whether income declarations are true, but at least they are carefully checked and there is no better source of information available. But do these records reflect the actual structure of income? Do they pertain to the whole income, or only to its taxable part? Do they comprise the whole population, or only its tax-paying part? The differences may be quite considerable. Very low income groups are usually exempted from income tax. Some other groups may also be exempt (e.g. civil servants). If this is the case such statistics will not give the full picture of the distribution of income.

In such cases there are two possible solutions from the point of view of the statistician: either to forgo the secondary material and carry out, if possible, a direct inquiry; or to use the secondary material as it is and to qualify the conclusions to allow for its incompleteness. Sometimes it may be worth while to fill the gap from another source, even if by a rough estimate, since even somewhat distorted data may throw some light on the problem if we take into account the type and dimension of the distortions.

In any case, one basic guiding principle concerning the use of administrative data for statistical purposes follows from the above examples and discussion: the statistician, as well as the research worker who uses statistics, must know exactly how the administrative documents are drawn up, must understand their purpose, and know how they compare with the reality which the statistics are supposed to depict. Disregarding this requirement must lead to erroneous conclusions. The statistician should always analyse and comment upon the  meaning and significance of the statistical reports he prepares, and the research worker using them should take into account all the existing reservations. Unfortunately this postulate is often disregarded, and this is one of the main reasons why statistics is often accused of being at odds with reality.

In spite of all these reservations administrative material contains an abundance of very valuable information which is rarely used.

As far as registration is concerned, certain difficulties may arise from the fact that the date of making out an administrative document often differs from the date on which the registered event occurred (e.g. the date of making out the birth certificate may be different from the date of birth). Sometimes this is of no importance, but in certain cases it may lead to errors. However, the administrative document, as a rule, contains enough information to establish the right date. Anyhow, the statistician or any person using statistics must know whether the dates refer to the moment when the event occurred or to the moment when the document was made out. If they refer to the time of making out the document then he should find out the length of time by which these two dates differ.

If the content of the administrative document is unsatisfactory from the point of view of statistics, but the registration of the facts in which we are interested is sufficiently complete, we can take advantage of this registration to conduct a direct statistical enquiry. The administrative records may be helpful in obtaining the required information which may be quite difficult in a direct investigation. The collecting of statistical material then consists of the filling in of special statistical questionnaires. An example of this procedure can be found in foreign trade statistics. It is a regular routine that each shipment of goods from and to the country must be declared at the customs office. It would seem that statistics could be based on customs declaration, but this would be too inconvenient technically, and also inadequate since they do not contain all the data that the statistician would like to have. If it is not possible to include additional questions in the customs declaration form it might be advisable to require the completion of a statistical declaration in addition to the customs declaration and have it mailed to the statistical office for further processing. The advantages may be considerable since the statistical office is thus certain to receive all the needed information if, as can be taken for granted in a well organized state, there is no considerable smuggling of goods. In this way the statistical office receives the information in the form convenient from the point of view of data processing and the customs office, which is only an intermediate link in collecting and passing over the information, is not burdened with statistical work.

Another example of combining administrative work with collecting statistical data can be found in population statistics. A direct registration of births, deaths and marriages for statistical purposes is very difficult, and almost never used. But the registration of these facts is necessary from the point of view of civil legislation and in most countries is organized with great accuracy. Under these circumstances the persons responsible for keeping the records of such events may be instructed to prepare additional statistical reports. Information contained in such reports may be based partially on the vital statistics certificates issued and partially on the specially obtained statistical information.

A separate technical problem is the method of using the secondary material possessed by a given administrative unit. The question to be settled is: by whom and how should the statistical tables be prepared on the basis of individual data? It may be done by the clerk who handles the administrative material in question. This would be "unseparated" statistics, permissible, as we already know, only in the cases of very simple tabulations. In all cases in which we want to have more complex tables it is necessary to give a statistical worker direct access to the accumulated material. This can be done in several ways:

(1) The administrative unit loans the documents to the statistical clerk for the duration of the study. However, this is almost always impossible because the documents are needed for current administrative work unless they pertain to problems that have ceased to be current, in which case they reach the statistician with too much delay, and will thus usually be of little practical value.

(2) The statistical clerk is assigned to the administrative unit concerned and works on the material there. This solution is also seldom used since such statistics may upset the regular administrative routine.

(3) The documents in question are made out in two identical copies; one of them is used for administrative purposes and the other is sent to the statistical bureau where it becomes a statistical document. In this way the statistical bureau may receive, e.g. an additional copy of the registration licence bought by industrial and commercial establishments. This method of making the material available is very good since it does not constitute a burden on the administrative unit and ensures the prompt delivery of the document to the statistical bureau.

(4) If it is not possible to have the document made out in more than one copy then an additional copy should be made out as soon as possible by an administrative clerk or a statistical clerk specially assigned for this purpose.

(5) Much less work is involved if instead of making out an additional copy only the information needed for statistical purposes is extracted. Only in very rare cases is all the information contained in the document needed for statistical purposes. Also the design of the administrative document is usually much more complex than is necessary from the purely statistical point of view. The extract, on the other hand, is usually very simple, especially if it is in the form of a list and not individual cards.

The situation is different, of course, when we have to make out a separate statistical document on the basis of administrative registration.

As we can see, the use of secondary material for statistical purposes usually requires quite a lot of work in making copies of documents or extracts from them. However, even when we make full sopies it is much less expensive to use, secondary material than to resort to original research for which we have to create a special organization to collect material.

Later we shall discuss special ways of lowering costs in statistics, both in secondary and original investigation.

## 4. PARTIAL STATISTICAL ENQUIRY

Statistical enquiry may be exhaustive: it may include the whole population studied. All units belonging to the population are described and the results tabulated. Quite often, however, such an exhaustive investigation is impossible or not necessary either because the population is too large and it would not be technically possible to investigate all the units, or because the financial and technical means at our disposal do not permit us to engage in an exhaustive research, or because sufficiently precise results can be obtained in some other way. The first case often occurs in the natural sciences. Let us suppose that the statistical enquiry is to relate to the leaves of the birch—the example that we used before. An exhaustive research would here involve the measuring and description of all the leaves on all the birch trees in a given forest. This would not be feassible and, in fact, would be pointless, since the same objective can be fully achieved by investigating only some of these leaves. Also in the social sciences we often either cannot, or do not want to engage in such an exhaustive research. Instead of making a census of all the population of a country we can confine ourselves to a certain part of this population and on this basis arrive at conclusions concerning the whole. The advantages of such a procedure are obvious: we can undertake tasks which could not be carried out by exhaustive research; we can widen the scope of our research to include new fields, or deepen our research by a more comprehensive approach to the problem. By thus saving money on some enquiries we can undertake new ones. The essential question to be determined is whether and under what conditions a partial enquiry can produce satisfactory results, i.e. when it will permit us to draw valid and sufficiently precise conclusions about the whole population.

We cannot now give the proof of our answer since it is based on the theory of probability which will be discussed later. However we can give a commonsense answer based on intuition.

The application of the results of partial research to the whole population may be understood in two ways. Either we wish to find the total number of units in a population on the basis of the number of units in a certain part of this population, or we want to find out what relations prevail in the whole population and what its structure is, by studying a part of the population. Both are possible under certain circumstances. In order to establish the size of the population on the basis of the size of a part we have to know how big is the part studied. We can determine the number of red corpuscles in the blood of a person if we know how many on the average appear in a sample viewed through a microscope and what is the proportion of the blood seen in the microscope to the person's total blood. The second problem can also be solved easily if we have a right to assume that the structure of the whole population is the same as the structure of the part investigated. Then we simply extend to the whole population our findings concerning the relations in the part of the population.

Thus we have the first condition that must be satisfied in a partial enquiry if we are to base our inference on it: the relations among the units selected for investigation must be the same as the relations in the whole population. This means, with reference to our first example of blood analysis, that the proportion of red corpuscles in the blood taken for analysis is the same as in all the blood of the given person. In the second case we assume that the structure of the whole population is basically the same as the structure of the part analysed.

These requirements are obvious. The difficulty consists only in finding a way of selecting units for enquiry that satisfy the requirements. Statistics tell us that the best guarantee of obtaining correct results is the random selection of units, adapted to the requirements of the study. It may appear, at first glance, that this would be contrary to our intuition which may lead us to believe that by random selection we expose ourselves to the danger of getting accidental results. The proof of the correctness of this procedure can be given only on the basis of probability theory. We can say, however, that random selection avoids the danger of bias in obtaining units for analysis and that for a large number of observations deviations in different directions will cancel out.

Partial investigation based on random selection is called *sampling*.

It is not always possible, however, to arrange for the right kind of random selection. In such cases we should try to find a method of selecting a sample that will ensure the correct result. We can try to select by conscious choice those units which can represent the whole population. But we should, by all means, avoid one error which we may instinctively commit. The population is not properly represented by only those units which are most characteristic of it (or average) and which do not deviate much one way or another from the most common type. They do not represent the population sufficiently because it is necessary to characterize not only the average type but also the deviations from it. For this reason the sample should also comprise deviations from the norm and, moreover, the number of deviating units should be included in an appropriate numerical proportion. Sometimes we may be able to find a correct solution by investigating certain compact parts of the population of which we have a right to think that they are characteristic of the whole. For instance, in studying the relations among the peasant population we may select for investigation a number of villages in the country and analyse them completely. We can assume that within these villages we shall find not only the same general level as among the whole peasant population, but also similar deviations. The difficulty lies in making a proper selection of these villages. To do so we may be guided by our knowledge of peasant relations, and choose typical villages in different parts of the country. It would be erroneous, however, to select a part of the country and subject it to an exhaustive investigation; it is quite likely that the relations in that part of the country will differ from those in the country as a whole.

The above example indicates that before making a choice we should be well acquainted with the problem that we want to analyse. This is the weak side of this type of procedure: the result largely depends upon subjective factors which cannot be properly controlled. Besides, the condition that we should be well acquainted with the problem may not always be statisfied, e.g. when we begin to investigate a new problem. However, with sufficient care we may achieve quite satisfactory results. On occasions we may also be able to check the results either by logic or by comparison with other studies.

It should be emphasized that in undertaking a partial enquiry we should exercise great care concerning the procedure, should know the subject well and should take all the circumstances into consideration.

The second condition that a partial enquiry has to satisfy if the results are to be correct is that the number of observations must be sufficiently large. This condition is intuitively obvious: if there are too few observations in a sample the results will be accidental. Only with the help of probability theory will it be possible to determine either the degree of reliability of a result obtained with a given number of observations in the sample, or the number of observations that should be made in order to achieve the desired degree of reliability. Without resorting to the theory of probability it would be impossible to determine precisely what number of observations can be regarded as sufficient. Intuitively we can say that the number of observations should be greater, the more heterogeneous the population from the point of view of the characteristics being analysed. If the people in a given territory are more or less of the same height it would suffice to measure the height of relatively few people to determine the average height. If, on the other hand, the height of the population varies considerably we have to obtain a greater number of measurements to achieve the same degree of accuracy.

A partial investigation, as described above—even if it is not sampling in the strict meaning of the word, based on random selection and subject to the laws of probability theory—consists in making a certain number of observations on the population in such a way as to ensure, as far as possible, that the relations between the selected units are approximately the same as the relations in the whole population. The number of observations should be sufficiently great in order that random deviations should cancel out. This kind of enquiry is just as statistical as an exhaustive enquiry comprising the whole population. The difference consists in a different method of collecting material and in a different degree of accuracy of the results, obtained, but otherwise the whole procedure, from beginning to end, is a statistical one.

Sometimes when we cannot investigate the whole population, a different method can be used. We can select a certain small number of units that can be regarded as typical for the whole population and analyse them thoroughly. Here the law of large numbers does not operate, the deviations do not cancel out, and we cannot say precisely to what extent the results obtained prevail in the whole population. What we can say about the population is true only to the extent that the selected units are actually typical. Nevertheless, we can sometimes achieve valuable results in this way. This kind of probing reality enables us to make a thorough analysis of samples dug out, so to say, from the greatest depth, and to discover the really characteristic features. For this reason this method, sometimes called a *typological* method, is often used in research, particularly for studying social phenomena. We shall not discuss it here since it is not a statistical method, although it may make use of statistics.

## 5. SUBSTITUTES FOR STATISTICAL ENQUIRY

Sometimes a direct investigation of a population either by exhaustive or by partial enquiry is impossible. In such cases we have to seek a method of obtaining the missing information in an indirect way, which is sometimes possible. Such indirect methods of obtaining numerical material we shall call substitutes for statistical enquiry. We shall briefly describe two such methods: statistical estimate and interpolation.

a. *Statistical estimate.* In the strict sense of the phrase, statistical estimate in mathematical statistics is an estimate of the value of a certain quantitative characteristic of the population obtained on the basis of analysis of a sample drawn from the population. Here we use this word in a general and not very strict sense: we regard as a statistical estimate each procedure by which, on the basis of certain known characteristics of a population, we can state numerically its other, unknown characteristics, or by which, on the basis of certain characteristics of a known population, we can determine certain characteristics of an unknown population. Of course, such an estimate is possible only when there is a definite and numerically determinable relationship between those characteristics that are known and those that we want to determine. If this relationship can be determined in a precise manner we deal, not with an estimate but with an ordinary mathematical calculation. If we know the number of marriages in a given period of time we also know automatically the number of persons that have been married, at least in a monogamous country: it is twice as great as the number of marriages.

Statistical estimates are used when there is a statistical relationship or correlation between the characteristics. It exists when, to a definite value of one characteristic there corresponds not one definite value of another, but a number of differing values whose average corresponds to the value of the other characteristic. For instance, we know from anthropology that there is a relationship between the length of the arm bone and the height of a man. Although men with a certain length of arm will differ with respect to height, the average height of men with a given length of arm bone has a more or less precisely determined value. Thus if we know the length of the arm bones of a certain number of men and the relationship between the arm length and height, we can determine the average height of those men. This will only be an approximation and its accuracy will depend on the strictness of the relationship between the two characteristics and on the number of units measured. The conditions for obtaining correct results are then the same as in a sampling survey. If the existing relationship is precise, i.e. the men with a given arm length differ only little in height, the computation of the average height will be relatively precise even with a small number of observations. If men with the same arm length differ considerably in height, then we shall have to make a greater number of observations to attain the same degree of precision.

In practice the difficulty consists mainly in determining the numerical relationship between the known and unknown characteristics. Two alternatives are possible. Sometimes we can determine this relationship on the basis of a sample taken from the population that we want to study. This will be a statistical estimate in the strict sense of the word. If, for the whole population, we know the values of characteristic $A$ on the basis of which we want to determine the value of characteristic $X$ for the same population, we conduct a partial investigation of the population, determining for each unit in the sample the values of both $A$ and $X$. If, besides characteristic $A$, we also know the values of characteristics $B, C, D$, etc., of the population, which may be numerically related to $X$, it is well to extend the enquiry to include them, since we can then discover which of them is most closely related to the characteristic we want to determine. We shall thus be able to attain greater precision in the results.

More often, however, the situation is less favourable. We can determine the desired relationship, not on the basis of the same population, but of some other. In this case an additional question arises, to which we may not always be able to find the answer. The question is this: Do we have a right, and if so, within what confidence limits, to apply to one population the results obtained from an investigation of another? A few examples should help to clarify the problem involved.

Quite often we have to use statistical estimates in historical statistics, where we cannot make new censuses or other direct statistical enquiries, but where we may have fairly good statistical data on other problems which can help us draw conclusions on our own. A typical example is the population estimates for earlier periods in which there were no censuses, but where some secondary information is available. For instance, in Poland, in the eighteenth century a population estimate was made on the basis of the number of "chimneys", i.e. the number of houses, as taxable units.

In our example of "chimney" statistics the accuracy of the estimate, even if we disregard the problem of the reliability of government statistics, depends upon the method and accuracy of calculating the average number of persons per "chimney". If we can base our calculation on data from that period, if we can find cases for which we have information on both the number of "chimneys" and the number of people, if this information is sufficiently ample and comprises different regions of the country, and, finally, if the enquiry shows a relative stability of the numerical relationship between the number of "chimneys" and the number of people—then we can obtain a precise result. If, however, we have to estimate the average number of people per "chimney" on the basis of the data for some other country, or for the same country but for a different period, then we shall have to ascertain first whether this is permissible. The knowledge of history, even without concrete numerical data, may often help in solving the problem. Sometimes in such cases we can make a correction: the figure obtained under different circumstances may be used for our purposes after it is changed in a certain way. The results, of course, will then be less precise and, what is worse, less reliable since quite often we will not be in a position to determine to what extent, or even in what direction, they deviate from reality. But even this kind of estimate may be valuable. We can achieve a certain approximation to reality, can at least state the order of magnitude of the population, and this is better than a complete lack of knowledge.

In historical statistics this kind of estimate may produce relatively accurate results. In our example it turned out that the average number of persons living in one house did not fluctuate much and can be calculated with a fairly high degree of accuracy. It would be different if we tried to apply the same method to the present time.

Today houses are of different sizes and even in one country it would be risky to use for one part of the country figures obtained in another part, not to mention towns for which this method cannot be applied at all.

Let us take another example. It is possible to estimate population on the basis of births or deaths, which we sometimes know even when we have no direct data on the population. The numerical relationship between the number of births and deaths and the population is subject to considerable fluctuations. In Europe, several hundred years ago, in the earliest period for which we have even scanty information, there were 40–50 births per thousand persons. Before the war the corresponding figure often dropped to 15 or less per thousand, seldom reaching 30, and only in exceptional cases (in tropical countries) going as high as 40 or more. It is understandable that under these circumstances a population estimate on the basis of births is possible only when we know the category in which the country that we want to investigate should be included. Were we able to make this kind of calculation with sufficient precision our population estimates would also be relatively precise.

In historical statistics the situation is more simple because in earlier times the ratio of births to population fluctuated within fairly narrow limits and thus the same figure could be used for all countries.

The situation would be different if we were to base a population estimate on the death rates. In earlier times the death rate was very irregular and was subject to tremendous fluctuations from year to year in the same country. The death rate was always high but during epidemics it often reached terrifying proportions. A population estimate based on death rates will be possible only when we know that the death rates come from a relatively normal period, when there were no epidemics. In this respect there is much more uniformity in our times, although even now there are considerable differences between countries with different levels of civilization.

Let us consider a few more examples. Apart from the ways described above, population was also estimated on the basis of various other data, such as dues and taxes levied. For instance Ladenberger estimated Poland's population during the reign of Casimir the Great on the basis of tax records. If a tax is levied on the family as a taxable unit (e.g. when the tax is paid by the head of the family) then the number of persons in the family must be determined. Sometimes the criteria of contemporary vital statistics are applied in such cases, but this practice should be regarded as very risky. When there were no other data population was estimated on the basis of the area of the country, which implied a certain defined density of population. This procedure, although of dubious value, is sometimes permissible because it can be assumed that a certain population density corresponds to a certain level of economic development, under given physiographic and climatic conditions. The area of cultivated land was sometimes estimated according to the number of ploughs or teams of draft animals.

In modern statistics, for example, we estimate milk production on the basis of the number of milk cows and the average yield of a cow. This method is not very accurate because the milk yield per cow fluctuates within very wide limits and for a precise calculation of the average milk output per cow it would be necessary to know not only the total number of cows, but also the number of cows of particular breeds. Moreover, it would be necessary to know the methods of feeding and other factors upon which the milk outpot depends. Under ordinary conditions an estimate of milk output is only a rough approximation. An example of an even less accurate estimate is an estimate of fruit output. It is based on fruit tree statistics and an approximate average yield per tree. Neither kind of information—fruit tree and average yield statistics—are very accurate usually.

None the less, estimates of all kinds are a valuable and often necessary supplement to a direct enquiry. Even a rather rough estimate, providing it is not altogether unreal, gives us some idea about the population of which we would otherwise know nothing or have erroneous notions. For this reason we attach so much importance to the pioneering work of Graunt.

b. *Interpolation. Extrapolation.* Interpolation is a mathematical procedure which enables us to reproduce by calculation the missing links in a series in which the other links are known. In statistics such cases occur, for instance, when we are in possession of the data on certain events which took place in certain years and we reproduce by calculation the number of events which occurred in other years. Let us suppose that we know how many deaths were due to a certain disease in the consecutive years from 1925 to 1929 and from 1931 to 1934, but, for some reason, we have no data for 1930. The calculation of the number of deaths in 1930 on the basis of the data for the preceding and following years will be an interpolation. We have a similar case when on the basis of two population censuses, e.g. for 1920 and in 1930, we attempt to calculate the population in any of the intervening years, e.g. in 1925, or consecutively in all the inter-census years. We also use interpolation when on the basis of the frequencies for the longer intervals of a series we calculate the frequencies in shorter intervals, e.g. when from the population data from the census in 5-year age classes we calculate the population for each age separately. The special case in which we calculate the values of term outside the series, on the basis of the known terms of a statistical series, is called extrapolation. Thus, an example of extrapolation is the calculation of the population after 1930 on the basis of the data from several censuses, the last of which was made in 1930, or for the years before 1920 if the earliest census was made in 1920. Certain mathematical methods of interpolation are described in the Appendix. Here we shall confine ourselves to general comments.

Interpolation as a source of additional statistical information is of no great importance and should be resorted to only with great care. In order to calculate the values of the missing terms of a series we have to know how the series develops in the available section. We can seldom assume that the growth is uniform. For instance, if we have several population censuses which show a steady population increase we can assume that the increase was also uniform during the inter-census period. However, the notion of uniform increase is not always the same: an increase may be *arithmetic*—the same number of units for each unit of time—or *geometric*—the same ratio for each unit of time. And increase is often much more complex. Worse still, it is sometimes quite irregular.

When we speak of the general population increase of a country, the number of births and deaths may not show substantial fluctuations from year to year; the number of emigrants, however, varies within very wide limits, depending upon the economic situation of the country from which people emigrate and the country to which they emigrate.

In capitalist countries the production of goods which are affected by the business cycle may fluctuate considerably, and cannot be guessed for the periods for which there are no data available. For instance, if we had data concerning the production of some commodity for only two periods of prosperity, or for a few random periods of time, it would not be possible to determine by interpolation the level of production during a period of economic depression.[22]

A similar stituation may arise when we know the population figures for each five-year age class and would like to determine by interpolation the frequencies for each age. The task is feasible if the changes are uniform. If, however, there are distortions due to, say, a war during which the number of births fluctuated widely, it would be difficult or impossible to obtain correct results by interpolation.[23]

From the mathematical point of view the object of interpolation is to find the function most closely expressing the trend of a series in a given section, or, if it is impossible to find such a function, to choose an appropriate "mechanical" interpolation formula. For the statistician, however, something else is important: to decide on the basis of a knowledge of the subject of analysis whether interpolation is at all permissible. If the answer is negative there is no sense in seeking any interpolation formula; if it is positive very often the choice of formula is of secondary importance because even quite different formulae may produce sufficiently accurate results and almost invariably the error resulting from the nature of a given phenomenon will be greater than the error caused by the application of a less suitable formula.

The situation is somewhat more favourable when the determination of a figure by interpolation for a certain period is not our main objective, but is a means of supplementing the data for a longer period of time. For instance, if for a 10-year period the data on production are missing for one or two years, then by careful interpolation we can estimate the values for the two missing years with sufficient accuracy to obtain for the whole 10-year period a total not far removed from the actual figure.

All the reservations concerning interpolation apply also to extrapolation. Here, however, we are faced with an additional element of uncertainty: all the assumptions concerning the development within a certain section are based on the assumption that the development is affected by certain definite factors that we know. As far as interpolation is concerned we can either assume that within the given period of time these factors did not change, or we can, even though only approximately, determine the change that occurred. In extrapolation the factors on which the development depends may undergo changes completely unknown to us and unpredictable.

---

[22] The annual production of pig iron in pre-war Poland during the period 1925–38 amounted to: 315, 327, 618, 684, 704, 478, 347, 199, 306, 382, 394, 584, 724 and 879 thousand tons respectively. In so irregular a series it is difficult, of course, to talk of interpolation, not to mention extrapolation.

[23] The population of Warsaw in 1931 included: age 5–9: 107,039; age 10–14: 77,942; age 15–19: 103,069; age 20–24: 137,889.

There were 22,109 8-year-olds, 18,897 10-year-olds 10,538 14-year-olds, and 28,079 20-year-olds. It is doubtful if even a most elaborate calculation based on 5-year age classes could establish the fact that the group of 14-year-olds (born in 1917) was the smallest.

To avoid misunderstandings we should add that not every calculation of the missing terms of a series is an interpolation. Interpolation is a purely mathematical procedure which determines the missing links by calculation based on a mathematical assumption concerning the trend of a series in the missing selection. Sometimes however, we have information that enables us to calculate the missing links with great precision. If, on the basis of population censuses, we know the population of a country at certain definite times and, if we also have information concerning births and deaths as well as immigration and emigration for each year, then we can determine the population figure for each year during the inter-census period and for each year after the last census for which we have vital statistics and migration data. The results will be quite accurate if the census and vital statistics are accurate. This will de different from interpolation and extrapolation in a mathematical sense. We sometimes call it an *estimate,* in contrast to the data obtained directly from the census, although this is not quite correct since the estimate is based on actual figures and a precise calculation.

Sometimes a combination of such calculations with interpolation may produce much more accurate results than interpolation itself. Using the same example of a population estimate let us suppose that of the two factors which affect population changes—natural population changes and migration—we have only the data on one of them. We know, for instance, the number of births and deaths but not the number of emigrants and immigrants. In this case we can calculate accurately how the population would grow if there were only natural population changes and apply interpolation to the second factor—migration. If in a given country migration does not play an important part, the accuracy of our calculations will be very high in comparison with a direct interpolation not taking into account natural population changes.

# CHAPTER 3

# THE PROCESSING OF STATISTICAL MATERIAL
# THE PRESENTATION OF STATISTICAL DATA

## 1. THE DESIGN OF STATISTICAL TABLE

a. *How to design a table.* The raw material of statistics contains individual data on particular units of the population. For each unit a number of characteristics included, which are important from the point of view of a given enquiry, are established. In their finished form statistical data are given in a table showing, in appropriate columns, the number of units possessing the various characteristics, or the sum of values for a group of units. An example of the first case is a table showing the number of farms with an area of from 2 to 5 hectares; of the second case, a table showing the total area of these farms. The task of processing statistical material consists in counting the units with a certain characteristic, or in summing up the values for a group of such units so that the corresponding figures can be written in the corresponding columns of the table. This task actually consists of two separate tasks: designing a proper statistical table and—a purely technical problem—transferring the individual data to the table.

A correct solution of the first problem—the design of a statistical table—is of basic importance, since the practical or scientific usefulness of an enquiry depends upon this design. An error in the substance of an enquiry may render it partially or completely useless, and a technical error makes it more difficult to use. For this reason great care should be exercised in designing tables.

From the formal point of view a statistical table is composed of a number of vertical columns and horizontal rows. At the head of every column and on the side—usually the left—of every row there are appropriate legends explaining the contents of the columns and rows. In the intersection cells of appropriate rows and columns we write down the figures corresponding to given combinations of characteristics. Each column and each row may be considered separately as a statistical series, a basic element in statistics.

The basic principle of proper table design is that every item of information of scientific or practical value be presented so as to facilitate the proper use of the results. This means, first of all, that all essential characteristics of the units of which the population is composed should be shown in the tables.

The presentation may take different forms. Each characteristic may be treated and shown separately, e.g. separate divisions of farms by size, by the number of employees, by the number of agricultural machines possessed, etc. This kind of presentation is possible but gives only a small part of what should be included in a full presentation. The point is that each characteristic can be fully appraised only when it is combined with other characteristics to which it is related. In our example we should design the table in such a way as to show the data on the use of labour power, not separately but in conjunction with the size of the farm, i.e. so that the classification according to the number of employees be shown separately for each group based on the size of the farm. Similarly the use of agricultural machines should be shown in conjuction with the size of the farm and possibly with the number of employees.

Were we to follow this principle rigidly we should have to combine every characteristic of the population analysed with each other characteristic. Then we could be sure that nothing would be lost from our material and that every research worker could select the combination of characteristics that interests him. However, this is possible only in very simple enquiries with few characteristics. Where there are a large number of characteristics the tables would be too complicated, cumbersome, difficult to read, and therefore not useful. The material would be so dispersed that in particular panels and even in certain parts of the table there would be empty spaces or just single observations from which we could not possibly draw any valid conclusions. The combining of characteristics to such an extent is unnecessary since not all the combinations produce essential information. It follows that before designing a table or tables we should analyse the substance of the enquiry. In our example of farms it would have to be a socio-economic analysis and possibly also an agricultural analysis. In new studies, however, when we cannot take advantage of previous experience, we may not always be able to determine in advance which combinations of characteristics are of essential importance. We may have to make many attempts before we decide on the scope of our study.

If it turns out that certain characteristics or combinations of characteristics may be useful, but are not essential, we should follow the principle that we should neither unduly expand the table by including everything that may have some possible value nor show only what is of a strictly utilitarian value. Efficiency here consists not only in avoiding useless tasks, but also in performing those tasks that can and should be performed. The actual solution of this problem in practice depends, as always, on the means available.

In practice the proper processing of complex material often means the substitution of several tables, each containing some combinations, for one table with all possible combinations of characteristics. Certain characteristics and even certain combinations of characteristics may be repeated in different tables. An example will best clarify the proper procedure.

Suppose we want to study peasant farms with an area of less than 50 hectares.

We consider the following characteristics: the size of the farm, the number of hired hands, the number of draft animals (horses, oxen), and the number of cows. For simplicity we disregard other characteristics which could also be included in our study. Let us suppose, further, that for different characteristics, the following classification has been accepted: the size of the farm (6 groups)—less than 1 hectare, 1–2, 2–5, 5–10, 10–15, 15–50 hectares; the employment of hired hands (5 groups)— farms with no hired workers and those employing 1, 2, 3–4, 5 and more; the draft animals (5 groups)—farms without draft animals and those with 1, 2, 3–4, 5 and more draft animals; the cows (5 groups)—the same as for the draft animals. The classification is rather formal: in a real enquiry it should be based on a socio-economic analysis. After the table has been designed and filled in it may turn out that the accepted classification is not quite appropriate with regard, say, to the size of the farm. In such cases appropriate changes should be introduced. To avoid the trouble of doing the whole thing over it is advisable to design a trial table based on part of the material before reaching a final decision concerning classification.

Let us suppose now that we have to combine all four characteristics. Technically this can be done by placing two characteristics at the top of the table and two on the side. If we place at the top the data on draft animals and cows it will look like this.

| Farms with draft animals (number) | | | | | | | | | | |
|---|---|---|---|---|---|---|---|---|---|---|
| 0 | | | | | 1 | | | | | |
| with cows (number) | | | | | | | | | | |
| 0 | 1 | 2 | 3–4 | 5 and more | 0 | 1 | 2 | 3–4 | 5 and more | etc. |

On the side of the table we place the remaining two characteristics. This can be done in the following way:

| The area of the farm<br>The number of hired hands |
|---|
| *Farms of less than 1 hectare*<br>without hired hands<br>with 1 hired  ,,<br>,, 2 ,,  ,,<br>,, 3–4 ,,  ,,<br>,, 5 or more hired hands<br>*Farms of 1–2 hectares*<br>without hired hands<br>with 1 hired  ,,<br>,, 2 ,,  ,,<br>,, 3–4 ,,  ,,<br>,, 5 or more hired hands, etc. |

In this way we have $5 \times 5 = 25$ vertical columns and $6 \times 5 = 30$ rows: in the whole table there will be $25 \times 30 = 750$ panels which will have to be filled in with figures.

However, this is not all. The table now contains all possible combinations of the selected characteristics, but is very cumbersome from the practical point of view, because it only contains combinations, and no totals. For example, we cannot find out from it directly how many 1-hectare farms with 1 horse here were, without adding up five items; or many farms without cows, with 1, 2, 3–4, 5 and more cows. In order to find the total number of 1-hectare farms we have to sum up $25 \times 5 = 125$ items, and in order to get the total number of farms included in the table we must sum all 750 items. Since in using statistical tables we also have to use totals, the table as designed above is not practical.

All the required totals could be placed in the table as shown on p. 84. In comparison with the first design we have added 11 items at the head of the table and 12 items on the side. Altogether we now have 36 columns and 42 rows and in the whole table we have $36 \times 42 = 1512$ panels. The table is large, not very clear or convenient. And we have used a rather simple example since the classification of characteristics is not very detailed: 5 groups for each of the three characteristics and 6 for one of them.

Let us now consider how to simplify the design, considering the economic significance of the characteristics and the combinations of the characteristics shown in Table 3.1.

The size of the farm is undoubtedly related to its socio-economic role and so is the number of hired hands. This enables us to separate the farms that rely exclusively or almost exclusively on family labour from those using hired hands to a limited extent and those with a large number of hands (in our example, 5 or more) which are owned by the richer farmers (*kulacks*), and use a capitalistic-type method of production. In order to characterize a farm it is not enough to consider one of these characteristics. The area by itself or the number of hired hands does not tell the whole story. Both have to be treated jointly and combined in the table. There may be small farms of a capitalistic type, using intensive farming methods and employing hired hands, and there may be relatively large farms, engaged in extensive agriculture and using only family labour. The next characteristic—the number of draft animals — provides further information on the economic strength of the farm and should be treated jointly with the previous two. In this way we get a table containing the combination of three characteristics which can be placed in the table so that, e.g. the number of draft animals is shown at the top and the size of the farm and the number of hired hands on the side as before. There remains one characteristic, the number of cows. This information also throws light on the economic position of the farm and it, too, should be treated in conjunction with the other characteristics—the size of the farm and the number of hired hands.

TABLE 3.1. PEASANT FARMS BY AREA, NUMBER OF HIRED HANDS, NUMBER OF DRAFT ANIMALS AND NUMBER OF COWS

| Area of farm / Number of hired hands | All farms | | | | | | Farms with draft animals | | | | | | | | | | | | | |
|---|---|---|---|---|---|---|---|---|---|---|---|---|---|---|---|---|---|---|---|---|
| | number of cows | | | | | | 0 | | | | | | 1 | | | | | | 2 | etc. |
| | total | 0 | 1 | 2 | 3-4 | 5 and more | total | number of cows | | | | | total | number of cows | | | | | | |
| | | | | | | | | 0 | 1 | 2 | 3-4 | 5 and more | | 0 | 1 | 2 | 3-4 | 5 and more | | |
| *All farms* Total | | | | | | | | | | | | | | | | | | | | |
| without hired hands | | | | | | | | | | | | | | | | | | | | |
| with 1 hired hand | | | | | | | | | | | | | | | | | | | | |
| with 2 hired hands | | | | | | | | | | | | | | | | | | | | |
| with 3-4 hired hands | | | | | | | | | | | | | | | | | | | | |
| with 5 and more hands | | | | | | | | | | | | | | | | | | | | |
| *Farms of less than 1 hectare* Total | | | | | | | | | | | | | | | | | | | | |
| without hired hands | | | | | | | | | | | | | | | | | | | | |
| with 1 hired hand | | | | | | | | | | | | | | | | | | | | |
| with 2 hired hands | | | | | | | | | | | | | | | | | | | | |
| with 3-4 hired hands | | | | | | | | | | | | | | | | | | | | |
| with 5 and more hands | | | | | | | | | | | | | | | | | | | | |
| *Farms from 1 to 2 hectares* Total | | | | | | | | | | | | | | | | | | | | |
| without hired hands, etc. | | | | | | | | | | | | | | | | | | | | |

We can show it in the second table: at the top—the number of cows, and on the side, as before—the size of the farm and the number of hired hands.

Now we have two tables and each of them gives a combination of three characteristics.

There remains the question of the combination of the number of draft animals and the number of cows. We decide that it is not worth while to show this combination together with the other three characteristics lest the table become too complex, but we may, nevertheless, feel that by itself this combination may add something of value to the general economic description of the farm. We can show this combination together with the size of the farm and get another table combining three characteristics. Thus we have three tables and each of them, after introducing all the necessary totals, will have 252 panels (by coincidence all three tables turned out to be of the same size). Together we shall have 756 panels instead of the 1512 that we got with the joint combination of all four characteristics. This is half of what we had before and, moreover, the tables are clearer and more convenient. If, then, our socio-economic analysis proves that the tables now give all that can be expected from the material available we shall have a better solution than we had got by combining all four characteristics.

b. *The technique of table design.* When we were discussing the essential features of designing statistical tables we also touched upon many technical points. The technical problem can actually be reduced to one main concern: to design a table in such a way as to make it most convenient. Starting from this basic premise we should try, within the limits of the main objective of the enquiry, to make a table design as simple and as clear as possible. Let us stress that this should be within the limits of the objectives of the enquiry because they must be decisive in doubtful cases. We have to distinguish between tables shown in publications containing basic statistical data and those in analyses based on this material and prepared for scientific or popular consumption. In the original publications which offer information to specialists no essential information should be omitted and the convenience of the reader is less important. In scientific and popular studies the objective is also of decisive importance but the need to show a special problem of limited scope and content makes it easier to make the table simple and readable. The condition of simplicity is of particular importance in publications intended for the public.

To design a table well is not an easy task. We shall show here a very striking example of a poorly designed table from which it is very difficult to decipher the information that it is supposed to provide.

The table was published in 1922 in a supplement to a newspaper and looked like this:

In this form the table is a real puzzle and would qualify for a humour column in any newspaper. First of all, according to the title of the table the accidents

TABLE 3.2. OFFICIAL STATISTICS ON MOTOR VEHICLE ACCIDENTS IN THE LAST TWO YEARS

| | Military vehicles | Private vehicles | Number of accidents | Number of accidents in 1921 | Number of accidents involving people | Number of accidents |
|---|---|---|---|---|---|---|
| | 1 | 2 | 3 | 4 | 5 | 6 |
| 1. Number of military and private vehicles | 339 | 2000 | — | — | — | — |
| 2. Accidents caused by military vehicles | — | — | 393 | — | 176 | 217 |
| 3. Accidents caused by private vehicles | — | — | 177 | — | 133 | 44 |
| 4. Accidents caused by military vehicles | — | — | — | 43 | 23 | 20 |
| 5. Accidents caused by private vehicles | — | — | — | 35 | 22 | 13 |
| *Total* | *339* | *2000* | *570* | *78* | *354* | *294* |

were to be given "for the last two years". Since the table was published in 1922 we surmise that the years are 1920 and 1921. But in the table only the year 1921 is shown at the head of column 4. In this column there are figures in rows 4 and 5 and in the total at the bottom. Since, except for the total, the figures in column 4 seem to be the sums of the figures in columns 5 and 6 for each row respectively we can assume that they also pertain to 1921. In this case the figures in column 3 probably show accidents in 1920. It would follow that the figures in columns 5 and 6 for rows 2 and 3, whose sums appear to be shown in column 3, also pertain to 1920. But there does not seem to be any clue as to the year for columns 1 and 2. It is also peculiar that the figure in column 2 ("Private vehicles") ends with three zeros which would indicate the lack of exact information. The last column (6) probably shows accidents where no people were involved. This conclusion is based on the fact that for particular rows the sums of the figures shown in columns 5 and 6 correspond to the figures in columns 3 and 4. Apart from this confusion the whole design of the table is poor. For a total of 30 panels (not counting the bottom row for the totals) only 14 panels are filled in, and the remaining 16 panels do not, and cannot, contain figures because of the headings given at the top and on the side. The totals at the bottom have different meanings. For columns 1 and 2 there are no sums, but at the bottom the figures are repeated from row 1 ("The number of vehicles")—in an unknown year. The sums of columns 3 and 4—if our surmise is correct—refer to the total number of accidents in 1920 (column 3) and 1921 (column 4). The totals for columns 5 and 6 have still another meaning since they show the total number of accidents in both years, with those involving people shown in column 5 and others in column 6.

We do not often encounter tables as poorly designed as the one just described, although its author had probably tried to do his best. Nevertheless, even now we occasionally come across faults in design which create unnecessary difficulties in understanding tables.

After corrections—assuming that our a deductions are correct—the table could be designed as follows:

TABLE 3.2a. STATISTICS ON MOTOR VEHICLE ACCIDENTS
in 1920 and 1921

| Type of vehicle | Number of vehicles | Accidents | | | | | |
|---|---|---|---|---|---|---|---|
| | | total | | involving people | | others | |
| | | 1920 | 1921 | 1920 | 1921 | 1920 | 1921 |
| *Total* | *2339* | *570* | *78* | *309* | *45* | *261* | *33* |
| Military | 339 | 393 | 43 | 176 | 23 | 217 | 20 |
| Private | 2000 | 177 | 35 | 133 | 22 | 44 | 13 |

The table now contains 21 panels, all filled in and provides much information not previously shown. The only thing missing is the total number of accidents in both years, previously shown at the bottom of columns 5 and 6. This information, however, is of little interest and can be easily introduced into the table by adding three more columns. We still do not know to what year the figures on the number of vehicles refer. Apart from this the design of the table is clear and all possible misunderstandings have been eliminated.

An alteration of the table such as is shown above is not the only possible solution. The classification by the type of accident could be shown on the side and the types of vehicle on the top: the years could be shown on the side instead of at the top. Practical considerations should decide which solution is the best. The important thing is to make the table clear and easy to understand.

The art of designing table cannot be learned from a set of rules. It can only be acquired through experience and by studying model designs. Like every technical skill it requires a certain innate ability which can only partially be replaced by routine. We shall describe here only some general rules. The table should not be too big or too complex. It is seldom possible to make a table clear if it shows a combination of more than four characteristics. When an investigation involves more characteristics, we should try, always remembering the main object of the study, to present the material in several tables. If we have more than two characteristics we should try to maintain some balance in placing them at the top and on the side of the table. This was shown in the first example in which we have put two characteristics at the top and two on the side. This, however, is not a necessary condition. There is no hard and fast rule about it, and we should be guided by practical considerations. In designing tables technical questions should be taken into account. Among them, the size of the page on which the table is to appear is always of great importance. Tables which are spread horizontally over more than one, or at the most two, pages are difficult to read; it is easier to read multi-page tables if they extend from top to bottom, even if they are continued on the following pages. In most cases willingness and skill enable us to overcome these difficulties without any harm to the problem analysed and without unduly increasing the space provided for the tables and without raising the cost.

All the headings of the table, and primarily those at the top and on the side should be worded briefly, but clearly and precisely, without ambiguities. The same rule applies to all the necessary comments: they should be placed next to the table. If more extensive comments or general remarks are needed and if it is more convenient not to place them right next to the table (e.g. a general introduction to the enquiry) it is desirable to give an appropriate reference mark in the table.

The vertical columns of the table are usually separated from one another by lines. If several consecutive columns constitute a logical group it may be worth while to separate such a group from other groups by thick or double lines. In very simple tables vertical lines are not absolutely necessary. Rows are usually not separated by lines, but we should be careful to place the figures clearly and distinctly and, if possible, to leave a lot of space between them for easier reading. Sometimes it is advisable to use different types of print. In particular, the totals and data of a more general nature should stand out. Certain types of information (e.g. percentage figures as distinct from absolute figures) are often printed in italics. As a rule totals should be shown in the table either at the bottom right, or at the top left. It seems that the latter is more logical, and more convenient for statistical tables. In statistical enquiry we start from the total which we divide, according to certain characteristics, first in a general way, and only then we go over to the details; therefore it might be preferable to place general information at the beginning and not at the end of the table.

A desire to economize is sometimes behind a tendency to squeeze a lot of material into a small space. This is understandable, because the cost of printing statistical tables is high. It is better however, to achieve economy by skilful design of the table. There is no important objection to the use of such technical devices as placing several essentially different tables under one common heading (at the top, or on the side). It is a bad practice, however, to condense the table at the expense of clarity.

Another technical problem that can be solved in somewhat different ways is rounding off. An original study usually deals with particular units. But a publication, even if it is an original source, usually does not require this degree of accuracy. What is more, giving the results in too small units may give a false impression of precision and thus encourage misleading conclusions on the true accuracy of the material. If shipments of bulk goods are shown in railway reports in kilogrammes it does not follow that the figures in statistical tables should also be expressed in kilogrammes, because nobody needs them, and tons or even thousands of tons would be just as good, or even better. Estimates of milk production, which are obtained by multiplying the average milk output per cow by the number of cows, are expressed in litres. However, the accuracy of the estimate is so small that rounding off the results not even to the nearest thousand, but to the nearest million is just an ordinary and natural precaution. The general principle may be formulated as follows: there is no need, and it is inadvisable even in original enquiries, to give more significant figures than indicated by the accuracy of the study. In more general or popular publications the results may be rounded off even farther, so long as the sense is sufficiently clear. Even in popular publications, however, we should avoid going to the other extreme since too much rounding off may blur certain important details.

The rounding off may result in certain technical difficulties, since it may mean that the components do not add up exactly to the total obtained by adding the figures before they have been rounded off. Differences of one or two units in the last digit are quite common. This is particularly noticeable in percentage calculations when the sum of the components is 99 or 101, or even 98 or 102, instead of 100. Actually there is no reason why the figures should not be given as they are calculated, without bothering about the discrepancies. Indeed, this is the most correct procedure. For practical reasons, however, the discrepancies are often removed and this can only be achieved by a not too accurate rounding off. If one of the components amounts to say, 27·4 and should be correctly rounded down to 27, but if by so doing we are one unit short of the total, we will not commit a great error by rounding it up to 28 instead of 27. This kind of inaccurate rounding off should be done with the figure in which the error will be the smallest. This means that for an inaccurate rounding off we should pick the figure as close to 5 as possible. On the other hand, we commit a smaller error when we introduce a correction to a large number than to a small one. Whether we get 48·2 per cent or 48·3 per cent does not usually much matter, but the difference between 1·2 and 1·3 per cent may be quite essential. Observing these principles we may try to reconcile the total with the sum of the components, It is always possible, of course, to change the total and not the components, but this is not always logical and permissible, especially when we deal with percentages which have to add up to 100 and cannot be changed. Besides, it is often inconvenient to change the total if it is repeated in several tables in which, of course, it should always be the same. The components may also appear in different tables and then they should also be the same. The reconciliation of figures in complex statistical studies is often very troublesome but—even if only for aesthetic reasons—it should be done consistently. A study in which this rule is not observed creates a poor impression and appears untidy and careless. It is imperative, however, that the clerk responsible for reconciling the figures should receive precise instructions concerning the procedure.

## 2. THE PREPARATION OF RAW STATISTICAL DATA
## FOR TABULATION

The preparation of raw data consits mainly in counting the units with certain characteristics or combinations of characteristics, and inserting the figures thus obtained in statistical tables. Except for very simple cases, the processing of these data requires a special technique which is described below.

a. *Direct counting*. Only in exceptional cases, and for very simple reports, is it possible to arrive at the figures required for the table by simply reading off the data from the documents and by direct counting. Let us suppose that we want to determine the number of births on the basis of birth registration records. We obtain the total number of births by counting the entries or by simply taking the number of the last entry if they are numbered. If we have to introduce a very simple classification, e.g. by sex, we can read off and count from entries how many boys were born. After writing down the result and repeating the process to count the number of girls, we check whether the sum of these two figures is the same as the total number of births previously established. If it is, the job is finished: if not, we have to check our calculation again and find the error.

This procedure can be used when classification is simple and there are few groups; it can almost never be used when we have a combination of several characteristics. But it can be used even for very long, extensive reports if they are not complex. Thus, for instance, in enquiries as large as population censuses the enumerators who collect the material are sometimes instructed to prepare summaries containing information not only concerning the total population by districts but also its break-down according to certain characteristics, such as sex, nationality, children of school age, etc. To facilitate these tasks the census enumerators get—in addition to the main questionnaires for the persons living in particular homes—special "summary sheets" in which the required items are shown; "total population", "among these: children of school age", "males", "females", etc. Reading off the main questionnaire, the enumerator counts the units in different groups and write the figures down in the summary sheat. Each line of the summary sheet corresponds to one questionnaire. After handling all the questionnaires the figures in the summary sheet are added up from the top to the bottom to obtain the totals for the district for which the enumerator is responsible. By transferring the totals to the summary sheets of a higher order we can easily get the totals for the locality, country and the whole country. In this way we can quickly obtain the preliminary totals for the whole census, which can be used for rapid analysis. Afterwards we can check the whole operation and work out all the details.

Sometimes the collection of statistical data is so organized that we require those who collect them to give, not individual information about particular units, but simple, prepared reports in tabular form. This is the case when we instruct the registrar to send summary sheets with the number of births or deaths registered during a given period and with a classification according to such simple characteristics as sex, age group, etc.

For the census taken in Poland in 1946 the enumerators were instructed to give for each home the number of persons living there with a break-down by sex, chief nationalities, and chief age groups (below 18, 18–60, 60 and over). This type of census is called a summary census.

This kind of procedure means that the person reporting (the registrar or enumerator) is obliged to prepare tabular summaries by "direct counting". This has considerable advantages: it speeds up the total results and substantially reduces the cost. The disadvantage is that the reports have to be simple and that there is a certain rigidity. For instance, the combination of characteristics used cannot be changed for later studies, even if it turns out that another would be better. In studies based on individual data such changes are possible although they may be quite costly.

In all complex reports we have to use special technical devices without which complex tabulation would be impossible. We shall describe here the "stroke" method and the card method.

b. *Counting by the "stroke" method.* To count by the "stroke" method we start by preparing a sheet of paper with panels for all the characteristics and combinations of characteristics that we want to show in our study. This does not mean that the layout of the sheet has to be identical with the design of the table in which we want to include this information. There is no need to provide panels for the totals and it is sufficient to include all the necessary combinations of characteristics. The order of the columns may also be different if it facilitates the work. The columns have to be sufficiently wide to provide enough room for entries. Onto this sheet we transfer information from the raw statistical data in our possession by putting a stroke in the appropriate column for each event. Instead of a stroke we may, of course, use any other sign, such as a point. After going through the whole material we merely count the strokes of the points in each panel of our work sheet and thus get all the basic elements of our final table. What remains to be done is to sum up the columns and rows.

It is awkward to count strokes placed close to each other. This we can simplify—for example, after writing down four strokes we can cross them with a fifth, producing sets of five strokes that can easily be counted. Thus if we have the following marks:

$$\cancel{||||} \quad \cancel{||||} \quad \cancel{||||} \quad \cancel{||||} \quad //$$

we can easily read off the number 22. The fifth stroke may be put down in any manner, providing the whole thing is easy to read. The points may also be grouped in sets of fives. All kinds of variations are permissible so long as the result is good.

The stroke method is easy, simple, cheap, and does not require any technical equipment. All that is needed is a sheet of paper appropriately ruled. The stroke method can generally be used in all studies, even the most complex. However, it requires a great deal of concentration from the worker since it is easy to put a stroke in a wrong panel and it may be very difficult to correct such an error. The error may come out if in several reports the same totals appear, as a result of separate counting. If the results from two tables give the same total this can be considered as sufficient proof that the counting was done correctly. If there are differences, this means that there must be an error which should be found and corrected. When we use the stroke method we can find and correct an error only by doing the whole work from the beginning at least up to the place when we discovered the error. This is a tremendous amount of work. In major studies it is almost impossible to avoid errors and in consequence each job would have to be done twice or even several times. If it is impossible to check the results by comparing the totals obtained by different, independent countings we would actually have to do the same work several times to make sure that the result is correct. For this reason the stroke method is used in relatively small studies in which the repetition of the same work does not present much trouble, and for which the use of the card method is not indicated because it requires a special preparation of raw data. In more extensive studies we can divide the whole material into smaller groups, since then it is easier to find and correct an error.

Sometimes the work consists, not in counting certain events with definite characteristics, but in summing up the figures which characterize these events. For example, in farm statistics we may want to establish not only the number of farms of different types but also the total area of all the farms in a certain class and the area used for different types of cultivation: arable land, meadows, pastures, etc. This kind of adding up cannot, of course, be done by marking strokes. If we do not choose the card method, then we will have to write down on a separate sheet the items that are to be added up. Since we also have to divide them into groups we should take as many sheets as there are combinations of characteristics. If we want to show in the table the combination of farms by size and by the number of hired hands, as in the example given above, we shall have $6 \times 5 = 30$ combinations of the characteristics and as many work sheets, each of which will contain only the farms of one group regarding area and one regarding the number of hired hands. In this case we do not have to use the stroke method, because we can simply add up the number of items on each sheet and obtain the result that we previously got by using the stroke method. The whole procedure requires the copying of the material that is to be added up and this is rather costly and troublesome.[24]

c. *Counting by the card method.* In the card method all information that requires statistical processing is written down on a separate card for each unit; thus we have as many cards as there are units in the population. Then we sort the cards according to the characteristics involved in the enquiry. After sorting them we count the cards in each group, write down the results in the appropriate panels of the table and thus complete the job.

Let us consider this method by means of an example from which we can get some practical hints. We shall again use the example discussed above for preparing the abbreviated version of three tables. We have as many cards as there are farms included in our enquiry. On each card we have all the pertinent information on each farm, i.e. the area, the number of hired hands, the number of draft animals and cows. Each card should contain information which enables us, if needed, to identify the farm in question. If the cards are copied from another document it is enough to place on each an appropriate reference number. If they are filled in during a direct field survey the name of the farmer and the address should be given. It is also advisable to number the cards for eventual checking to make sure that none is lost.

The work starts with the determination of the total number of units which belong to the population. If the cards are numbered the total is simply the highest number: if they are not numbered—we have to count them. The total should be written down and all the other results of our analysis have to check with this total. Then we start sorting the cards according to the first selected characteristic, e.g. the area of the farm. After reading off the entries on the cards we sort them into separate groups each containing only farms belonging to one group, according to the division previously accepted. In our example we have six such groups. After the cards have been sorted we count them separately for each pile and thus get the breakdown of farms by size. The results should be written down and checked by adding them up. The sum should be the same as the total number of farms in the population. The counting of the cards, writing down of the results and checking by addition should be done for control purposes after the completion of each

---

[24] Only in exceptional cases, when we have an adding machine which prints results, can we add directly so that one person selects the required data and dictates them to another person who adds them on the machine. Checking can be done by adding in different combinations.

stage of our work, even though it may not be necessary from the point of view of the final design of the table.

Having already divided the farms by size, we sort out the cards in each pile according to the number of hired hands. In this way we get 30 bundles of cards each containing the farms of only one class as far as area is concerned, and one class as far as the number of hired hands is concerned. Keeping this division we further divide each of the 30 bundles according to the number of draft animals. Thus we get 30 × 5 = 150 smaller bundles. After counting the number of cards in each of them we get the basic figures for the first table; if we have already counted the intermediate results we also have all the necessary totals.

In order to prepare the second table we put the bundles together according to the number of draft animals but keep the division according to size and the number of hired hands. A new sorting according to the numbers of cows gives us the figures for the second table.

If the third table is to contain only the combination of the number of draft animals and cows we can cancel from the second table the classiffication by area and the number of hired hands, keeping only the division by the number of draft animals. By segregating the cards according to the number of cows we get the figures needed for the third table. If the table is also to give the combination with a breakdown by area we only cancel the previous division according to the number of hired hands.

It is advisable to cancel a division which is not needed for further sorting because keeping too detailed a breakdown may unnecessarily complicate the work. In addition, the order in which we start sorting according to particular characteristics is not a matter of indifference. The point is to do it so that we can keep the segregation needed for the following tables since in this way we can avoid going back to the same characteristic and thus avoid doing the same sorting over again. In extensive studies it may require some ingenuity to do this and even at that it may not always be possible. In any case, the amount of effort put into this type of work depends, as a rule, upon the proper order of sorting.

The advantages of the card method are its simplicity, the ease of performing the work and the possibility of its universal application to different types of studies, even the most complex, with resultant speed and low cost. The card method does not require as much attention as the "stroke" method, and consequently the workers are less tired and commit fewer errors. In this method the results can easily be controlled by checking whether after each sorting all the cards in on bundle have the same combination of characteristics according to which they have been sorted and, if necessary, by counting again the number of cards in each bundle. This sort of checking can be done at any stage of the work.

To use the card method it is necessary, of course, to have a separate card for each unit of the population. The whole problem is simplified if the collection of raw data has been based on individual cards. If the system of records was used, however, we have to make out these cards especially for sorting purposes. But even if the individual cards were used for collecting information they may not be suitable for counting purposes, because the requirements for filling in the cards are different from those used in sorting. The former have to be relatively large, should contain the full text of questions and answers and should leave enough space for writing down the answers: the latter should be small and handy to facilitate the job of sorting. The former may be printed on poor quality, cheap paper; the latter should be made of durable and stiff paper, so that they do not wear out numerous sortings.

If the individual cards obtained in collecting information are too inconvenient for further processing either because they are too large or because their layout is not quite suitable, there are two solutions: either to resort to the stroke method, which is rather troublesome here, or to make copies of individual cards adapted for sorting. In such cases we can also use special devices to facilitate work. Thus, the cards should be small and the paper stiff; individual entries should be arranged for expediency in sorting rather than to fit the table design. The entries should be legible and the writing should not be too small. Comments and remarks that are to be disregarded in sorting should be as inconspicuous as possible, in small print and placed so that they do not catch the eye and do not disturb the process of sorting. The relevant information may be abbreviated or given in symbols understandable only to those who know the key for decoding it. All kinds of devices used in the card index system may also be used here: cards in different colours to facilitate the distinction between basic characteristics, cut off corners, signs placed in the corners of the card, etc.

The card method may also considerably facilitate the addition of those items that are to give the total value of the characteristics expressed in some unit of measurement. We may place the appropriate information along one of the edges of the card. For example, we can put at the top of the card the area of each farm, the area of arable land, meadows, pastures, etc. Then, after sorting the cards into basic groups for which the data are to be given (e.g. after sorting the farms according to size in combination with the number of hired hands), we place the cards in each group above one another so that the top of the lower card sticks out far enough from underneath the upper card so that we can read off the appropriate data. In this way the figures to be added are placed one beneath the other, as in an ordinary table or column prepared for summing up. For the data that are to be summed up we may use all edges of the card and if necessary the other side.

In using the card method, when we have and adding machine at our disposal, we may in simple cases and up directly from the sorted cards, even if the figures are not placed along the border of the card.

d. *The machine card method.* In very extensive studies the manual card system described above can be usefully replaced by the machine card method in which the sorting and counting of cards is done mechanically by special machines. To make possible the use of machines we have to fill the cards in, not by writing but by marking them so that the machine can read off the information. This is done by using punch cards, i.e. cards with small holes punched in them in appropriate places to record the required information.

A punch card is an elongated rectangle, is made of cardboard and is divided into several dozen narrow vertical columns. The number of columns varies with the need. In the punch card machines now in use it may reach 80. Each column has spaces marked from the top to the bottom by numbers from 0 to 9. In each such space we can punch a hole. In addition three holes can be punched at the top of the card, above the figure. In this way we have at our disposal 13 spaces in each column.

To mark the required information on the card we earmark for each characteristic one or several columns, depending upon the need. If the characteristic is expressed in figures, the matter is very simple: we punch holes in appropriate spaces in the column, and for the numbers with more than one digit we use as many columns as there are digits. The age of 27 years is marked by punching the hole marked 7 in the column for units and the hole marked 2 in the column for tens of units. If the information is not expressed in numbers we have to introduce an appropriate code, e.g. designate man by the number 1 and woman by the number 2, and then start punching the information on the card. In this way, if we have a sufficient number of columns we can transfer all the required information on to the card. If necessary, we can also mark in this way the information needed, not for sorting but for the identification of the card: the area to which the unit belongs, its number, etc. If the population is to be divided into several groups according to a characteristic, these groups should be numbered and only the number of the group should be shown on the card. For instance, in our example the number 1 will be given to the farms below 1 hectare, the number 2 to those between 1 and 2 hectares, etc.; the actual area of the farm does not have to be shown on the card unless the areas of all the farms have to be added together. The eleventh and the twelfth space on the card can be used for marking the figures 11 and 12; in this way we may be able to put into one column, instead of two, information that may require two-digit numbers, (for instance, for marking the month of the year). We may also use these additional spaces for special notations, e.g. to the effect that there is no information available concerning the characteristic in question. Special punching machines are used to punch the holes. The operator reads off the information from the document and punches a hole in the card by pressing the appropriate key. The work on the punching machine can be done with great speed; if the entries are simple a skilled operator may be able to punch several hundred cards an hour.

After being punched a card should be verified. We may want to verify all cards, or only some of them, depending how much confidence we have in the operators, and how important it is to have the data free from error. The checking may be done semi-mechanically on special veryfying machines which are similar to the punching machine.

After punching and verifying we put the cards through the sorting machine. We set the machine to read a specific column and then set it in motion. The machine reads off each card separately and, according to the space in which the hole had been punched, places it in the appropriate compartment. Thus, in each compartment we get cards with identical entries, i.e. with holes punched in the same space. At the same time special meters count both the total number of cards that have been put through the machine and the number of cards collected in each compartment. After all the cards have passed through the machine the sorting is finished and we can read off the results from the meters and write them down. Certain types of machines record the result mechanically on paper so that we do not have to read off the figures and this saves much time. There are also special counting machines which can read off the results from several columns simultaneously. For instance, if we have sorted the cards twice and thus divided the farms according to area in combination with the number of hired hands, then after putting the cards through the counting machine once we obtain information concerning both the number of farms with a given number of draft animals in each group, and the number of farms with a given number of cows. In this way we get two finished tables at once. The results are at the same time recorded mechanically.

Sorting and counting machines work with great precision and speed, and without error. We can put through them, depending upon the method and conditions of sorting, from several thousand to about fifteen thousand cards per hour. Thus, even very extensive studies can be completed very quickly.

The third type of statistical machine is a tabulating machine used for adding the numerical entries. The tabulating machine reads off the figures from the cards that have previously been sorted, adds them up and records either only the final result or also all the components. Several series of figures can be added simultaneously so that after putting the cards through the machine once, we can get at once the total area of the farms, the area of arable land, meadows, pastures, etc. Thus the operations done on the tabulating machine can also, be completed very quickly, although the number of cards that can be put through it within an bour is not as great as it is in the sorting machine.

Statistical machines greatly surpass all manual methods in both speed and accuracy. The cost of using machines, however, must be carefully estimated in each case. The problem is that in using the machines we add one more operation: the preparation of the cards. This is fairly expensive, both because the good quality card is relatively expensive and because of the cost of punching. These additional costs may be too high in small enquiries. In extensive studies, however, substantial savings can be achieved, especially when the sorting has to be done many times or when a lot of tabulating is involved. Whether or not it is worth while to use statistical machines largely depends on the ratio of labour cost to the cost of using machines.

When statistical machines are used many problems arise, both of a technical and basic nature. In solving them expert knowledge and experience are essential. An improper sorting plan may create considerable difficulties and raise costs substantially, much more so than in the case of the manual system. On the other hand the technique of operating the machines involves many specific elements that have to be taken into account. In spite of difficulties in the organization of machine operations the use of statistical machines opens up great possibilities, unattainable by manual methods. These possibilities exist not only in technique but also in content, but only an experienced and able worker can take full advantage of them.

In any case, today in all major statistical enquiries statistical machines are used, and it is difficult to imagine how large statistical offices could function efficiently without them.

The machines of the kind described above were first used in the United States for processing the result of the census in 1890. They rapidly became popular in Europe as well. At present statistical machines are manufactured in various countries, including the Soviet Union where the production of certain types of machines is ahead of the western countries.

## 3. CHECKING AND CODING

The purpose of checking statistics is, of course, the elimination of errors. Checking should be done at every stage of processing: it should start when we collect raw data and end with the completed reports and the analysis of the results. The ways of obtaining good statistical material were discussed above. Now we shall describe the checking of more advanced stages of processing.

Raw statistics have to be thoroughly checked before actual processing starts. First of all the formal aspects of control have to be satisfied. We have to know that: (1) the material is complete, (2) all the panels of the forms have been properly filled, in, (3) there are no omissions. Then we have to check that there are no faulty entries. This can be done only in some cases. Usually the easiest error to discover is one caused by a misunderstanding of the question, and an answer out of context. Contradictions in answers can also be caught easily. If in the census forms a 2-year-old girl is referred to as "widow", then we undoubtedly have an error either in the age or in the marital status. Sometimes, however, we can only suspect that there is an error, but cannot be sure. If we are told that on a 2-hectare farm there are 45 cows we know that it is unlikely, though not impossible: it may be a dairy farm using purchased fodder. We may suspect an error, but we cannot be sure that it exists.

Control by logic should be based on everything that may help to discover errors; thus we should not only be alerted to contradictions in information pertaining to the same unit, but also to contradictions in information on different related units, e.g. on parents and children: if the father or mother is 25–30 years old, the age of the child cannot be 20 years. Control by logic is also based on a knowledge of the subject studied and it enables us to catch both obvious nonsense and improbable information. The psychology of the person who answers the questions should be taken into account. There may be a tendency to make certain typical, repeated errors, sometimes because the questionnaire is not well designed, and sometimes for other reasons. For example, it is a well known fact that most members of the family on a small farm work on the farm, or as it is expressed technically—they help the head of the family. It often happens that the space for an answer to the question on this subject is left blank not because the members of the family do not work on the farm, but because this is considered so obvious both by the farmer and the census enumerator, that it is hardly worth mentioning. Because the space is left blank the members of the family may be included in the wrong category of "not employed" dependants instead of "members of the family helping on the farm".

If an error is found an appropriate correction may be introduced. Returning to our previous example, if a child 2 years of age is said to be a widow and from other data it appears that the age is stated correctly (e.g. if she is a child of very young parents) then we can safely replace the word "widow" by "single". However, such possibilities of discovering and correcting errors are rare. It is much more likely that when an error is discovered there will be no indication in the remaining answers as to how it should be corrected. If we find an error which we cannot correct right away, there are two ways out. The first is to go back to the source information and get the right answer. In large enquiries comprising hundreds of thousands or millions of questionnaires this can be done only in exceptional cases, either when the matter is of great importance or when a certain type of error is repeated very often. In smaller enquiries and when there are no difficulties in returning the questionnaire for correction all the questionnaires with important errors may be returned. If this is impossible, there is another alternative: to cross out the wrong answer and state in the proper panel that no information is available concerning this characteristic of this specfic unit. In the statistical table these units will appear in the panel as "unknown". Such items often appear in tables and are inevitable. It is undesirable, however, to have too many such "unknowns" in relation to the total number of units in a group. This would indicate a lack of care in conducting the enquiry or the inclusion of a question to which, under the circumstances, no proper answer can be given.

It is obvious that even with the best of control there will be a certain number of errors in the completed questionnaires. This is unavoidable and should be taken into consideration in every statistical enquiry. It is also inevitable to have a certain number of "unknowns".

Another function is usually related to the checking of questionnaire to possible later studies. This consists, first of all, in removing technical defects (e.g. illegible writing) that can create difficulties in later studies. Very often we make use of coding. The purpose is to make any further work on tabulation—whether by the "stroke", manual card, or mechanized card method—as mechanical as possible, so that the worker need not ponder over the contents of the entries, but will recognize them visually and automatically perform the operation: put a stroke in the right column, put the card on the right pile, or in mechanized operations, press the right key of the punching machine. Such mechanization of operations is possible only when the entries on the card are short and easy to read. Only very infrequently do we get such entries on the questionnaire directly from the enquiry. Usually the card has to be especially prepared for sorting. Another consideration is still more important. Very often while sorting we can classify a certain event not just by reading off the answer but by performing a mental operation. If the questionnaire states that the area of the farm is 7 hectares, we have to think for a moment before we decide to include the farm in the "5–10 hectare" group. Sometimes a simple arithmetical operation has to be performed. This is the case, for instance, when the raw data provide only the date of birth and the classification is based on age at the time of the census. Even more involved mental processes are necessary for including the persons queried in an appropriate socio-professional category. This usually necessitates the perusal of quite a few answers concerning the person and sometimes also the members of the family. In machine processing special difficulties arise when certain characteristics described in words have to be expressed by a number. In these cases we have to remember the code so that we know which number to use in a given case.

It is necessary to separate all the operations that require thinking from other mechanical operations involved in data processing or in transferring data on to the machine card. This means that before the work on data processing is begun all the entries in raw data that cannot easily be read should be replaced by short signs, the data concerning the size of the unit should be replaced by a symbol of the size class to which it belongs, all the necessary computations should be performed, verbal entries should be replaced by numerical symbols, etc. All these operations we call *coding*.

Coding may be usefully combined with checking the material, because these operations are similar: in both of them the mind should be alert to the logical essence of the phenomena whereas in such operations as marking strokes, sorting or transcribing the data onto machine cards the work is done mechanically.

In more extensive studies those engaged in coding should be provided with all the necessary special equipment. In addition to detailed instructions they should receive coding keys, computation tables, etc. In simple enquiries in which coding would be too expensive certain decisions concerning work simplification may be delegated to those who do the sorting and punching. This considerably diminishes the efficiency of their work but under certain circumstances may be more economical.

The operations of coding and checking are intended to make the statistical document as convenient as possible to use and to eliminate errors. However, errors may occur in the process of tabulating, and therefore it should also be thoroughly checked.

Each stage of work should be checked to reduce the chance of errors appearing in the table. However, they cannot be completely eliminated, and therefore the table itself should also be checked. The checking will be primarily of an accounting type: the table has to balance and the totals across and from top to bottom must balance. The figures pertaining to the same phenomenon shown in different tables should also agree and therefore cross-checking is also necessary.

If errors or inconsistencies are discovered they should be removed by checking particular stages of the tabulation and, if necessary, by referring to the original document. Errors are often due to mistakes in writing down the figures or to some obvious blunder: such errors are relatively easy to discover. Quite often, however, the sources of error are not easy to find. If inconsistencies due to errors constitute only a small percentage of the total then—although this is not a desirable practice—we may, and sometimes even must, remove them mechanically by simple changing the figures so that they balance. In order to find an error we might have to go through the whole or a large part of the material all over again. This is both troublesome and expensive and may be worth while only in very important cases. A minor "juggling" of figures may be a lesser evil since a difference of several units on large items is without much significance in statistics. We should be most careful, however, and under no circumstances can such corrections be entrusted to auxiliary personnel, especially to those directly engaged in the processing since it might encourage them to thus conceal major errors due to carelessness.[25] First of all, though, we should strive to reduce the number of errors through good organization and constant checking of all phases of the work.

A purely arithmetical check of the table is not the only possible form of control. Equally important is checking by logic which consists in analysing the contents of the table. Sometimes it is very simple as certain panels of the table should remain blank since they contain combinations of characteristics that never appear

---

[25] A practical hint: auxiliary personnel should not be allowed to erase the wrong figure and replace it by the correct one. The wrong figure should be lightly crossed out and the correct figure be written above or beside it.

in practice. In tables of population data such panels may be some of those in which age is combined with marital status since there are no persons married or widowed below a certain age. If, then, there is a figure in such a panel, we can be sure that there is an error. It is desirable that on working sheets such panels as cannot contain any figures be marked in some special way, e.g. by putting crosses in them. This indicates at once that they are not empty by mistake.

The situation is not always so simple. Quite frequently a given event may occur, but is unlikely. We cannot then simply reject the figures that fall into such panels, but we have to consider it as a possible warning that warrants special checking. If a large number appears in such a panel the likelihood of error is considerably greater. There may be panels in which too large or too small figures may be such that an error can be spotted immediately. In certain cases the middle values are always large and the extreme ones small: there are always more people of medium height than very tall or very short ones. If the table shows some other pattern then we can be sure that there is an error. There are quite a few such special situation peculiar to a certain phenomenon; of course, one has to be an expert in the field and know the probable and improbable situations, to be able to intercept an error. For this reason final checking of the tables before they are published should be done by someone who knows the subject well. This type of control is necessary if the user of the table is to be protected from unpleasant surprises. In the course of further investigation or in practical applications of the results further errors may be discovered but then it is usually too late to eliminate them.

In discovering errors the computation of ratios or averages may be of some help. For instance, if in a group of farms with areas of from 5 to 10 hectares there were 720 farms and the total area was given as 1200 hectares then the average size of a farm would be slightly over 1·6 hectares, which is impossible since the farms are of no less than 5 hectares. If we divide the output of a certain commodity by the number of persons employed in its production or by the number machines used in production we may discover that the figures, if not obviously erroneous, are questionable.

An error in the table does not necessarily have to be an error in tabulation. It may be an arithmetically correct reflection of faulty statistical data. An analysis of the table may bring to light certain errors in documents that we might not be able to discover otherwise.

If we have individual data concerning, say, the height of a group of adult men we will not question their correctness if they all fall within certain probable limits, e.g. 140–190 cm (55–74 in). If the figures show, however, that the numbers of men are almost equal in the different height groups 140–5, 165–70, and 185–90 cm then we can be sure that the figures have been forged, though incompetently, with the object of concealing the forgery. The culprit, in his naiveté, hoped that he would not be discovered if all the people were evenly divided into different height groups.[26]

An interesting example of the discovery of a forgery by an analysis of statistical reports is provided by birth statistics. A report on births by months in many countries showed an unaccountable drop in December and an increase in January of the following year. To check this phenomenon more thoroughly instructions were issued—first in Italy and then in other countries—to make a breakdown not by months, but by the days on which the births occurred. It turned out that in many countries the number or births drops considerably toward the end of December and increases rapidly in the first days of January, reaching a level more than several times the daily average for other periods of the year. The conclusion was obvious: many parents make their children "younger" by declaring the beginning of January as the date of birth rather than the end of the preceding year when the birth actually took place. A more thorough analysis conducted in Poland showed unwarranted increases in births not only at the beginning of the year, but also, although to a much smaller extent, on the first day of each month at the expense of the last days of the last days of the preceding month, and even on each "round" date, e.g. the 10th, 15th, or 20th of each month.[27]

In this example it would be impossible to discover which particular document had been forged, unless we instituted a special investigation in each case. A statistical analysis, however, enables us to establish beyond doubt the prevalence of mass forgeries. Naturally we cannot eliminate such errors by improving our statistics; statistics, however, help discover them and may thus bring about measures designed to correct the situation.

No matter how much care we exercise in processing statistical data and what methods we use for checking, it is hard to imagine a major statistical report without at least a small number of errors. We shall now consider the significance of such errors from the point of view of using the results of a statistical enquiry.

We shall discuss primarily errors due to inexact information obtained from the person queried and to incorrect entries made by the person who fills in the questionnaire.

From the point of view of their origin such errors can be divided into two categories: inadvertent and deliberate errors. The former may be the result of carelessness or ignorance. Quite often, when the level of culture is low, the owner of a small farm cannot give the exact area of different types of land; or some people may not be able to give the exact date of their birth. Sometimes such ignorance or carelessness may lead to peculiar deviations from reality, e.g. the preference

---

[26] This example is authentic, and is taken from the report on the heights of recruits sent to the Warsaw Committee on Statistics before World War I by a rural community.

[27] This analysis was made in Poland for December 1929 and January 1930, and for the whole year 1932.

for round figures: 40 instead of 39 or 41, etc., analysis having substantial clusters at round numbers gives evidence of this kind of errors and the extent of rounding off indicates the size of the error. Care in collecting the data may substantially reduce the number of accidental errors. It is important to have proper forms with clearly formulated questions and good instructions, but even more important is the quality of work of the enumerator—his skill in asking questions, gaining people confidence, extracting answers, appraising the credibility of the answers, suggesting ways of establishing the fact more precisely, etc.

The second category of erroneous answers—deliberate misinformation—appears particularly often when people fear an undesirable consequence of telling the truth. This kind of misinformation is most common in financial matters because of the fear of increased taxation or other burdens. However, it may be due to other reasons (e.g. a man may be afraid to give his correct age for fear of being drafted). The registration of the wrong date of birth also belongs in this category. Sometimes the motives are different, e.g. the vanity that induces older people to deduct a few years from their age. The motives may vary considerably, and the range of incorrect answers of this kind is very wide. The results of a statistical enquiry usually cannot expose the error directly and therefore later checking is rather difficult. This makes care in collecting material all the more important. Much will depend upon the advance publicity, but the most important part is played by the census enumerator who collects the material.

From the point of view of statistical results it is important to distinguish these from random errors which are as likely to deviate in either direction. Deliberate errors usually tend to go in one direction and inadvertent errors almost always deviate in both directions. However, there may be exceptions to this rule. Very old people who do not remember their age may be inclined to state it too high. Here, although there is no desire to distort the truth, the distortion will be in one direction. On the other hand, if somebody does not want to give his right age because he considers it dangerous, he may hide it by stating it either high or low; this is deliberate but not necessarily biased in one direction.

From the point of view of the results random errors which are equally likely to go in one direction as another, are the least dangerous; if many observations are recorded they will almost completely cancel out. Biassed errors, however, are always very dangerous and a large number of observations will not tone down the bad effects. Even the errors of the first kind, however, are not always negligible. If a certain number of people round off their ages by giving the figure a year or two higher or lower than the actual age it may not affect the average age of the whole population, but it may make it impossible to find the frequencies in particular years though ingenious devices are sometimes used to smooth out a series distorted by the tendency to round off the age.

Now that we already know that it is almost impossible to have statistics without errors, we have to concentrate on determining the type of error, its direction and probable magnitude. When we establish these we can use statistical data, even those which considerably deviate from reality, both for practical and scientific research purposes. A careful analysis of errors will protect us against jumping to hasty conclusions and enable us to make the necessary corrections as well as use the material at our disposal, even though to a more limited extent and with less confidence than if our material were free from error. The utilization of information that is not too precise is common and inevitable not only in the field of statistics.

A knowledge of the nature of the errors is a necessary condition. For this reason both the institutions and the individuals who publish statistical data should be required to provide exact information concerning the reliability of the statistics published. This applies both to raw data—since without it we could not properly make use of these data—and to studies in which the author draws conclusions on the basis of the data he collected. The reader must be in a position to check the validity of such conclusions. This kind of information concerning the reliability of data should apply both to the collection of raw data and their processing and tabulation.

## 4. TECHNICAL EQUIPMENT IN STATISTICS

Statistical enquiries require many, sometimes cumbersome computations. Thus it is very important to make as extensive use as possible of equipment, machines, tables and other devices that facilitate computations. We have already discussed special statistical machines. Now we shall describe briefly the most important other types of equipment.

Calculating machines usually do not perform all, but only some specialized arithmetical operations: adding and subtracting or multiplying and dividing. Even though adding machines can be used for multiplication, and calculating machines can be used for adding and subtracting, these operations are performed much less efficiently than on the appropriate specialized machines. We shall now describe these two types of machines.

a. *Calculating machines and equipment.* The simplest adding device is an abacus, long known in Russia, less common in Poland and other countries. It consists of a frame and a number of horizontal metal rods, each with ten wooden balls that are moved from side to side in counting. Experienced operators can add subtract with it very quickly and almost automatically which is very important from the point of view of efficiency. They can also multiply by consecutive adding. To multiply 725 by 42 they add 725 twice and then 7250 four times. Using abbreviated adding methods an experienced operator can achieve a considerable speed.

More convenient than the abacus, although based on the same principle, are various types of small plates on which by pushing pins, we move metal bands with numbers from 0 to 9; the result appears in a window at the top. By using the reverse side of the plate we can subtract in the same way. If for example, the plate contains nine bands we can add or subtract figures up to 999 million.

Much more efficient in statistical work are various types of adding machines. They are equipped with keyboards and to add a number we press the appropriate keys; the figure thus obtained is shown in a special window. If we then press the addition key this figure is typed on a paper tape which is inserted in the machine and is also recorded in the inner mechanism so that each consecutive figure is added to the previous sum. When a special key is pressed the sum appears on the tape. The machine can also be used for subtracting or multiplying (as on the abacus). Subtotals can also be obtained and recorded on the tape. There are manually operated adding machines and electric ones: the latter are of course much more efficient. In general, adding machines are very effective and reliable. Since all the items are recorded on the tape we can easily check whether there is an error.

Other types of such machines perform specialized operations. For example, on some of them two or more independent summations can be made.

Calculating machines are also of several types. There are calculating machines which are used mainly for division and multiplication. They have a special mechanism for setting the required figure and by turning the handle we transfer it to the "carriage" part in which the result of the operation is shown. Apart from the hand-operated machines there are also electric calculators. They can also be used for adding and subtracting, but since each figure has to be set first, they are relatively slow. There are different types of calculating machines, but the basic elements are the same.

For quick multiplication and division slide rules can be used. This simple but ingenious device gives the result up to three significant digits. This degree of precision is usually sufficient for calculating percentages or for obtaining approximate results of multiplication. Since calculations can be done very quickly the slide rule can be used to obtain preliminary results and sometimes even for final calculations. The statistician should always have it handy and use it particularly when calculating machines or writing would take too much time. Besides multiplying and dividing, the slide rule raises to a power, extracts roots, makes logarithmic and trigonometric calculations. There are special slide rules for technical calculations and for other special purposes. The degree of precision depends upon the length of the scale. Most common are slide rules with a scale of 25 centimetres, although some are twice or half as long. By using special cylinders with a large diameter the scale can be extended to several metres, thus showing the 4th and even the 5th digit. However, the speed of work is then correspondingly reduced.

b. *Statistical tables. Graphs.* Various kinds of tables are very helpful in statistical work. Some, such as logarithmic tables, are used primarily for other purposes but also facilitate work in statistics. There are multiplication tables which give the products of two numbers up to $1000 \times 1000$, or $100 \times 10\,000$ or percentage tables which give the percentage ratio of two figures of up to three-digits each. Such tables avoid cumbersome calculations. There are also tables which reduce the work, e.g. the calculation of percentages can be done by adding a few components. Very useful for work with calculating machines are reciprocal ratio tables give quotients, $1 : x$.[28] There are also tables especially prepared for statistical purposes which contain the finished or semi-finished results of common calculations which require much work. There are several collections of such tables. The most extensive is Pearson's *Tables for Statisticians and Biometricians* (London, 2 volumes). More useful for some purposes is *Statistical Tables for Biological, Agricultural and Medical Research* by R. A. Fisher and F. Yates (2nd ed., London, 1948). In Polish there are short statistical tables by J. Wiśniewski *Tablice liczbowe* (*Numerical Tables*) (Warsaw, 1939).[29] Moreover, certain tables are usually included in textbooks on statistics. Some general and statistical tables are included in the Appendix to this book.

When using tables we must remember that most of them give only approximate results. Of course, the approximation, must be sufficient to prevent a major error in the final result. On the other hand—and this is very important in practical applications—the tables should be only as exact as is absolutely necessary. Too much precision renders the tables too awkward to use For example, consider logarithmic tables. Seven-digit tables given up to 100,000 fill a volume of about 100 pages. Five-digit tables up to 10,000 comprise 20 pages, and four-digit tables only 2 pages. For many calculations four-digit tables are quite sufficient and the required number can be found in them much faster than in five-digit, to say nothing of seven-digit tables. The same applies to tables of reciprocals: four-digit tables to 1000 are often quite sufficient and require only two pages whereas for five-digit tables to 10,000 need about twenty pages. In all extensive studies, then, tables of only the required accuracy should be used. In short calculations, of course, this consideration is of less importance.

In statistical calculations graphs are very helpful to solve equations. Let us take a function of the type: $y = x^2$. We substitute different values of $x$ to find $y$ and plot the results with $x$ as the abscissa and $y$ as the ordinate. We then have the curve representing the function. From it we can read off the value of $y$ for each value of $x$ with an accuracy depending on the scale of the graph. In the same way we can obtain the value of $x$ for a given $y$. Such graphs are widely used in technical work, and save a great deal of time compared with the method of solving each equation directly. They are also more convenient to use than numerical tables. Graphs can give solutions even to very complex equations. Solutions can be given

---

[28] A number of tables very useful for statistical work can be found in *Barlow's Tables of Squares, Cubes, Square Roots, Cube Roots and Reciprocals*.

[29] These tables were published just before the war, and unfortunately there are only very few of them left.

on ordinary rectangular coordinates, as in the above example, and they can also be given in relation to two or more arguments with a great number of possible solutions from the point of view of drawing technique. For a graph to serve its purpose it has to be easily readable and sufficiently accurate. If the required degree of accuracy cannot be achieved, e.g. because it would require too large a scale, inconvenient to use, it is better not to use the graph at all.[30]

In statistics, as in engineering, there are many problems that can be solved mathematically only with a lot of work. Tables provide ready solutions, but many of these solutions can also be given in graphic form. For this reason the collections of tables mentioned above also contain graphs.

## 5. STATISTICAL DIAGRAMS

a. *The purpose of a diagram.* Diagrams are also effective means of presenting numerical data. But a diagram has its specific qualities which fit it for use in special circumstances and for special purposes.

A good diagram is not a simple repetition of numerical data from the table. It shows a problem in a more condensed form, so to say, synthetically. It is a result of an analysis, of thinking about the problem. Moreover a diagram provides a clearer picture, with a more direct appeal. Being a result of an analysis it is, in a sense, a product of the thinking processes of its author, and not just an objective presentation of reality. In this respect it does not always differ from a tabular presentation, since a synthetic table is also a product of a mental process. If it is to produce a synthetic picture a graph should not, and cannot, contain as many details as the table. A graph which is a simple and detailed repetition of the data from the table is conceivable but it loses the qualities that it should possess, and is boring and superfluous.

The purposes of a diagram may be varied. It may be designed to present certain statistical data in a form most easy for the general public to comprehend, in this way to make certain facts generally known. This type of diagram may replace numerical data or may be shown with such data to supplement it. Other types of diagrams, used in special statistical publications or in scientific studies, serve to emphasize special aspects of a problem and this can usually be more easily achieved by a diagram than by figures. Such diagrams are shown as proofs of certain statements, as an illustration of the conclusions. Finally, diagrams may be a tool of direct scientific analysis; certain problems become easier to understand in diagram form. Between these three basic types there are, course, many intermediate types.

The form of the diagram depends upon its purpose. If it is prepared for the

---

[30] There is an extensive work on nomograms in Polish by Bolesław Konarski *Nomografia*, Warsaw, 1937, pp. VIII, 328.

general public it should catch the eye and be easy to understand. Thus is should be simple unambiguous, and attractive. Bright colours are desirable, especially when the diagram is to be seen from a distance, e.g. when it is placed in a shop window in the street, on a bill-board etc. Then the same techniques should be used as in poster advertising.

There are certain dangers in the use of diagrams. Since they result from syntheses and interpret raw data, they express the individual judgment of the maker more than a table would. He may go to extremes and give a one-sided interpretation or even distort the facts. Such distortions are induced by the fact that a diagram does not always create the same impression as the figures it presents. Optical illusions often play an important part. Disregarding them may lead to a false presentation of the facts. This may not even be due to a lack of good will, but rather to a lack of skill and experience. Quite often, of course, it is done on purpose, and the type of presentation is so selected as to mislead or give a biased presentation of certain facts.

The diagrams below are examples of optical illusions which may arise.

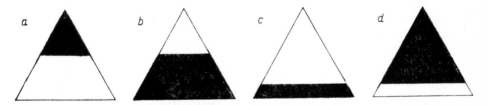

FIG. 3.1. Optical illusions.

If we mark one fourth of the area of a triangle at its top part (drawings *a* and *b*) we get an exaggerated impression of the area marked, and if we mark one fourth of the area at the bottom (drawings *c* and *d*), it appears relatively small.[31] In this way we can give a completely false impression even though the actual area is shown correctly. This sort of trick was used by the Germans in 1921 when they presented their losses from World War I: the pre-war population of Germany was represented by a triangle and the losses were shown at the top.[32]

It is also important which part of the drawing is shaded and which is white; the same part appears bigger when it is white than when it is shaded (compare drawings *a* and *b* or *c* and *d*).

We shall now discuss certain technical aspects of making diagrams. We shall

---

[31] The reader may check that the area of the narrow strips at the bottom of the triangle in drawings *c* and *d* is the same as the area marked at the top in drawings *a* and *b*.

[32] The diagram in question was shown in *Wirtschaft und Statistik*, Statistical Office of the German Reich, Berlin, 1921, Vol. 2, p. 95.

describe in greater detail the graphs used for a simple presentation of the facts. We shall discuss later the methods used in a scientific analysis of statistical data.

b. *Line, bar, area pictorial charts.* The simplest type of diagram consists of segments of straight lines, one beside the other, so that their lengths represent the respective sizes of the populations that we want to compare. By such straight lines we can present the lengths of different rivers. We can also use them for comparing all kinds of numerical data: the populations of different countries, the areas, the production of a certain commodity in different years, etc. This kind of presentation is not very spectacular, but is adequate.

The lines may be of varying thickness or, rather, instead of lines we can use rectangles or *bars* placed beside each other or one above the other. The principle is the same and the length of the rectangle is the important thing as it previously was the length of the segment. The picture is clearer, however, and more pleasing, especially when in colour. With different colours or different types of shading we can also present different phenomena which we want to compare. If we want to compare births and deaths in different countries we can choose different colours or differents kinds of shading for births and deaths and place the bars in pairs for each country, one beside the other. Moreover, the difference between the rectangles representing births and deaths shows the natural population increase: the excess of birth over deaths or vice versa (see Fig. 3.2).

The use of bars instead of lines essentially enlarges the scope of presenting statistical data. If we divide the rectangle of the bar into parts and distinguish them, e.g. by different colours or shadings, we can show the structure of the population. Thus we can compare two things simultaneously: the total size of the population (the area of the whole rectangle) and the structure of the population (the division of the rectangle into parts). In this method, as in the previous one, only one dimension of the rectangle is changed, usually the longer side. In this way the visual comparability of absolute measurements is maintained, both with regard to the total size of the population, and with regard to its component parts. From the point of view of the structure of the population this method has certain disadvantages, because it is not immediately apparent how the particular parts of the population compare with each other. To overcome this difficulty we may divide the rectangle into parts along the side that does not vary in size; most frequently the comparison of total size is transferred to the varying, shorter side, and the division into parts is shown along the unchanged, longer side. We can also abandon the comparison of absolute figures and show the structure in percentages on bars of the same length and width.

All three methods shown above refer to the number and size of flats in Warsaw and Łódź, based on the census of 1931.

A comparison of the first two shows that Fig. 3a enables a better comparison of total populations and Fig. 3b is better for comparing their structure, because

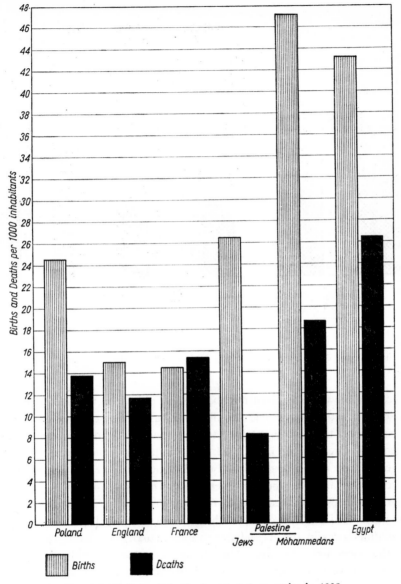

FIG. 3.2. Births and deaths in selected countries in 1938.

changes along the shorter side are not very clear. The second method can be used
when less emphasis is laid on differences in total size than on differences in structure. If the differences between total populations are small they will not be very
visible on this type of graph. In Fig. 3c, in which the rectangles are of the same
length and width, only a comparison of structures in shown.

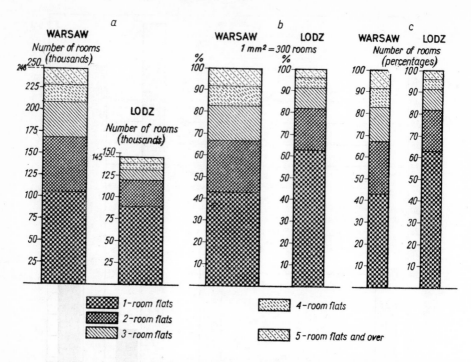

FIG. 3.3. a,b,c. Flats in Warsaw and Lodz by the number of rooms in 1931.

The scale in the first and third method may be placed on the side, as in Fig. 3c. In the second method (rectangles of different bases) the scale should be placed at the bottom, at the base of each rectangle separately; more frequently an area equivalence is given, as in Fig. 3b (1 mm² equals a certain number of units). When we use bars of the same height but different width we can also show a vertical percentage scale, as in the third method shown above.

In the rectangles described above, one dimension—the height or the base—remains unchanged and consequently the differences in total quantities are shown by *linear* differences in the second dimension; actually, however, these diagrams express the phenomena by area. Thus it appears that there should be another type of graph with figures in which both dimensions change. For this purpose we can use primarily regular polygons, equilateral triangles, squares, or circles. Figures with more than four sides are not suitable. The advantage of using these figures when differences between populations are great is that it is easier to place them side by side in the same scale than it is when we use rectangles of the same base, since sometimes the use of the same scale might require too much space. This technical advantage does, however, have can associated weakness—the eye does not properly judge the ratios between areas, as can be seen from the example below.

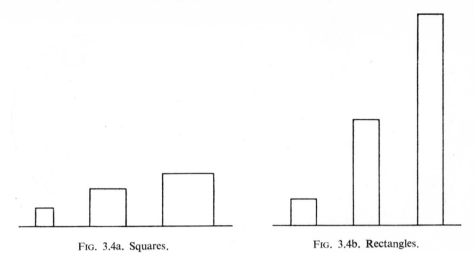

FIG. 3.4a. Squares.          FIG. 3.4b. Rectangles.

For both the squares and the rectangles the ratios of the areas are 1 : 4 : 8. There is no doubt that the squares provide a much less clear picture than do the rectangles with the same base.

However, with figures in which two dimensions change, the structure of the population can be very well presented. This is particularly true with reference to squares and circles. If a population is presented in the form of a circle its sectors will represent the structure. The eye easily catches differences in angles in different circle, regardless whether they are the same size, providing the angles are not too small. Therefore, if our prime purpose is to draw attention to the differences in structure and if the differences in the size of the population are of secondary importance, then the sectors of the circle are very suitable. We draw circles so that their areas (i.e. the radius squared) are proportional to the total populations being compared, and the division into sectors corresponds to the structure of these populations. It is desirable to establish for all circles one uniform starting point and one direction in which the graph should be read. For instance, we can start from the upper vertical radius and read clockwise.

The structure of a population can also be very well presented by a square. There are many different possibilities. Instead of dividing a square, as we do a rectangle, into an appropriate number of vertical or horizontal strips corresponding in width to the frequencies of particular components, we can divide it by thin lines into the desired number of small squares and then shade or colour enough of them to indicate the ratio of the given part of the population to the total. Perhaps, the most convenient method, is to divide the square into one hundred small squares, because in this way we get immediately the percentage the part is of the total population. As in the case of circle, with squares we can better compare the structures of different populations than their total sizes.

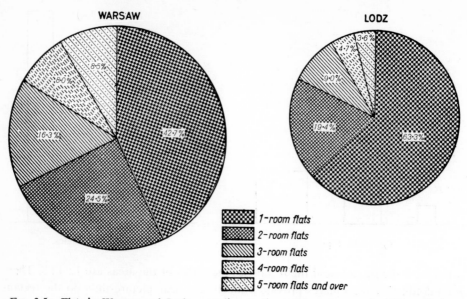

FIG. 3.5a. Flats in Warsaw and Lodz according to the number of rooms in 1931 — Circles.

Sometimes good results can be obtained by using semicircles instead of full circles, as in the example below, where the upper semicircle represents the division of farms by size, and the lower semicircle, the area occupied by farms of different sizes.

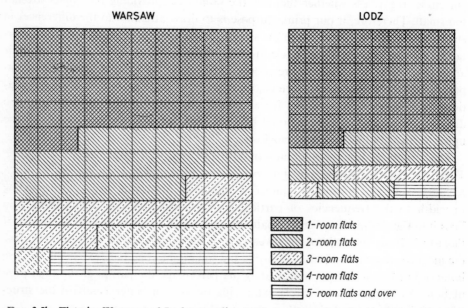

FIG. 3.5b. Flats in Warsaw and Lodz according to the number of rooms in 1931 — Squares.

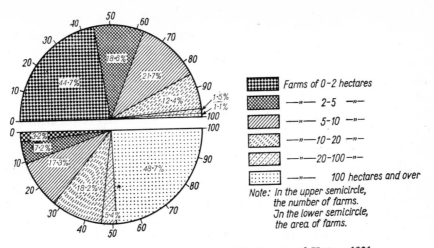

FIG. 3.6. Farms according to size. The County of Kutno, 1931.

Geometrical figures other than rectangles, squares and circles are rarely used in statistics since, if they are improperly used, they can cause optical illusions and thus can misrepresent reality (see p. 109).

The question may arise whether it would not be desirable to use three-dimensional drawings of solids to represent statistical quantities. It is possible, of course, but there is not much point to it. The objection is the same as, and stronger than, that against the use of areas of circles and regular polygons to compare total populations: the eye does not properly estimate the differences in size between drawings of solids.

For this reason this method is almost never used in serious studies. It may be used, however, in popular presentations, particularly in conjunction with pictures, e.g. a number of men whose height corresponds to the total populations of the countries, each of them carrying on his back a bag whose sive expresses the amount of taxes levied. In this way the ratio of the size of the bag to the height of the man vividly expresses the tax burden in the country. The presentation is ingenious and eye-catching, but not very precise.

In this example we are faced with another problem—the use of pictures in sizes proportional to the total sizes of the populations compared. In this way, of course, we can ochieve better effects, but in designing the diagram we encounter so many difficulties that cannot be overcome without infringing upon the principle of statistical honesty, that the use of pictures is considered permissible only in exceptional cases. Let us imagine how difficult it is to draw a human figure of a size proportional to the size of the population. If we change the height in proportion to the population the question arises what to do with other dimensions. If all figures are made equally thin, regardless of height, the effect will be ridiculous. If we make the whole figure proportional to the height we shall completely distort the visual effect since big figures will appear disproportionately large in comparison with the small ones. To be guided by the "volume" of the human figure is also not satisfactory.

This does not mean that figures or pictures should never be used in statistical charts; they should only be used *properly*. Pictorial presentation serves its purpose when it is used to attract attention, or is related to the subject of the chart and not to its numerical and statistical content which is also presented independently of the pictures. If we present the prevalence of blindness, in a chart to be hung on the wall, for example at a hygiene exhibition for the general public, it will be appropriate to paint a colourful picture pertaining to the theme of the exhibition— perhaps a blind person led by a dog. If the picture is attractive the viewer will be drawn to it by the theme and technique, and having stopped he will also look at the main charts which are the chief points of the exhibition. Such pictures are not of a graphical or statistical type, but a medium of attracting attention, and they are therefore outside the scope of this book. But in the method that we are going to discuss presently, the picture is directly connected with the manner of presenting a phenomenon in a chart.

c. *The quantitative and quantitative-symbolic method.* During the third decade of the 20th century a new method of presenting statistical data became very popular. It was called the Viennese method since it was used extensively by the Socio-Economic Museum in Vienna. This method is also in common use in other countries, including the Soviet Union. Here the size of a population is expressed not by the length of a line, the area of a figure, or the volume of a geometrical solid, but by repeating a certain symbol expressing a definte number of units—as many times as it is contained in the total. Thus, if such a symbol stands for 1 million persons and the population of a country is 25 million, the symbol is repeated 25 times. This method—which in contradistinction to the linear, area or volume methods can be called a quantitative one—is statistically correct, and at least as expressive as, for example, the method of rectangles with the same base and varying heights. Without a special scale we can read off the figures on the chart by counting how many the symbol is repeated.

We can use any symbols: points, circles, squares or anything else. The Viennese method consists in using small drawings which vividly present the phenomenon in an abbreviated and stylized form. We can use drawings of loaded railway cars for coal shipments, boats for traffic in a seaport, etc. When symbols are well chosen and carefully drawn the impression may be very direct and vivid, as, for instance, when we use a drawing of infants in swaddling-clothes for births or coffins for deaths. The comparative frequency of births and deaths is particularly well emphasized when we show them side by side.

For the Viennese method the charts should be particularly well prepared both as to choice of symbol and drawing technique, or else the chart may completely fail. The symbol must be simple, schematic, and yet readable and understandable without explanations. It should also be aesthetic in appearance. If it is well done the results achieved may be excellent. This method may be wearying if used to excess, e.g. in major statistical complications. Also, it does not provide much scope for subtle distinctions. A symbol should represent a considerable number of units or it may have to be repeated too often—thus destroying the desired simplicity. For this reason, the Viennese method may be considered as a very valuable achievement of diagram technique but its application is rather limited. It can be more widely used in posters for exhibition than in books (see Fig. 3.7.).

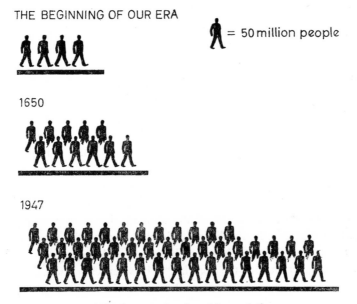

FIG. 3.7. The growth of world population.

All the types of figures or charts described above are used primarily to demonstrate certain points. We have discussed in general terms the principle on which they should be based, without going into details. For the statistician as well as for the artist there is a large scope for initiative and invention, particularly when we are bent on forcing a reluctant viewer to take note of a statistical representation of reality.

When we said that the diagrams described so far are used mainly for demonstration purposes we did not mean to say that they cannot be helpful in scientific analysis although this will seldom be the case. On the other hand, the diagrams that we shall presently discuss possess not only a very high demonstration value but are also excellent tools of statistical analysis.

d. *Graphs.* In mathematics graphs are used to present functions. Two lines intersecting at right angles are the axes. On them, from the point of intersection, we measure positive values to the right and upward, and negative values to the left and downward. The horizontal axis, which is called the abscissa or the x-axis, represents the independent variable and the vertical axis, called the ordinate or the y-axis, the dependent variable. Points on the graph representing pairs of values satisfying the function are found as the points of intersection of lines perpendicular to the axes, drawn from the points on the axes determined by the values of the variables.

In statistical graphs the situation is usually simplified by the fact that, as a rule, we do not deal with negative values and consequently the graph is confined to the upper right-hand quadrant.

Graphs on rectangular coordinate axes are basically used in statistics in three cases:

(1) For a graph of a frequency distribution we measure the numerical values of a certain characteristic along the abscissa, (e.g. height in centimetres), and on the ordinate the frequency with which the given value of the characteristic appears (e.g. the number of persons of a given height) (see Chapter 4, Part II).

(2) For a graph of the development of a phenomenon in time we measure the units of time along the abscissa (e.g. months or years), and along the ordinate the number of events coresponding to a given unit of time (e.g. the number of tons of coal extracted in a given month or year) (see Chapter 9, Part II).

(3) For a graph of the correlation of characteristics we measure on the abscissa the values of one variable and along the ordinate the corresponding values of the other, e.g. on the x-axis the height in centimeters and on the y-axis the weight corresponding to a given height. These graphs correspond very closely to a mathematical graph of a function, but the correlation between characteristics in statistics is a different notion from the concept of functional dependence in mathematics (see Part IV).

For statistical graphs a logarithmic or semi-logarithmic scale is sometimes used. In the latter case, to one of the coordinates, usually the ordinate, a scale is used proportional, not to the numbers, but to their logarithms.

Graphs are a fundamental tool of statistical analysis. Different types will be discussed in detail in appropriate sections of this book.

Under certain circumstances polar coordinates are used instead of rectangular coordinates.

e. *Cartograms.* Cartograms represent a geographical distribution of statistical events and will be discussed in detail in Chapter 8, Part II. Here we shall confine ourselves to enumerating the basic technical methods used in cartograms.

The basis, of course, is a map or a drawing, usually in a schematic form on which only the most essential features or reference points are shown. e.g. only the administrative boundaries of states, provinces or counties. Statistical events may be marked on them in a variety of ways.

(1) In the appropriate place on the map we draw *conventional signs* or symbols specifying the appearance of a phenomenon in that area. As symbols we can use points, circles of different diameters, etc. which denote settlements of different sizes; or pickaxes may be placed where mines exist; or sugar loafs to mark the location of sugar factories; and so on.

(2) The *area* method. The whole map is divided into districts, e.g. provinces or counties; for each district we calculate the average intensity of a phenomenon: population density, crop yields in hundredweights per hectare; after selecting an appropriate scale (shading of different densities of colouring of different intensities) we designate in an appropriate manner the area of each district. This method is perhaps the most common in statistical cartograms.

(3) The *isorithmic* method (from the Greek words: *isos,* equal and *arithmos,* number) or the method of lines of equal values. This is the way, meteorological charts are prepared—*isotherms* join points with the same temperature, *isobars* points with the same barometric pressure, etc. In geography, on a hypsometric map lines are shown that join points of the same elevation above sea-level.

Under certain circumstances it is also possible to denote statistical phenomena in this way. The belts between the lines can be marked by shading or colours, as in the area method. In this way on a hypsometric map, layers will be marked as belts with elevations above sea-level defined by the two neighbouring equal elevation lines, e.g. not less than 200 metres and not more than 300 metres.

(4) The *point* method. We assume that a point (or some other sign) represents a fixed number of units of a population e.g. 1000 inhabitants or 1000 heads of cattle, and at each point on the map we place the number of signs corresponding to the number of units of the population located there. In this way the distribution of signs expresses in absolute figures the actual geographical distribution of a phenomenon; the density of signs reflect the density of distribution. By choosing signs of different shapes and colours we can present different distributions simultaneously, e.g. the number of horses, cattle, pigs. etc.

(5) By placing in appropriate spots on the map different diagrams in the form of rectangles, circles or squares we can show the geographical distribution of both total frequencies of given phenomena and the structures of particular populations. For instance, the distribution of farms and the agrarian structure can be shown by placing in each district a circle of an area corresponding to the total number of farms in the district and showing the number of farms of different sizes by the areas of particular sectors.

(6) The movements on a given territory can be expressed by appropriately placed arrows which indicate, e.g. the direction of emigration from this territory. The intensity of the movement can be denoted on the map by bands of varying thick-

ness; for instance, bands of different thickness drawn along a railway line may express the quantities of car-loads carried.

The technique of preparing diagrams is discussed in some statistical textbooks. A very thorough exposition of making charts and graphs is given by L. A. Byzov in *Graficzne metody w statystyce, planowaniu i ewidencji (Graphical Methods in Statistics, Planning and Registration)*, translated from the Russian (Polskie Wydawnictwa Gospodarcze, 1951).

# PART II
## Statistical Series

# INTRODUCTION

## 1. STATISTICAL SERIES

A statistical series is a succession of statistical quantities ordered according to a defined criterion. The series is presented in two columns, one of which describes the contents of the consecutive items and the other gives the number of units in a category of objects or phenomena, or the sum of values corresponding to the category. For instance, if we deal with different categories of farms, then the first column describes these categories (farms of less than 1 hectare, from 1–2 hectares, etc., or farms with and without draft animals, or farms situated within a 15 km radius of a city, from 15–30 km, etc.). In the second column either the number of farms in a given category is listed, or their total area. In foreign trade statistics the first column contains the names of exported or imported commodities, and the second—the number of units of a given commodity (e.g. the number of exported or imported cars), or more frequently, the total weight or value of a given imported or exported commodity.

The particular items of the series may be shown either vertically—from top to bottom, or horizontally—from left to right. The arrangement is not essential from the point of view of statistical method; it can be chosen at will and for the convenience of presentation.

This is the most general definition of a statistical series. Series are divided into several types depending upon their content. Not all of them are of equal importance as far as statistical research methods are concerned.

a. *In the first group of statistical series* we include statistical quantities which are placed in numerical order because they possess some common aspect, but which do not add up to one complete entity. One example would be an enumeration of the more important commodities produced in a country and the amount of each produced, when these do not account for the whole production. Another example is a series in which we show for a given district the area, population, number of villages and towns, number of farms and industrial and commercial establishments. Such enumerating series—as we may call them—are of little interest from the point of view of statistical method. They can also be studied, although only to a limited extent and only by general methods, such as the computation of indices. Generally speaking, they do not require a specifically statistical approach, and therefore we shall not discuss them here separately.

Incomparably more important from the point of view of statistical methods and as a starting point for a scientific investigation are other types of statistical series such as geographical, time and structural series.

b. *Geographical series* represent geographical distributions of statistical quantities, e.g. the number of traffic accidents in particular parts of town, or the density of population in particular counties in a country.

c. *Time series* (sometimes called *chronological series*) show the succession in time of certain events which occur in consecutive time intervals, e.g. the number of cars registered on January 1 in consecutive years, or the number of deaths in consecutive months.

d. *Structural series* show the structure of a population, its division into groups according to some material criterion. One such series, for instance, gives a break-down of traffic accidents which occurred in a certain period of time, according to the cause of accident or the resulting damage; another is a break-down of tax-payers according to the amount of tax paid.

Structural series are divided into two sub-groups depending upon the nature of the characteristics used as a criterion of division. Consider the example of traffic accidents. Their causes may be specified as follows: a collision of two motor-vehicles, a collision of a motor-vehicle with a horse-drawn vehicle, damage to a steering mechanism, intoxication of the driver, etc. Or, if we divide people according to the colour of their hair, the divisions are: blond, brown, black, etc. In other words these are characteristics which a given unit in the population either has, or does not have. There exists a different situation when we divide the population according to height or the tax-paying citizens according to the amount of tax paid. In these cases each person has the characteristic in question—the height or tax paid—and it would be meaningless just to state that this is actually the fact. The important and relevant thing is to measure each unit from the point of view of the characteristic concerned: to establish its height in centimeters or the amount of tax in monetary units. Only this type of measurement provides a basis for the division of the population into groups and consequently for a presentation of its structure.

Thus in structural series we deal with two types of characteristics: measurable ones which must, therefore, be measured as in the case of height or tax paid, and non-measurable ones with regard to which we just state whether a given unit does or does not possess a given characteristic, as in the case of the causes of traffic accidents or the colour of hair. According to this distinction structural series are divided into two sub-groups: series based on measurable characteristics and the series based on non-measurable characteristics.[33]

---

[33] Sometimes the terms variable (instead of measurable) and constant (instead of non-measurable) characteristics are used. The terms quantitative (measurable) and qualitative (non-measurable) characteristics are also used, but they are rather awkward. With reference to structural series based on measurable characteristics the term "frequency distribution" is often used; the latter term will be used most frequently in this book.

Of all these types of series the structural series based on measurable characteristics plays the most important part in the theory of statistics. Such series require different kinds of statistical approach and are most helpful in introducing the reader directly to the essence of statistical methods. Thus, we shall start our exposition with them. Before we do so, however, we shall briefly discuss statistical tables.

## 2. STATISTICAL TABLES

From the formal point of view a statistical table is a collection of statistical series: and vice versa, we can look upon a statistical series as a component part of a statistical table. Each horizontal row and each vertical column in a table may be regarded as a separate series. The logical content of a table may vary depending upon the way of combining the series in the table.

A table may contain a mechanical combination of series bound by a common subject or only by a common division shown at the head or on the side of the table. If on the side we have a territorial division, e.g. provinces listed from top to bottom, next may appear series concerning: (1) the areas of these provinces, (2) the number of administrative units (e.g. counties) in each of them, (3) the number of towns, (4) the number of other settlements, (5) the population, and (6) the density of population. All these series together characterize the administrative division of the country, although they pertain to different problems and are not logically related to each other (except for the population density which follows from two other items: the population and the area). It sometimes happens that information included in a statistical table is not exactly related to the subject, but is shown because there is space available. This would be the case if to the table mentioned above we added extra columns concerning, e.g. (7) the number of peasant farms, (8) the number of meteorological stations. (9) the number of registered radio receivers, etc. This sort of filling in the empty space may be excused on the grounds of economy, but has nothing to do with statistical methods. It may happen that in a table in which statistical series refer to the same subject, as in the table described above concerning the administrative characteristics of a certain territory, there are few problems that have to be solved by statistical methods proper. In such cases decisions concerning not only the statement of the problem to which the data in the table refer but also its solution, should be taken from the point of view of the branch of science concerned rather than from the point of view of statistical methods. This reservation concerns the table as a whole, and not the particular series shown in it. The latter should, of course, be considered from the statistical point of view.

There are other tables in which the series are significantly related to one another. To this group belong, first of all, tables in which different types of series serve as a basis of division at the top and on the side of the table. For instance, on the side of the table a division by territories may be shown, and at the top a division according to some characteristic which refers to the structure of the population, e.g. nationality. Most characteristic of this group are tables in which a combination of two structural series is shown. Both series may be based on measurable or non-measurable characteristics, or one on measurable and the other on non-measurable characteristics. For instance, the population of 7-year old children may be divided according to the combination of height (at the top of the table) and weight (on the side of the table). These are two measurable characteristics. The population of a country may be divided according to the combination of nationality and the ability to read and write (both are non-measurable characteristics). White-collar workers may be divided according to the combination of education and monthly earnings (the combination of a non-measurable and a measurable characteristic). Tables of this kind cannot be regarded as a purely mechanical combination of series. They constitute a comprehensive entity and require the use of special methods of statistical research which are different from the methods used for analysing the series. Part IV of this book in which we discuss the method of analysis of interdependence between the characteristics deals with these methods. Tables of this kind could be called "complex statistical populations" as distinct from series which might be called "simple statistical populations".

# CHAPTER 4

# FREQUENCY DISTRIBUTIONS

## 1. THE ARRANGEMENT OF SERIES: CLASSIFICATION

For each unit of the population, the raw data on which statistical series are based contain information on the value assumed by the characteristic for a given unit, e.g. its height in centimeters, the sum of its annual income, etc. If people are listed in the order in which the measurements were taken, e.g. the height of the first person is 175 cm, of the second, 178 cm, of the third, 166 cm, this will not be a statistical series. On the other hand, if we arrange these individual observations in increasing or decreasing values of height we can call the result a series. We may content ourselves merely with arranging the data if observations are few—several or several dozen. Usually, however, we determine the number of units of the population with a particular value of the characteristic. For this purpose we should (1) divide the whole range within which the characteristic varies into groups, which we shall call *classes,* and (2) determine the number of units in each class, and write down the figures in appropriate class panels. Thus we get two columns, the first containing the values of the variable, in a decreasing or increasing order, and second, the frequencies with which these values appear. The task of determining the number of units in each class in purely technical and consists in a simple sorting which can be done in one of the ways described in Part 1, Chapter 2. The question of dividing the range of value into classes is, however, a new problem, and should be considered from the point of view of both technique and substance.

Let us state at the beginning that the division of a population into classes may be a matter of technique—when we adapt the raw data to the requirements of statistical research by statistical methods, or it may be a matter of substance —when by forming possibly homogeneous groups we attempt to describe the structure of the population from some clearly defined point of view.

Let us begin with the latter.

On the basis of the population census of 14 February 1946, we can establish the distribution of Poland's population according to age (see Table 4.1, on the page 128).

The purpose of this division is obvious: in the middle group are persons whose age implies unimpaired ability to work; in the first group are the children and teenagers who still cannot work or can work on a part-time basis only; in the last group are the old people unable to work or able to work only on a part-time basis. In this case the ability to work is the criterion of division.

TABLE 4.1. THE POPULATION OF POLAND
ACCORDING TO AGE
in 1946

| Age group | Population in percentages |
|---|---|
| *Total* | *100·0* |
| 0–17 | 36·7 |
| 18–59 | 54·4 |
| 60 and over | 8·9 |

Apart from the classification by age, there may also be other criteria. We can, for instance, single out women at child-bearing age; then we usually accept the age limit from 15 to 44 or 49. Children and teenagers may be divided into age groups on the basis of criteria related to the organization of education: (1) less than 3 years, (2) from 3–6 years—nursery school age, (3) from 7–13 years—elementary school age, (4) from 14–17 years—secondary school age. If the organization of education is changed the division by age groups must also be changed.

With the agrarian structure that prevailed in Poland before the war the farms were divided according to area into the following groups: less than 2 hectares, 2–5 hectares, 5–10 hectares, 10–15 hectares, 15–50 hectares, 50 hectares and over. This division was subject to reservations with respect to certain details, but the groups as specified had some socio-economic significance. Farms under 2 hectares could not be considered as a source of independent livelihood, but merely as a supplement to income from other sources, e.g. hired labour. Farms of from 2–5 hectares were small farms that under favourable conditions might provide a basis for livelihood, but would require supplemental income from other sources. Farms of from 5 to 10 and from 10 and 15 hectares were medium sized farms which could provide a full livelihood for the peasant's whole family, and on which mainly family labour would be used. These groups were intermediate between small farming and capitalistics methods of husbandry. Larger peasant's farms of from 15 to 50 hectares required much hired labour, although both the owner and his family participated in farm work. They were the farms of the village rich. And finally, farms of 50 hectares and over were large estates using mainly hired labour.

It is obvious that this particular division by area has socio-economic meaning only under given specific conditions. In some other country, e.g. the United States, completely different groups should be formed. Moreover, even in Poland in different districts the limits should be moved upwards or downwards, and the change in economic conditions that has taken place in People's Poland may warrant the application of a completely different division. As Lenin has shown[34] the division of farms by area not only is not the only possible division, but is not a good division as far as the determination of the socio-economic importance of the farm is concerned. Much more significant results are obtained when the number of hired labourers is used as a criterion, or the number of draft animals, the value of output, etc. Moreover, really valuable results can be arrived at only by considering various characteristic jointly, as was done in the combinations shown in the tables above (see p. 125–126). Lenin emphasizes that the final objective of a statistical enquiry is the formation of uniform groups to which some substance—in our example, socio-economic substance—corresponds. We engage here in economic analysis for which statistics provides raw data. In other instances it may be research of a biological, technical, meteorological, or some other type.

The division should be based on criteria outside the scope of statistics, and it cannot be permanent and generally binding. It depends upon the conditions existing at a given time and place, and upon the objective that we set for ourselves in each case. It does not lead to a simple description of the population, but to a description suitable for drawing conclusions, and often predetermining them *a priori*. Improper classification may lead to erroneous conclusions. For instance, an improper classification of farms by size may vitiate appraisal of an agrarian situation of the country. To choose a correct classification it is necessary to know the problem well and frequently to make a preliminary analysis, often of a statistical type. For this reason a certain knowledge of statistical technique and devices helps in selecting the kind of classification appropriate from the point of view of the subject of analysis. The kind of classification discussed below is just this sort of technical, statistical classification. We shall try to show how, starting with this sort of classification, we gradually come to the crux of the problem. We shall also point out the dangers involved when, in consequence of a formal approach, either no results are arrived at, or, even worse, incorrect ones are obtained.

In frequency distributions we may have *continuous* or *discontinuous* variables. For a discontinuous variable, the value may be expressed by figures changing by jumps, without continuity. Thus, a school may have 1, 2, 3 classes, etc., but obviously not a number, say, between 2 and 3. The number of petals of a flower, the number of cars in a train, etc., are discontinuous variables. A variable is continuous if the characteristic studied may assume any value within given limits, even when two values differ by a very small amount, the characteristic can assume a third value between them. Age or height are examples of such characteristics.

A discontinuous characteristic may sometimes assume either few or many values. The division of elementary schools according to the number of classes will obviously be limited to not more than 7 different possibilities if, in the given system of

---

[34] See especially *The Development of Capitalism in Russia* and *New Data on the Laws of Development of Capitalism in Agriculture.*

education, the number of classes in the elementary school is not greater than 7. The division of flowers according to the number of petals will be limited to 5 possibilities if the number of petals of the flower in question is not less than 8 and not more than 12. The number of cars in a train may vary within much wider limits and thus the characteristic may assume a much greater number of values.

A characteristic example of a discontinuous variable with a great number of possible values is the wage of a worker. The variable is discontinuous since the wage may only be expressed in a finite number of monetary units, between which there are no intermediate values. However, the number of possibilities may be expressed in tens of thousands.

Discontinuous variables with a great number of possible values approach the continuous variable in character, and may often be treated statistically and mathematically as continuous variables. They are called *quasi-continuous variables*.

The arrangement of a series based on a discontinuous characteristic with a small number of possible values does not present any difficulties. We write down all the values that the characteristic may assume, from the lowest to the highest, or vice versa, and beside each of them we write the number of units for which the characteristic has that value. For instance, if we are concerned with newly built flats classified according to the number of rooms, and there are no flats with more than 6 rooms then we can arrange the table in the following way:

TABLE 4.2a. NEWLY BUILT FLATS BY NUMBER OF ROOMS

| Number of flats | All flats | Flats with | | | | | |
|---|---|---|---|---|---|---|---|
| | | 1 room | 2 rooms | 3 rooms | 4 rooms | 5 rooms | 6 rooms |
| | 17,284 | 3392 | 6207 | 4300 | 2237 | 767 | 381 |

If the variable can assume a greater number of values it may sometimes be desirable to form groups combining several values. Even in so small a series as the one presented above it may be desirable for certain specific purposes. We may divide the flats into 3 groups: (1) small flats with 1 or 2 rooms, (2) medium-sized flats with 3 or 4 rooms, (3) large flats with 5 or 6 rooms. The series will then look as follows:

TABLE 4.2b. NEWLY BUILT FLATS BY NUMBER OF ROOMS (IN GROUPS)

| Number of rooms in flat | Number of flats |
|---|---|
| *Total* | *17,284* |
| 1–2 | 9599 |
| 3–4 | 6537 |
| 5–6 | 1148 |

This, however, is the kind of division based not on purely statistical considerations, but related to the subject and purpose of study, since we have to decide which flats should be considered small and which medium or large.

If a series comprises a considerable number of possible values the combination of these values into groups becomes a necessity. In such cases we proceed in the same way as with series of continuous variables (see below).

For the time being we shall discuss the division into classes from the technical, statistical point of view, which is usually a first step to a preliminary analysis of raw data and which will eventually lead to a division based on considerations related to the subject of the study.

In grouping into classes a series based on a continuous or quasi-continuous variable we have to solve three separate, although related problems: (1) how many classes there should be and how large the class interval; (2) whether or not the intervals should be of the same size; (3) how the class limits should be set, e.g. should we count the years "from 15 to 25", "from 25 to 35", etc., or "from 10 to 20", "from 20 to 30", etc.

In trying to arrive at an appropriate number of classes we should be guided by the following rules: (1) too many classes (too small class intervals) do not produce a clear picture, and show random deviations irrelevant to the essence of the problem; (2) too few classes (too large intervals) obscure the essential features of the structure.

Let us take an example. The prices of rye paid to the farmers in January 1935 fluctuated in different counties in Poland from 13·43 zlotys to 22·88 zlotys. If we divide the whole range of prices into classes of 0·10 zlotys each and arrange the counties in the order of increasing prices than we obtain the series shown in Table 4.3a.

The series in this very detailed form contain 95 classes and undoubtedly does not present a clear picture. Although certain classes stand out because they have the greatest number of observations (they are: 14·60–14·69; 15·20–15·29; 15·60–15·69 and the following up to 15·99) but there is no regular pattern and there are many classes with no observations at all (e.g. 21 classes from 20·70 to 22·79 zlotys). The very fact that there are many classes makes the whole picture confusing.

A regular pattern is obtained when 0·50-zloty class intervals are used, i.e. when five consecutive classes in the previous table are combined into one. Thus we get the series shown in Table 4.3b.

The same series arranged in classes of 1 zloty each is shown in Table 4.3c and Table 4.3d.

By joining the classes and increasing the class interval to 0·50 zlotys we get 20 classes. The pattern of the figures is sufficiently regular. Certain irregularities in the second half of the series probably reflect the lack of uniformity in the popu-

### TABLE 4.3a.  PRICES OF RYE PAID TO FARMERS[35]

| Price in zlotys | Number of counties | Price in zlotys | Number of counties | Price in zlotys | Number of counties |
|---|---|---|---|---|---|
| 13·40–13·49 | 1 | 16·60–16·69 | 4 | 19·80–19·89 | 2 |
| 13·50–13·59 | 1 | 16·70–16·79 | 7 | 19·90–19·99 | 1 |
| 13·60–13·69 | 2 | 16·80–16·89 | 3 | 20·00–20·09 | 2 |
| 13·70–13·79 | 2 | 16·90–16·99 | 5 | 20·10–20·19 | 1 |
| 13·80–13·89 | 1 | 17·00–17·09 | 3 | 20·20–20·29 | 1 |
| 13·90–13·99 | — | 17·10–17·19 | 3 | 20·30–20·39 | 1 |
| 14·00–14·09 | 1 | 17·20–17·29 | 5 | 20·40–20·49 | — |
| 14·10–14·19 | 1 | 17·30–17·39 | 1 | 20·50–20·59 | — |
| 14·20–14·29 | 5 | 17·40–17·49 | 5 | 20·60–20·69 | 1 |
| 14·30–14·39 | 2 | 17·50–17·59 | 5 | 20·70–20·79 | — |
| 14·40–14·49 |   | 17·60–17·69 | 1 | 20·80–20·89 | — |
| 14·50–14·59 | 6 | 17·70–17·79 | 2 | 20·90–20·99 | — |
| 14·60–14·69 | 9 | 17·80–17·89 | 2 | 21·00–21·09 | — |
| 14·70–14·79 | 1 | 17·90–17·99 | 1 | 21·10–21·19 | — |
| 14·80–14·89 | 3 | 18·00–18·09 | 2 | 21·20–21·29 | — |
| 14·90–14·99 | 4 | 18·10–18·19 | 4 | 21·30–21·39 | — |
| 15·00–15·09 | 4 | 18·20–18.29 | 4 | 21·40–21·49 | — |
| 15·10–15·19 | 6 | 18·30–18·39 | 1 | 21·50–21·59 | — |
| 15·20–15·29 | 14 | 18·40–18·49 | 1 | 21·60–21·69 | — |
| 15·30–15·39 | 6 | 18·50–18·59 | 2 | 21·70–21·79 | — |
| 15·40–15·49 | 7 | 18·60–18·69 | 1 | 21·80–21·89 | — |
| 15·50–15·59 | 8 | 18·70–18·79 | — | 21·90–21·99 | — |
| 15·60–15·69 | 10 | 18·80–18·89 | 1 | 22·00–22·09 | — |
| 15·70–15·79 | 13 | 18·90–18·99 | 1 | 22·10–22·19 | — |
| 15·80–15·89 | 11 | 19·00–19·09 | 2 | 22·20–22·29 | — |
| 15·90–15·99 | 10 | 19·10–19·19 | — | 22·30–22·39 | — |
| 16·00–16·09 | 7 | 19·20–19·29 | 3 | 22·40–22·49 | — |
| 16·10–16·19 | 4 | 19·30–19·39 | — | 22·50–22·59 | — |
| 16·20–16·29 | 4 | 19·40–19·49 | 1 | 22·60–22·69 | — |
| 16·30–16·39 | 8 | 19·50–19·59 | 1 | 22·70–22·79 | — |
| 16·40–16·49 | 5 | 19·60–19·69 | 1 | 22·80–22·89 | 1 |
| 16·50–16·59 | 3 | 19·70–19·79 | — | *Total* | *241* |

lation. These irregularities disappear when class interval is increased to 1 zloty. There remains only one separated observation in the class 22·00–22·99, or 22·50–23·49. This is the price in the county of Żywiec which was over 2 zlotys above the price paid in the second highest-priced county. On the whole, it can be said that combining the data into classes with a class interval of 1 zloty (10 or 11 classes) does not obscure the pattern.

It is impossible to give general rules concerning the division into classes. The solution depends upon the circumstances of each particular case and upon the structure of the population. As a general hint it could be said that a division into 10–20 equal classes usually produces good results. However, it should not be re-

[35] *Statystyka cen* (*Price Statistics*), quarterly, Warsaw, 1935.

TABLE 4.3b. PRICES OF RYE PAID TO FARMERS

| Price in zlotys | Number of counties | Price in zlotys | Number of counties |
|---|---|---|---|
| 13·00–13·49 | 1 | 18·00–18·49 | 12 |
| 13·50–13·99 | 6 | 18·50–18·99 | 5 |
| 14·00–14·49 | 9 | 19·00–19·49 | 6 |
| 14·50–14·99 | 23 | 19·50–19·99 | 5 |
| 15·00–15·49 | 37 | 20·00–20·49 | 5 |
| 15·50–15·99 | 52 | 20·50–20·99 | 1 |
| 16·00–16·49 | 28 | 21.00–21·49 | — |
| 16·50–16·99 | 22 | 21·50–21·99 | — |
| 17·00–17·49 | 17 | 22·00–22·49 | — |
| 17·50–17·99 | 11 | 22·50–22·99 | 1 |
| | | *Total* | *241* |

TABLE 4.3c. PRICES OF RYE PAID TO FARMERS

| Price in zlotys | Number of counties |
|---|---|
| 13·00–13·99 | 7 |
| 14·00–14·99 | 32 |
| 15·00–15·99 | 89 |
| 16·00–16·99 | 50 |
| 17·00–17·99 | 28 |
| 18·00–18·99 | 17 |
| 19·00–19·99 | 11 |
| 20·00–20·99 | 6 |
| 21·00–21·99 | — |
| 22·00–22·99 | 1 |
| *Total* | *241* |

TABLE 4.3d. PRICES OF RYE PAID TO FARMERS

| Price in zlotys | Number of counties |
|---|---|
| 12·50–13·49 | 1 |
| 13·50–14·49 | 15 |
| 14·50–15·49 | 60 |
| 15·50–16·49 | 80 |
| 16·50–17·49 | 39 |
| 17·50–18·49 | 23 |
| 18·50–19·49 | 11 |
| 19·50–20·49 | 10 |
| 20·50–21·49 | 1 |
| 21·50–22·49 | — |
| 22·50–23·49 | 1 |
| *Total* | *241* |

garded as binding. Sometimes the number of classes should be less than 10 or more than 20. For instance, in presenting the population of a country by age groups we often use class intervals of 1 year which brings the number of classes to over 100.

In the examples given above the class-intervals were *equal*. In a preliminary statistical study the classes should be equal, if at all possible. This helps to give a good idea of the structure of the population and simplifies all computations. However, it is not always possible or advisable to divide the population into classes of equal interval width. If the structure of the population is not uniform, and particularly when the majority of observations are clustered around the lower values of the variable, it may be necessary to use intervals of different lengths in different parts of the series. With the type of agrarian structure prevailing in Poland before the war there were very many small and very small farms. It makes an essential difference whether the area of a farm was 1 or 2 hectares and the division into classes of small farms had to be very detailed, e.g. into classes of 1 hectare. So detailed a classification for all the farms would result in several hundred or even several thousand classes and would be absurd from both the technical and logical points of view since it would lead to a useless disintegration of classes for large farms where it obviously does not matter whether the area of the farm is 100 or 101 hectares. In this case the classification, of necessity, should be much more detailed for small than for large farms. In the census of 1921 the following classification was accepted (in hectares): up to $0 \cdot 5$; $0 \cdot 5-1$, $1-2$, $2-3$, $3-4$, $4-5$, $5-10$, $10-15$, $15-20$, $20-50$, $50-100$, $100-200$, $200-1000$, over $1000$. The payers of income tax were divided according to their annual income into the following classes (in thousands of zlotys): $1 \cdot 5-2 \cdot 6$, $2 \cdot 6-3 \cdot 6$, $3 \cdot 6-6 \cdot 0$, $6 \cdot 0-12 \cdot 0$, $12 \cdot 0-24 \cdot 0$, $24 \cdot 0-36 \cdot 0$, $36 \cdot 0-60 \cdot 0$, over $60 \cdot 0$. The classification for the lower income groups must obviously be more detailed than for the higher, especially since the number of people in low income groups is always very large and in the high income groups it is quite negligible. Without going into the details of this particular classification, which is perhaps not quite proper, we can say that in such cases we should not even attempt to group the population in equal classes. Sometimes the data may be divided into equal classes, but for some reason or other it is better to show a certain part of the series in greater detail. In such cases we may arrange the series so that the sizes of classes in the less detailed part are multiples of the sizes of classes in the more detailed part. For instance, if we decide that it should suffice to divide the population into 10-year classes, except for the earlier years, we can accept for the latter the classes of 1 or 5 years from which we can easily change to 10-year groups.

In the tables showing prices of rye the series has a class intreval of 1 zloty in two varieties: with the class limits in integral numbers of zlotys, e.g. $13-14 \cdot 99$, $14-14 \cdot 99$, etc. (Table 3c) and with class limits of $12 \cdot 50-13 \cdot 49$, $13 \cdot 50-14 \cdot 49$ zlotys, etc. (Table 3d). It is hard to say *a priori* which table better describes the population. In general, the choice of class limits is usually of secondary importance. It is more important only when for some values of the variable there is a noticeable artificial rounding off. In population statistics by age the figures for particular age groups are often incorrect because of the fairly common practice of giving not the true age, but the nearest number ending with 0 or, less frequently, with 5. This emerges very clearly in a series with 1-year age groups in that the frequencies for the years ending with 0 or 5 are too high and for the neighbouring years too low; there are many more persons 40 years old than 39 or 41; to a lesser extent the frequencies for the ages 38 and 42 are artificially decreased. Similarly the number of people 45 years of age is inflated at the expense of those aged 44 and 46. In such cases it is better to arrange the series in such a way as put in the middle of the class the values around which the observations appear to cluster artificially, instead of having them at the beginning or the end of the class; thus we decrease the likelihood of distortions due to the inclusion of too few or too many units in the class. If we set the class limits from 40 to 49 then this class will include a certain number of people who gave their age as 40 although they were 39 or 38 years old, but on the other hand it will not include those aged 49 or 48 who incorrectly have their age as 50. Only in exceptional cases will these two deviations—plus and minus—cancel out exactly and the frequency for the whole 10-year class will rarely correspond to reality. It is because of this tendency towards rounding off the age that population statistics in Great Britain use class limits from 25 to 34, from 35 to 44, etc. In this classification the ages 25, 35 etc. at which rounding off also appears but is much smaller, are at the beginning, so that we can expect the totals shown in the table for age groups 25–34, 35–44, etc. to correspond to reality more closely than the totals for the age groups 30–39, 40–49, etc. Since rounding off also appears for numbers ending with 5, we could surmise that the classes least removed from reality would be those beginning and ending neither with zeros nor with fives, e.g. classes beginning with 3 and ending with 2. This kind of classification is not appropriate for general demographic tables, but sometimes is used in special studies.

If rounding off is very common for the years ending with zero the table cannot be arranged into 5-year groups, as can be seen from Table 4.4. This table presents the population of five central provinces in Poland, on the basis of the census of 1897.

TABLE  4.4.  POPULATION  OF  THE  CENTRAL  PROVINCES
BY  AGE  WOMEN  AGED  40–69
(in  1897)

| Age | Population in thousands |
| --- | --- |
| 40–44 | 221·8 |
| 45–49 | 165·7 |
| 50–54 | 203·8 |
| 55–59 | 123·4 |
| 60–64 | 132·6 |
| 65–69 | 60·1 |

The frequencies decrease as the age increases, but they decrease irregularly. In the age groups 45–49, 55–59, 65–69 there are far fewer people than in the age groups preceding them. But in the age group 50–54 there are many more people than in the group 45–49 and in the group 60–64 more than in the group 55–59. These irregularities obviously do not correspond to reality and result from the fact that rounding off is much stronger for the years ending with zero than for the years ending with 5. The errors in the census prevent us from using 5-year age groups and it would appear that the population figures in 10-year age groups, particularly those beginning with 5 (45–54, 55–64, etc.) are perhaps the most correct.

In wage statistics certain values of the variable will also stand out although not because of errors in recording wages, but because of the tendency to set wages in some round figures, e.g. in ten, hundreds, or thousands. The frequencies in consecutive classes will then be correct regardless of where we set the class limit. Nevertheless, it is better to set the limits so that the values for which the frequencies are particularly inflated are exactly in the middle of the class. This is important because in many calculations based on frequency distributions it is assumed that the average value of the variable for each class equals the arithmetic mean of the values of the upper and lower limits of the class. This assumption, of course, never exactly corresponds to reality, but the error will be greatest when values with a particularly large number of observations are located close to the upper or lower limit of the class.

If we deal with a phenomenon familiar to us and the degree of accuracy of the data is known, the division into classes is facilitated in so far as we can use old and tried patterns. However, if we are studying a new phenomenon, or when the reliability of the data is not quite known we would be well advised to make first a detailed analysis, beginning with very small class intervals, or even with individual observations. The advisability of such an analysis can be best shown by an example concerning the weighing of newly born infants in a clinic.

The variable in this case is continuous. However, since the weighing can be done only with a definite degree of accuracy, individual observations will appear to be of a discontinuous type. This is shown in Table 4.5a.

In the table the individual weight of each infant is shown, but some values appear to be much more frequent than others. For instance the weight of 2700 grammes occurs 10 times, the weight of 2900 grammes 12 times. There were no weights having values not shown in the table.

A casual glance at the table reveal immediately that the weights were not obtained with an accuracy greater than 10 grammes; all the figures, with but one exception (3285 g) end in zero. After a closer investigation, however, it turns out that the observations are particularly numerous for weights ending in two zeros, and to a lesser extent, for those ending in 50. Intermediate values appear only infrequently which would indicate that the actual accuracy of weighing did not exceed 50 grammes, and often even 100 grammes. Let us try to arrange these observations into a series with a class interval of 100 grammes so that the figures most rounded off (ending with two zeros) are located in the middle of the class. Thus we get the classes of 2050–2150 grammes, 2150–2250 grammes, etc. However, in this sort of classification there will be a great number of observations for the border values between two adjacent classes. For instance, for the class of 3150–3250 grammes we have 6 boys weighing 3150 grammes each and 8 boys weighing 3250 grammes each. One half of these borderline cases can be placed in the lower class and one half in the higher class, so that in the 3150–3250 class we

TABLE 4.5a. WEIGHT OF NEW-BORN MALE INFANTS

| Weight (g) | Number of observations | Weight (g) | Number of observations | Weight (g) | Number of observations |
|---|---|---|---|---|---|
| 1 | 2 | 3 | 4 | 5 | 6 |
| 2100 | 1 | 3140 | 1 | 3600 | 18 |
| 2150 | 1 | 3150 | 6 | 3620 | 1 |
| 2250 | 1 | 3160 | 1 | 3650 | 13 |
| 2360 | 1 | 3180 | 1 | 3670 | 1 |
| 2400 | 2 | 3200 | 24 | 3680 | 1 |
| 2430 | 1 | 3250 | 8 | 3700 | 17 |
| 2450 | 1 | 3270 | 1 | 3720 | 2 |
| 2460 | 1 | 3280 | 1 | 3750 | 8 |
| 2500 | 5 | 3285 | 1 | 3800 | 19 |
| 2550 | 1 | 3300 | 30 | 3850 | 4 |
| 2600 | 7 | 3310 | 1 | 3860 | 2 |
| 2650 | 1 | 3320 | 3 | 3900 | 13 |
| 2700 | 10 | 3330 | 2 | 3950 | 4 |
| 2750 | 3 | 3350 | 7 | 3970 | 1 |
| 2760 | 1 | 3360 | 1 | 4000 | 21 |
| 2800 | 9 | 3380 | 1 | 4030 | 2 |
| 2850 | 6 | 3400 | 30 | 4050 | 3 |
| 2870 | 1 | 3420 | 2 | 4070 | 2 |
| 2900 | 12 | 3450 | 13 | 4100 | 5 |
| 2950 | 1 | 3470 | 1 | 4150 | 1 |
| 2960 | 1 | 3480 | 1 | 4200 | 6 |
| 3000 | 43 | 3500 | 32 | 4250 | 1 |
| 3010 | 1 | 3510 | 1 | 4300 | 3 |
| 3040 | 1 | 3520 | 1 | 4350 | 1 |
| 3050 | 5 | 3540 | 1 | 4400 | 2 |
| 3080 | 1 | 3550 | 8 | 4450 | 1 |
| 3090 | 1 | 3560 | 1 | 4500 | 2 |
| 3100 | 21 | 3570 | 1 | 4550 | 1 |
| 3120 | 1 | 3590 | 1 | | |
| | | | | Total | 478 |

shall include 3 boys weighing 3150 grammes each, and 4 boys weighing 3250 grammes each. Thus the total frequency in this class will be: $3 + 1 + 1 + 24 + 4 = 33$. If the number of observations for the borderline values is old then we obtain numbers ending in one-half when we divide the number between two classes. Hence the decimals in the series in Table 4.5b which is derived from the series shown in Table 4.5a.

The practice of using halves in arranging certain series is justified only when the measurements have been taken with great precision, and when there may be some sense in striving for maximum accuracy. Were we not to insist on placing in the middle of the class the values most rounded off, we could set the class limits at values which do not appear in the data at all, say, at 2175, 2275 etc. or for 2125, 2225, etc. Thus the class limits would be: 2075–2175, 2175–2275 etc., or 2025–2125, 2125–2225, etc.

TABLE 4.5b. WEIGHT OF NEW-BORN MALE INFANTS

| Weight (g) | Number of observations |
|------------|------------------------|
| 1 | 2 |
| Total | 478 |
| 2050–2150 | 1·5 |
| 2150–2250 | 1·0 |
| 2250–2350 | 0·5 |
| 2350–2450 | 4·5 |
| 2450–2550 | 7·0 |
| 2550–2650 | 8·0 |
| 2650–2750 | 12·0 |
| 2750–2850 | 14·5 |
| 2850–2950 | 16·5 |
| 2950–3050 | 49·0 |
| 3050–3150 | 30·5 |
| 3150–3250 | 33·0 |
| 3250–3350 | 46·5 |
| 3350–3450 | 44·0 |
| 3450–3550 | 47·5 |
| 3550–3650 | 32·5 |
| 3650–3750 | 31·5 |
| 3750–3850 | 25·0 |
| 3850–3950 | 19·0 |
| 3950–4050 | 27·5 |
| 4050–4150 | 9·0 |
| 4150–4250 | 7·0 |
| 4250–4350 | 4·0 |
| 4350–4450 | 3·0 |
| 4450–4550 | 3·5 |

We see that the pattern of the series in Table 4.5b is irregular, with strikingly higher frequencies in the classes 2950–3050, 3450–3550, and 3950–4050, than in the classes adjoining them. They are the classes comprising the values of full kilograms or of half kilograms. Checking this observation against Table 4.5a we find that, in fact, for the values of 3, 3·5 and 4 kg the number of observations is much higher than for other values. Thus it turns out that the weighing was not consistently accurate even to the order of 100 g. This fact considerably undermines confidence in the reliability of these data since obviously the weighing must have been done not only inaccurately— which could, perhaps, be excused by imprecise scales—but also carelessly. We can see how in this case a purely technical, statistical analysis has led to the discovery of essential shortcomings in the statistical material.

Disregarding for the moment the accuracy of the data let us try to arrange the series more smoothly by making the class interval larger. In Table 4.5b we have 25 classes. Joining them in twos we get 13 classes in two variables, depending on how we join them.

| TABLE 4.5c. WEIGHT OF NEW-BORN MALE INFANTS | | TABLE 4.5d. WEIGHT OF NEW-BORN MALE INFANTS | |
|---|---|---|---|
| Weight (g) | Number of observations | Weight (g) | Number of observations |
| *Total* | *478* | *Total* | *478* |
| 2050–2250 | 2·5 | 1950–2150 | 1·5 |
| 2250–2450 | 5·0 | 2150–2350 | 1·5 |
| 2450–2650 | 15·0 | 2350–2550 | 11·5 |
| 2650–2850 | 26·5 | 2550–2750 | 20·0 |
| 2850–3050 | 65·5 | 2750–2950 | 31·0 |
| 3050–3250 | 63·5 | 2950–3150 | 79·5 |
| 3250–3450 | 90·5 | 3150–3350 | 79·5 |
| 3450–3650 | 80·0 | 3350–3550 | 91·5 |
| 3650–3850 | 56·5 | 3550–3750 | 64·0 |
| 3850–4050 | 46·5 | 3750–3950 | 44·0 |
| 4050–4250 | 16·0 | 3950–4150 | 36·5 |
| 4250–4450 | 7·0 | 4150–4350 | 11·0 |
| 4450–4650 | 3·5 | 4350–4550 | 6·5 |

These series also lack a completely smooth pattern. In both of them frequencies are higher in those classes which contain full 3 kg: 2850–3050 or 2950–3150. These irregularities are not caused by an essential characteristic of the population but by the lack of accuracy in weighing. A satisfactory degree of smoothness can be obtained only after joining the observations into classes of 300 grammes each, as shown in Table 4.5e.

TABLE 4. 5e. WEIGHT OF NEW-BORN MALE INFANTS

| Weight (g) | Number of observations |
|---|---|
| *Total* | *478* |
| 1950–2250 | 2·5 |
| 2250–2550 | 12·0 |
| 2550–2850 | 34·5 |
| 2850–3150 | 96·0 |
| 3150–3450 | 123·5 |
| 3450–3750 | 111·5 |
| 3750–4050 | 71·5 |
| 4050–4350 | 20·0 |
| 4350–4650 | 6·5 |

However, we cannot have full confidence even in a table arranged in this way, because of faults in the data which have been revealed in the course of trying to design the table in the best possible way. This very possibility of discovering faults in the statistical material is one of the reasons why it is necessary to engage in such detailed trials before we arrive at a decision concerning the final design of the table.

As it turns out, a smooth pattern is not always obtained by simply joining into

10*

larger classes the arrangement first tried. Sometimes we have to start from the beginning, using different class limits.

We purposely selected example with carelessly taken measurements in order to show, on the one hand, how by making the classes sufficiently large and by appropriately selecting the class limits we can obtain a smooth series from chaotic individual data, and to point out, on the other hand, that the smoothness of pattern in a series does not prove that the data are reliable.

However, another reservation is more important. We are not always justified in trying to arrange a frequency distribution in such a way to obtain a smooth pattern. In this case our attempts were justified by a desire to smooth over the faults in the statistical material. Quite often, however, an irregular pattern is a consequence of irregularities in the phenomenon studied. The series should not obscure or hide such irregularities but, on the contrary, should bring them fully to light. We shall return to this subject later on.

Sometimes in statistical publications we encounter series in which the upper and lower limits are not defined, e.g. at the beginning we have "below 20", and at the end "140 or more". This type of arrangement is very undesirable since it clouds the picture and makes it difficult to perform the computations required to analyse the series. However, this sort of arrangement may be unavoidable when at the beginning or the end of the series there are very few units scattered over a long range of values of the variable. For instance, in the example on p. 133 (Table 4.3b) the class "20·00–20·49" in which there are 5 counties, could be followed by the class "20·50 or more". In this open class we would have only two observations.

When relatively few observations are scattered over a very long range of the values of the variable the formation of open classes becomes a necessity for technical reasons. It should be remembered, however, that in the open classes at the beginning and the end of a series there should not be too many observations in relation to the total. In wage statistics for the manufacturing industries published before the war by the Central Statistical Office, weekly wages were given in classes of 10 zlotys (less than 10 zlotys, 10–20 zlotys, etc.). The upper class was marked: "80 zlotys or more". In 1938 in the wood industry there were only 0·1 per cent of all workers in this class and therefore this kind of classification was acceptable. However, in the printing industry, in the class "80 zlotys or more", there were 11·6 per cent of all workers and in the "70–80 zlotys" class there were only 5·2 per cent. There is no doubt that the wages of the workers in the printing industry considerably exceeded 80 zlotys, and possibly even 90 and 100 zlotys. The open upper class spoils the pattern of the series.[36] Similar examples of improper classification, from the statistical point of view, can be found in post-war earnings statis-

---

[36] *Concise Statistical Yearbook (Mały Rocznik Statystyczny)*, 1939, p. 273.

tics for August 1949, where in some industries (wool, clothing) in the open lower class of earnings (up to 12,000 zlotys a month) there were 40 per cent of all workers, whereas, on the other hand, a very high proportion of the engineering and technical personnel (in mining, 45·2 per cent) were included in the open upper class (40,001 zlotys a month or more). This practice of including a high proportion of all observations in open classes considerably reduces the value of data.[37]

An even worse example can be found in the table "Dwellings and Density of Occupancy in Selected Countries".[38] The dwellings were divided into those with 1, 2, 3, 4, 5 and more rooms. In the last, top class there were in Warsaw 8·5 per cent of all dwellings and this can be considered a reasonable percentage to be included in an open class. But in the Hague there were 53·6 per cent of such dwellings and in London 72·4 per cent of the total. A table arranged in this way gives us only the information that in the Hague and even more so in London, large flats of 5 or more rooms predominate, but it does not tell us what the actual structure of the dwellings in those cities really is. Unfortunately, technical considerations often encourage this sort of improper classification. The last example could be excused on the grounds that the main object of the table was to show the number of small dwellings to emphasize the problem of overcrowded dwellings. If so, then the statement that in certain cities there is only a negligible number of small, or too small dwellings whereas in other cities there are very many such dwellings, provides some relevant information. However, in this way we do not get a full picture of the dwelling situation of the inhabitants of those cities. Thus, for instance, in spite of a great number of large dwellings there may also be overcrowded dwellings. Indeed, the table cited above informs us that in London there were 5·4 per cent of overcrowded dwellings, i.e. those in which there were more than 2 persons per room. In those dwellings lived 9·4 per cent of the inhabitants of the city. Moreover, there is no information on whether the poorer inhabitants of London could find the required accomodation at all. We know from other sources that in the working class districts of London living conditions are poor.

In some extremely asymmetrical series the use of open upper classes (and less frequently open lower classes) may be a necessity. For instance, in the statistics on taxpayers it is difficult to divide income above a certain limit into separate classes. However, without this information the series loses some of its information value which would increase considerably were we able to give not only the number of persons with income above a certain limit, but also the sum of their income. In the table on the size of dwellings the same kind of supplementary information would be the total number of rooms in dwellings with 5 or more rooms, in addition to the number of dwellings in this class.

We should now say a few words on several technical problems concerning the

[37] *Statistical Yearbook (Rocznik Statystyczny)*, 1949, pp. 135–6.
[38] *Concise Statistical Yearbook (Mały Rocznik Statystyczny)*, 1939, p. 61.

determination of class intervals. There are two systems in use: either the number denoting the upper limit of the lower class also denotes the lower limit of the higher class (10–15, 15–20, 20–25, etc.); or the number denoting the upper limit of the lower class one unit smaller than the number denoting the lower limit of the higher class (10–14, 15–19, etc; or $10 \cdot 0$–$14 \cdot 9$, $15 \cdot 0$–$19 \cdot 9$; $10 \cdot 00$–$14 \cdot 99$, $15 \cdot 00$–$19 \cdot 99$, etc., depending upon whether we use figures accurate to one unit, or to one or two decimal points).

When the variable is continuous, the former method of notation is natural; the number expressing the upper limit of one class and the lower limit of another class is the mathematical limit of the two classes. If the value of some observations are exactly equal to the value of the limit, half of them should be included in one class and half in the other. Thus we may get fractional numbers of observations as shown in the Tables 4.5b–4.5e on pp. 138–9. If we consider this kind of accuracy often more imaginary than real—as superfluous, then we can decide that the values equal to the class limits should always and consistently be included either in the higher or in the lower class. In such cases the denotation: 20–30, 30–40, should be interpreted as meaning: "20 to less than 30, 30 to less than 40, etc.", or "over 20 up to and including 30", "over 30, up to and including 40", etc. The notations should be written in such a way as to leave no doubt where values equal to class limits should be included, or some additional explanatory comments should be provided.

When the variable is by nature discontinuous the number at the end of each class will be one unit smaller than the number with which the next class begins. This also applies to quasi-continuous variables.

A few words should be said about the method of rounding off. When the variable is continuous we shall always have to round off the number, if only because measurements can never be completely exact. In statistical practice values are given with a definite degree of accuracy: to one unit or to one or two decimal places, and so on. Usual by rounding off is done so that the figures differing from a given figure by less than one significant unit are rounded up or down, so that, for example, when the degree of accuracy is $0 \cdot 1$ the figure $20 \cdot 0$ denotes values from $19 \cdot 95$ to $20 \cdot 05$. Then observations with values measured as exactly $19 \cdot 95$ and $20 \cdot 05$, depending upon the practice agreed upon, will be included either half in $19 \cdot 9$ and half in $20 \cdot 0$, or in $20 \cdot 0$ and in $20 \cdot 1$, or else they will all be included either in the lower or in the higher class.

Another practice of rounding off is also in common use—that of rounding only downwards. It is often used in determining age. If we say that somebody is 20 years old we usually mean that this person was 20 on his or her last birthday but has not yet reached 21; consequently in determining the class limits we should write: 20–21, 21–22, etc. If the class interval was 5 years we would have: 20–25, 25–30, etc. Sometimes we may also write 20, 21, 22 years of age, or 20–24, 25–29, etc.

Which way it is written does not much matter, but we should know exactly what the figures mean. In the examples just mentioned the class 20–25 would mean the same as the class 20–24 i.e. people who are over 20 but not yet 25 years old.

The method of rounding off may be quite important for the interpretation of the results, particularly when the unit chosen is relatively large. For instance, people whose age was given as 20 average $20 \cdot 5$ if the accepted method of rounding off was that of rounding down. Were we rounding up or down, depending upon the circumstances, as is also often done, the average age of those people would be exactly 20 years.

It follows that the method of rounding off should always be obvious from the way the series is arranged or should be explained in notes, and should always be taken into account in analysing the data.

Sometimes the centre of the class is given instead of the class limits. Then, e.g. in the series from Table 4.5e (p. 139) we would write 2100, 2400, etc. instead of 1950–2250, 2250–2550, etc. Which method we choose does not really matter. For some computations it may be more convenient to use the centre of the class rather than the class limits.

Information on the structure of the population may be presented in yet another manner. Instead of giving the number of units in the classes of values from $x_1$ to $x_2$, from $x_2$ to $x_3$, we can give the number of units for which the variable assumes values less than $x_1$, $x_2$, $x_3$, etc., or more than $x_n$, $x_{n-1}$, $x_{n-2}$, etc. In this way we get Table 4.6a or 6b (p. 144) instead of Table 4.3d. A series arranged in this way is called a cumulative series. It is formed out of a frequency distribution by adding consecutive frequencies beginning from the top (Table 4.6a) or from the bottom (Table 4.6b). Frequencies in a cumulative series increase steadily, and for the last item we get the total number of observations. If a certain number is repeated several times it means that in some classes of the frequency distribution there are no observations. In Table 4.6a the figure 240 is repeated twice, and in Table 4.6b the figure 1 is repeated twice since in the class $21 \cdot 50$–$22 \cdot 49$ (Table 4.3d) there are no observations.

The most rapid increase in frequencies in a cumulative series is noticeable, of course, in those sections in which the classes in the frequency distribution are most numerous. In our example they are between $15 \cdot 50$ and $16 \cdot 50$.

Similarly as we can form a cumulative series out of a frequency distribution by adding consecutive frequencies, so we can form a frequency distribution out of a cumulative series by subtracting consecutive frequencies (by differencing).

The values of the variable in a cumulative series should be denoted as shown in the example above: less than $13 \cdot 50$, less than $14 \cdot 50$ and $22 \cdot 50$ and more, $21 \cdot 50$ and more, etc. Were the class intervals in the frequency distribution marked: $12 \cdot 51$–$13 \cdot 50$, $13 \cdot 51$–$14 \cdot 50$, etc., we would write in the cumulative series $13 \cdot 50$ and less, $14 \cdot 50$ and less; and over $22 \cdot 50$, over $21 \cdot 50$, etc.

| TABLE 4.6a.  PRICES OF RYE PAID TO FARMERS Cumulative Series 1. | | TABLE 4.6b.  PRICES OF RYE PAID TO FARMERS Cumulative Series 2. | |
|---|---|---|---|
| Price in zlotys | Number of counties | Price in zlotys | Number of counties |
| Less than   13·50 | 1 | 22·50 and more | 1 |
| ,,    ,,    14·50 | 16 | 21·50  ,,    ,, | 1 |
| ,,    ,,    15·50 | 76 | 20·50  ,,    ,, | 2 |
| ,,    ,,    16·50 | 156 | 19·50  ,,    ,, | 12 |
| ,,    ,,    17·50 | 195 | 18·50  ,,    ,, | 23 |
| ,,    ,,    18·50 | 218 | 17·50  ,,    ,, | 46 |
| ,,    ,,    19·50 | 229 | 16·50  ,,    ,, | 85 |
| ,,    ,,    20·50 | 239 | 15·50  ,,    ,, | 165 |
| ,,    ,,    21·50 | 240 | 14·50  ,,    ,, | 225 |
| ,,    ,,    22·50 | 240 | 13·50  ,,    ,, | 240 |
| ,,    ,,    23·50 | 241 | 12·50  ,,    ,, | 241 |

Cumulative series usually present a less direct picture of the structure of the population than frequency distributions, but under certain circumstances they may be more useful for statistical analysis.

## 2. GENERAL ANALYSIS OF A FREQUENCY DISTRIBUTION

a. *Graphical presentation.* A frequency distribution based on a variable characteristic can be presented graphically in a rectangular system of coordinates; the values of the variable are shown as abscissas and the number of observations as ordinates. For most statistical graphs we use the upper, right-hand quadrant of the coordinate system, and only in exceptional cases the upper left; in the nature of things, the number of observations is always positive, and the values of the variable are only very rarely negative. Therefore in statistical graphs usually only the upper right-hand quadrant is shown. A graphical solution is illustrated by the following example. Let the following series concerning the age of male and female workers covered by a pension scheme be given:

We shall now deal with the column in which the distribution of men according to age is shown in absolute figures. We have to assume that the age was given in years completed and the limiting values of the classes are figures ending with 0 and 5. The scale of the abscissa in the graph is marked accordingly. The scale, contrary to the rules accepted in mathematics, does not begin from zero at the origin. For a statistical graph this is not necessary and, could make a statistical presentation awkward. We should start the scale from the lowest value that we need. The scale on the ordinate, however, should start from zero.

TABLE 4.7. WORKERS COVERED BY PENSION SCHEMES IN DECEMBER 1935[a]

| Age of workers | Number of workers | | | |
| | absolute | | in percentages | |
| | men | women | men | women |
|---|---|---|---|---|
| *Total* | *847,130* | *504,200* | *100·0* | *100·0* |
| 10–14 | 1340 | 2170 | 0·2 | 0·4 |
| 15–19 | 52,020 | 58,950 | 6·1 | 11·7 |
| 20–24 | 119,300 | 134,470 | 14·1 | 26·7 |
| 25–29 | 179,230 | 107,140 | 21·2 | 21·2 |
| 30–34 | 156,080 | 64,980 | 18·4 | 12·9 |
| 35–39 | 110,970 | 44,720 | 13·1 | 8·9 |
| 40–44 | 75,680 | 31,500 | 8·9 | 6·2 |
| 45–49 | 57,800 | 24,540 | 6·8 | 4·9 |
| 50–54 | 41,350 | 15,860 | 4·9 | 3·1 |
| 55–59 | 29,030 | 11,450 | 3·4 | 2·3 |
| 60–64 | 19,160 | 6370 | 2·3 | 1·3 |
| 65–69 | 5170 | 2050 | 0·6 | 0·4 |

[a] Social Insurance Agency *Insurance Statistics for 1935*, Warsaw 1938, p. 38.

*Note.* The above table includes only workers whose ages are known. The original publication includes in addition 19,590 men and 5070 women whose ages were not known. The last age group in the original publication was denoted "65 and more". For simplicity we have used 65–69 years of age. Because of a relatively low frequency in this class and a rapid drop in frequency in comparison with the preceding classes we can make this change without fear of committing a serious error. The calculation of percentages after deducting those whose ages were not known is tantamount to assuming that the distribution of workers of unknown age is the same as of the workers whose age is known.

In Fig. 4.1 we have plotted in the usual way the points corresponding to particular entries of the series; in this case concerning the number of workers in particular age groups. The points are placed so that they correspond to the values in the middle of the class on the abscissa. This is a correct procedure when not the particular values of the variable are given, but the classes of these values as in this example.

There is a variety of ways in which the graph may be drawn.

(1) We can draw rectangles on particular segments of the horizontal axis with heights determined by the class frequencies. The areas of the rectangles will be proportional to the frequencies of the classes, and the total area of the figure will correspond to the total number of units in the whole population. This kind of graph is called a *histogram*.

(2) We can join by straight lines the points plotted as before. Thus we get a broken line which is usually extended to the right and to the left to meet the horizontal axis in the centres of the classes just above and just below the values that appear in the series. In our example this will be to the right in the middle of the class of 70–75 years, and to the left up in the middle of the class of 5–10 years.

On this way we get a figure with a straight line at the bottom and a broken line on the other sides. A figure of this kind is called a *frequency polygon*.

Note that the total area of such a polygon is equal to the total area of the histogram. Indeed the triangle *ABC* cut off from the histogram by the line *AC* is equal to the triangle *CED*, which is added to the histogram (equal angles, side *AB* equal to side *DE*). The same is true of every pair of triangles cut off and added, down to the last triangles on the right and left side. But the area marked by the broken line for each segment corresponding to the class interval is not equal to the area of the corresponding rectangle in the histogram since the triangle *CED* is not equal to the triangle *EFG*, and moreover, the broken line cuts off from the highest rectangle two triangles, without adding any. From this point of view a frequency polygon does not correctly represent the structure of the population.

(3) Instead of a broken line we can draw a smooth curve which is called a *frequency curve*. When the variable is continuous or quasi-continuous this is the most natural way. For a graphical solution to be correct the curve must be drawn so that the areas bounded by the curve, the ordinates and the corresponding segments of the abscissa, are proportional to the frequencies of the corresponding classes. It follows that the curve will not pass through the points which served as a basis for determining the heights of the rectangles in Fig. 4.1, nor will it pass through the points at which the line breaks in Fig. 4.2. The zero points will cor-

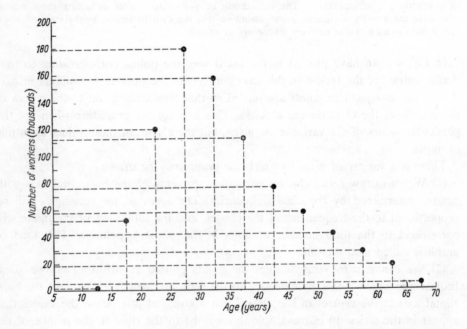

FIG. 4.1. Age of male workers insured in December 1935.

respond to the lower limit of the lowest class and the upper limit of the highest class. The technical difficulties in drawing correct frequency curves are rather formidable. The reader may compare the shape of the broken line with that of the curve and both of them with the histogram.

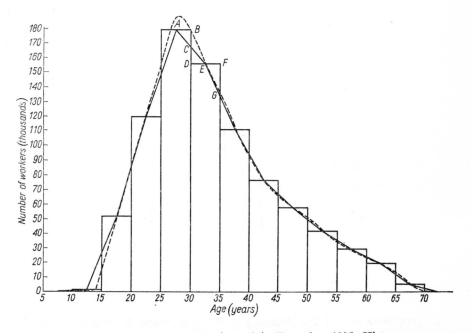

FIG. 4.2. Age of male workers insured in December 1935. Histogram. Frequency polygon. Frequency curve.

When the class intervals are not equal, the drawing of a graph presents certain difficulties. Let us imagine that the series from Table 4.7 is arranged in 5-year age groups only up to the age of 49, and above that the age groups are of a 10-year duration. We shall then have $41,350 + 29,030 = 70,380$ workers in the age group 50–59, and $19,160 + 5170 = 24,330$ workers in the age group 60–69. On the axis of abscissas we shall now have to make the segments from 50 years upwards twice as long as before. But the ordinates cannot be taken as the segments corresponding to 70,380 and 24,330 since then the areas of the rectangles would be twice as big as they should be, and the whole picture would be completely false. To make it right we have to change the scale on the ordinate appropriately as we change the class interval, i.e. we have to diminish the scale in the same ratio as we increase the class interval or vice versa, increase the scale in the same ratio as we decrease the class interval. Or, what amounts to the same thing, we have to reduce appropriately the frequencies corresponding to the classes in question. In our example we would have to mark off on the ordinate segments corresponding not to the figures 70,380 and 24,330 but to figures half as big. This procedure is shown in Fig. 4.3. For the classes from 50 years up the continuous line shows a correct solution and the dotted line an incorrect solution.

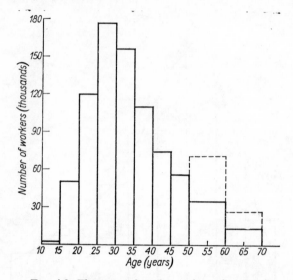

FIG. 4.3. The age of male workers insured in December 1935. Histogram. Change in class intervals.

The general nature of the structure of the population determined on the basis of the new histogram will be the same as that determined from Fig. 4.2, with the difference that the picture will be less precise for the higher classes.

In some special cases—contrary to the custom in mathematics—the values of the independent variable may be measured not along the horizontal but along the vertical axis. An example of such a special type of graph is an age pyramid used in demography to present the structure of the population with regard to age and sex. The graph is drawn in the following way: from the middle of the horizontal axis we draw a perpendicular axis along which age is measured; on the horizontal line the frequency scale is shown—to the left of the perpendicular line for men and to the right for women. Fig. 4.4 refers to the population of the former western provinces in 1900; age is shown in 5-year groups.

An age pyramid is very suitable for comparing the structure of the population by age. Of course we can also use an ordinary graph measuring the age scale on the abscissa (see Fig. 4.5).

Let us now consider how to draw a graph for a cumulative series. The figures from Table 4.7 referring to men will then be arranged as shown in Table 4.8 and will be graphically presented as shown in Fig. 4.6.

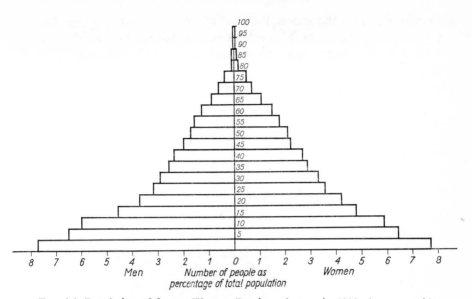

FIG. 4.4. Population of former Western Provinces by age in 1900. Age pyramid.

TABLE 4.8. WORKERS COVERED BY PENSION SCHEMES BY AGE
Cumulative Series

| Age of workers | Number of workers |
|---|---|
| less than 15 years | 1340 |
| ,, ,, 20 ,, | 53,360 |
| ,, ,, 25 ,, | 172,660 |
| ,, ,, 30 ,, | 351,890 |
| ,, ,, 35 ,, | 507,970 |
| ,, ,, 40 ,, | 618,940 |
| ,, ,, 45 ,, | 694,620 |
| ,, ,, 50 ,, | 752,420 |
| ,, ,, 55 ,, | 793,770 |
| ,, ,, 60 ,, | 822,800 |
| ,, ,, 65 ,, | 841,960 |
| ,, ,, 70 ,, | 847,130 |

Both in the series and in the graph the individual points correspond to the number of persons younger than the age marked on the abscissa. The most natural graphical presentation will be a broken line as shown in the graph, or by a smooth curve.[39] Rectangles are not suitable in this case to present the frequency distribution. The slope of the line will be the greater, the greater the population increase

[39] When we use broken lines, the breaks occur at the limits of the classes, and when a smooth curve is used it goes exactly through the points corresponding to the values of the cumulative series located at the limits of the classes.

in a given segment, i.e. the greater the frequencies in the corresponding classes of the frequency distribution. In this case the line is steepest within the segment of 25–30 years where there is the greatest number of observations in Table 4.7.

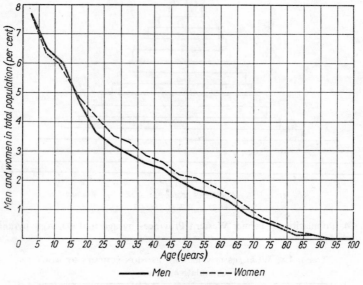

FIG. 4.5. Population of former Western Provinces by age in 1900.
Frequency polygon.

and the highest ordinate in Fig. 4.1 and 4.2 p. 146 and p. 147. In the initial and final segments, where the frequencies are low, the slope is very small. The ordinate corresponding to the last and highest point of the curve expresses the total number of observations in the population, as does the last item in the cumulative series. A curve of this type is called an *ogive*.

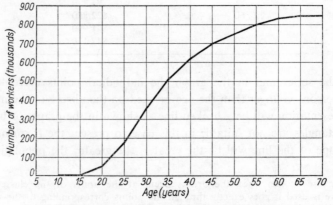

FIG. 4.6. Age of workers insured in December 1935. Ogive.

An ogive is not so expressive as the types of graphs previously described, but it may be useful for special purposes. e.g. for a graphical calculation of certain numerical characteristics.

Graphs are used primarily for comparing the structure of different populations. As an example of this kind of application we shall make a comparative analysis of the age structure of male and female workers for which the figures were given in Table 4.7. It would be inconvenient to compare graphs based on absolute values taken directly from the table because the sizes of the two populations differ. To make the data comparable we shall show the number of workers in different age groups in percentages, separately for men and for women. Frequency polygons will then look as shown in Fig. 4.7.

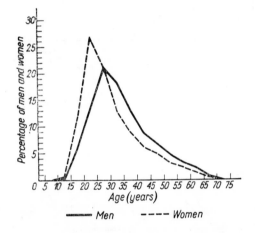

Fig. 4.7. Age of male and female workers insured in December 1935. Frequency polygons.

A similar result could be obtained by using the absolute figures and applying to each population a different scale for the ordinate. In this case we would have to use a bigger scale for women than for men in the ratio of 847,130 : 504,200, i.e. roughly 1·7 : 1. Then the areas of both figures will be approximately the same. The second scale may be marked either on the same (left) vertical line, on its other side, or on the right side of the graph. However, this method is cumbersome, and when more than two populations are to be compared it would give a picture rather difficult to decipher because of the need to show more than two scales on the graph.

Looking at the graph we see that both for men and for women the group of young workers is rather outstanding: for women 20–25 years old and for men 25–30 years old. After these peak points the frequencies drop off rapidly in both directions, although they drop faster to the left than to the right. This means that there are relatively, many workers of both sexes who are considerably older than those at the most frequently observed age. On the basis of the graph we can determine the differences between men and women as follows: (1) the whole graph relating to women is shifted to the left, which means that the women are generally younger than the men; (2) the peak point of the curve for women is shifted still more to the left which means that the most common age is lower for women than for men; (3) the peak of the curve for women is higher and the curve drops more steeply than for men which means that for women the concentration around one age group is more marked than for men.

The same conclusions, of course, can be drawn from the figures in the table but the graph undoubtedly makes the task easier. Presented in the form of ogives the figures from the table give the following picture:

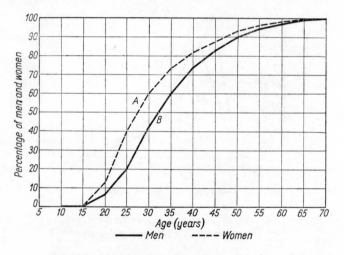

FIG. 4.8. Age of male and female workers insured
in December 1935. Ogives.

The fact that the curve for women is shifted farther to the left and is steeper in the initial segment than is the curve for men indicates their relative youth. A relatively more horizontal shape of both curves in the upper part of the graph in comparison with the lower part indicated an asymmetric arrangement of figures for both men and women.

An analysis of the ogive leads generally to the same conclusions as the analysis of the previous graph although, as we pointed out before, the ogive produces a less clear picture.

b. *The General structure of the population judged from the frequency distribution.* The general structure of the population can be seen directly from the order of the absolute values expressing the frequency of the appearance of the phenomenon in particular classes. The structure can be seen more clearly when the class frequencies are shown in figures relative to the total population, e.g. in percentages. A graph presents an even more expressive picture.

The general structure of the series gives a general idea of the phenomenon which we want to study in relation to the given population. We shall describe below certain typical structures. It might seem at the first glance that classification according to the type of structure is of a rather formal nature. However, a detailed review of particular cases from different fields indicates that this formal analysis may lead to important conclusions and, what is more, may often show in which direction further investigation should proceed.

(1) *Symmetric series with a single maximum.* Let us take as an example a series showing the height structure of draftees. The numerical and graphical pictures are presented in Table 4.9 and Fig. 4.9 respectively.

TABLE 4.9. HEIGHTS OF DRAFTEES IN POLAND[40]
born in 1906–1909

| Height (cm) | Number of draftees (percentages) |
|---|---|
| 137·5–140·5 | 0·1 |
| 140·5–143·5 | 0·1 |
| 143·5–146·5 | 0·2 |
| 146·5–149·5 | 0·4 |
| 149·5–152·5 | 1·2 |
| 152·5–155·5 | 2·9 |
| 155·5–158·5 | 6·4 |
| 158·5–161·5 | 11·9 |
| 161·5–164·5 | 17·1 |
| 164·5–167·5 | 19·8 |
| 167·5–170·5 | 17·3 |
| 170·5–173·5 | 11·8 |
| 173·5–176·5 | 6·6 |
| 176·5–179·5 | 2·8 |
| 179·5–182·5 | 1·0 |
| 182·5–185·5 | 0·3 |
| 185·5–188·5 | 0·1 |
| *Total* | *100·0* |

The greatest number of observations is centred at the middle of the series (the maximum of the curve). The drop in frequencies on both sides of the maximum is almost completely symmetric except that the left side extends a little farther than the right side.

---

[40] Jan Mydlarski: Budowa fizyczna młodzieży męskiej roczników 1906 do 1909 w świetle materiałów Komisji poborowych (The Physical Structure of Young Men Born in 1906–09), *Lekarz Wojskowy (The Army Physician)*, Vol. XXII, Nos. 1, 2, 3, 4, Warsaw, 1933.

This typical picture may sometimes be interpreted as meaning that there is a certain average value of the variable that is most common in the population, from which there are many deviations up or down. These deviations are equally frequent in both directions and their frequency decreases as the magnitude of deviation increases. This average value of the variable could be called normal. Curves representing repeated measurements of the same quantity are such statistical curves. Since the instruments used for measuring as well as the human senses are imperfect, individual measurements deviate from the true value for the object. The greater the deviations, the less frequent they are. If there is no bias in the instrument or in the work of the investigator the curve should be symmetric.

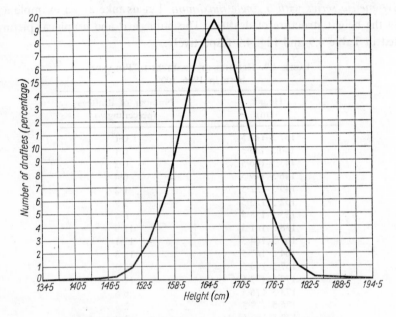

FIG. 4.9. Height of draftees in Poland born in 1906-09.

It should be noted that the curve is fully symmetric only if the class limits are properly chosen; otherwise the symmetry disappears. Strictly speaking, of course, it does not actually disappear, but improper classification fails to reveal it. Thus, to determine whether a series is symmetric it is important to choose the proper class interval or else special and complicated methods of mathematical analysis have to be used.

This kind of symmetric curve or series with a unique maximum is often encountered in the natural sciences. Others are more common in populations related to man in human society and to his activities, and they are discussed below.

(2) *Asymmetric series with a unique maximum.* Let us take as an example the data concerning the weight of girls 12½ years old.

TABLE 4.10. WEIGHT OF GIRLS AGED 12½ YEARS[41]

| Weight (kg) | Number of girls |
|---|---|
| *Total* | *883* |
| 20–22 | 4 |
| 23–25 | 24 |
| 26–28 | 104 |
| 29–31 | 220 |
| 32–34 | 182 |
| 35–37 | 152 |
| 38–40 | 80 |
| 41–43 | 49 |
| 44–46 | 27 |
| 47–49 | 18 |
| 50–52 | 13 |
| 53–55 | 4 |
| 56–58 | 5 |
| 59–61 | 1 |

In this example the deviations from the most common weight upwards are much more frequent than downwards and the maximum is closer to the lower limit of the series. We can say that for special reasons very large deviations of the weight downwards are impossible whereas even quite substantial deviations upward may occur. A similar picture is obtained from the series shown above (Table 4.7 on p. 145) and (Fig. 4.2, p. 147), concerning the number of workers by age groups. The most common age of the worker is relatively low but deviations from this age upward are much more frequent than downward, particularly for women. This is not surprising since the most common age is 25–29 years which is relatively young and there may be workers as old as 65–69 (i.e. about 40 years older) but of course, there could not be any workers 40 years younger than the most common age group of 25–29 years. If the maximum of the curve is shifted to the left, as in the examples mentioned above, we say that the curve is positively skewed (left asymmetry). In other cases the curve may be negatively skewed (right asymmetry).

In our examples the asymmetry has a biological and socio-economic significance. From the biological point of view there are always fewer old than young people and therefore there must be fewer old workers; children below a certain age cannot work at all. From the biological point of view, however, there is no explanation why there should be so clear a maximum at the age of 25–29 years for men, and 20–24 years for women. From the socio-economic point of view the clear maximum occurs for a relatively young age group because: (a) a developing industry attracts

[41] Jan Mydlarski: Sprawność fizyczna młodzieży w Polsce (Physical Fitness of Youth in Poland), *Przegląd Fizjologii Ruchu*, Warsaw, 1934, table 4a.

primarily young people from other trades and from agriculture; (b) the capitalist employer prefers to lay off older workers who tire more easily and therefore are less efficient, and to replace them by young ones.

The table below shows the percentages of women in different age groups who died in the United States in 1936 from: (1) diseases of the circulatory system, (2) tuberculosis of the respiratory tracts. (Table 4.11 and Fig. 4.10).

TABLE 4.11. DEATHS OF WOMEN BY AGE AND CERTAIN CAUSES
IN THE UNITED STATES[42]
in 1936

| Age of deceased (years) | Cause of death | |
| --- | --- | --- |
| | Diseases of the circulatory system | Tuberculosis of the respiratory tracts |
| | (percentage) | |
| Total | 100·0 | 100·0 |
| 0–4 | 0·2 | 1·3 |
| 5–9 | 0·3 | 0·4 |
| 10–14 | 0·5 | 1·2 |
| 15–19 | 0·5 | 6·7 |
| 20–24 | 0·6 | 13·2 |
| 25–29 | 0·8 | 14·2 |
| 30–34 | 1·0 | 11·0 |
| 35–39 | 1·5 | 9·5 |
| 40–44 | 2·1 | 7·5 |
| 45–49 | 3·2 | 6·1 |
| 50–54 | 4·4 | 5·6 |
| 55–59 | 6·2 | 5·2 |
| 60–64 | 9·0 | 5·0 |
| 65–69 | 12·5 | 5·1 |
| 70–74 | 15·2 | 3·5 |
| 75–79 | 17·1 | 2·8 |
| 80–84 | 13·2 | 1·2 |
| 85–89 | 7·9 | 0·5 |
| 90–94 | 3·0 | 0·0 |
| 95–99 | 0·7 | 0·0 |
| 100 and over | 0·1 | 0·0 |

Both the table and the graph show a very strong negative skewness with regard to the age of those who died from diseases of the circulatory system. The greatest number of deaths occurred in the 70–79 age group, but there were quite a few also in the 80–84 and even 85–89 age groups. It is all the more striking that we are dealing here with the absolute numbers of the dead and not with the dead as percentages of the living, of whom there are very few at so advanced an age. One fact comes out very clearly: diseases of the circulatory system are a formidable cause of death,

---

[42] *Mortality Statistics 1936.* (The data refer to white women. The details differ somewhat for Negro women).

particularly in old age. On the other hand, the curve of deaths due to tuberculosis shows a clear maximum at the early age of 20–29 years. A comparison of the two curves gives us a significant picture of these two diseases. (See Fig. 4.10.)

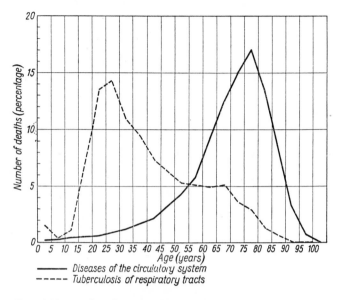

FIG. 4.10. Deaths of women by age and selected causes in the United States in 1936.

A characteristic feature of the curves described above, both symmetrical and asymmetric, is a drop on both sides of the maximum, first gradual, then more rapid, and then again gradual (so that the curve approaches the $x$-axis at an acute angle on one side and almost as an asymptote on the other).

(3) *Extremely asymmetric series—monotonically decreasing or increasing*. The greatest frequency usually appears at the smallest, and less often, at the greatest values of the variable. A typical example of this kind of series is the age structure of the population of a country. Under normal conditions the most numerous population group is the youngest, immediately after birth, as can be seen from the example shown in Table 4.12 in which the age structure of the population of the former western provinces of Poland is given according to the statistics for 1900.

Care should be taken not to place a statistical series in this category too hastily. Sometimes the maximum frequency appears at the beginning or at the end of the series only because the division into classes is not sufficiently detailed. Very characteristic in this respect is the example given in Table 4.13a concerning deaths from diphtheria according to the age of the deceased, taken from Italian statistical literature. The youngest age group dominates the older age groups completely: almost

TABLE 4.12. POPULATION OF THE FORMER WESTERN
PROVINCES BY AGE[43]
in 1900

| Age (years) | Population (thousands) |
|---|---|
| Total | 3462·6 |
| 0–4 | 530·7 |
| 5–9 | 447·1 |
| 10–14 | 410·8 |
| 15–19 | 323·5 |
| 20–24 | 275·2 |
| 25–29 | 235·9 |
| 30–34 | 215·9 |
| 35–39 | 190·5 |
| 40–44 | 175·2 |
| 45–49 | 144·9 |
| 50–54 | 132·5 |
| 55–59 | 118·6 |
| 60–64 | 95·7 |
| 65–69 | 70·1 |
| 70–74 | 47·1 |
| 75–79 | 29·0 |
| 80 and over | 19·9 |

TABLE 4.13a. DEATHS DUE TO DIPHTHERIA BY AGE
OF DECEASED IN ITALY[44]
in 1937

| Age of deceased (years) | Number of deaths |
|---|---|
| Total | 2748 |
| 0–4 | 2000 |
| 5–9 | 551 |
| 10–14 | 114 |
| 15–19 | 32 |
| 20–24 | 9 |
| 25–29 | 10 |
| 30–34 | 7 |
| 35–39 | 5 |
| 40–44 | 5 |
| 45–49 | 5 |
| 50–54 | 2 |
| 55–59 | 4 |
| 60–64 | 2 |
| 65–69 | 1 |
| 70–74 | 1 |

[43] Zagadnienia demograficzne Polski (Demographic Problems in Poland), *Statystyka Polski*, Series C, No. 41, Warsaw 1936, p. 15 (see also Figs 4.4 and 4.5).
[44] *Statistica delle Cause di Morte nell' Anno 1937*.

73 per cent of all the deceased were below 5 years of age and deaths at the age of 20 or over occurred only very rarely. Hence the apparent conclusion that the younger the patient the more dangerous is diphtheria. However, this conclusion is wrong. If we divide the first five years of age into 1-year groups we get the following picture:

TABLE 4.13b. DEATHS FROM DIPHTHERIA AT AGE 0-4
YEARS, ITALY
1937

| Age of deceased (years) | Number of deaths |
|---|---|
| 0-4 | 2000 |
| 0 | 264 |
| 1 | 656 |
| 2 | 416 |
| 3 | 364 |
| 4 | 300 |

Thus it appears that the greatest number of deaths occurs at 1 year of age. There are relatively few deaths of infants below 1 year—in any case fewer than those of children aged 2, 3 or 4 years. A clearer picture still is obtained after dividing the first year of age into months: in the first month of life only 15 infants died and in the remaining 11 months, 249. The correct conclusion now is that diphtheria is most dangerous to very young children, but not to those immediately after birth. On the contrary, infants right after birth only rerely die of diphtheria.

(4) *Symmetric and asymmetric series with a unique minimum.* Series with high frequencies at the extreme values of the variables and low frequencies at middle values appear only rarely in statistical populations. An example from the field of meteorology can be used to illustrate this kind of series. Cloudiness is denoted by the figures from 0 to 10: 0 means that there are no clouds and 10 means that the sky is completely covered with clouds, whereas the figures from 1 to 9 denote various degrees of partial cloudiness. The data presented in Table 4.14 were obtained for the city of Wrocław (in 1876–85).[45]

C. *Irregularities of distribution in statistical series.* An irregular run of frequencies is usually an important indication concerning the nature of the population. The pattern of the series in Table 4.12 shown as an example of an extremely asymmetric type of series (the largest numbers at the beginning) is not by any means accidental, but is related to the nature of the phenomenon. It is obvious that in a normally developing society the largest population figures will be obtained for the earliest age groups and will decline for later age groups, providing the number of births in consecutive periods of time increases, remains the same, or

---

[45] Cited from Yule: *Wstęp do teorii statystyki (An Introduction to the Theory of Statistics),* Warsaw 1921, p. 123.

TABLE 4.14. CLOUDINESS OF THE SKY OVER WROCŁAW
in 1876–85

| Degree of cloudiness | Number of days |
|---|---|
| *Total* | *3653* |
| 0 | 751 |
| 1 | 179 |
| 2 | 107 |
| 3 | 69 |
| 4 | 46 |
| 5 | 9 |
| 6 | 21 |
| 7 | 71 |
| 8 | 194 |
| 9 | 117 |
| 10 | 2089 |

decreases only slightly. Therefore, if the figures show a different pattern it is an indication of the presence of factors disturbing the normal growth of the society, such as, for instance a temporarily or permanently declining birth rate, or the impact of strong migration movements. The population census of 1931 in Poland showed a smaller number of people at 10–19 years of age than at 20–29, because the age group from 10 to 19 contained those born during the First World War when the birth rate declined considerably. In Sweden in 1935 the frequencies in the first five 5-year age groups expressed in percentages of total population were as follows:

TABLE 4.15. POPULATION OF SWEDEN BY AGE
(0–24 years) in 1935

| Age (years) | Percentage of total population |
|---|---|
| 0–4 | 6·6 |
| 5–9 | 7·2 |
| 10–14 | 8·4 |
| 15–19 | 8·7 |
| 20–24 | 8·8 |

In the first five age groups frequency decreases as the age decreases, and only the 25–29 age group shows the reverse trend, having a smaller frequency than the 20–24 age group. A similar population picture for the first four 5-year age groups was also noted then in other countries, notably in England and Germany.

A similar disturbance in the population pattern was discovered in Warsaw (see Table 4.16), but is was for a different reason. High frequencies in the middle age-groups, particularly in those between 20–29 years, were due to the fact that Warsaw was a large city which attracted people in their prime looking for work.

TABLE 4.16. POPULATION OF WARSAW BY AGE
in 1931

| Age (years) | Population (thousands) |
|---|---|
| *Total* | *1171·9* |
| 0–9 | 196·8 |
| 10–19 | 181·8 |
| 20–29 | 268·7 |
| 30–39 | 194·6 |
| 40–49 | 141·8 |
| 50–59 | 95·2 |
| 60–69 | 62·1 |
| 70 and over | 28·2 |
| Unknown | 3·5 |

Far more striking disturbances in the structure of population by age appeared in Warsaw in 1946, as shown in the age pyramid in Fig. 4.11. These disturbances come out with particular clarity when they are compared with a „normal" structure, e.g. such as prevailed in the former western provinces in 1900 (see Fig. 4.4, p. 149).

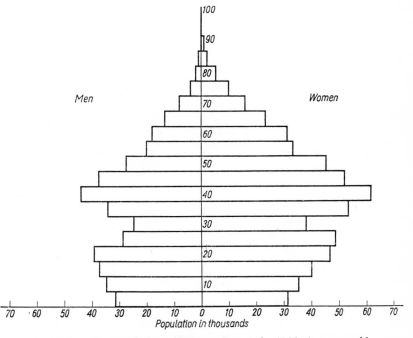

FIG. 4.11. The population of Warsaw by age in 1946. Age pyramid.

The structure of the population of Warsaw in 1946 exhibits exhels a noticeable gap at the ages of 20–34 for men and 25–34 for women. There are two reasons for this:

(1) the deportation and extermination of a part of the population by the Nazi occupiers: thus the gap is more marked for men than for women;

(2) a sudden drop in the birth rate during the First World War (this caused the gap at the ages of 25–29 years).

The narrowing of the base of the pyramid starting at 15 or 20 years was caused by three factors:

(1) the birth rate in Warsaw before the Second World War declined markedly;

(2) the number of those at the earliest age was reduced by a drop in the birth rate during the Second World War;

(3) a relative increase of those in the middle age-groups was due to the migration to large cities (more strongly marked for women than for men).

As can be seen from these examples, an irregular pattern points to the existence of disturbances in the phenomenon itself and to the nature and intensity of these disturbances and thus induces the research worker to dig deeper for the reasons. This is the only way probe the reality behind a series or a curve.

It should be emphasized, however, that a knowledge of the problem is indispensable for establishing the existence of disturbances. Without such knowledge peculiarities of the particular method of registration may easily be taken for basic disturbances in the phenomenon itself.

Especially characteristic are disturbances that cause the existence of two or more maxima. The origin of a series of this kind can best be explained by an example.

TABLE 4.17. YIELDS PER HECTARE IN QUINTALS
in 1934–38

| Yield per hectare (quintals) | Number of counties | | |
|---|---|---|---|
| | Old territories | Regained territories | Total |
| *Total* | *161* | *124* | *285* |
| 7 | 1 | — | 1 |
| 8 | 2 | — | 2 |
| 9 | 15 | — | 15 |
| 10 | 30 | — | 30 |
| 11 | 30 | — | 30 |
| 12 | 23 | 5 | 28 |
| 13 | 21 | 7 | 28 |
| 14 | 18 | 11 | 29 |
| 15 | 16 | 19 | 35 |
| 16 | 2 | 15 | 17 |
| 17 | 2 | 23 | 25 |
| 18 | 1 | 23 | 24 |
| 19 | — | 8 | 8 |
| 20 | — | 6 | 6 |
| 21 | — | 4 | 4 |
| 22 | — | 1 | 1 |
| 23 | — | 1 | 1 |
| 24 | — | 1 | 1 |

This example pertains to the average yield in 1934–8 from 1 hectare (2·5 acres) of rye in the counties that are now within Poland's boundaries. The figures for the old and the regained territories (including the Free City of Gdańsk) are shown separately, and the totals given for both old and regained territories (Table 4.17). These three series are shown in Fig. 4.12.

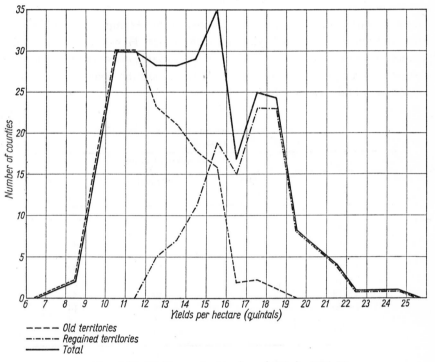

- - - - Old territories
- · - · · - · - Regained territories
——— Total

Fig. 4.12. Yields per hectare in quintals in 1934–38.

Each curve of the separate types of regions is more or less asymmetric. The curve for the old territories has one maximum for the class of 10–11 quintals per hectare, and the curve for the regained territories has two maxima: one for the class of 15 quintals per hectare and another for the class of 17–18 quintals per hectare. The shape of the curve for the old territories is somewhat irregular and we shall discuss it later on. Generally, yields per hectare were much greater in the regained territories than in the old territories. Adding the two series, we get a curve with three maxima, for the classes 10–11, 15 and 17 quintals per hectare: they are separated by two minima, for the classes 12–13 and 16 quintals per hectare. How these maxima and minima were formed is quite obvious. For the classes of 10–11 quintals there is a maximum for the old territories, in the classes from 12–14, the number of counties in the old territories is declining, and in the regained territories it is still quite small and therefore the total is smaller than the maximum for the old territories in the classes of 10–11 quintals. The very clearly marked second maximum of the combined series in the class of 15 quintals per hectare corresponds to the first maximum for the regained territories, with a still considerable number of counties for the old territories. Finally, the third maximum of the combined series (the class of 17 quintals) corresponds to the second maximum, for the regained territories.

The series with several maxima was formed in our example by combining areas of low yield and areas of high yield into one series. However, the combining of populations with different levels of values of the variable does not always lead to the formation of a series with two maxima. If we divide the counties into classes of 2 hectares we obtain Table 4.18.

TABLE 4.18. YIELDS PER HECTARE IN QUINTALS
in 1934–38

| Yields per hectare in quintals | Number of counties | | |
|---|---|---|---|
| | Old territories | Regained territories | Total |
| *Total* | *161* | *124* | *285* |
| 7–8 | 3 | — | 3 |
| 9–10 | 45 | — | 45 |
| 11–12 | 53 | 5 | 58 |
| 13–14 | 39 | 18 | 57 |
| 15–16 | 18 | 34 | 52 |
| 17–18 | 3 | 46 | 49 |
| 19–20 | — | 14 | 14 |
| 21–22 | — | 5 | 5 |
| 23–24 | — | 2 | 2 |

In spite of the fact that we combined the same basically different populations we obtain a joint curve with only one maximum although its top is unusually wide. This example shows how, by making the class interval too large, we can obscure the essential features of the structure of the population.

All irregularities in the shape of the curve—the appearance of more than one maximum, flattened tops, unexpected inflections, etc.,—suggest that the composition of the population in question is not uniform. In our case this is true with regard not only to the combined series, but also to the original series. For the regained territories there are two maxima. Indeed, there are areas of very high yield per hectare (primarily the Opole–Silesia District and the Lower Silesia District) and areas where the yield is lower. For the old territories we have only one maximum, but the top is flattened; here the areas of high yield per hectare are the districts of Poznań, Bydgoszcz and Katowice. By using four separate territorial groups instead of two, we would have obtained four curves of a much more regular shape.

Thus when we come across a series with an irregular pattern we should attempt, first of all, to split the population into homogeneous classes. This procedure will enable us to draw the proper conclusions. It may not always be possible to split a population into classes by purely statistical means. It is usually necessary to examine the essence of the subject to which a given population is related. Moreover, this kind of analysis may enable us to rearrange the population into uniform parts even before we start a statistical investigation. Under no circumstances, however, can we disregard the indications of the lack of uniformity in the population arrived at by statistical analysis.

Another example of an irregular series is found in the age distribution of those who died of pleurisy.

TABLE 4.19. DEATHS OF WOMEN BY PLEURISY IN THE
UNITED STATES
in 1936[46]

| Age of deceased (years) | Number of deceased (percentages) |
|---|---|
| *Total* | *100·0* |
| 0 | 23·4 |
| 1 | 5·3 |
| 2 | 1·9 |
| 3 | 0·9 |
| 4 | 0·7 |
| 0–4 | 32·2 |
| 5–9 | 1·7 |
| 10–14 | 1·1 |
| 15–19 | 1·0 |
| 20–24 | 0·9 |
| 25–29 | 1·3 |
| 30–34 | 1·4 |
| 35–39 | 1·7 |
| 40–44 | 2·0 |
| 45–49 | 2·2 |
| 50–54 | 2·8 |
| 55–59 | 3·2 |
| 60–64 | 4·7 |
| 65–69 | 6·7 |
| 70–74 | 8·0 |
| 75–79 | 10·3 |
| 80–84 | 9·0 |
| 85–89 | 6·2 |
| 90–94 | 2·8 |
| 95–99 | 0·7 |
| 100 and over | 0·1 |

[46] Mortality Statistics, 1936.

The first part of the series decreases monotonically. The greatest number of deaths occurs in the first year of life and then the numbers decrease rapidly. In youth, except for early childhood, deaths are few, but in later life the percentage of deaths by pleurisy increases, reaching a distinct maximum at the ages of 75–79 years. The irregularity of the series indicates clearly the specific, double significance of pleurisy as a cause of death.

Another example given in Table 4.20 is taken from socio-economic literature. The series has two distinct maxima: the first, very clear maximum occurs at low earnings, 10–20 zlotys; the second, less marked but still distinct, occurs at earnings of 60–70 zlotys. Very numerous—much more so than in any other industry—is the open, upper class of earnings, 80 zlotys and over.

TABLE 4.20.   WEEKLY EARNINGS OF WORKERS EMPLOYED
IN THE PRINTING INDUSTRY IN POLAND
(August 1935)

| Weekly earnings in zlotys | Number of workers in percentages |
|---|---|
| *Total* | *100·0* |
| Below 10 | 12·0 |
| 10–20 | 23·8 |
| 20–30 | 16·1 |
| 30–40 | 12·3 |
| 40–50 | 7·3 |
| 50–60 | 5·6 |
| 60–70 | 6·1 |
| 70–80 | 5·2 |
| 80 and over | 11·6 |

The reason is obvious: in the printing industry are employed, on the one hand, highly skilled specialists with very high earnings (such as type-setters, clickers, machinists, bookbinders) and on the other hand, many auxiliary workers—mainly unskilled women—workers who are also classified as employees of the printing industry. It follows that if we wanted to abide by Lenin's principle of forming groups uniform from the socio-economic point of view we would have to present the earnings of workers in the printing industry in at least two series: one for skilled workers and another for auxiliary, unskilled workers.

# NUMERICAL CHARACTERISTICS OF FREQUENCY DISTRIBUTIONS

## STATEMENT OF THE PROBLEM

A general description of a series of the type we have discussed above provides valuable information, but it does not suffice in statistical enquiries. It lacks precision, since it is based on general impressions rather than on the exact establishment of the true state of affairs, and it is not sufficiently concrete since it is confined to a qualitative description. We shall explain by an example what we should strive for in giving a quantitative characterization of a series if its essential features are to be grasped.

In the Polish *Concise Statistical Yearbook* (1939, p. 273) there are data on the weekly earnings of the workers employed in heavy and medium heavy industries. Table 5.1 gives the earnings of the workers employed in the wood, construction and printing industries as presented there.

TABLE 5.1. WEEKLY EARNINGS OF WORKERS IN HEAVY AND MEDIUM
HEAVY INDUSTRIES
in August 1938

| Industry | Percentage of workers whose weekly earnings were (zlotys) | | | | | | | | |
|---|---|---|---|---|---|---|---|---|---|
| | less than 10 | 10–20 | 20–30 | 30–40 | 40–50 | 50–60 | 60–70 | 70–80 | 80 and over |
| Wood | 20·5 | 49·6 | 20·8 | 6·7 | 1·6 | 0·4 | 0·2 | 0·1 | 0·1 |
| Construction | 10·0 | 21·0 | 23·8 | 21·0 | 10·8 | 6·8 | 4·1 | 1·4 | 1·1 |
| Printing | 12·0 | 23·8 | 16·1 | 12·3 | 7·3 | 5·6 | 6·1 | 5·2 | 11·6 |

For the time being we shall disregard the data for the printing industry, for reasons already mentioned on p. 166 and to which we shall return later on. The series concerning the wood and construction industries are presented graphically in Fig. 5.1.

An analysis of Fig. 5.1. leads to the following conclusions:

(1) The earnings of construction workers are on average higher than those of

workers in the wood industry. This is shown by a shift to the right of the broken-line curve in comparison with the solid-line curve.

(2) The earnings of the wood industry workers are more markedly centred around a most frequent level than are those of the construction workers. This is shown by a more distinctly marked maximum, and a more rapid drop on both sides of the maximum for the solid-line curve than for the broken-line curve.

(3) Both curves are asymmetric. The right arms of both curves are longer than the left, so that we have a case of positive skewness (left asymmetry). It is difficult to say from the diagram alone for which group of workers the skewness is more pronounced until we decided how to measure the degree of skewness.

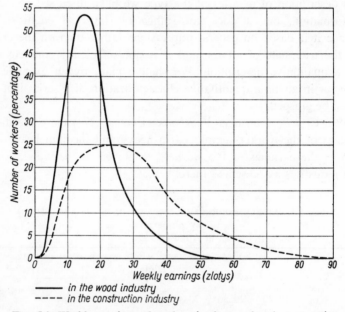

— in the wood industry
---- in the construction industry

FIG. 5.1. Weekly earnings of workers in the wood and construction industries.

The reader is advised to compare this with Fig. 4.7. (p. 151) where the differences between the two curves were of a similar character.

To generalize, we can say that a population may be characterized from three points of view:

(1) By determining the general level of the value of the variable within each population. Expressing the same thing graphically we talk about the position of the figure depicting the population in relation to the abscissa and about it being shifted to the right or to the left. The numerical characteristics used for this purpose are called *averages*.

(2) By determining the degree of concentration of the values corresponding to particular observations around some centre, or, vice versa, the degree of dispersion of the values corresponding to particular observations. The numerical characteristics used for this purpose are called *measures of dispersion.*

(3) By determining the direction and degree of asymmetry. For this purpose we use the *measures of asymmetry.*

# CHAPTER 5

# AVERAGE

## 1. DEFINITION AND TYPES OF AVERAGES IN STATISTICS

An average of a population, in the broad sense of the word, can be defined as any value of the variable lying between its extreme values, and uniquely determinable mathematically. From among an infinite number of averages that can be obtained in this way only a few are useful in statistics, in which numerical measures are used to characterize reality. We shall discuss below only the more important averages used in statistics.

They are divided into two groups:

A. Averages obtained by calculation based on all the values of the variable appearing in the population. The property of these averages is that by substituting an appropriate average for the particular values of the variable we obtain for the whole population the same result as we would get by taking into account individual values corresponding to particular observations. For the calculation of these averages it is not necessary to arrange the observations into a series; nor are the averages affected by the order in which particular observations are arranged for computation.

To this group belong the arithmetic mean, the geometric mean, the harmonic mean, the power means.

B. Averages obtained by taking into account the frequencies in a frequency distribution. Graphically these averages determine certain characteristic points on the horizontal axis on the basis of the shape of the frequency curve. The following averages of this type, also called location averages, are used in statistics: the mode, the median (and related to it quartiles, deciles, percentiles or, more generally, quantiles).

The choice of an average of the variety described in $A$ is determined by the problem and is a consequence of the definition according to which the substitution of the average for the individual values does not change the final result. Averages of the type described in $B$ can be used at will, depending upon which one is deemed most suitable for a given case. We can also describe a population by using simultaneously different averages of the $B$ type and an appropriate average of the $A$ type so that each of these averages throws some light on the population from a different angle.

170

## 2. THE ARITHMETIC MEAN AND ITS COMPUTATION

The arithmetic mean is calculated by adding up the values of the variable corresponding to particular observations and dividing the total by the number of observations. Denoting the particular values of the variable $x$ by $x_1$, $x_2$, etc., up to $x_n$, and the arithmetic mean of the values of $x$ by $\bar{x}$, we have:

$$\bar{x} = \frac{x_1 + x_2 + \cdots\cdots + x_n}{n} \tag{V.1}$$

or, by introducing the symbol $\sum$ to denote summation

$$\bar{x} = \frac{\sum x}{n} \tag{V.2}$$

or[47]

$$\bar{x} = \frac{1}{n} \sum x. \tag{V.2a}$$

It follows from formula (V. 2) or (V. 2a) that

$$\bar{x}\, n = \sum x. \tag{V.3}$$

This means that by multiplying the arithmetic mean by the number of observations we get the same result as we would by adding up all the individual values of the variable. In other words, the arithmetic mean, substituted for the particular values, fulfills the condition of keeping the sum unchanged.

On the basis of this observation we can define the logical meaning of the arithmetic mean as the value each individual observation would have if they were all equal and their sum remained unchanged. Thus, the arithmetic mean of the income of a group of people would be the income that would accrue to each person if the total income were equally divided among all. It is a clear and precise notion. On the other hand, however, the abstract nature of the arithmetic mean and its independence of reality are clearly emphasized here, since the very essence of the distribution of income amongst individuals is its inequality. Nevertheless, the arithmetic mean, which states the average level of income, is one of the most important numerical characteristics.

One reservation, however, should be made here. It makes sense to calculate the arithmetic mean only when we deal with a *homogeneous* population. Otherwise, the calculation of the arithmetic mean is meaningless and leads to false conclusions. As extreme cases of this let us consider a few examples. A city may have special

---

[47] Strictly speaking we should write $\bar{x} = \frac{1}{n} \sum_{i=1}^{n} x_i$, to indicate that the summing up of the individual values of $x$ is done consecutively for all observations, from the first to the $n$th. For the sake of simplicity we shall use the symbols as shown in the text above, when there is no possibility of a misunderstanding.

homes for children and for the aged: to calculate the average age of those who live in such institutions would be obvious nonsense. Or let us imagine a factory in which some of the workers use old, traditional methods and some employ new, modern methods. The productivity of labour in these two groups will be quite different and the differences may be considerable. Under these circumstances it is very dangerous to calculate the average productivity for the whole factory. A rise in the average in two consecutive periods of time will be interpreted as an achievement. Yet this increase may be due to a more widespread use of modern methods or to an increased efficiency in both groups, or to a combination of both these factors. And it is by no means a matter of indifference how this increase was achieved. Therefore, in cases like these, we should calculate separate averages of the productivity of both groups of workers, in addition to, or instead of, an overall general average. Having both these averages and knowing the conditions of work in the factory, we shall be able to determine by how much and in what way the total efficiency in the factory can be improved.

From the three frequency distributions of workers earnings in Table 5.1. (p. 167) in the wood and construction industries, even though the distributions are very asymmetrical, no special groups seem to stand out so that the calculation of the arithmetic mean may be justified. However, in the printing industry the situation is different. As we mentioned before, in the printing industry there are two different groups of workers: highly skilled workers and auxiliary unskilled workers. In this case the arithmetic mean for the two groups together would be completely meaningless.

In countries where the areas of farms differ considerably—from undersized "dwarf" farms to large estates—there is no point in calculating the average size of the farm. Even if we confine ourselves only to peasant farms, say below 50 hectares, the calculation of averages (e.g. the average number of livestock, the average number of hired hands per farm) may be misleading, and by obscuring the differences that exist may lead not only to meaningless conclusions but even to a distortion of reality.

Lenin pointed out that averages may be calculated only for uniform populations which constitute logical entities. In the field of economics these populations would have to constitute entities from the economic point of view. An example of the excellent application of averages are Lenin's works, particularly *The Development of Capitalism in Russia*. We may calculate the average number of livestock per farm for small peasant farms and for capitalistic peasant farms separately, but we should not combine both these types of farms into one. We can calculate the average number of workers per handicraft establishment, say, in the textile industry, but there would be no sense in calculating the average for the "population" of such establishments in all industries in general. We should remember that the average, like all other numerical characteristics, is only an auxiliary tool of analysis; the proper description of the population is provided by the frequency distribution and by its graphical presentation.

Let us consider a few examples that will show how—by using formally proper averages—the picture of reality can be distorted, or even completely falsified.

According to the census of 1931 the average occupancy of apartments in Warsaw was 2·1 persons per room, and in 1947 it was 2·2 persons per room. The increase is not surprising, since we all know that accomodation in Warsaw was destroyed by war. However, after a closer look at apartment occupancy, and considering the size of the apartment, we get a completely different picture. It turns out that in 1-room apartments the average occupancy per room dropped from 4·0 to 3·2 persons, in 2-room apartments it dropped from 2·4 to 2·0 persons, but in 3-room apartments it increased from 1·7 to 1·8 persons, in 4-room apartments it increased from 1·3 to 1·8 persons and in apartments with 5 or more rooms it increased from 0·8 to 1·9 persons. In 1947 the occupancy density for all apartments from 2 rooms was more or less the same and the housing situation of a large portion of the population had improved considerably. Even though 1-room apartments still accomodated 3·2 persons per room and the occupancy density of apartments with 2 rooms or more was still very high, and even though there were still many apartments occupied by more than one family—in other words even though many important housing problems still awaited solutions—the achievements in comparison with the pre-war period were considerable. However, they were not reflected in the overall occupancy average mentioned above.

Obviously misleading statistics concerning income *per capita* are published annually in the *Statistical Yearbook of the United States* in the table "Income Payments to Individuals". An explanatory note states that income includes: (1) salaries and earnings; (2) owner's income from industrial, commercial and agricultural establishments; (3) "estate" income such as dividends, interest, etc.; (4) social security, insurance and pension payments. Total income and the average per head are given. The latter is obtained by dividing total income by total population, thus providing misleading information on the average standard of living (which it is supposed to reflect), since hired workers and retired people are treated in the same way as the entrepreneurs whose income often reaches the millions. Also misleading are such statistics as national income per head in capitalist countries, since it is commonly known that a major portion of national income is controlled by business magnates.

When the number of observations is small the arithmetic mean can be calculated directly by adding up and dividing the total by the number of observations. With many observations this method would be cumbersome. Besides, the form in which we get statistical data often makes the use of this procedure impossible. Sometimes statistical tables provide the total sum of all the values of the variable in addition to the total number of observations; e.g. in taxation statistics, apart from the total number of income tax payers in different income brackets, the total of their income is also given; or in farm statistics the total area is given in addition to the number of farms of different sizes. In these few cases we can obtain the average income of the taxpayers and the average size of the farm by simple division. In most cases, however, the average has to be calculated from a frequency distribution which gives only the number of units in each class. We shall illustrate the method of calculating the average by several examples.

When the variable is discontinuous and the number of individual values is limited, and when all of them are shown in the series the procedure is quite simple. Let us take the series showing the distribution of apartments by the number of rooms in two districts of Warsaw.[48]

TABLE 5.2. APARTMENTS IN WARSAW BY NUMBER OF ROOMS

| Number of rooms $(x)$ | District IV Muranów | | District XXIII Ochota | |
| | Number of apartments $(f)$ | Total number of rooms $(fx)$ | Number of apartments $(f)$ | Total number of rooms $(fx)$ |
|---|---|---|---|---|
| 1 | 900 | 900 | 2550 | 2550 |
| 2 | 1289 | 2578 | 592 | 1184 |
| 3 | 2227 | 6681 | 126 | 378 |
| 4 | 905 | 3620 | 37 | 148 |
| 5 | 413 | 2065 | 15 | 75 |
| 6 | 160 | 960 | 5 | 30 |
| 7 | 39 | 273 | 1 | 7 |
| 8 | 6 | 48 | 1 | 8 |
| 9 | 2 | 18 | — | — |
| Total | 5941 | 17,143 | 3327 | 4330 |

In the original source only the columns marked $x$ (the number of rooms in the apartment) and $f$ (the number of apartments in individual classes) were given. To obtain the total number of rooms in the apartments of a given size we have to multiply the number of rooms in the apartment by the number of apartments in the corresponding class, thus finding the products $fx$. The sum of these products, which may be denoted by $\sum fx$, gives the total number of rooms. Dividing this sum by the total number of apartments, i.e. $n = \sum f$, we get the arithmetic mean.

We shall write the formula as follows:

$$\bar{x} = \frac{\sum fx}{\sum f} \quad \text{(V.4)} \quad \text{or} \quad \bar{x} = \frac{\sum fx}{n}. \quad \text{(V.4a)}$$

The series for District IV (Muranów) differs considerably from the series for

---

[48] Obtained from the real estate property and flat census in Warsaw in 1919. *Prace Wydziału Statystycznego m. st. Warszawy (Works of the Statistical Office of the Capital Warsaw)*, No. 2, vol. II, Warsaw, 1923, pp. 56 and 58.

District XXIII (Ochota). The first is markedly asymmetric with the maximum in the class of 3-room apartments. The second series is extremely asymmetrical, with the greatest number of apartments (over three-quarters of the total) in the 1-room class, with relatively few 2-room apartments and less than 6 per cent of 3-room and larger apartments. These differences in the structure are reflected in the difference in the arithmetic means: in Muranów the mean is 17, 143/5941, or 2·89 rooms per apartment, and in Ochota it is 4380/3327, or 1·32 rooms.

The computation is somewhat more difficult when the variable is continuous, or when, for a discontinuous variable, the classes of values instead of individual values of the variable are given. In such cases we have to make an assumption concerning the value corresponding to the observations which belong to one class. In principle we should take the arithmetic mean for each class. However, since it is impossible to find this arithmetic mean by elementary methods it is usually assumed that the value located in the middle of the class interval corresponds to all observations in a given class. Further steps are the same as in the case of a discontinuous variable with all the individual values shown in the series. The technique of calculation is as follows:

TABLE 5.3. WORKERS COVERED BY PENSION PLAN BY AGE[49]
Social Insurance Office in Warsaw. Women employed in December 1935

| Age group (x) | Centre of class (x') | Number of insured (f) | Joint age (fx') |
|---|---|---|---|
| 10–14 | 12·5 | 170 | 2125 |
| 15–19 | 17·5 | 12,030 | 210,525 |
| 20–24 | 22·5 | 26,490 | 596,025 |
| 25–29 | 27·5 | 22,100 | 607,750 |
| 30–34 | 32·5 | 12,850 | 417,625 |
| 35–39 | 37·5 | 9400 | 352,500 |
| 40–44 | 42·5 | 5920 | 251,600 |
| 45–49 | 47·5 | 4620 | 219,450 |
| 50–54 | 52·5 | 3200 | 168,000 |
| 55–59 | 57·5 | 1940 | 111,550 |
| 60–64 | 62·5 | 1270 | 79,375 |
| 65 and over | 67·5 | 290 | 19,575 |
| Total | . | 100,280 | 3,036,100 |

We have excluded from the above table a small number of the insured whose ages were unknown.

Data are given only for two columns: age groups (5-year classes) and the number of insured. We want to find the arithmetic mean of the age of the insured: to do this we have to know the combined age of all the insured. Since we cannot multiply the age groups as shown in column x by the number of insured we replace the

---

[49] Social Insurance Office: *Insurance Statistics for 1935*, Warsaw 1938, p. 39.

numbers in column $x$ by the numbers corresponding to the centres of the class interval. We have denoted these figures by $x'$ (12·5, 17·5, 22·5, etc.). We write 12·5, 17·5, 22·5, etc., and not 12, 17, 22, etc., because age is given in years on the last birthday and the class limits are the ages 10, 15, 20, etc. Further calculation proceeds as shown in the example on p. 174: we compute products $fx'$ and the sum of these products we divide by the total number of workers. Finally, the arithmetic mean is

$$\bar{x} = \frac{\sum fx'}{\sum f} = \frac{3,036,100}{100,280} = 30 \cdot 28.$$

From now on we shall denote the centre of the class not by $x'$ but by $x$.

We should now consider the problem of the accuracy of such calculations since it is obvious that the centre of the class interval may not correspond to the average value of the variable within a given class. There are several possible sources of error.

(1) *Random errors resulting from an insufficient number of observations.* When the number of observations is small the average value of the variable within the class may accidentally be far from the centre of the class. Hence the conclusion that the calculation of the arithmetic mean for a small population is less accurate than that for a large one. But we must remember that of decisive importance to the error in calculating the arithmetic mean are not the errors in each product $fx$ separately, but the error of the sum $\sum fx$. In computing the sum, errors of computation for individual components partially cancel out, and increasingly so the greater the number of components. On the other hand, the greatest errors from determining $x$ are to be expected in those classes in which $f$ is the smallest (usually these classes are located at the beginning and at the end of the series). But in this case the product $fx$ will also be small and the error will not much affect the sum $\sum fx$. Therefore, even when the population is small the computation of $\sum fx$ and thus also of the arithmetic mean may produce relatively accurate results.

(2) *Errors in determining individual values of the variable and particularly errors due to rounding off.* As an example we gave the rounding off of age in population censuses. In determining wages there are also many rounded figures ending with zeros. If these rounded figures do not happen to be located in the middle of the class a large error may result, and in extreme cases it may happen that all the values are located at the beginning or the end of the class interval. Let us suppose that we have a series arranged into classes of 100 zlotys (200–99, 300–99, etc.) and that all actual wages are given in hundreds of zlotys (200, 300, etc.). By taking the centres of the classes (250, 350, etc.) to calculate the arithmetic mean we always deviate from the actual average of the class by 50 zlotys and the arithmetic mean will be 50 zlotys too high. Thus, if for some values of the variable, the frequencies are relatively high we should try to arrange the series so that the values for which

frequencies are exceptionally high fall in the centres of the class intervals. In our example the classification should be: 150–249, 250–349, etc. In population statistics according to age, the years ending with zero should be located in the middle of the class, etc. When we deal with data already arranged in series and which cannot be rearranged, it is sometimes possible to estimate the error and introduce the appropriate correction.

(3) More important than these random errors or errors due to the specific nature of the statistical material available are *biassed errors resulting from the nature of the statistical series*. Replacing all the values of the variable belonging to a given class by the mid-value is not a correct procedure because only in exceptional cases will the centre of the class be equal to the arithmetic mean for this class. The error in this instance results from the shape of the frequency curve which may rise in certain sections and drop in others, or rise or fall over the whole range when the frequencies per unit of value of the variable increase or decrease as we move from lower to higher values of the variable. Such an arrangement of the series causes systematic errors when the centre of the class is taken instead of the actual average of the class. This also causes errors in computing the product $fx$. In sections in which the frequencies increase the mid-point of the class has a lower value than the arithmetic mean of the class and in sections where the frequencies decrease it has a higher value, since within each class a larger number of observations occur in the part that adjoins the class with a greater number of observations and this causes a shift of the actual value of the arithmetic mean of the class in this direction. For instance, if in Table 5.3 the consecutive frequencies in the first three classes are 170, 12,030 and 26,490 then we can be sure that in the class 10–14 years a very considerable part of the insured in this class will be close to the upper age limit, very few will be close to the age of 10 years, and the average age of the workers in this class will be considerably higher than 12·5 years. Similarly in the class 15–19 the actual average age will be higher than the accepted 17·5 years. But starting with the class 25–29 years of age the centres of the class intervals accepted by us have higher values than the actual average age of the workers in these classes. The shift of the centre of the class interval in relation to the actual average is greater the steeper the curve. It also depends upon whether the curve in the section is convex or concave. Only the class whose centre coincides with the apex of the curve is free of this error, provided the shape of the curve is symmetric on both sides.

Theoretical considerations, as well as experience have shown that errors of this kind cancel out in symmetric or moderately asymmetric series so that in effect the value obtained for $\sum fx$, and consequently for the arithmetic mean, is correct. But in monotonically decreasing or increasing series all the deviations are in one direction, and the computation of the average of the series is subject to a biassed error, and is not accurate.

Let us consider several examples for which the precise actual value of the arithmetic mean can be computed and compared with the arithmetic mean calculated from the series.

The first example pertains to average monthly temperatures in Warsaw over the years 1826–1910.[50] For each month, the average is calculated in two ways: (1) from the individual data by addition of the average temperatures for a given month in individual years and by dividing the total by the number of years; (2) from the frequency distribution. Let us take the calculations for the month of October.

TABLE 5.4. AVERAGE TEMPERATURES IN WARSAW IN OCTOBER
in 1826–1910

| Average temperature of the month | Centre of the class (x) | Number of years (f) | Combined temperature (fx) |
|---|---|---|---|
| 3·0–3·9° | 3·45° | 1 | 3·45° |
| 4·0–4·9° | 4·45° | 3 | 13·35° |
| 5·0–5·9° | 5·45° | 6 | 32·70° |
| 6·0–6·9° | 6·45° | 14 | 90·30° |
| 7·0–7·9° | 7·45° | 26 | 193·70° |
| 8·0–8·9° | 8·45° | 12 | 101·40° |
| 9·0–9·9° | 9·45° | 12 | 113·40° |
| 10·0–10·9° | 10·45° | 7 | 73·15° |
| 11·0–11·9° | 11·45° | 3 | 34·35° |
| 12·0–12·9° | 12·45° | 1 | 12·35° |
| Total | · | 85 | 668·25° |

The values 3·45, 4·45, etc., were used as centres of the classes. The values of monthly averages are given at the source with an accuracy of 0·1°. If the computation of averages, as can be assumed, was done by rounding off to the nearest tenth of a degree the temperature of 3·0° includes values from 2·95° to 3·05°, the temperature of 3·9° values from 3·85° to 3·95° and the actual limits of the first class are 2·95° and 3·95°. Hence we have

$$\left( \frac{2 \cdot 95 + 3 \cdot 95}{2} \right)^\circ = 3 \cdot 45°.$$

The same is true of the other classes.

The calculation of the arithmetic mean gives

$$\bar{x} = \frac{668 \cdot 25°}{85} = 7 \cdot 86°$$

or after rounding off to 0·1° it amounts to 7·9°. A direct computation (the

---

[50] Wł. Gorczyński and S. Kosińska: *O temperaturze powietrza w Polsce* (*Temperature of the Air in Poland*), Warsaw, 1916, pp. 9 and 43.

addition of the particular data and division by the number of years) gives 7·905° which is slightly greater than that we obtained before, but after rounding off to 0·1°, it also gives 7·9°.

Similar calculations have been made for all the months of the year. In most cases the results achieved coincide with the results of direct computation in tenths of a degree; the difference never exceeds 0·1°.

In the above example on temperatures we deal with moderately asymmetric series, although for some months the asymmetry is more marked than in the month of October shown above. The class intervals selected here are rather large, and in some months with small temperature fluctuations the number of classes is 7–8. In spite of this the results can be considered quite satisfactory.

The next example deals with the calculation of the average weight of new-born children. It is based on the weighings described above (pp. 135–9) which are very inaccurate. A smooth shape has been achieved only after combining the observations into large classes of 300 g. The computation is based on Table 4.5e.

TABLE 5.5. WEIGHT OF NEW-BORN MALE INFANTS

| Weight in grammes (centre of class) ($x$) | Number of infants ($f$) | Combined weight ($fx$) |
|---|---|---|
| 2100 | 2·5 | 5250 |
| 2400 | 12·0 | 28,800 |
| 2700 | 34·5 | 93,150 |
| 3000 | 96·0 | 288,000 |
| 3300 | 123·5 | 407,550 |
| 3600 | 111·5 | 401,400 |
| 3900 | 71·5 | 278,850 |
| 4200 | 20·0 | 84,000 |
| 4500 | 6·5 | 29,250 |
| Total | 478·0 | 1,616,250 |

The computation of the arithmetic mean gives

$$\bar{x} = \frac{1,616,250}{478} = 3381 \text{ g.}$$

The result obtained by direct calculation—by adding up all the individual weights—was 3385 g, an almost identical result. With so small a number of observations (478) the arithmetic mean may be subject to a random error much larger than 4 g. This shows that, even when the arrangement of individual values is very irregular, the calculation of the arithmetic mean from the series may produce a formally correct result even with large class intervals, providing the classes are arranged so that their centres are close to the values for which frequencies are high.

The fact that the result here is formally correct means only, that the arithmetic mean calculated from the series agrees with the arithmetic mean computed directly, but it does not mean that the average weight of the new-born infants was, in fact, approximately 3881 g, since the weighings themselves are open to doubt.

Let us now consider an example of an extremely asymmetric series.

TABLE 5.6. MALE POPULATION IN WARSAW BY AGE
(Ages 70–99) in 1931

| Age group (years) | Centre of class (x) | Number of men (f) | Combined age (fx) |
|---|---|---|---|
| 70–74 | 72·5 | 5802 | 420,645·0 |
| 75–79 | 77·5 | 2440 | 189,100·0 |
| 80–84 | 82·5 | 931 | 76,807·5 |
| 85–89 | 87·5 | 310 | 27,125·0 |
| 90–94 | 92·5 | 116 | 10,730·0 |
| 95–99 | 97·5 | 48 | 6680·0 |
| Total | — | 9647 | 729,087·5 |

The series is monotonically decreasing. If we compute from this series the arithmetic mean of the ages of men from 70 to 99 we get:

$$\bar{x} = \frac{729,087 \cdot 5}{9647} = 75 \cdot 58$$

This result can be *a priori* regarded as wrong. Over the whole range studied the frequencies decrease steadily and by replacing the average age in each class by the centres of the classes (72·5, 77·5, etc.) we use numbers consistently higher than the actual average age in each class.

We have no means of checking directly since we do not know the age of each particular inhabitant of Warsaw but we can perform our calculation using 1-year instead of 5-year age groups, which should reduce the error considerably since it can constitute only a small part of the class interval. The calculation based on 1-year age groups produces the result

$$\bar{x} = 75 \cdot 17$$

which is about 0·4 years less than before. Even this value is still too high, but the error is smaller.

It is possible to calculate the arithmetic mean for monotonically decreasing or increasing series by complex mathematical methods consisting in approximating the function corresponding to a given series, and calculating the area under the curve. Apart from this method—which cannot always be applied—the error may be considerably reduced by using as small class intervals as possible.

It should be added that the errors in the increasing and decreasing part of the series cancel out only when we deal with a series having equal class intervals.

The series concerning the height of draftees described above (Table 4.9. p. 153) and divided into six classes has the following arithmetic mean:

TABLE 5.7. HEIGHT OF DRAFTEES BORN
in 1906–9

| Height in centimetres (centre of class) ($x$) | Number of draftees in percentages ($f$) | Combined height ($fx$) |
|---|---|---|
| 139 | 0·2 | 27·8 |
| 148 | 1·8 | 266·4 |
| 157 | 21·2 | 3,328·4 |
| 166 | 54·2 | 8,997·2 |
| 175 | 21·2 | 3,710·0 |
| 184 | 1·4 | 257·6 |
| *Total* | *100·0* | *16,587·4* |

$$\bar{x} = 165 \cdot 87.$$

For this calculation very large class intervals were used (only 6 classes 9 cm each), and yet the result obtained is very accurate: the calculation with small intervals of 3 cm gives the average height of 165·89 cm, which is an almost identical result. However, the results obtained with unequal class intervals are significantly different.

Let us consider two arrangements with unequal intervals.

| TABLE 5.7a. CLASSIFICATION A | | TABLE 5.7b. CLASSIFICATION B | |
|---|---|---|---|
| Height (cm) | Number of draftees in percentages | Height (cm) | Number of draftees (percentage) |
| 138–140 | 0·1 | 135–143 | 0·2 |
| 141–143 | 0·1 | 144–152 | 1·8 |
| 144–146 | 0·2 | 153–161 | 21·2 |
| 147–149 | 0·4 | 162–170 | 54·2 |
| 150–152 | 1·2 | 171–173 | 11·8 |
| 153–155 | 2·9 | 174–176 | 6·6 |
| 156–158 | 6·4 | 177–179 | 2·8 |
| 159–161 | 11·9 | 180–182 | 1·0 |
| 162–170 | 54·2 | 183–185 | 0·3 |
| 171–179 | 21·2 | 186–188 | 0·1 |
| 180–188 | 1·4 | | |
| *Total* | *100·0* | *Total* | *100·0* |

In the first case the class intervals are small (3 cm) in the increasing part of the series and large (9 cm) in the decreasing part. In the second case the situation is reversed. The computation of the arithmetic mean for classification A gives $\bar{x} = 166 \cdot 18$ cm, 0·29 cm more than the accurate calculation and for classification

B we get $\bar{x} = 165 \cdot 58$ cm, $0 \cdot 41$ cm too small. Thus we can see that large errors that arise in classes with large intervals are not completely offset by small errors in the opposite direction for classes with small intervals. In classification B the large intervals are in the decreasing part of the series, and the centres of the class intervals (used instead of the actual averages for each class) are too large and they are not sufficiently offset by undervalued figures in the increasing part of the series; hence the arithmetic mean is too high. In classification B the large intervals are in the increasing part and the dominant error is of the opposite sign and the arithmetic mean is too low. The difference between the results obtained for A and for B is $0 \cdot 7$ cm and is very large considering that the tables are based on a very large number of observations and a random error cannot be very large.

Let us now discuss the determination of the value of the variable in the class that should be multiplied by the number of observations to calculate the arithmetic mean ($x$ in the product $fx$).

The first case: individual values of a discontinuous variable (see Table 5.2. on p. 174: Flats according to the number of rooms). This case does not raise any questions or doubts.

The second case: a discontinuous variable grouped into classes (Flats with 1–2, 3–4, 5–6 rooms, etc.). The centres of the classes are: $(1 + 2)/2 = 1 \cdot 5$; $(3 + 4)/2 = 3 \cdot 5$ etc. Doubts may arise when the classes are below 3, 3–5, 5–7 rooms, etc. This sort of classification should be avoided since it is awkward. But it is sometimes used, especially when the discontinuous variable assumes a large number of values. In such cases it should be decided in which class the end values should be included. In the above example, since in the first class we have "below 3", we should assume that in the first class are flats with 1 or 2 rooms, in the second, with 3 or 4 rooms, etc. and the centres of the classes will be as above: $1 \cdot 5$, $3 \cdot 5$, etc.[51]

The third case: a continuous variable with the upper values of the lower class equal to the lower value of the higher class (age: 15–20, 20–5, etc.). The centre of the class is the sum of the values of the class limits divided by 2 ($17 \cdot 5$, $22 \cdot 5$, etc.).

The fourth case: a continuous variable, the upper value of the lower class is one unit ($1$, $0 \cdot 1$, $0 \cdot 01$, etc.) less than the corresponding value of the higher class (age 15–19, 20–4, etc.).

The way in which measurements were rounded off should be determined. In the case of age rounding down is common: 15 means from 15 at the last birthday up to, but not including, a full 16, 24 means 24 on the last birthday up to but not

---

[51] When the variable is discontinuous a classification such as used above (3–5, 5–7, etc.) is not only awkward, but also incorrect. If we want to write a series based on a discontinuous characteristic as a series based on a continuous characteristic, repeating the figures that constitute the class limits, it should be assumed that 3 represents the values from $2 \cdot 5$ to $3 \cdot 5$ the values from $3 \cdot 5$ to $4 \cdot 5$ etc. and we should write: $2 \cdot 5$–$4 \cdot 5$ rooms, $4 \cdot 5$–$6 \cdot 5$ rooms, etc., but this would look very strange.

including a full 25, and so on. Then 15–19, 20–24 years means the same as 15–20, 20–25 years and the centres of the class intervals will be as above: 17·5, 22·5, etc. However, if we round off to the nearest integer up or down then 15 years means from 14·5 to 15·5; 19 years, the age from 18·5 to 19·5, etc., and the class limits are: 14·5, 19·5, 24·5, etc. More correctly we should then write: 14·5–19·5, 19·5–24·5. The centres of the class are

$$\frac{14\cdot5 + 19\cdot5}{2} = 17 \text{ years}; \quad \frac{19\cdot5 + 24\cdot5}{2} = 22 \text{ years}; \quad \text{etc.}$$

(Compare also Table 5.4 on page 178 and the reasoning presented there).

In general, the problem of rounding off may sometimes present serious difficulties. It is not always obvious from the table how the figures were rounded off and only a careful analysis of all the circumstances can clarify the situation. In some cases rounding off is by custom done in a certain way, as is the case with age. Sometimes we may obtain information on how the measurements were taken, but there may be cases when intuition will be our only lead.

An error in calculating the arithmetic mean due to a disregard for the method of rounding off may be considerable. We may note that the error of the arithmetic mean is equal to the error committed in determining the centres of the classes.

*An abbreviated method of calculating the arithmetic mean.* The computation of the arithmetic mean from the series sometimes involves operating with large numbers, but it is possible to simplify the calculation and obtain the same result

We have to calculate the arithmetic mean for the variable $x$, which assumes $n$ different values $x_1, x_2, \ldots, x_n$. We denote by $x_0$ an arbitrary value of the variable $x$. The difference $x - x_0$ we denote by $t$. We can then write

$$x = x_0 + t.$$

In this equation $t$, like $x$, has $n$ different values, but $x_0$ is constant. We sum both sides of the equation. On the left side we have $x_1 + x_2 + x_3 + \ldots + x_n = \Sigma x$, and on the right side the constant $x_0$ repested $n$ times which equales $nx_0$, and the sum of all the values of $t$ which amounts to $t_1 + t_2 + t_3 \ldots + t_n = \Sigma t$.

Thus we have

$$\Sigma x = nx_0 + \Sigma t.$$

Dividing both sides by $n$ we get

$$\frac{\Sigma x}{n} = x_0 + \frac{\Sigma t}{n}.$$

$\dfrac{\Sigma x}{n}$ is the arithmetic mean of variable $x$ and we can write

$$\bar{x} = x_0 + \frac{\Sigma t}{n}. \tag{V.5}$$

If we calculate from the frequency distribution we write

$$\bar{x} = x_0 + \frac{\sum ft}{\sum f} \qquad \qquad (V.5a)$$

which is analogous to formulae (V.4) and (V.4a), p. 174. The arithmetic mean, then differs[52] from $x_0$ by the quotient $(\sum t)/n$ or $(\sum ft)/\sum f$, where $t = x - x_0$. In accordance with the above argument the origin $x_0$ can be arbitrarily chosen since the choice of its value does not affect the final result. When the origin $x_0$ is properly selected the computation of $(\sum t)/n$ is much easier than that of $(\sum x)/n$.

Let us consider the example of temperatures is October in Warsaw (Table 5.4). As $x_0$ we select $7 \cdot 45°$ i.e. the centre of the class $7 \cdot 0 - 7 \cdot 9°$. On the basis of the arrangement of the frequencies we can surmise that value will be close to the arithmetic mean sought. Them, for the centre of the class $3 \cdot 0 - 3 \cdot 9°$, for example, $t$ will have the value $3 \cdot 45 - 7 \cdot 45 = -4$. In general, for values lower than $7 \cdot 45°$, $t$ will be negative, and for those higher than $7 \cdot 45°$, positive.

The calculation proceeds as follows.

TABLE 5.8. CALCULATION OF THE ARITHMETIC MEAN OF TEMPERATURE
IN WARSAW IN OCTOBER
(1826–1910)

| Average monthly temperature | Centre of class ($x$) | $x - x_0 = t$ | Number of years ($f$) | Product ($ft$) |
|---|---|---|---|---|
| $3 \cdot 0 - 3 \cdot 9°$ | $3 \cdot 45°$ | $-4$ | 1 | $-4$ |
| $4 \cdot 0 - 4 \cdot 9°$ | $4 \cdot 45°$ | $-3$ | 3 | $-9$ |
| $5 \cdot 0 - 5 \cdot 9°$ | $5 \cdot 45°$ | $-2$ | 6 | $-12$ |
| $6 \cdot 0 - 6 \cdot 9°$ | $6 \cdot 45°$ | $-1$ | 14 | $-14 \; -39$ |
| $7 \cdot 0 - 7 \cdot 9°$ | $7 \cdot 45°$ | $0$ | 26 | $0$ |
| $8 \cdot 0 - 8 \cdot 9°$ | $8 \cdot 45°$ | $+1$ | 12 | $+12$ |
| $9 \cdot 0 - 9 \cdot 9°$ | $9 \cdot 45°$ | $+2$ | 12 | $+24$ |
| $10 \cdot 0 - 10 \cdot 9°$ | $10 \cdot 45°$ | $+3$ | 7 | $+21$ |
| $11 \cdot 0 - 11 \cdot 9°$ | $11 \cdot 45°$ | $+4$ | 3 | $+12$ |
| $12 \cdot 0 - 12 \cdot 9°$ | $12 \cdot 45°$ | $+5$ | 1 | $+5 \; +74$ |
| Total | . | . | 85 | $+35$ |

$$\frac{\sum ft}{\sum f} = + \frac{35}{85} = + 0 \cdot 41°,$$

Hence

$$\bar{x} = 7 \cdot 45° + 0 \cdot 41° = 7 \cdot 86°.$$

The result, of course, is identical with the result previously obtained.

It should be remembered that $\sum ft$, and thus also the correction $v_1$, may be positive or negative.

---

[52] The correction $\dfrac{\sum t}{n}$ or $\dfrac{\sum ft}{f}$ we shall later denote by the Greek letter $v_1$ (See Chapter VI.2).

It is advisable to choose $x_0$ as close to the arithmetic mean as possible because in this way we use small numbers. We can also select as $x_0$ the lowest value of $x$, in our case $3 \cdot 45°$; in this way we deal with positive values only, which reduces the chance of error. If the class intervals are not units the whole calculation can be carried out in assumed units equal to class intervals. If we denote the class interval by $l$, then instead of the actual values of $t$ we have these values divided by $l$. Hence both $\sum ft$ and $(\sum ft)/f$ will be divided by $l$, and in order to obtain the correct value we have to multiply the result by $l$. This procedure simplifies the computation considerably.

How the computation should be done will be shown later, in an example on standard deviation.

## 3. THE GEOMETRIC MEAN

Let us start with an example. Let the population of a certain settlement be 1000 at the start, 1500 after 10 years and 1650 after the next 10 years. The absolute increase in the first period is 500, and in the second, 150, 650 altogether. We can get this result directly by subtracting the original value from the final population: $1650 - 1000 = 650$.

Hence we get the average absolute increase per decade: $650/2 = 325$. This is an arithmetic mean. Adding to the original population twice the figure 325 we get the final result—after 20 years—1650, the true value.

The relative increase in the first decade was $1500/1000 = 1 \cdot 5$, i.e. the population increased $1 \cdot 5$ times. The relative increase in the second decade was $1650/1500 = 1 \cdot 1$. However, the average relative increase per decade cannot be calculated as the arithmetic mean: $(1 \cdot 5 + 1 \cdot 1)/2 = 1 \cdot 3$. If in every decade the population increased $1 \cdot 3$ times (in the ratio $1 \cdot 3 : 1$), then after 10 years the population would be $1000 \times 1 \cdot 3 = 1300$, and after 20 years: $1300 \times 1 \cdot 3 = 1690$, i.e. 40 more than was actually the case. Thus the actual relative increase in both periods combined in not $1690/1000 = 1 \cdot 69$ as would follow from the calculation above, but $1650/1000 = 1 \cdot 65$. We get the same result by multiplying $1 \cdot 5$ by $1 \cdot 1$ which gives us $1 \cdot 65$. The arithmetic mean in this case does not satisfy the condition which an average should meet, because it does not lead to the same result.

The correct result is obtained by the use of the *geometric mean*: the square root of the product of the two values:

$$\sqrt{1 \cdot 5 \cdot 1 \cdot 1} = \sqrt{1 \cdot 65} = 1 \cdot 2845.$$

If in every decade the population increases in the ratio of $1 \cdot 2845 : 1$ then after 20 years it will amount to 1650, as in fact, was the case. $1000 \times 1 \cdot 2845 = 1284 \cdot 5$; $1284 \cdot 5 \times 1 \cdot 2845 = 1650$. This is obvious since $1 \cdot 2845^2 = 1 \cdot 65$.

The general formula for calculating the geometric mean is

$$G_x = \sqrt[n]{x_1 \times x_2 \times x_3 \times \ldots \times x_n}, \tag{V.6}$$

13

where $x_1$, $x_2$, $x_3$, etc. are the particular values of the variable, $n$ is the number of observations and $G$ the geometric mean.

We can express this as follows: the geometric mean is the $n$th root of the product of $n$ values of the variable.

Let $a_1$, $a_2$ ... $a_{n+1}$ be the absolute values of a variable corresponding to different moments of time, taken at equal intervals. Let us further suppose that we are dealing with the production of a certain commodity in consecutive calendar years, from the first year to the year $(n+1)$. We record the production during $n$ calendar years. Then the figures

$$x_1 = \frac{a_2}{a_1}, \ x_2 = \frac{a_3}{a_2}, \ ..., \ x_n = \frac{a_{n+1}}{a_n}$$

will express the ratio of the production figures in two consecutive years, and multiplying together $a_1$, $x_1$, $x_2$, ... $x_n$ we get $a_{n+1}$ as we can easily check by substituting for $x_1$, $x_2$, etc. the corresponding ratios $\frac{a_2}{a_1}$, $\frac{a_3}{a_2}$, etc.

$$a_1 \times \frac{a_2}{a_1} \times \frac{a_3}{a_2} ... \frac{a_{n+1}}{a_n} = a_{n+1}.$$

We have to find a value $z$ such that the product $a_1$ times $z$ repeated $n$ times: $a_1 \times z \times z \times z \times ... \times z = a_1 z^n$ also gives $a_n + 1$. This quantity is the geometric mean, since as follows from formula (V.6)

$$G_x^n = x_1, \ x_2, \ x_3, \ ..., \ x_n.$$

The geometric mean which keeps the product unchanged should be used to calculate the average ratio.

If we wanted to calculate not the average ratio, but the average difference, we should use the arithmetic mean, as is pointed out above on p. 185.

The geometric mean should be calculated using logarithms. By applying logarithms to formula (V.6) we get

$$\log G_x = \frac{\log x_1 + \log x_2 + \log x_3 + ... + \log x_n}{n}, \tag{V.7}$$

Thus the logarithm of the geometric mean is equal to the arithmetic mean of the logarithms of the particular values of the variable.

When the starting value of the variable $a_1$ and the end value after $n$ periods $a_{n+1}$ are known there is no need to calculate the ratio $x$ for each period separately, since the average ratio of increase corresponding to one period can be obtained directly from the formula

$$G_x = \sqrt[n]{\frac{a_{n+1}}{a_1}}, \tag{V.8}$$

as the average absolute increase is calculated from the formula

$$A = \frac{a_{n+1} - a_1}{n}.$$

It should be noted, however, that the calculation of the geometric mean from ratios can be done only when the final result is obtained—as in the example above—by multiplying the ratios.

Let $q_1$ denote the price index (the ratio of prices in two different periods) for commodity 1, $q_2$ the price index for the same periods for commodity 2, etc., $q_1$, $q_2$, $q_3$, ..., $q_n$ are ratios, but it would be a complete fallacy to calculate the average index for all commodities as the geometric mean $\sqrt[n]{q_1\, q_2\, q_3\, ...\, q_n}$. The product $q_1$, $q_2$, $q_3$, ..., $q_n$ has no mean in this case.[53]

The basic reservations concerning the use of the geometric mean are the same as those made with reference to the arithmetic mean. From the formal point of view the geometric mean is calculated correctly when the product is unchanged. However, such a calculation does not always make sense.

Let us suppose that a 6-year plan envisages uniform production increases of the same percentage every year. In fact the plan is exceeded by different amounts in different years, so that the rate of growth varies from year to year. In this case it is justified to calculate the average actual increase in production in the 6-year period as the geometric mean.

## 4. THE HARMONIC MEAN

Let us again start with an example. Suppose that three workers produce the same commodity. The length of the working day is the same for all: 8 hr = 480 min, but the intensity of their work is not the same. In the first day worker A produces 120 pieces, requiring 4 min per piece, worker B produces 80 pieces at the rate of 1 piece in 6 min and worker C produces 40 pieces at the rate of 1 piece in 12 min.

In one day all three workers produce 120+80+40 = 240 pieces and the average productivity is 240/3 = 80 pieces a day. This is the arithmetic mean, and it is correctly calculated, since if every worker produced 80 pieces then all 3 would produce 240 pieces—as is actually the case.

How much time do the workers use on the average to produce one piece? We can calculate this directly. In all, the 3 workers used 480×3 = 1440 min and produced 240 pieces, so the production of 1 piece takes 6 min (1440/240). If, however, we add up the time used up by individual workers: 4+6+12 = 22 min and divide by 3 (the arithmetic mean), we get 22/3 = $7^1/_3$ min which is of course a wrong result. At this pace of work only approximately 218 pieces could be pro-

---

[53] The problem of calculating average indices will be discussed in Part III.

duced in 1440 min and not 240 pieces. The time needed to produce 240 pieces would be not 1440 min, or 24 hr, but 29 hr 20 min.

The correct result in this case is obtained by the harmonic mean.

The general formula for calculating the harmonic mean is:

$$\frac{1}{H_x} = \frac{\dfrac{1}{x_1} + \dfrac{1}{x_2} + \cdots + \dfrac{1}{x_n}}{n}, \tag{V.9}$$

$$\text{i. e. } H_x = \frac{n}{\dfrac{1}{x_1} + \dfrac{1}{x_2} + \cdots + \dfrac{1}{x_n}}, \tag{V.9a}$$

which can be expressed by saying that the harmonic mean equals the reciprocal of the arithmetic mean of the reciprocals of the particular observations.

In our case we reason as follows. If the total working time of each worker is given ($T$ min) as well as the length of time needed to produce one piece ($t$ min) the number of pieces produced by one worker is $T/t$, and if we have $n$ workers and each of them works $T$ minutes but requires different lengths of time to produce one piece ($t_1$, $t_2$, ..., $t_n$) then the total number of pieces produced is

$$\frac{T}{t_1} + \frac{T}{t_2} + \cdots + \frac{T}{t_n} = \sum \frac{T}{t}.$$

The object is to find an average value $t_s$ such that the sum of $n$ components

$$\frac{T}{t_s} + \frac{T}{t_s} + \ldots + \frac{T}{t_s} \text{ i.e. } n \cdot \frac{T}{t_s} \text{ will be equal to } \sum \frac{T}{t},$$

$$\text{i.e. } n \frac{T}{t_s} = \frac{T}{t_1} + \frac{T}{t_2} + \ldots + \frac{T}{t_n}$$

$$\text{or } \frac{n}{t_s} = \frac{1}{t_1} + \frac{1}{t_2} + \ldots + \frac{1}{t_n}.$$

Solving this equation for $t_s$ we get the harmonic mean

$$t_s = \frac{n}{\dfrac{1}{t_1} + \dfrac{1}{t_2} + \ldots + \dfrac{1}{t_n}}$$

(see formula V.9a).

Indeed, the harmonic mean of 4, 6 and 12 min is 6 min.

$$\frac{3}{\dfrac{1}{4} + \dfrac{1}{6} + \dfrac{1}{12}} = 6.$$

The above example is somewhat of a paradox, which we shall be able to explain later after discussing the weighted average (see Chapter 5, p. 191).

In calculating harmonic means tables of reciprocals are very helpful.

## 5. POWER MEANS

The power mean can be written in the following general form:

$$_kP_x = \sqrt[k]{\frac{\Sigma x^k}{n}}, \qquad (\text{V}.10)$$

where $k$ may assume different values: 1, 2, 3, etc. In particular, if $k = 1$ we get

$$_1P_x = \frac{\Sigma x}{n}, \qquad (\text{V}.11 = \text{V}.2)$$

or the *arithmetic mean*.

If $k = 2$ we get the *square mean*

$$_2P_x = \sqrt{\frac{\Sigma x^2}{n}}, \qquad (\text{V}.12)$$

Let us suppose that on a certain piece of land there are square plots of areas $p_1, p_2, ..., p_n$ with sides $x_1, x_2, ..., x_n$.

We want to divide this land into squares of equal area and equal sides. The number of squares is to remain unchanged. The average area of such a square is calculated as the arithmetic mean

$$\bar{p} = \frac{p_1 + p_2 + ... + p_n}{n}.$$

The calculation will be different if we have to calculate not the arithmetic mean of the area but the average length of side. Let the length of the side be $x_s$. Since the area of the square is equal to the square of its side we can write

$$nx_3^2 = x_1^2 + x_2^2 + ... + x_n^2,$$

Hence $x_s = \sqrt{\dfrac{\Sigma x^2}{n}}$, which is the square mean (see formula V.12).

The situation would be similar if we wanted to replace circles of different radius and thus of different areas by the same number of circles with the same radius (and thus the same area), without changing the total area. Since the area of a circle is proportional to the square of its radius we have to use the square mean to calculate the average radius.

Let us consider an example of the cubic mean. We have spheres different diameters $r_1, r_2, ..., r_n$ and we want to replace them by the same number of spheres with the same diameter $r_s$ so that the volume of all the spheres (and thus their weight if they are made of the same material) remains unchanged. The volume of the sphere is $4/_3 \pi r^3$, and therefore

$$n \cdot \frac{4}{3} \pi r_s^3 = \frac{4}{3} \pi r_1^3 + \frac{4}{3} \pi r_2^3 + \dots + \frac{4}{3} \pi r_n^3,$$

Hence we easily get

$$n r_s^3 = r_1^3 + r_2^3 + \dots + r_n^3$$

and

$$r_s = \sqrt[3]{\frac{\sum r^3}{n}},$$

which is the cubic mean of the diameter of the spheres:

$$_3P_x = \sqrt[3]{\frac{\sum x^3}{n}}. \tag{V.13}$$

The most important rôle in statistics is undoubtedly played by the arithmetic mean. The geometric mean, harmonic mean or power means are rarely used, although one of the most important statistical measurements—the standard deviation—is a power mean.

It should be stressed again that the choice of the average should not be made at will, but should depend upon the circumstances and object of the study. The purpose of the preceding remarks was to explain which average should be used under different circumstances.

There is a relationship between the values of different averages calculated from the same individual data. The value of the harmonic mean is always smaller than that of the geometric mean, and this, in turn, is smaller than the arithmetic mean. The values of power means increase with the exponent. If we denote a power mean with the exponent $k$ by $_kP$, then

$$_kP < _{k+1}P < _{k+2}P < _{k+3}P < \dots < _{k+n}P.$$

Considering that the arithmetic mean may be interpreted as a power with the exponent 1 we can write

$$H_x < G_x < \bar{x} < _2P_x < _3P_x < _4P_x \dots \tag{V.14}$$

## 6. WEIGHTED ARITHMETIC, GEOMETRIC, HARMONIC AND POWER MEANS. AVERAGES OF AVERAGES. AVERAGES OF QUOTIENTS.

If in calculating the arithmetic mean particular values of the variable appear more than once, each value should be included as many times as it appears in the population and the figure in the denominator of the fraction should not reflect the number of different values of the variable, but the number of observations, allowing for the fact that different values of the variable may appear more than once.

This was the case when we were calculating the arithmetic mean of the number of rooms per flat in Table 5.2. (p. 174). We then obtained the formula for the arithmetic mean

$$\bar{x} = \frac{\sum fx}{\sum f}.$$

This type of arithmetic mean is called the *weighted arithmetic mean*. The general formula for this average can be written as follows:

$$_w\bar{x} = \frac{w_1 x_1 + w_2 x_2 + \ldots + w_n x_n}{w_1 + w_2 + \ldots + w_n} = \frac{\sum wx}{\sum w}, \tag{V.15}$$

where $x_1$, $x_2$, ..., $x_n$ denote, as usual, the particular values of the variable, and $w_1$, $w_2$, ..., $w_n$ denote the numbers by which we multiply these values. These numbers are called *weights*.

We can say that the weighted arithmetic mean of variable $x$ is equal to the sum of the separate values of the variable multiplied by the corresponding weights and divided by the sum of the weights.

"Weighing" can be used in calculating the arithmetic mean, the geometric and power means.

In the case of the geometric mean it is necessary to form a product of the particular values of the variable. If $x_1$, $x_2$, $x_3$, ..., $x_n$ denote the geometric means of partial populations then within each partial population we have the product $x_1$, $x_1$, $x_1$, ..., $x_1$ (times $w_1$), or $x_2$, $x_2$, ...., $x_2$ (times $w_2$), etc. repeated as many times as there are units of $w$ in each partial population, i.e. $x_1$, repeated $w_1$ times, $x_2$ repeated $w_2$ times, etc.: in other words: $x_1^{w_1}, x_2^{w_2}, x_3^{w_3}, \ldots, x_n^{w_n}$, and in all partial populations

$$x_1^{w_1}, x_2^{w_2}, x_3^{w_3}, \ldots, x_n^{w_n}.$$

From this product we have to extract a root of a power equal to the number of observations—in this case $\sum w$. In this way we arrive at a formula for calculating the geometric mean for a total population on the basis of the geometric means of the partial populations.

$$_wG_x = \sqrt[\sum w]{x_1^{w_1}, x_2^{w_2}, x_3^{w_3}, \ldots, x_n^{w_n}}. \tag{V.16}$$

An example in which the weighted geometric mean should be used can be obtained by modifying the example on pp. 185 and 186. There we assumed that the population of the settlement increased in 10 years from 1000 to 1500, i.e. in the ratio $1 \cdot 5 : 1$, and in the next 10 years from 1500 to 1650, i.e. in the ratio $1 \cdot 1 : 1$. If the increase from 1000 to 1500 took place not in 10 years but in 40 years we should have to calculate, first, the geometric mean of the relative increase in each decade in the first period: $\sqrt[4]{1 \cdot 5} = 1 \cdot 1067$ and then the combined geometric mean for both periods

$$\sqrt[5]{1 \cdot 1067 . 1 \cdot 1} = \sqrt[5]{1 \cdot 65} = 1 \cdot 105.$$

We can obtain the same result directly by dividing the final population figure by the original population: $1650/1000 = 1 \cdot 65$ and by extracting the 5th root:

$$\sqrt[5]{1 \cdot 65} = 1 \cdot 105.$$

If we have to calculate the geometric mean from a frequency distribution then, as follows from formula (V.16), we cannot use the centre of the class as one half of the sum of the upper and lower limits of the class since the formula contains the product of geometric means. As an approximation we could take the geometric mean of the upper and lower limits of the class, i.e. a value lower than the centre of the class used in the arithmetic mean. Only when the class intervals are very small would both values differ so little that it might be permissible to replace one by the other. However, it is hard to imagine a case in statistics for which it should be necessary to calculate the geometric mean from a series.

The calculation of the weighted geometric mean is done, of course using logarithms. By applying logarithms to formula (V.16) we get

$$\log {_w}G_x = \frac{w_1 \log x_1 + w_2 \log x_2 + \ldots + w_n \log x_n}{w_1 + w_2 + \ldots + w_n} = \frac{\Sigma w \log x}{\Sigma w}. \qquad \text{(V.17)}$$

This means that the logarithm of the weighted geometric mean is the weighted arithmetic mean of the logarithms of the particular values of the variable.

In the case of the harmonic mean we get

$$_wH_x = \frac{\Sigma w}{\Sigma \dfrac{w}{x}}, \qquad \text{(V.18)}$$

where $x$ is the harmonic mean of the partial populations.

In calculating the harmonic mean from a frequency distribution we should take as the centre of the class the harmonic mean of the upper and lower limits of the class.

A special case is the calculation of the average of averages and more generally, of the average of quotients. This case should be discussed in greater detail.

According to the *Polish Concise Statistical Yearbook* of 1939 (p. 272, Table 31) the average weekly earnings of the workers in the leather industry in 1938 were $34 \cdot 8$ zlotys, and in the wood industry only $17 \cdot 2$ zlotys. In the leather industry 6200 workers were employed and in the wood industry 54,900 workers. If we want to calculate the average earnings of both these groups of workers we cannot confine ourselves to adding up the average earnings and dividing the sum by 2 which would give

$$(34 \cdot 8 + 17 \cdot 2)/2 = 26 \text{ zlotys.}$$

This calculation would be correct only if the number of workers were the same in both industries. Actually there were many more workers in the wood industry earning only 17·2 zlotys than there were relatively well paid workers in the leather industry. The actual average earnings for both groups are much lower than 26 zlotys.

To obtain the correct result we have to know the combined earnings of both groups of workers and divide tham by the total number of workers. The combined earnings can easily be obtained by multiplying the average earnings of the group by the number of workers. The calculation is as follows

$$(34·8 \times 6·2 + 17·2 \times 54·9)/(6·2 + 54·9) = 19·0.$$

The correctly calculated earnings for both groups together are only 19 zlotys.

We shall outline below the general reasoning involved. Let us suppose that we have a certain number of partial populations, and that for each of them one of the averages described above has been calculated. From these partial averages we can calculate a general average, which would characterize the total population as a sum of partial populations, if we know the number of observations in each partial population. We can consider the partial average as a particular value of the variable repeated as many times as there are units in the corresponding partial population. In the case of the arithmetic mean we add these values and in the case of geometric mean we multiply them. If we denote by $\bar{x}_1, \bar{x}_2, \bar{x}_3, ..., \bar{x}_n$, the average values of the variable within partial populations and by $w_1, w_2, w_3, ..., w_n$ the corresponding number of observations in these populations, then in the case of the arithmetic mean the sums of the values of the variable within partial populations, in accordance with the definition of the arithmetic mean are: $w_1\bar{x}_1$, $w_2\bar{x}_2, w_3\bar{x}_3, ..., w_n\bar{x}_n$, and the total sum of all the values of the variable for the whole population is $w_1\bar{x}_1 + w_2\bar{x}_2 + w_3\bar{x}_3 + ... + w_n\bar{x}_n$, or $\sum w\bar{x}_n$. The total number of observations in the general population is $w_1 + w_2 + w_3 + ... + w_n$, or $\sum w$.

In this way the arithmetic mean for the whole population is

$$_w\bar{x} = \frac{\sum w\bar{x}}{\sum w}.$$

This formula is identical with formula (V.15) on p. 191.

The formula that we used in calculating the arithmetic mean from a frequency distribution

$$\bar{x} = \frac{\sum fx}{\sum f}$$

is basically the same as the above formula for calculating the arithmetic mean from averages. In calculating the arithmetic mean from a frequency distribution, individual classes constitute partial populations and the centre of each class is equivalent to the arithmetic mean of the class.

The situation is similar when we calculate the average of relative numbers obtained by dividing two statistical quantities.

Let us take the density of population as an example: the ratio of population to area. The area of Warsaw in 1946 was 141 square kilometers and the population according to the 1946 census was 478,755 inhabitants. Hence the population density was 3395 persons per square kilometer. The population of the County of Warsaw was 326,768 and the area 1766 square kilometers; hence the population density was 185 persons per square kilometer. If we wanted to calculate the joint population density of the City and County of Warsaw within which the City is located, we can perform the computation directly by adding the population and the area of both units and dividing the total population by the total area

$$(478{,}755 + 326{,}768)/(141 + 1766) = 422.$$

Adding the figures expressing the population density and dividing them by two we get a different, and, of course, incorrect, result:

$$(3395 + 185)/2 = 1790$$

But the result will be correct if we calculate the weighted average according to the formula $_w\bar{x} = \dfrac{\sum wx}{\sum w}$, taking the areas of both units as weights. Indeed, the product of the population density by the area gives the population and so $\sum wx$ expresses the total population of the City and the County and $\sum w$ is the sum of the areas.

According to the Census of 1931 the percentage of illiterates among the population of 10 years of age and over was $12 \cdot 2$ per cent in urban and $27 \cdot 6$ per cent in rural areas. These percentages were obtained by dividing the 100 times the number of urban and rural persons aged 10 or over who could not read and write by the number of people 10 years old or older, both urban (6,962,000) and rural (17,005,000). The combined percentage of illiterate population should be calculated as a weighted average in which the population figures are weighted

$$\frac{12 \cdot 2 \times 6962 + 27 \cdot 6 \times 17{,}005}{6962 + 17{,}005} = 23 \cdot 1.$$

The result is closer to the percentage of rural than urban illiterates since the rural population (weight) is larger than the urban.

This method of calculating the arithmetic mean as a weighted average must always be used when we compute the average of quotients. Weights must be used since only in this way can we obtain a result equivalent to the direct calculation based on absolute figures. It follows from the above argument that in computations of the arithmetic mean of quotients the denominator will always be a weight.

Weighted averages are also used in statistics when different importance is attached to different values of the variable. In such cases we select weights proportional to the values of the variable and calculate the weighted average instead of the simple mean.

A very great difficulty in using weighted averages is the frequent lack of criteria for selecting weights. In such cases a certain degree of arbitrariness is unavoidable. We shall return to this subject later on during the discussion of certain methods of calculating group index numbers, method of standardization, etc. (see Part III).

It is obvious that weighted averages will be closer than ordinary averages to those values of the variable whose weights are greater.

Only in exceptional cases is it permissible to calculate a simple mean where the circumstances indicate the choice of a weighted average.

Let us suppose that in a large country with hundreds of counties the population density of the counties has been calculated and that we have to calculate the density of population of the whole country on the basis of the densities in separate counties. We should use a weighted average and the weights should be the areas of the counties, since the population density is a quotient of the population of the county divided by its area. It may happen, of course, that the counties of very large or very small areas have population densities much higher or much lower than others. However, if this relationship between the area and the population density is accidental, then the deviations in opposite directions will cancel out, and when the number of counties is large—as we have assumed—the simple arithmetic mean will give approximately the same result as that obtained by using the weighted arithmetic mean. In practice, however, there may exist a definite relationship between the area of the county and the population density. For instance, counties with large areas may have, on the whole, a lower than average population density, and counties with small areas may have a higher of population density than the average. Then, of course, the simple arithmetic mean will produce a distorted result; in this case the average density will be too high since the weights that should be used are large for the counties with low population densities and small for those with high population densities.

Generalizing, we can say that the use of a simple average instead of a weighted average is permissible when: (1) it can be assumed that there is no relationship between quantity $a$ for which we are to compute the average, and quantity $b$ which is used as a weight; in other words, when we know that smaller values of $b$ do not systematically correspond to larger values of $a$, or vice versa; (2) the number of units from which we compute the average is sufficiently large so that random deviations in opposite directions cancel out.

As we have seen, weighted averages may be calculated, depending upon the circumstances, as arithmetic, geometric, harmonic or power means. This means that weighted averages cannot be regarded as a separate type of average, in addition to the types already known to us, but should be regarded as a specific method of calculating them used under certain circumstances.

With regard to the technique of computing weighted averages it should be noted that instead of the figures corresponding to weights other figures, proportional to them, can be used. Evan if they are not exactly proportional the result will not differ much from the exact values, provided the number of observations from which the arithmetic mean is to be computed is sufficiently large. This may considerably facilitate the work, especially when large weights are replaced by smaller or rounded off ones. The object of the study, and if necessary some trial calculations, will determine how far we can go in simplifying our work. It is often desirable, especially when the same weights are to be used for different computations, to reduce the weights so that their sum is expressed by some round figures like 1000. When we deal with the arithmetic mean, which is most commonly used, this device eliminates the necessity of a division since it suffices to put the decimal point at the right place.

In calculating the arithmetic mean of quotients we can obtain a correct result by using denominators as weights. In calculating the harmonic mean numerators should be used as weights.

The proof is simple.

Let us write

$$\frac{a}{b} = c \qquad (V.19)$$

$a$ and $b$ and therefore also $c$ are variables which can assume $k$ different values. $a$ may represent a population, $b$ an area, and $c$ the population density of particular regions. The properly calculated population density $c$ is equal to the quotient of the total population by the total area

$$c = \frac{\sum a}{\sum b}. \qquad (V.20)$$

We obtain this result by calculating the weighted arithmetic mean if the weights are particular of $b$

$$c = \frac{\sum bc}{\sum b}, \qquad (V.21)$$

since it follows from formula V.19 that $bc = a$.

But we get the same result by computing the harmonic mean with $a$ as weights

$$c = \frac{\sum a}{\sum \frac{a}{c}}, \qquad (V.22)$$

since it follows from formula (V.19) that $a/c = b$.

Let us try this calculation in an example. Table 5.9 (p. 197) gives information on the area of particular provinces and the length of hard surface roads in those provinces.

The road density in a given territory can be expressed in two ways: (1) by calculating the length of roads in kilometers in a defined unit of the area, e.g.

100 km² (column $c$ in the table), or (2) by calculating the number of square kilometers of area per kilometer of roads. (column $d$ in the table). In the first case the larger $c$ is the better the situation, and in the second case the smaller $d$ is the better the situation. It follows from the figures that the highest road density is in the Silesia and Wroclaw provinces and the lowest in the Lublin and Bialystok provinces.

It follows from the formulae that the quantities $c$ and $d$ are reciprocals of one another, multiplied or divided by 100 because $c$ is calculated for 100 km².

The overall averages for Poland which are denoted by $C$ and $D$ are calculated in the table directly on the basis of the total area and total length of roads in the

TABLE 5.9. HARD SURFACE ROADS IN POLAND[54]
(1 November 1947)

| Province | Area (km²) $a$ | Length of roads km $b$ | Per 100 km² of area there are $c$ km of roads $c = \dfrac{100b}{a}$ | Per km of road there are $d$ km² of area $d = \dfrac{a}{b}$ |
|---|---|---|---|---|
| Poland | 311,730* | 96,605 | 31·0 | 3·2 |
| Warszawa | 30,338 | 6050 | 19·9 | 5·0 |
| Lodz | 20,234 | 5969 | 29·5 | 3·4 |
| Kielce | 18,060 | 3390 | 18·8 | 5·3 |
| Lublin | 25,747 | 3546 | 13·8 | 7·3 |
| Bialystok | 23,201 | 3254 | 14·0 | 7·1 |
| Olsztyn | 19,319 | 6828 | 35·3 | 2·8 |
| Gdansk | 10,725 | 4211 | 39·3 | 2·5 |
| Pomorze | 20,029 | 5897 | 29·4 | 3·4 |
| Szczecin | 30,252 | 10,996 | 36·3 | 2·8 |
| Poznan | 39,244 | 13,503 | 34·4 | 2·9 |
| Wroclaw | 24,740 | 13,729 | 55·5 | 1·8 |
| Silesia | 15,369 | 8693 | 56·6 | 1·8 |
| Krakow | 15,918 | 6154 | 38·7 | 2·6 |
| Rzeszow | 18,201 | 4385 | 24·1 | 4·1 |

* Omitting the cities of Warsaw and Lodz

country. The same averages can be obtained from the data for the provinces as weighted averages, the weights, depending upon the circumstances, being either areas or the lengths of roads.

In the first case we have

$$C = {}_w\bar{c}_n = {}_wH_c = \frac{\sum ac}{\sum a} = \frac{\sum b}{\sum b \times \dfrac{1}{c}} = \frac{9,658,400}{311,730} = 31\cdot0.$$

[54] *The Statistical Yearbook 1949*, pp. 16–17 and 81.

In the case of the arithmetic mean, the weight must be the area as the quantity in the denominator; in the case of the harmonic mean it is the length of roads as the quantity in the numerator. The computations for the arithmetic mean and the harmonic mean must give the same results, since $ac = 100\,b, a = 100\,b \times \dfrac{1}{c}$.

In the second case we have

$$D = {}_w\bar{d} = {}_wH_d = \frac{\sum bd}{\sum b} = \frac{\sum a}{\sum a \times \dfrac{1}{d}} = \frac{311,483}{96,605} = 3\cdot2.$$

The proof is the same as above.

The minor differences in the numerators and denominators in comparison with the data from the table are due to the fact that the quantities $c$ and $d$ are rounded off to $0\cdot1$. If the computation were made with greater accuracy there would be no differences in the integers.

We can now explain the apparent paradox in calculating the average time needed to produce one object in the example on p. 187 *et seq*. The average time is the quotient of the total time used divided by the number of objects produced and therefore to calculate the combined average a weighted average should be used. The non-weighted harmonic average gave the correct result only because the dividend which should be a weight in harmonic averages, is the same in all three cases (all workers worked 8 hr or 480 min). But in calculating the arithmetic mean the weight is the number of pieces produced by each worker (120, 80, 40). We can easily show that the properly calculated weighted arithmetic mean gives the correct result:

$$\frac{4 \times 120 + 6 \times 80 + 12 \times 40}{120 + 80 + 40} = \frac{3 \times 480}{240} = 6.$$

If the number of minutes of work was not always the same, e.g. if 120 pieces were made not by 1 but by 3 workers who together used $480 \times 3 = 1440$ min, 80 pieces were made by 2 workers $(480 \times 2 = 960$ min$)$ and 40 pieces were made by 1 worker (480 min) the simple harmonic mean would not produce the correct result. We should use as weights the number of minutes, or the numbers of workers proportional to them

$$_wH_x = \frac{6}{\dfrac{3}{4} + \dfrac{2}{6} + \dfrac{1}{12}} = \frac{6 \times 12}{9 + 4 + 1} = \frac{72}{14} = 5\cdot14.$$

The same result will be obtained by calculating the weighted arithmetic mean if we use as weights the number of pieces produced by each of the three groups of workers:

$$\bar{x} = \frac{4 \times 360 + 6 \times 160 + 12 \times 40}{360 + 160 + 40} = \frac{2880}{560} = 5\cdot14.$$

The same result is also obtained by direct calculation: the division of the total number of minutes used by all the workers by the total number of pieces produced.

If it ever happens that the simple harmonic mean gives the correct result and the simple arithmetic mean the wrong one, or vice versa, then this means that the weights are the same in one case and different in another; or else, in the quotients the numerators are the same once and the denominators different (then the correct result is obtained by using the simple harmonic mean) and then again the denominators are the same and the numerators are different (then we can use the simple arithmetic mean).

Let us take another common example—prices expressed either in monetary units per unit of commodity, or in the number of units of the commodity that can be bought for a certain amount of money. Let us suppose that the price of one commodity is 25 zlotys and that of another 50 zlotys. Then for 100 zlotys we can buy:

$$\frac{100}{25} = 4 \text{ units of commodity 1}$$

$$\frac{100}{50} = 2 \text{ units of commodity 2}$$

The average price of the two commodities is obtained as the arithmetic mean $(25 + 50)/2 = 37 \cdot 5$ zlotys. Calculating the arithmetic mean of the number of units $(4 + 2)/2 = 3$ we obtain a different average price since when we receive 3 units for 100 zlotys we pay $33 \cdot 3$ zlotys per unit. But when we calculate the harmonic mean of the number of units:

$$H = \frac{2}{\dfrac{1}{4} + \dfrac{1}{2}} = 2 \cdot 67,$$

the average price per unit is $100/2 \cdot 67 = 37 \cdot 5$ zlotys, as in the case of the arithmetic mean computed directly. We get the same number of units by calculating the weighted arithmetic mean

$$\frac{4 \times 25 + 2 \times 50}{75} = \frac{200}{75} = 2 \cdot 67.$$

The calculation of the average price as the arithmetic mean $(25 + 50)/2$ corresponds to the assumption that we buy one unit (or the same number of units) of each commodity. However, if we assume that we buy not the same number of units of each commodity but the same amount of money's worth then it should be expressed as follows:

$$\frac{100}{4} = 25 \text{ zlotys for commodity 1,}$$

$$\frac{100}{2} = 50 \text{ zlotys for commodity 2,}$$

and the average price should be calculated as the weighted arithmetic mean

$$\bar{x} = \frac{25 \times 4 + 50 \times 2}{6} = 33 \cdot 3 \text{ zlotys,}$$

or as the simple harmonic mean

$$_wH_x = \frac{2}{\dfrac{1}{25} + \dfrac{1}{50}} = \frac{100}{3} = 33 \cdot 3 \text{ zlotys.}$$

The reader should become thoroughly familiar with these aspects of calculating averages since this will guard against misunderstandings and wrong conclusions.

The practical conclusion from all this is that we can always use the arithmetic mean instead of the harmonic mean and vice versa providing the weights are used appropriately. We should use the average that is easier to compute. In most cases, but not always, it will be the arithmetic mean.

## 7. LOCATION AVERAGES

As we know location averages, are calculated on the basis of frequencies in a frequency distribution. They cannot be calculated from the individual values of the variable, like the averages discussed above, but only from a series of values arranged in ascending or descending order, or from a frequency distribution arranged in classes. On the other hand, it is not always necessary to know the whole series; sometimes it is enough to know a part of it.

The number of conceivable location averages is unlimited but only some of them are useful and can be applied in statistics.

a. *The arithmetic mean of the highest and lowest value of the variable* (the mid-range). If the highest income is 1000 zlotys and the lowest 500 zlotys the average is

$$(1000 + 500)/2 = 750 \text{ zlotys.}$$

This average is the easiest to compute but not very useful in statistics since it is very easily affected by random events. Very high or very low earnings in a given group of workers may be due to irrelevant circumstances not all related to the general level of wages in the group. Therefore, we use the mid-range only if no other method can be used, or when only the highest and lowest values of the variable are given. This kind of information is sometimes encountered in price statistics when for some reason the average or most common price is not given, but only the highest and the lowest. This information and the average that is based on it makes sense only when those who supply it know that they should not give *exceptional* extreme highest or lowest prices (e.g. for a lame or race horse) but the lowest and highest prices *normally* paid under the given circumstances.

If we have to compute a general average from the averages prices so computed, we proceed as if they were ordinary arithmetic means. If agricultural correspondents give the range within which the prices of livestock fluctuate, we can calculate the average for each correspondent as a middle value between the high and the low, and overall averages for counties or provinces as arithmetic means of these averages, simple or weighted, e.g. by the number of quotations in the country or province.

b. *The mode.* The great majority of statistical series have a maximum at some point. This means that certain values of the variable appear more frequently than other. The mode is the value of the variable having the greatest number of observations or, more generally, around which observations appear in the densest cluster. The first definition is applicable only to certain cases with a discontinuous variable; when the variable is continuous, and frequently also when it is discontinuous, we can only talk about a value around which the observations are most densely clustered. In a graphic presentation the mode is determined by the point on the horizontal axis at which the frequency curve reaches its maximum.

The mode is a useful characteristic of a population which we shall easily comprehend when we apply it to specific cases. The mode in a study workers' earnings is the wage that is most frequently paid; when we study height, it is the most frequent height, and so on. This is a more real notion than the arithmetic mean which, in a sense, is an abstract concept, although reflecting reality when properly used.

Unfortunately the calculation of the mode presents serious difficulties. It can be determined approximately by indicating in which class it is located and this can be read off directly from the series if the class intervals are of equal length. In this way, however, we can only say that the mode is located between certain values of the variable, but exactly where we cannot say. What is worse, it cannot be uniquely determined since the result depends upon the length of the class interval and the location of the class limits. In other words a different classification of the same values may produce a different mode.

In Table 4.3b on p. 133 the prices of rye paid to farmers are arranged into classes of 0·50 zloty, and the class limits star at the price of 13·00 zlotys. The most numerous class (52 counties) is at the prices 15·50–15·99 zlotys, and we can say that the mode is located within these limits. But we can arrange the 0·50-zloty classes in some other way, taking as a basis the figures in Table 4.3a (p. 132).

Depending upon how we set the class limits we shall have the mode in the class 15·30–15·79 zlotys, or 15·40–15·89 zlotys, or (as above) 15·50–15·99 zlotys, or 15·60–16·09 zlotys, or between 15·20 and 16·19 zlotys, i.e. within the range of 1 zloty, because if the class limits are set at 14·70, 15·20, etc., the classes 15·20–15·69 and 15·70–16·19 have the same frequencies.

This kind of determination of the location of the mode is satisfactory only in exceptional cases.

14

To determine the location of the mode precisely, it would be necessary to find the function corresponding to a given frequency distribution and to calculate the value of the variable at which the function reaches its maximum. It is only possible to approximate a function representing a frequency distribution. The computations are so complex that they can only rarely be used in practice. Doubt will remain as to whether the function selected properly represents the frequency distribution or whether it distorts reality by trying to force it into a mathematical formula. For this reason an approximation is usually considered sufficient.

Such an approximation can be based on the assumption that the shape of curve within the range of the most numerous and the two adjacent classes is a parabola. This is a simplification considered mathematically permissible as a first approximation. With this assumption the solution of a differential equation (which we shall not show here) leads to a very simple formula for calculating the mode. Let us introduce the following notations:

$x_0$, the lower limit of the most numerous class (i.e. the class in which by definition the mode should be located)

$f_0$, the frequency of the most numerous class

$f_{-1}$, the frequency of the class preceding the most numerous one

$f_1$, the frequency of the class following the most numerous one

$l$, the class interval.

The formula for determining the mode is

$$D_x = x + l \times \frac{f_0 - f_{-1}}{(f_0 - f_{-1}) + (f_0 - f_1)}. \tag{V.23}$$

Removing the brackets in the denominator we can write:

$$D_x = x + l \times \frac{f_0 - f_{-1}}{2f_0 - (f_{-1} + f_1)}. \tag{V.23a}$$

We can use these two formulae as checks on our computations.

Let us analyse formula (V.23). If the class preceding the most numerous one is as numerous as the class following the most numerous class, i.e. if $f_{-1} = f_1$, then $f_0 - f_{-1} = f_0 - f_1$ and the fraction by which $l$ should be multiplied has the value $\frac{1}{2}$. This means that the mode will be located precisely in the middle of the most numerous class whose lower limit we denoted as $x_0$. If the preceding class is more numerous than the following one ($f_{-1} > f_1$) then $(f_0 - f_1) > (f_0 - f_{-1})$, the fraction next to $l$ is less than $\frac{1}{2}$ (the denominator is more than twice as large as the numerator) and the value $D_x$ lies nearer the lower limit of the most numerous class. If $f_{-1} < f_1$, then the fraction next to $l$ is larger than $\frac{1}{2}$ and the value $D_x$ lies nearer the upper limit of the most numerous class. Intuition confirms this statement.

To calculate the mode according to the above formula is very easy. Unfortunately, the result is not very accurate, since the curve is usually not a parabola. Therefore the value of the mode thus calculated is only an approximation, which may however, suffice for practical purposes.

We can reduce the margin of error by making the class interval smaller. But this is permissible only to a certain extent and under the following conditions: (1) when the number of observations is sufficiently large, so that the frequencies of smaller classes are not too strongly affected by random events, (2) when the nature of the material on which the series is based does not indicate a bias in favour of certain values of the variable which could lead to increased frequencies in some classes and reduced frequencies in others.

In both these cases better results are obtained with somewhat larger intervals so arranged that the frequencies of particular classes are as much as possible independent of outside factors. The size of error may be explained by example by performing calculations for the same series, changing the class limits several times. If the formula can give an accurate result the latter should not depend upon the location of the class limits. In fact, however, the difference may be quite large, as can be seen from the examples below.

We can also take into consideration four, instead of three, middle classes and assume that within those four classes, one of which is the most numerous, the curve is of the third degree. In most cases we obtain in this way a somewhat more accurate result than by using a parabola. Taking the limit between the two middle classes as a starting point, i.e. selecting $x_0$ so that we have two classes below $x_0$ and two classes above we write

$$D = x_0 + t. \tag{V.24}$$

The value of $t$ calculated from the formula is

$$t = \frac{-b \pm \sqrt{b^2 - 3ac}}{3a}, \tag{V.25}$$

where

$$a = \frac{f_2 - f_{-2}}{6} - \frac{f_1 - f_{-1}}{2},$$

$$b = \frac{f_2 + f_{-2}}{4} - \frac{f_1 + f_{-1}}{4},$$

$$c = \frac{5(f_1 - f_{-1})}{4} - \frac{f_2 - f_{-2}}{12}.$$

As before $f_{-2}, f_{-1}, f_2, f_1$ here denote the frequencies of classes starting with the lowest to the highest values of $x$, so that $x_0$ is the limit of the classes whose frequencies are $f_{-1}$, and $f_1$.

14*

The computations are much more complex than in the case of a parabola, but still the result is not accurate. If we have a choice between two methods, neither of which will produce the accurate result, we usually choose the simpler one.

As an example let us consider the computation of the mode of the height of draftees born in 1906–9. We arrange the data in classes of 3 cm each, and we take three different class limits. The table shows only classes close to the maximum since they suffice for calculating the mode.

TABLE 5.10. HEIGHT OF DRAFTEES

| I | | II | | III | |
|---|---|---|---|---|---|
| Height (cm) | Number of draftees* | Height (cm) | Number of draftees* | Height (cm) | Number of draftees* |
| 157·5–160·5 | 100 | 158·5–161·5 | 119 | 159·5–162·5 | 141 |
| 160·5–163·5 | 155 | 161·5–164·5 | 171 | 162·5–165·5 | 186 |
| 163·5–166·5 | 194 | 164·5–167·5 | 198 | 165·5–168·5 | 191 |
| 166·5–169·5 | 181 | 167·5–170·5 | 173 | 169·5–171·5 | 157 |
| 169·5–172·5 | 142 | 170·5–173·5 | 118 | 171·5–174·5 | 99 |

* (per thousand of all the draftees in all classes of height)

We shall perform our calculations on the basis of Section I of the table according to formula (V.23) i.e. assuming that the curve is a parabola within the three middle classes

$$D = x_0 + l \times \frac{f_0 - f_{-1}}{(f_0 - f_{-1}) + (f_0 - f_1)}.$$

The greatest number of observations are in the class 163·5–166·5 cm, and so $x_0 = 163·5$ cm. The frequency of this class $(f_0)$ is 194, the frequency of the preceding class $(f_{-1}) = 155$ and the frequency of the following class $(f_1) = 181$. The class interval is 3 cm. Substituting in the formula we get

$$D = 163·5 + 3 \times \frac{194 - 155}{(194 - 155) + (194 - 181)} = 163·5 + 3 \times \frac{39}{52} = 165·75.$$

To check this result let us perform another calculation using formula (V.23a).

$$D = x_0 + l \times \frac{f_0 - f_{-1}}{2f_0 - (f_{-1} + f_1)},$$

$$D = 163·5 + 3 \times \frac{39}{388 - 336} = 163·5 + 3 \times \frac{39}{52} = 165·75 \text{ cm.}$$

Computation according to Section II leads to a somewhat different result:

$$D = 164·5 + 3 \times \frac{27}{27 + 25} = 166·06 \text{ cm.}$$

From Section III we obtain

$$D = 165 \cdot 5 + 3 \times \frac{5}{39} = 165 \cdot 89 \text{ cm.}$$

The difference between the highest and the lowest of the above values is $166 \cdot 06 - 165 \cdot 75 = 0 \cdot 31$ cm, i.e. over 3 units in the first decimal place.

We shall now show the calculation for the cubic curve on the basis of Section I of the table (see formulae V.24 and V.25 on p. 203).

We can consider either the first 4 classes (from $157 \cdot 5 - 169 \cdot 5$ cm) or the last 4 classes (from $160 \cdot 5$ to $172 \cdot 5$ cm). Taking the first 4 classes we have $f_{-2} = 100$, $f_{-1} = 155$, $f_1 = 194$, $f_2 = 181$; $x_0$ equals $163 \cdot 5$ cm. After substituting we have

$$a = \frac{181 - 100}{6} - \frac{194 - 155}{2} = -6,$$

$$b = \frac{181 + 100}{4} - \frac{194 + 155}{4} = -17,$$

$$c = \frac{5 \times (194 - 155)}{4} - \frac{181 - 100}{12} = 42.$$

Hence

$$t = \frac{17 \pm \sqrt{289 + 3 \times 6 \times 42}}{(-3 \times 6)} = \frac{17 \pm 32 \cdot 326}{-18}.$$

This equation gives two values of $t$:

$$t' = \frac{17 + 32 \cdot 326}{-18} = -2 \cdot 74,$$

$$t'' = \frac{17 - 32 \cdot 326}{-18} = +0 \cdot 85.$$

This leads to two values of the mode:

$$D' = 163 \cdot 5 - 3 : 2 \cdot 74 = 155 \cdot 28 \text{ cm,}$$

$$D'' = 163 \cdot 5 + 3 : 0 \cdot 85 = 166 \cdot 05 \text{ cm.}$$

Of these two results only the second satisfied the conditions of the problem, thus we object the first.

The calculation from the class $160 \cdot 5 - 172 \cdot 5$ cm gives

$$D = 165 \cdot 46 \text{ cm.}$$

Calculations based on Sections II and III of the table lead to still different results. If the assumptions were precise, all the results would be identical.

Thus the example confirms the theoretical conclusion that the calculation of the mode is possible only as a rough approximation, which can be considered sufficient for practical purposes. Calculations based on the cubic curve gave results as inconclusive as those based on a parabola. Thus it does not seem worth while to use more complex computations.

The cubic curve should be used when the frequencies of the two middle classes are identical. The computation will then be somewhat simplified, since when $f_1 = f_{-1}$ the second expression will disappear in the formula for calculating $a$, and the first expression will disappear in the formula for calculating $c$, so that we shall have

$$a = \frac{f_2 - f_{-2}}{6},$$

$$c = \frac{f_2 - f_{-2}}{12}.$$

In series with two or more maxima the mode can be calculated for each maximum separately either by determining the classes in which the frequencies are the greatest or by assuming, as above, that the curve within the classes containing the maxima and those neighbouring them has the shape of a parabola, according to formula (V.23) or (V.23a). Since series with two or more maxima are frequently created by combining different populations (see above) the facility of calculating both maxima would be worth while if it were also possible to determine separately the location of the mode for each of the component populations. This is possible to a certain degree of approximation only in cases when the separate maxima are far apart. Generally, the modes corresponding to particular maxime in a non-uniform population are not the modes of the component populations of which this non-uniform population consists, since maxima in a combined population are created by a mutual superimposition of particular series, and are liable to be shifted in relation to the maxima in the component series. In the combined series the lesser maximum is shifted to the right and the greater maximum is shifted to the left in relation to the maxima in the series that have been combined.

c. *The median. Quantiles.* Imagine that we have arranged an odd number of persons, say 101, in the order of height from the shortest to the tallest. If we measure the height of the 51st person the value of his height will split the whole population arranged in the order of height into two equal parts in such a way that there will be as many persons who are shorter than the middle person as there are taller persons. The value that thus halves the ordered population is called the median height. If the number of observations is even, e.g. 100, this value cannot be precisely determined. In this case the condition of dividing the arranged population into halves is satisfied by any height greater than the height of the person in the 50th place and less than the height of the person in the 51st place. In such cases we consider as the median the value of the variable corresponding to the arithmetic mean of the values corresponding to the 50th and 51st persons.

The median is then the value of the variable that divides the population so that the number of units with values of the variable lower than the median is equal to the number of units with values of the variable higher than the median. This definition, like the definition of the mode, is quite concrete. The median is a good and logical measure.

The calculation of the median is very simple. Let us take as an example the data on weekly earnings in the metal industry in August 1938.

The reasoning is as follows. There are 1000 workers. Of course, it is a matter of indifference whether the figure is relative or absolute. We have to find the earnings of the worker who is located in the series between the 500th and 501st

TABLE 5.11. WORKERS EMPLOYED IN THE METAL INDUSTRY BY WEEKLY EARNINGS[55]

| Weekly earnings in zlotys | Number of workers in per mil. | Cumulative series |
|---|---|---|
| $x$ | $f$ | $\Sigma f$ |
| Less than 10 | 98 | 98 |
| 10–20 | 169 | 267 |
| 20–30 | 184 | 451 |
| 30–40 | 179 | 630 |
| 40–50 | 126 | 756 |
| 50–60 | 85 | 841 |
| 60–70 | 59 | 900 |
| 70–80 | 36 | 936 |
| 80 and more | 64 | 1000 |
| Total | 1000 | — |

place, or, more exactly half way between. It is most convenient to take the cumulative series as a starting point. The earnings of this worker will be more than 30 zlotys per week, since there are only 451 workers earning less than 30 zlotys, and will be less than 40 zlotys. In order to determine the earnings of the worker in between the 500th place and the 501st we have to assume that the earnings in the class 30–40 zlotys increase in a uniform way, i.e. that each worker receives as much more than his predecessor as gets less than the worker following him. Counting from the lower limit of the class, the number of places separating the lower limit from the median is $500 \cdot 5 - 451 = 49 \cdot 5$ places. Therefore we divide 10 zlotys, i.e. the length of the interval of the class in which the median is located in the ratio $49 \cdot 5 : 179$.

In the numerator of the fraction we have the number of places needed to reach the half and in the denominator—the total number of units in the class containing the median. The number of zlotys thus obtained should be added to the value of the lower limit of the appropriate class—in our case to 30 zlotys.

---

[55] *The Concise Statistical Yearbook 1939*, p. 273. In the source the number of workers is given in percentages with one decimal place.

Let us denote by

$n$,   the total number of observations,

$_sf_0$,  the number of observations in the cumulative series corresponding to the lower limit of the class containing the median,

$f_0$,  the number of observations in the class containing the median,

$x_0$,  the value of the variable corresponding to the lower limit of this class,

$l$,   the class interval.

We can now write

$$M_x = x_0 + l \times \frac{\dfrac{n+1}{2} - {_sf_0}}{f_0}, \qquad (\text{V}.26)$$

We can also count from the upper limit of the class containing the median. Introducing the appropriate notations $_sf_1$, and $x_1$ we write

$$M_x = x_1 - l \times \frac{{_sf_1} - \dfrac{n+1}{2}}{f_0}. \qquad (\text{V}.26\text{a})$$

The results of the calculation from the two varieties of the formula should, of course, be identical. In our example we get

$$M = 30 + 10 \times \frac{500 \cdot 5 - 451}{179} = 30 + \frac{495}{179} = 32 \cdot 77$$

or

$$M = 40 - 10 \times \frac{630 - 500 \cdot 5}{179} = 40 - \frac{1295}{179} = 32 \cdot 77$$

We can also calculate the median from the graph representing the cumulative series. We find on the curve the point corresponding to the ordinate $(n+1)/2$ (one half of the number of observations increased by one). The median is the abscissa of the corresponding point on the curve. Within the limits of the accuracy of the graph this determination of the median should give the same result as the arithmetic computation if the points corresponding to the particular values of the cumulative series are joined by straight lines. If we use a smooth curve instead of a broken line the graphical solution may be even more precise than the calculation (see Fig. 5.2).

The determination of the median both by graphical and arithmetic methods is very easy. But substantial errors are possible because of the underlying assumption of a uniform change in the values in the class containing the median. These errors will be smaller if we use smaller class intervals, but then there is a danger of random deviations due to the insufficient number of observations. A more precise computation of the median would be possible if we knew the function representing the curve. We could also reduce the error by using, e.g. parabolic interpolation.[56]

---

[56] Compare S. Fogelson: Mediana i jej wyznaczanie (The Median and Its Determination), *Kwartalnik Statystyczny (Statistical Quarterly)* 1930, vol. VII, Book 2, pp. 866–81.

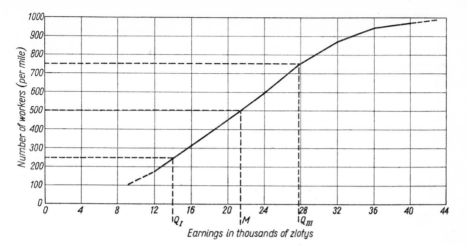

FIG. 5.2. Workers employed in the leather industry by weekly earnings in August 1949. Graphical determination of the median and quartiles.[57]

However, complex parabolic interpolation is, as a rule, not used to determine the median. The results of linear interpolation will be the more precise, the more the curve corresponding to the cumulative series approaches a straight line in the segment corresponding to the median.

In addition to the median there are other similar measures used in statistics. The median halves the arranged series. In a similar way we can calculate the values cutting off $\frac{1}{4}$ or $\frac{3}{4}$ of all observations. Thus we obtain *quartiles* (Q).

The first, or lower quartile ($Q_1$) is the value of the variable below which there are $\frac{1}{4}$ of all observations and above which there are $\frac{3}{4}$ of them. Analogously, the third or upper quartile ($Q_3$) is the value below there are $\frac{3}{4}$ of all observations and above, $\frac{1}{4}$ of them. The second quartile ($Q_2$) in this interpretation would be the median. Quartiles may be used to characterize the population just as well as other measures. They have a clear logical meaning. Moreover, they can be used to measure dispersion: this will be discussed later.

The population can be divided into an even greater number of parts, say 10, and then we have *deciles* or, say 100, and then we get *percentiles*. Both deciles and percentiles are sometimes used to characterize series. They are especially often used in psychological studies. The calculation of quartiles, deciles and percentiles is done in a way analogous to the calculation of the median.

[57] *The Statistical Yearbook 1949*, p. 136.

A general name for the measures of this type is *quantiles*.

It should be added that for location averages calculated for two or more types of populations we cannot, as we did for the averages of the first kind (pp. 192 *et seq.*), calculate joint averages for combined populations without adding up the frequencies and forming a new series for combined populations.

## 8. GENERAL COMMENTS ABOUT AVERAGES

We have discussed the averages which are used in statistical research to characterize frequency distributions. Of these averages the arithmetic mean plays the most important part. If we use the definition of the average of the first kind which we gave on p. 170 it will turn out that under certain circumstances we have to use the geometric mean, harmonic mean, etc., instead of the arithmetic mean. These averages cannot be substituted for each other at will. However, in addition to these averages and independently of them we can use at will the mode, the median and other quantiles providing the arrangement of the series makes their use logical (e.g. there cannot be a mode in an extremely asymmetrical series in which the highest frequencies occur for the lowest or highest values of the variable). Each of these averages has its own specific logical sense and should be properly interpreted.

From this point of view we may sometimes give preference to one type of series over an other. For instance, if the spread of a population is very wide, which means that it contains units with very different characteristics, then the cognitive value of the arithmetic mean will be rather small. When we study the size of the farm and have in our population small peasant farms as well as large estates then the statement that the average size of the farm (the arithmetic mean) is a certain number of hectares is meaningless, and does not only say nothing about the population but can be misleading. But we can calculate the mode for such a series and state that the most common size of farm is 3·75 hectares, this is a concrete statement characterizing one aspect of the problem. Yet this characteristic is not exhaustive because in addition there is a question of the existence of a larger or smaller number of large estates, large peasant farms, undersized "dwarf" farms, etc. If we study the age structure of the population of a country composed of a great number of small children, a smaller but still considerable number of young people, a still smaller number of adults and relatively few old people, it would be meaningless to calculate the arithmetic mean of age. It would be more sensible to use the median or the quartiles—the age below which there are $\frac{1}{4}$ or $\frac{3}{4}$ of the total population.

More useful and descriptive is the arithmetic mean with reference to populations with a relatively narrow range of values of the variable clustered around a centre, i.e. those populations which are not only a mechanical combination of different units but lend themselves to logical interpretation.

Generally speaking the averages should always be treated as convenient and necessary tools of learning, particularly in comparing populations, but it should be remembered that the actual picture of reality is the series itself and not the statistical measures of dispersion and asymmetry which will be discussed in Chapter 6.

Sometimes technical considerations may decide the type of average. For instance, the calculation of the arithmetic mean of a monotonically decreasing or increasing series leads to biased errors, especially when the class intervals are large. Similarly it is not possible to calculate with sufficient accuracy the arithmetic mean of a series with an open upper or lower class if the frequencies of the open classes are large. We can then often calculate the median or the mode which we should use instead of the arithmetic mean.

Similarly, a situation may arise in which, for technical reasons, it will not be possible to calculate the median or the mode. To calculate the mode by elementary methods we must have equal class intervals at least in the part in which the mode is located. An irregular shape of the curve and the lack of well defined maxima also interfere with the calculation of the mode. For the calculation of the median the class intervals must not be too large in the part containing the median, particularly if the shape of the curve differs much from a straight line. If these conditions are not satisfied it may be advisable to calculate some other average, for purely technical reasons, even if basically the choice of the mode or the median is indicated.

There is a certain characteristic dependence between the numerical values of the arithmetic mean, median and mode of the same series.

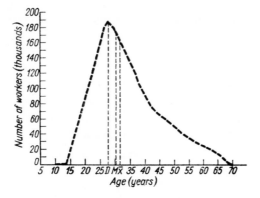

FIG. 5.3. Age of male workers insured in December 1935.
Mode, median and arithmetic mean.

Fig. 5.3. refers to the problem discussed earlier in this book: the age distribution of men covered by pension plans in 1935. The letters $D$, $M$ and $\bar{x}$ denote the points on the horizontal axis corresponding to the mode, median and arithmetic mean respectively.

The vertical line from point $D$, in accordance with the definition, meets the highest point of the curve: this is the largest ordinate. The perpendicular line from point $M$ divides the area under the curve into two equal parts: the number of observations with values less than the median is equal to the number of observations with values greater than the median, and, as we know, in a graphical presentation equal frequencies are represented by equal areas. With respect to the arithmetic mean we can say that the perpendicular line from point $\bar{x}$ on the horizontal axis passes through the centre of gravity of the set. In other words, if we cut the whole figure out of cardboard and suspend it at point $\bar{x}$ the abscissas will be horizontal and the ordinates vertical. We can express this mathematically by saying that the sum of the products of the distances from point $\bar{x}$ by the corresponding ordinates will be the same to the left as to the right of point $\bar{x}$. But if we cut the cardboard along the vertical line from point $\bar{x}$ the weight of the two parts will not be the same. It would be the same, through, if we cut the cardboard along the ordinate drawn from point $M$.

These three averages have the same value in a symmetric series. In asymmetric series, however, both the median and arithmetic mean ar shifted away from the mode in the direction of the longer arm of the curve and the arithmetic mean occupies the extreme position so that in the case of left asymmetry (positive skewness) we can write

$$\bar{x} > M_x > D_x,$$

and in the case of right asymmetry (negative skewness)

$$\bar{x} < M_x < D_x.$$

Karl Pearson has proved that in certain series, not exceedingly asymmetric, there is a definite relationship between the values of these three averages:

$$\bar{x} - D_x = 3(\bar{x} - M_x),$$

i.e. the difference between the arithmetic mean and the mode is three times as great as the difference between the arithmetic mean and the median. From this relationship it is sometimes possible to calculate the value of the mode on the basis of known values of the arithmetic mean and median, namely:

$$D_x = \bar{x} - 3(\bar{x} - M_x) \qquad (\text{V.27})$$

or

$$D_x = M_x - 2(\bar{x} - M_x). \qquad (\text{V.27a})$$

This method of calculating the mode is recommended by British statisticians. Unfortunately the relationship described here between the arithmetic mean, the median and the mode occurs, strictly speaking, only in series of a certain type that can be expressed by a special function. The application of formulae (V.27) and (V.27a) to other cases may lead to serious errors, especially since the median cannot be accurately calculated by elementary methods.

# CHAPTER 6

# MEASURES OF DISPERSION, ASYMMETRY AND CONCENTRATION

We shall now discuss measures of a second type which indicate to what degree particular observations are concentrated about a common centre. The degree of spread (scatter) of the values of the variable is called the dispersion. Greater concentration is indicated graphically, by a curve with a distinctly marked maximum, and greater dispersion by a curve of a rather flattened shape (see above pp. 167 *et seq.*).

## 1. RANGE OF VARIATION. QUARTILE DEVIATION. MEAN DEVIATION

The simplest measure of dispersion would be the difference between the highest and the lowest value of the variable in a given population. For instance, if in one population group the height of the shortest person is 158 cm and that of the tallest 168 cm, and in another group the height of the shortest person is 142 cm and that of the tallest 192 cm, the range of the extreme values in the first case is 10 cm, and in the second 50 cm. In statistics the difference between the extreme values is called the *range* of variation. This measure may sometimes be useful in giving a general idea, but it is imprecise, and may be misleading. We have already pointed out that extremely large or small values may appear as chance fluctuations, so that the range on one occasion be wide, and on another quite narrow in populations which do not differ much from one another in the form of their distributions. In studies of the weights of male students in academic institutions in Warsaw in 1946, it turned out that at of 20 and 23–24 years of age, the range was 74 kg (the lowest weight was 45·5 kg, and the highest 119·5 kg), whereas in other age groups the range did not exceed 48–50 kg. This was due to the random fluctuations, since in both the 20 and the 23–24 age groups there happened to be one man with an extremely abnormal weight close to 120 kg (264 1b).

A correct measure of dispersion must be based on the whole frequency distribution of the series, and not only on individual values. One such type of measure is the *quartile deviation*. It is based on the notion of quartiles (see pp. 209–10). We compute the difference between the first and the third quartile. It follows from the definition that within these limits are one-half of all the observations. Usually a half of the difference between the quartiles is used. Denoting the quartile deviation by Q we have

$$Q = \frac{Q_3 - Q_1}{2}. \qquad (VI.1)$$

This measure is easy to compute, and sufficiently precise. Bearing in mind the reservations about the accuracy of calculating quartiles in general (see p. 208–9), this measure can always be used if it is not necessary to apply other measures, especially the standard deviation, during further analysis of the series.

Other measures of dispersion are based on the following reasoning. Let us suppose that for a given series we have computed the average height, weight, or some other measurable characteristic. Let us disregard, for the time being, which average we have selected. Then we calculate the differences between the values of particular observations and this average. It is obvious that the greater the deviations from the average, the wider the dispersion. Depending on the average used two measures of dispersion are distinguished: the *mean deviation* and the *standard deviation*.

The mean deviation is the arithmetic mean of the absolute values of the deviations from the average of the series. From mathematical point of view it is correct to calculate the average deviation from the median, so the formula is written as follows:

$$d_x = \frac{\sum |x - M_x|}{n}. \qquad (VI.2)$$

In statistical practice the deviation is often calculated not from the median, but from the arithmetic mean:

$$d'_x = \frac{\sum |x - \bar{x}|}{n}. \qquad (VI.3)$$

The mean deviation reaches a minimum when it is calculated using the median as the average so that we always have

$$d'_x > d_x.$$

Note that we are dealing here with the absolute values of the differences between the variate values and the mean. Were we to take the sign into account, the mean deviation measured from the arithmetic mean would always equal zero (the sum of the deviations from the arithmetic mean, as we know, equals zero). The mean deviation measured from the median does not equal zero because the median is not identical with the arithmetic mean; but the value of the mean deviation would depend more upon the difference between the arithmetic mean and the median than upon actual dispersion of observations.

The computation of the mean deviation is simple if we use the individual values of the variable. After arranging the series in the order of magnitude, we calculate the median and then the diffferences between, the particular observations and the median, and finally we obtain the arithmetic mean of these differences ignoring the sign of the difference. If we take the arithmetic mean as a starting point, the procedure is the same.

If, as is usual, we deal not with individual observations but with statistical series, we calculate first the differences between the centres of individual classes and the median or the arithmetic mean of the series. These difference should be multiplied by the class frequencies, and the products added without paying attention to the sign. The total thus obtained divided by the total number of observations gives the value of the mean deviation. The formula is

$$d_x = \frac{\Sigma f |x - M_x|}{\Sigma f} \qquad\qquad (VI.4)$$

or

$$d'_x = \frac{\Sigma f |x - \bar{x}|}{\Sigma f}, \qquad\qquad (VI.5)$$

depending on whether we measure the deviations from the median or from the arithmetic mean.

It is also possible to calculate the mean deviation of a series by a simplified method, analogous to the simplified method used in calculating the arithmetic mean (see above p. 183 *et seq.*) and the standard deviation, which we shall discuss later on. However, the formula for such a calculation is fairly complex, and makes certain simplifying assumptions. Since, in addition, the mean deviation is rarely used in statistics we shall not give this formula.[58]

## 2. STANDARD DEVIATION

The standard deviation is the square mean of the deviations from the average, which in this case is always the arithmetic mean. We denote the standard deviation by the Greek letter $\sigma$ (sigma)

$$\sigma_x = \sqrt{\frac{\Sigma (x - \bar{x})^2}{n}}. \qquad\qquad (VI.6)$$

In other words we can say that the standard deviation is the square root of the arithmetic mean of the square of deviations from the arithmetic mean, or the root mean of the deviations from the arithmetic mean. The plus or minus sign of the difference $x - \bar{x}$ does not matter here, since the differences are squared. It can be proved that the sum of the squares of the deviations (and hence $\sigma$) is a minimum when the deviations are measured from the arithmetic mean (see pp. 218–19).

---

[58] G. U. Yule and M. G. Kendall: *An Introduction to the Theory of Statistics,* 13th ed., London 1945, pp. 146, 153 and 546.

Instead of $\sigma$ the quantity $\sigma^2 = \mu$ is sometimes used as a measure of dispersion

$$\sigma^2 = \mu = \frac{\sum (x - \bar{x})^2}{n} \tag{VI.7}$$

It should be noted that $\mu$ is not a characteristic but a measure of the characteristic, i.e. of the dispersion. It is called the *variance*.

The standard deviation and the variance are by far the most important measures of dispersion and are used in one way or another as a basis for almost all conclusions. For this reason we can treat all other measures of dispersion as of secondary importance.

With the help of simplified methods of calculation the standard deviation is not any more difficult to obtain than the average deviation.

If we deal with individual values of the variable the computation of the standard deviation according to formula (VI.6) on p. 215 is done by calculating first the arithmetic mean, then the differences between the individual values of the variable and their arithmetic mean, then by squaring the differences, adding the squares, dividing their sum by the number of observations and extracting the square root of this quotient.

We shall illustrate the method by a simple example. Let us suppose that variable $x$ assumes 5 different values: 1, 3, 5, 7 and 9.

|                     | $x$ | $x - \bar{x}$ | $(x - \bar{x})^2$ |
|---------------------|-----|---------------|-------------------|
| First observation   | 1   | −4            | 16                |
| Second ,,           | 3   | −2            | 4                 |
| Third ,,            | 5   | 0             | 0                 |
| Fourth ,,           | 7   | +2            | 4                 |
| Fifth ,,            | 9   | +4            | 16                |
| Total               | 25  | 0             | 40                |

The arithmetic mean of $x$ is $25/5 = 5$. The differences $x - \bar{x}$ are negative for the first two observations and positive for the last two. The sum of these differences is zero.

The mean deviation is calculated by summing the differences, disregarding the sign: $4 + 2 + 2 + 4 = 12$. 12 divided by 5 gives the mean deviation

$$d_x = \frac{\sum |x - \bar{x}|}{n} = \frac{\sum |x - M_x|}{n} = \frac{12}{5} = 2 \cdot 4.$$

In the given symmetric series the median is, of course, equal to the arithmetic mean.

The standard deviation is

$$\sigma_x = \sqrt{\frac{\sum (x - \bar{x})^2}{n}} = \sqrt{\frac{40}{5}} = \sqrt{8} = 2 \cdot 83.$$

The deviations of individual values of the variable from the arithmetic mean we shall denote by capital letters from now on:

$$x - \bar{x} = X,$$

$$y - \bar{y} = Y, \text{ etc.}$$

In other words $X$, $Y$, etc. denote the values of the variable measured from the arithmetic mean.

In a direct calculation from a frequency distribution the procedure is analogous: we calculate the differences between the values corresponding to the centres of the classes, square them and multiply the squares of the differences by the frequencies of the corresponding classes. The square root of the sum of these products divided by the number of observations is the standard deviation. In this way formula (VI.6) on p. 215 is modified:

$$\sigma_x = \sqrt{\frac{\sum f(x - \bar{x})^2}{\sum f}} = \sqrt{\frac{\sum fX^2}{\sum f}}, \tag{VI.8}$$

where $f$ stands for the frequencies of particular classes and $x - \bar{x} = X$ is the difference between the centres of particular classes and the arithmetic mean.

To this formula a correction is sometimes introduced. In calculating the average of the squared deviations from the arithmetic mean an error arises due to the assumption that the average value of the variable within each class is equal to the value of the centre of the class interval. In calculating the mean deviation and the standard deviation these errors do not cancel out, and the sum of squared deviations thus obtained is always too large. The English statistician W. F. Sheppard showed that under certain conditions this sum is too large by $\frac{1}{12}$ th of the square of the class interval.

Allowing for this error, instead of formula (VI.8) we have

$$\sigma_x = \sqrt{\frac{\sum fX^2}{\sum f} - \frac{l^2}{12}} \tag{VI.9}$$

where $l$, as always, denotes the class interval.

This correction is applied to distributions of continuous or quasi-continuous variables with curves approaching the horizontal axis gradually on both sides of the maximum. For a discontinuous variable this correction should not be used. If the class intervals are not large the expression $\frac{l^2}{12}$ under the square root sign is small in comparison with the arithmetic mean of the squared deviations from the arithmetic mean, and therefore this correction is often disregarded, particularly when the whole population is small or the series is irregular, since in such cases the random error may be much larger than the correction.

15

When using shortened method of calculation we proceed in the same way as in calculating the arithmetic mean: we selected an arbitrary origin—preferably the centre of the class—if possible close to the arithmetic mean, and compute first the sum of squared deviations of the centres of the classes from the arbitrary origin, in units equal to the class interval. In this way small figures are usually obtained, which simplifies the calculation. An appropriate correction is introduced later. The value of this correction is arrived at in the following way.

Denote by $v_1$ the difference between the arithmetic mean and an arbitrary value of the variable $x_0$

$$x_0 = \bar{x} - v_1.$$

Subtracting both sides of this equation from $x$ we have

$$x - x_0 = x - \bar{x} + v_1 = X + v_1.$$

Squaring both sides of the equation we get

$$(x - x_0)^2 = X^2 + 2v_1 X + v_1^2.$$

There will be as many such equations as there are individual values of $x$, i.e. as many as there are observations. We add up both sides of these equations for all the values of $x$. Remembering that $v_1$ is constant we write

$$\Sigma (x - x_0)^2 = \Sigma X^2 + 2v_1 \Sigma X + nv_1^2.$$

In this equation $\Sigma X$, as the sum of deviations from the arithmetic mean, equals zero, and the middle expression on the right side disappears. Dividing both sides by $n$ we get

$$\frac{\Sigma (x - x_0)^2}{n} = \frac{\Sigma X^2}{n} + v_1^2.$$

Since $\dfrac{\Sigma x^2}{n}$ is the square of the mean deviation we finally get

$$\sigma_x^2 = \frac{\Sigma (x - x_0)^2}{n} - v_1^2. \tag{VI.10}$$

In this equation the expressions $\sigma_x^2 = \dfrac{\Sigma X^2}{n}$ and $\dfrac{\Sigma (x - x_0)^2}{n}$, (in whose numerators the sums of squares appear and in whose denominators the number of observations) are always non-negative. Therefore, in every case, when $x_0$ does not equal $x$, i.e. when $v_1$ does not equal zero

$$\sigma_x^2 < \frac{\Sigma (x - x_0)^2}{n}.$$

We have thus proved the theorem stated without proof on p. 216, that the sum of squared deviations from the arbitrary origin is a minimum when the arithmetic mean is made the origin.

Formula (VI.10) can be used for a simplified calculation of the average deviation. Denoting the auxiliary quantity $\dfrac{\Sigma (x - x_0)^2}{n}$ by $v_2$ we get

$$\sigma^2 = v_2 - v_1^2 \tag{VI.11}$$

and

$$\sigma = \sqrt{v_2 - v_1^2} \tag{VI.12}$$

$v_1$ here plays the part of the correction we used above in an abbreviated calculation of the arithmetic mean

$$v_1 = \frac{\Sigma t}{n} = \frac{\Sigma (x - x_0)}{n}$$

or, if we calculate from the frequency distribution

$$v_1 = \frac{\Sigma ft}{\Sigma f} = \frac{\Sigma f (x - x_0)}{\Sigma f}.$$

Counting in class intervals we obtain values divided by $l$

$$v_1 = \frac{1}{l} \frac{\Sigma f (x - x_0)}{\Sigma f},$$

$$lv_1 = \frac{\Sigma f (x - x_0)}{\Sigma f}.$$

Similarly

$$v_2 = \frac{\Sigma (x - x_0)^2}{n}.$$

When we calculate from the series

$$v_2 = \frac{\Sigma f (x - x_0)^2}{\Sigma f}$$

and in class intervals

$$v_2 = \frac{1}{l^2} \frac{\Sigma f (x - x_0)^2}{\Sigma f},$$

$$l^2 v_2 = \frac{\Sigma f (x - x_0)^2}{\Sigma f}.$$

Then, if we want to count in units equal to class intervals we write formula (VI.12) as

$$\sigma = l \sqrt{v_2 - v_1^2}, \tag{VI.13}$$

and, allowing for Sheppard's Correction,

$$\sigma = l \sqrt{v_2 - v_1^2 - \frac{1}{12}} \tag{VI.14}$$

15*

(in all the expressions under the square root $l$ appears to the second power and we can take it out of the square root sign).

Just as the calculation of the auxiliary quantity $v_1$ was much simpler than the direct computation of the arithmetic mean, so the calculation of the auxiliary quantity $v_2$ is much easier than the direct computation of $\sigma^2$, particularly when the calculation is done in class intervals.

An example of the calculation will be given later.

## 3. RELATIVE DEVIATIONS

All the measures of dispersion described above, like the averages, are expressed in the same units of measurement as the values of the variable. This may create difficulties in comparisons. Suppose that we are analysing the dispersion of the weekly wages of workers and monthly salaries of clerical personnel. Let the average weekly wage of the worker be 40 zlotys with a standard deviation of 10 zlotys, and the average monthly salary of the clerks 320 zlotys with a standard deviation of 40 zlotys. The standard deviation of the salaries of white collar workers is four times as great as the standard deviation of the wages of factory workers. We have to consider, however, that the average level of the monthly salary of clerical personnel is eight times as great as the level of weekly earnings of factory workers. In order to decide in which case the dispersion is greater in relation to the level of earnings we calculate the ratio of the standard deviation to the arithmetic mean

$$V_x = \frac{\sigma_x}{\bar{x}}.$$

This ratio is usually expressed in percentages

$$V_x = \frac{100\,\sigma_x}{\bar{x}}. \tag{VI.15}$$

$V_x$ is a measure of the relative dispersion and is called the *coefficient of variation*. In our case we have for the workers

$$V_x = \frac{10 \times 100}{40} = 25\%,$$

and for the clerical personnel

$$V_x = \frac{40 \times 100}{320} = 12 \cdot 5\%.$$

The earnings of the clerical personnel in this example are much more evenly distributed than the earnings of the factory workers. In a similar way we can calculate relative deviations, taking as a starting point mean or quartile deviations. If the mean deviation is measured from the median it will be most natural to put the median in the denominator; similarly in the case of quartile deviation. Then we have

$$\frac{d}{M_x} \quad \text{and} \quad \frac{Q}{M_x}$$

When we use relative measures of dispersion we can sometimes compare dispersions even when the quantities compared are expressed in different units of measurement. It would be interesting to find out, for instance, which is less uniform in man: height of weight.

A study of university students made in Warsaw in 1946 disclosed that for girls aged 20, the standard deviation of height was 5·39 cm at an average height of 160·73 cm, and the standard deviation of weight is 6·95 kg at the average weight of 58·76 kg. A direct comparison of 5·39 cm with 6·95 kg would not make sense, but it is possible to compare the coefficients of variation as abstract numbers. Thus we get

$$\text{for height} \quad V_x = \frac{5 \cdot 39 \times 100}{160 \cdot 73} = 335\%,$$

$$\text{for weight} \quad V_y = \frac{6 \cdot 95 \times 100}{58 \cdot 76} = 11 \cdot 83\%.$$

Thus the dispersion of weight is several times greater than that for height.

However, it is not always possible nor necessary to calculate relative dispersion.

From the example quoted above we find that the standard deviation for monthly temperatures in Warsaw in 1826–1910 was 3·17° in January and 2·39° in March. The average temperature over a period of years was −4·2° in January and +0·8° in March. Hence we obtain the coefficient of variation for January as 75·5 per cent and for March as 298·7 per cent. However the high coefficient for March is explained by the fact that the temperature in this month was close to zero. If by any chance the average temperature of the months were zero, the coefficient of variation would equal infinity, which has no sensible interpretation. The computation of the coefficients of variation for temperatures would perhaps be permissible only if temperatures were measured from absolute zero.

It should be remembered that relative deviations are not measures that can be treated like other measures, e.g. the standard or mean deviation. They are simply quartile, mean or standard deviations expressed in relative numbers.

## 4. MEASURES OF ASYMMETRY (SKEWNESS)

The measure of asymmetry of a series can be based on the observation that in a symmetric series the arithmetic mean, mode and median are identical, and in an asymmetric series they differ from each other, and the greater the asymmetry the greater the difference. Thus we can measure asymmetry by the difference between the arithmetic mean and the mode.

This difference however, has dimensions, and depends upon the units of measurement and the level of the variable for a given phenomenon. We obtain a dimensionless ratio by taking the ratio of the difference between the averages to one of the numerical characteristics of the series which has the same dimension. It is natural to relate this difference to the standard deviation which characterizes the dispersion of the variable.

In this way we develop the concept of the coefficient of asymmetry expressed by the formula

$$As. = \frac{\bar{x} - D_x}{\sigma_x} \qquad (VI.16)$$

This measure is positive if the arithmetic mean is greater than the mode (the right arm of the curve is the longer and the maximum is less than the mode) the maximum shifted to the right. Thus the plus sign corresponds to left asymmetry and the minus sign to right asymmetry. In a symmetric series $\bar{x} = D_x$ and therefore the coefficient of asymmetry is zero. The precision of calculation depends, of course, upon the accuracy of calculating the mode.

Another measure of skewness is based on the observation that in a symmetric distribution the difference between the third quartile and the median is always the same as the difference between the median and the first quartile. In an asymmetric series the difference between these differences will be greater, the greater the asymmetry. We can write

$$As. = \frac{(Q_3 - M_x) - (M_x - Q_1)}{(Q_3 - M_x) + (M_x - Q_1)}. \qquad (VI.17)$$

This is also a dimensionless number. We can easily show that this value is zero when the series is symmetric (because then $Q_3 - M_x = M_x - Q_1$); it is positive when we have left asymmetry (because then $Q_3 - M_x$ is greater than $M_x - Q_1$) and negative when we have right asymmetry ($M_x - Q_1$ is greater than $Q_3 - M_x$). The extreme values are $+1$ or $-1$, and are achieved only if one of the guartiles equals the median.

The measures of asymmetry are less important in analysing distributions than the averages and the measures of dispersion discussed above.

## 5. THE CALCULATION OF THE NUMERICAL CHARACTERISTICS
### OF A FREQUENCY DISTRIBUTION

We give below examples of calculations of all the basic measures discussed above, with emphasis on the technique and convenience of calculation, and the possibility of checking the results. We shall also give a number of examples to emphasize the merits of different measures.

In the first example we have data on the deaths of married men by age in the former Western Provinces of Poznan, Pomorze, Sląsk in 1932.[59] We have selected the deaths of married men, and not those of the whole population because the pattern for the latter is irregular: the highest values immediately after birth, a strongly marked minimum at the age of about 13 and an equally strongly marked maximum at the age of 65–69. This kind of series does not lend itself to description by averages and measures of dispersion.

The original series contains columns 1 and 5: the age of the decreased in 5-year intervals, and the number of the decreased for each class. We have added columns 2 and 8 to these two columns. Column 2 denotes the age of the deceased as the centre of the class interval, and in column 8 we have the cumulative series which we shall need in calculating the median and the quartiles. In this column the figure 1 in the first row means than 1 person died before reaching the age of 20, the number 79 in the second row that 79 persons died before the age of 25, etc. In column 2 we have chosen the average of $102 \cdot 5$ for the open, upper class of the age of 100 and over, which is 5 years from the centre of the preceding class, the same as for the whole series. This should be the most likely value if we consider the whole pattern of the series. Besides, a possible error committed here is on no consequence since in the class of 100 and over there is only one death out of the total of 10,793.

Columns 3, 4, 6 and 7 are used for the calculation of the arithmetic mean and standard deviation. In column 3 we have chosen as the arbitrary origin $x_0$ the centre of the class 60–64 years, and have expressed the centres of the other class intervals as deviations from this origin; these deviations are expressed in units equal to the class interval (which is why the column is headed: $\frac{x - x_0}{l}$).

Trying to estimate visually the location of the arithmetic mean we might be doubtful whether the class 60–64 years or 55–59 should be selected. In fact, as we shall see, the arithmetic mean is $59 \cdot 24$ years, and so it is located in the class 55–59. As we already know, however, the choice of the arbitrary origin does not affect the result. If we choose a point further removed from the centre of the distribution the only consequence is that the computation may be somewhat more difficult.

The next column 4 contains the squares of these differences, i.e. $\frac{(x - x_0)^2}{l^2}$ needed for the calculation of the standard deviation. Columns 6 and 7 contain the products $\frac{f(x - x_0)}{l}$ and $\frac{f(x - x_0)^2}{l^2}$ needed for the calculation of the auxiliary quantities $v_1$ and $v_2$. The computation can be checked here by first calculating

[59] Małżeństwa, urodzenia, zgony (Marriages, Births, Deaths), 1931, 1932. *Statystyka Polski* (*Statistics of Poland*), Series C, No. 102. Warsaw, 1939, p. 239.

column 7 directly (the product of the figures in columns 4 and 5) and then by multiplying the figures in the previously calculated column 6 by the figures in column 3. Of course

$$f \times \frac{x - x_0}{l} \times \frac{x - x_0}{l} = f \frac{(x - x_0)^2}{l^2}.$$

This double checking ensures the correctness of the calculation of both columns 6 and 7.

At the bottom the required totals are shown in column 5 (the total number of the deceased), column 6 $\sum \dfrac{f(x - x_0)}{l}$ and $\sum \dfrac{f(x - x_0)^2}{l^2}$. Other columns cannot be added up and therefore the sign—is placed in the row marked *Total*. In column 6 the sums of positive and negative values are given separetely.

TABLE 6.1. DEATHS OF MARRIED MEN BY AGE. FORMER WESTERN PROVINCES (1932)

| Age of the deceased | | $\left(\dfrac{x - x_0}{l}\right)$ | $\dfrac{(x - x_0)^2}{l^2}$ | Number of deceased ($f$) | $\dfrac{f(x - x_0)}{l}$ | $\dfrac{f(x - x_0)^2}{l^2}$ | Cumulative series $sf$ |
|---|---|---|---|---|---|---|---|
| class intervals | centre of class ($x$) | | | | | | |
| 1 | 2 | 3 | 4 | 5 | 6 | 7 | 8 |
| 15–19 | 17·5 | −9 | 81 | 1 | −9 | 81 | 1 |
| 20–24 | 22·5 | −8 | 64 | 78 | −624 | 4992 | 79 |
| 25–29 | 27·5 | −7 | 49 | 409 | −2863 | 20,041 | 483 |
| 30–34 | 32·5 | −6 | 36 | 554 | −3324 | 19,944 | 1042 |
| 35–39 | 37·5 | −5 | 25 | 592 | −2960 | 14,800 | 1634 |
| 40–44 | 42·5 | −4 | 16 | 596 | −2384 | 9536 | 2230 |
| 45–49 | 47·5 | −3 | 9 | 710 | −2130 | 6390 | 2940 |
| 50–54 | 52·5 | −2 | 4 | 934 | −1868 | 3736 | 3874 |
| 55–59 | 57·5 | −1 | 1 | 1141 | −1141 | 1141 | 5015 |
| 60–64 | 62·5 | 0 | 0 | 1313 | 0 | 0 | 6328 |
| 65–69 | 67·5 | +1 | 1 | 1408 | +1408 | 1408 | 7736 |
| 70–74 | 72·5 | +2 | 4 | 1359 | +2718 | 5436 | 9095 |
| 75–79 | 77·5 | +3 | 9 | 931 | +2793 | 8379 | 10,026 |
| 80–84 | 82·5 | +4 | 16 | 536 | +2144 | 8576 | 10,562 |
| 85–89 | 87·5 | +5 | 25 | 189 | +945 | 4725 | 10,751 |
| 90–94 | 92·5 | +6 | 36 | 38 | +228 | 1368 | 10,789 |
| 95–99 | 97·5 | +7 | 49 | 3 | +21 | 147 | 10,792 |
| 100 and over | 102·5 | +8 | 64 | 1 | +8 | 64 | 10,793 |
| Total | — | — | — | 10,793[a] | −17,303 +10,265 −7038 | 110,764 | — |

a Excluding 14 married men whose ages at death could not be established.

From these sums we calculate directly $v_1$ and $v_2$. We must remember that this calculation is in conventional units equal to the class interval and that the quantities $v_1$ and $v_2$ are expressed in those units. If we want to return to actual units we have to multiply $v_1$ by 5 and $v_2$ by $5^2 = 25$.

$$v_1 = \frac{-7038}{10{,}793} = -0 \cdot 6521, \quad v_1^2 = 0 \cdot 6521^2 = 0 \cdot 425,$$

$$v_2 = \frac{110{,}764}{10{,}793} = 10 \cdot 262.$$

The arithmetic mean calculated by formula (V.5a) p. 184 is

$$\bar{x} = x_0 + 5v_1 = 62 \cdot 5 - 5 \times 0 \cdot 652 = 62 \cdot 5 - 3 \cdot 26 = 59 \cdot 24.$$

The standard deviation calculated by formula (VI.14) p. 219, i.e. after allowing for Sheppard's Correction, is

$$\sigma_1 = l \times \sqrt{v_2 - v_1^2 - \frac{1}{12}} = 5 \times \sqrt{10 \cdot 263 - 0 \cdot 425 - 0 \cdot 083} = 5 \times \sqrt{9 \cdot 755}$$

$$= 5 \times 3 \cdot 1233 = 15 \cdot 62.$$

The computation of $v_2$, and even more of $v_1$, must be done to a relatively large number of decimal places, because the errors are magnified during the multiplication by the class interval and squaring. The final result, however, can be given to only two decimal places, since the calculation of statistical measures from the series cannot be done with greater accuracy. In calculating the standard deviation Sheppard's. Correction has been taken into account: $\frac{1}{12}$th has been deducted from the expression under the square root sign. The class intervals here are fairly large and disregarding the correction might lead to reduced accuracy (the standard deviation without the correction is $15 \cdot 68$, so that there is a considerable difference in the second decimal place).

Let us now calculate the mode. We look for it in the largest class of 65–69 years. To interpolate on the basis of the parabola we use formula (V.23) p. 202.

$$D = x_0 + l \times \frac{f_0 - f_{-1}}{(f_0 - f_{-1}) + (f_0 - f_1)} :$$

$x_0$ has here a different meaning from that used in calculating the arithmetic mean: it is here the lower limit of the largest class (65 years). $l$, as before, is the class interval (5 years). $f$ denotes the number of observations: $f_0$ in the largest class, $f_{-1}$ in the class preceding it and $f_1$ in the class following it.

$$f_0 = 1408, \quad f_{-1} = 1313, \quad f_1 = 1359.$$

Therefore

$$D_x = 65 + 5 \times \frac{1408 - 1313}{(1408 - 1313) + (1408 - 1359)} = 65 + 5 \times \frac{95}{144} = 68 \cdot 30.$$

Checking the calculation against formula (V.23a)

$$D_x = x_0 + l \frac{f_0 - f_{-1}}{2f_0 - (f_{-1} + f_1)},$$

we obtain the same result.

Let us now calculate the median. There are 10,793 observations in all, and the number is odd. The middle position is

$$\frac{10,793 + 1}{2} = 5397.$$

It follows from the cumulative series that this middle position is in the class 60–64 years. Applying linear interpolation according to formula (V.26) p. 208 we get

$$M_x = 60 + 5 \times \frac{5397 - 5015}{1313} = 60 + 1 \cdot 46 = 61 \cdot 46.$$

In computing quartiles, we also use linear interpolation. Calculating to the nearest integer we get

$$\frac{n}{4} = \frac{10,793}{4} = 2698,$$

$$\frac{3n}{4} = 8095.$$

Thus the first quartile is in the class 45–49 years and the third quartile in the class 70–74 years.

$$Q_1 = 45 + 5 \frac{2698 - 2230}{710} = 45 + 3 \cdot 30 = 48 \cdot 30,$$

$$Q_3 = 70 + 5 \times \frac{8095 - 7736}{1359} = 70 + 1 \cdot 32 = 71 \cdot 32.$$

The quartile deviation is

$$Q = \frac{Q_3 - Q_1}{2} = \frac{71 \cdot 32 - 48 \cdot 30}{2} = \frac{23 \cdot 02}{2} = 11 \cdot 51.$$

To find the mean deviation we calculate first the differences between the median (which after rounding off is 61·5 years), and the centres of the consecutive classes: 17·5—61·5 = —44, 22·5—61·5 = —39, etc. We multiply these differences by the corresponding frequencies (column 5, Table 6.1 p. 224) disregarding the sign: 44×1 = 44, 39×78 = 3042, etc. The sum of the products is 138,603; divided by the total number of the deceased (10,793) this gives the mean deviation

$$d_x = \frac{\Sigma f (x - M_x)}{\Sigma f} = \frac{138,603}{10,793} = 12 \cdot 84 \text{ years.}$$

The coefficient of asymmetry calculated according to formula (VI.16) p. 222 is

$$\frac{59 \cdot 24 - 68 \cdot 30}{15 \cdot 61} = -\frac{9 \cdot 06}{15 \cdot 61} = -0 \cdot 58.$$

The minus sign indicates right asymmetry (the maximum shifted to the right, the left tail of the curve longer than the right).

Let us now consider several statistical distributions of related populations, and a comparison of their numerical characteristics. The examples pertain to the deaths of married men and women, widows and widowers in the former Western provinces in 1932 (Table 6.2 p. 228). All these populations, arranged in the form of a frequency distribution, represent the type most frequently encountered in statistics: they begin and end with very small frequencies and have more or less clearly marked maxima and so are well suited for demonstrating the use of numerical characteristics. The populations are presented in the form of frequency distributions and cumulative frequency distributions, both in absolute figures and in percentages. The frequency distributions and the cumulative frequencies are presented in a graphical form (both in percentages). In the original population there are a certain number of deceased of unknown age; the number is significant—up to a dozen persons. We disregard these deaths altogether, so that the figures include only those of the deceased whose ages at the time of death were known.

The last class is marked at the source: "100 years and over". In our table we wrote "100–104 years" which in this case will certainly not produce a noticeable error. The numbers of married men are identical with the figures in Table 6.1 p. 224.

From the demographic point of view the following should be noted. The number of deaths at each age, and thus the total number of deaths in each population, depend upon two factors: the death rate, which increases with age, and the number of persons who can die, i.e. the number of live persons in each age group. In both respects the populations compared differ considerably from one another. The death rate for widowers and widows, especially when young age, is much greater than the death rate for married people. There are also differences in death rates for men and women, always in favour of women. Above all, however, there are differences in frequencies in the age groups of living persons in each of these populations. Naturally, in the youngest age group, below 20, there are very few married people and almost no widowers and widows.

For older age groups the number of married persons increases rapidly, and at first considerably exceeds the number of widowers and widows. Only toward the end of life is the ratio reversed: the number of widowed increases considerably, so that at old age the number of widows (if not the number of widowers) exceeds the number of married people. In the last decades of life the numbers of both drop rapidly; hence the number of deaths decreases in spite of the increasing death rate. There are fairly large differences between the populations of men and women:

TABLE 6.2. DEATHS BY AGE. FORMER WESTERN PROVINCES
(1932)

| Age of deceased in years | Men | | Women | | Men | | Women | |
|---|---|---|---|---|---|---|---|---|
| | married | widowers | married | widows | mar-ried | wid-owers | mar-ried | wid-ows |
| | (absolute values) | | | | (percentages) | | | |

## A. Frequency Distributions

| Age of deceased in years | married | widowers | married | widows | mar-ried | wid-owers | mar-ried | wid-ows |
|---|---|---|---|---|---|---|---|---|
| Total | 10,793 | 3283 | 7670 | 7604 | 100·0 | 100·0 | 100·0 | 100·0 |
| 15–19 | 1 | — | 29 | — | 0·0 | — | 0·4 | — |
| 20–24 | 78 | 1 | 325 | 3 | 0·7 | 0·0 | 4·2 | 0·0 |
| 25–29 | 409 | 2 | 608 | 14 | 3·8 | 0·0 | 7·9 | 0·2 |
| 30–34 | 554 | 14 | 635 | 26 | 5·1 | 0·4 | 8·3 | 0·3 |
| 35–39 | 592 | 11 | 674 | 52 | 5·5 | 0·3 | 8·8 | 0·7 |
| 40–44 | 596 | 18 | 591 | 80 | 5·5 | 0·5 | 7·7 | 1·0 |
| 45–49 | 710 | 27 | 588 | 122 | 6·6 | 0·8 | 7·7 | 1·6 |
| 50–54 | 934 | 47 | 592 | 191 | 8·6 | 1·4 | 7·7 | 2·5 |
| 55–59 | 1141 | 107 | 701 | 337 | 10·6 | 3·3 | 9·2 | 4·4 |
| 60–64 | 1313 | 198 | 799 | 549 | 12·2 | 6·0 | 10·4 | 7·2 |
| 65–69 | 1408 | 346 | 794 | 884 | 13·1 | 10·6 | 10·3 | 11·6 |
| 70–74 | 1359 | 575 | 694 | 1368 | 12·6 | 17·5 | 9·1 | 18·0 |
| 75–79 | 931 | 677 | 403 | 1519 | 8·6 | 20·7 | 5·3 | 20·0 |
| 80–84 | 536 | 635 | 184 | 1362 | 5·0 | 19·4 | 2·4 | 17·9 |
| 85–89 | 189 | 431 | 35 | 759 | 1·7 | 13·1 | 0·4 | 10·0 |
| 90–94 | 38 | 160 | 17 | 249 | 0·4 | 4·9 | 0·2 | 3·4 |
| 95–99 | 3 | 25 | 1 | 73 | 0·0 | 0·8 | 0·0 | 1·0 |
| 100–104 | 1 | 9 | — | 16 | 0·0 | 0·3 | — | 0·2 |

## B. Cumulative Frequency Distributions

| | | married | widowers | married | widows | mar-ried | wid-owers | mar-ried | wid-ows |
|---|---|---|---|---|---|---|---|---|---|
| Less than | 20 | 1 | — | 29 | — | 0·0 | | 0·4 | — |
| ,, | ,, 25 | 79 | 1 | 354 | 3 | 0·7 | 0·0 | 4·6 | 0·0 |
| ,, | ,, 30 | 488 | 3 | 962 | 17 | 4·5 | 0·0 | 12·5 | 0·2 |
| ,, | ,, 35 | 1042 | 17 | 1597 | 43 | 9·6 | 0·4 | 20·8 | 0·5 |
| ,, | ,, 40 | 1634 | 28 | 2271 | 95 | 15·1 | 0·7 | 29·6 | 1·2 |
| ,, | ,, 45 | 2230 | 46 | 2862 | 175 | 20·6 | 1·2 | 37·3 | 2·2 |
| ,, | ,, 50 | 2940 | 73 | 3450 | 297 | 27·2 | 2·0 | 45·0 | 3·8 |
| ,, | ,, 55 | 3874 | 120 | 4042 | 488 | 35·8 | 3·4 | 52·7 | 6·3 |
| ,, | ,, 60 | 5015 | 227 | 4743 | 825 | 46·4 | 6·7 | 61·9 | 10·7 |
| ,, | ,, 65 | 6328 | 425 | 5542 | 1374 | 58·6 | 12·7 | 72·3 | 17·9 |
| ,, | ,, 70 | 7736 | 771 | 6336 | 2258 | 71·7 | 23·3 | 82·6 | 29·5 |
| ,, | ,, 75 | 9095 | 1346 | 7030 | 3626 | 84·3 | 40·8 | 91·7 | 47·5 |
| ,, | ,, 80 | 10,026 | 2023 | 7433 | 5145 | 92·9 | 61·5 | 97·0 | 67·5 |
| ,, | ,, 85 | 10,562 | 2658 | 7617 | 6507 | 97·9 | 80·9 | 99·4 | 85·4 |
| ,, | ,, 90 | 10,751 | 3089 | 7652 | 7266 | 99·6 | 94·0 | 99·8 | 95·4 |
| ,, | ,, 95 | 10,789 | 3249 | 7669 | 7515 | 100·0 | 98·9 | 100·0 | 98·8 |
| ,, | ,, 100 | 10,792 | 3274 | 7670 | 7588 | 100·0 | 99·7 | 100·0 | 99·8 |
| ,, | ,, 105 | 10,793 | 3283 | 7670 | 7604 | 100·0 | 100·0 | 100·0 | 100·0 |

women marry earlier, and become widows much earlier than men become widowers. The total number of widows is much larger than the number of widowers. These circumstances account for the pattern of the series (see Fig. 6.1 and Fig. 6.2).

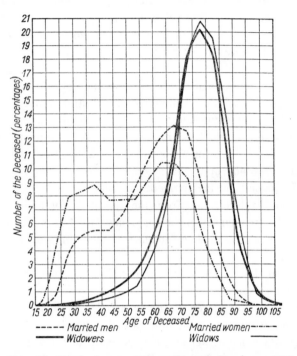

FIG. 6.1. Deaths by age. Former Western Provinces, 1932.
Frequency polygons.

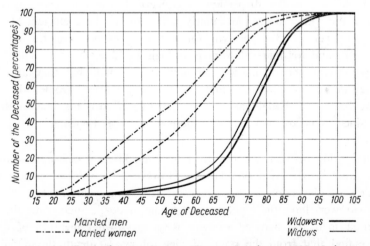

FIG. 6.2. Deaths by age. Former Western Provinces, 1933. Ogives.

Let us now analyse the shapes of the individual curves. All populations have approximately the same range of variation: the range of age is from 15 or 20 years to 100 or 105. But, as we can clearly see from the graph, the deaths of widowers and widows occur almost exclusively later in life, while the deaths of married men and women appear to be fairly high both at an early and at an advanced age. For married women there are two distinct maxima. For men the second maximum is not so clearly marked, but in the range 30–45 years a disturbance in the pattern is quite visible.

The cumulative distributions display corresponding patterns. We can very clearly follow here the growth of the cumulative distribution curve: for widows and widowers the curves start rising late, to rise slowly at first and then very rapidly; for married people the curves rise rapidly from the beginning but the rate of increase is not as great as it is for widowers and widows. Let us remember that the slope of the ogive depends upon the increase in frequencies per unit of age, i.e. upon the class frequencies in the frequency distribution.

We can see from Table 6.2 that from the age of 70 for men and from the age of 65 for women the frequencies in the frequency distribution, expressed in percentages, aee greater for widowers than for married men, and greater for widows than for married women.

After this general description of the populations we give below a comparison of basic statistical measures.

In these characteristics, differences in the married population on the one hand and the widows and widowers on the other are also clearly marked. The differences are in the averages (a much higher average age at death for widows and widowers), in the measures of dispersion (a lower dispersion for widows and widowers), and in the measure of asymmetry (much less marked asymmetry for widows and widowers). As far as the dispersion is concerned, the differences between the married and the widowed are particularly noticeable in the coefficient of variation, which for widowers is 13·8 per cent, for widows 15·4 per cent, for married men 26·4 per cent, and for married women as high as 32·6 per cent. There are also differences between the populations of men and women, but they are relatively minor; they are greatest between married men and married women. For married women we have two modal values corresponding to two maxima in the series; however, since there are two maxima, there is no basis for calculating a measure of asymmetry.

The relationship between different averages and different measures of dispersion is not the same in particular populations. However, the order of all averages and all measures of dispersion is the same; regardless of what measure we use we find that widowers have the highest average age at death, then come the widows, then married men and married women. Regardless what measure of dispersion we use we find that from the point of view of age at death the population of

TABLE 6.3. NUMERICAL CHARACTERISTICS OF THE SERIES CONCERNING DEATHS

| Statistical measures | | Men | | Women | |
|---|---|---|---|---|---|
| | | married | widowers | married | widows |
| *Averages* | | | | | |
| Arithmetic mean | $\bar{x}$ | 59·24 | 76·08 | 52·14 | 74·08 |
| Mode | $D_x$ | 68·30 | 78·54 | I 36·60 | 77·45 |
| | | | | II 64·76 | |
| Median | $M_x$ | 61·46 | 77·19 | 53·25 | 75·58 |
| 1st quartile | $Q_1$ | 48·30 | 70·43 | 38·38 | 67·98 |
| 3rd quartile | $Q_3$ | 71·32 | 83·46 | 66·33 | 82·05 |
| *Measures of dispersion* | | | | | |
| Standard deviation | $\sigma_x$ | 15·62 | 10·52 | 16·98 | 11·40 |
| Mean deviation | $d_x$ | 12·84 | 8·14 | 14·78 | 8·78 |
| Quartile deviation | $Q$ | 11·51 | 6·51 | 13·97 | 7·03 |
| Coefficient of variation | % | 26·37 | 13·83 | 32·57 | 15·39 |
| *Coefficient of asymmetry* | | | | | |
| $\dfrac{\bar{x}-D_x}{\sigma_x}$ | | −0·58 | −0·23 | | −0·30 |

widowers is most uniform, then come widows the population of married men is much less uniform and least uniform is the population of married women.

Finally, we find that in all cases $\bar{x} < D_x$ (right asymmetry)[60] and $Q < d < \sigma$.

The whole range of variation (the difference between the greatest and least age of the deceased) for married men is 90 years (105–15), and for the rest 85 years. These figures need not be considered representative since the frequencies in the upper and lower age classes are very low. For instance, in 1931 there was no known case of death of a married man below the age of 20 years, and for married women the last item (100 years and over) is not filled in. In any case, the differences in the range are negligible, whereas the more precise measures of dispersion display considerable differences. The whole range of variation is 5·8 times the standard deviation for married men, 5 times for married women, 8·1 times for widowers, and 7·5 times for widows. The last two figures are strikingly high; this confirms again our conclusion that the dispersion of the age of the deceased is particularly low for widowers and widows.

We should also note that the average age at death is lower for married women than for married men, and lower for widows than for widowers. This is apparently at odds with the known greater longevity of women. But it is also known that women marry at an earlier age than men, and become widowed earlier. It follows that there are more young married women than young married men, and the widows are, on the average, younger than the widowers. In consequence, the average age of the deceased women is lower than the average age of the deceased men, in spite of the fact that the death rate is higher for men than for women.

---

[60] This does not apply to married women for whom there are two maxima.

One further thing to be explained is the existence of the maxima in the death curve for married women and of the irregular pattern of the death curve for married men. To explain this, however, would involve us even further in a demographic analysis, which is outside the scope of this book.

As a rule, in statistical practice, it is not necessary to calculate so many different measures for one problem. Usually we confine ourselves to one or two averages, and one measure of dispersion. The average is almost always the arithmetic mean, and in addition, perhaps, the mode or median. Dispersion is usually expressed by the standard deviation.

We shall now give an example of the application of these measures to other fields. Let us take a case from meteorology. If we observed temperatures in a certain locality in particular months over a long period of time, and if we calculated the average for each month, we would find that the temperatures in particular months differ considerably from each other, and show a yearly cycle having lower values in the winter months and higher in the summer. If, however, we observed the temperatures of each months in particular years of the long period under study, then we should get values deviating somewhat from the average for each month for the whole period. In addition to the level of temperature there is the variation of temperatures.[61]

TABLE 6.4. AVERAGE MONTHLY TEMPERATURES AND STANDARD DEVIATIONS
WARSAW, 1826–1910
(degrees centigrade)

| Month | Average | | Average over the whole period | Standard deviation | Range[a] of variation |
|---|---|---|---|---|---|
| | highest | lowest | | | |
| January | −13·4 | +1·6 | −4·2 | 3·17 | 15·0 |
| February | −11·4 | +3·6 | −2·8 | 3·25 | 15·0 |
| March | −6·9 | +7·5 | +0·8 | 2·39 | 14·4 |
| April | +3·3 | +11·2 | +7·0 | 1·84 | 7·9 |
| May | +7·9 | +17·6 | +12·9 | 1·94 | 9·7 |
| June | +13·5 | +20·5 | +16·9 | 1·53 | 7·0 |
| July | +14·1 | +21·8 | +18·4 | 1·49 | 7·7 |
| August | +13·4 | +21·4 | +17·5 | 1·45 | 8·0 |
| September | +10·3 | +16·5 | +13·4 | 1·35 | 6·2 |
| October | +3·8 | +12·8 | +7·9 | 1·76 | 9·0 |
| November | −3·0 | +6·1 | +1·6 | 2·02 | 9·1 |
| December | −12·3 | +2·3 | −2·3 | 3·10 | 14·6 |

ᵃ The difference between the highest and the lowest temperature in a given month.

61 The variation of temperature can also be studied in another way—as the difference between average temperatures of two consecutive days, or the difference between the highest and the lowest temperature in one day. Here we are concerned with fluctuations in the average monthly temperature in particular years of a long period of time.

The table below shows the average temperatures in Warsaw for each month of the year, as well as the standard deviation of the temperature of each month. The data are for the years from 1826–1910.[62]

Apart from differences in the levels of temperature in different months we can notice another interesting phenomenon: the standard deviation of the temperatures in the winter months (December, January, February) is more than twice as large as in the months from June to September (summer and early autumn). Spring and late autumn occupy an intermediate position. Thus the average temperatures in the summer months are much more stable than in the winter months. These differences in the variation of temperatures in different months are as important a characteristic of the climate as differences in the levels.

As well as the mean deviation, the range of variation is provided. In this case these values provide fairly useful measures of dispersion, and with certain reservations, they can be used instead of the mean deviations.[63]

The calculation of the coefficient of variation of temperatures is not indicated.

The values from the table are presented in graphical form (Figs 6.3 and 6.4, p. 234–5). The first of these figures shows levels of temperature in individual months: the highest and the lowest temperatures over the 85 years, as well as the average temperatures. The distance between the upper and lower line gives the range in the period covered. We should be careful not to be misled by the fact that the highest temperatures in all months are above zero, and not to jump to the conclusion that in one year there was no month with the average temperature below zero, since these highest temperatures could have occurred, of course, in different years. In the second figure the dispersion of temperatures is presented both by the standard deviation and by the range. To make a comparison possible separate scales were used for the two curves. We can see that the pattern of the curves in basically consistent.

---

[62] *Sieć meteorologiczna warszawska.* XV *Spostrzeżenia meteorologiczne dokonane w r.* 1909 *i* 1910 *na stacjach sieci warszawskiej (Warsaw Meteorological Stations.* XV. *Meteorological Observations in* 1909 *and* 1910), *Warsaw at Warsaw Stations* 1913 pp. 126 and 128. Temperatures in the 85-year period were measured in different ways, and under different conditions. In calculating the averages for many years and the standard deviations, certain corrections had to be introduced to make the date comparable.

[63] A more pronounced difference between the two measures appears in March. The range of variation in this month is 14·40 which is almost as much as in the winter months, and the mean deviation is relatively small, 2·39°. Indeed, out of the 85 years analysed, in 80 the mean temperatures were within the limits from —3·7° to +3·9°; only in four years were the mean temperatures from 4·0 to 7·5 and in one year it was exceptionally cold and the temperature was —6·9° which was 3·2° less than in the second coldest year.

These random but considerable deviations directly increase range but effect the standard deviation to a much lesser extent since in the latter all deviations from the arithmetic mean are taken into account. A similar situation, although less pronounced existed in May, in which the temperature in one year was exceptionally low at 7·9° whereas the second lowest was 9·0°. These examples indicate to what extent the range depends upon random factors.

The average annual temperature in the period was $7 \cdot 25°$ in the coldest year the temperature was $4 \cdot 8°$ and in the warmest, $9 \cdot 1°$; the standard deviation was $0 \cdot 88$, much less than for any one month. This is natural since the average annual temperature is the average of separate months and the variation of the average is always smaller than the variations in individual data. We shall return to this problem in the final part of this book.

## 6. MEASURES OF CONCENTRATION

The measures of dispersion discussed above are universal, and can be applied to all frequency distributions. However, there are situations in which they are rather artificial, and more appropriate measures should be sought. This applies particularly

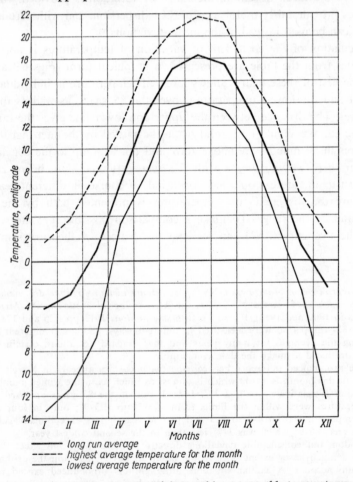

FIG. 6.3. Long run averages. Highest and lowest monthly temperatures in Warsaw, 1826–1920.

to extremely asymmetric distributions, such as, for instance, chose presenting the distribution of income by amount earned. In capitalistic countries there are many people with very low incomes and a few people with very high incomes. As opposed to this classification of people by size of income there is the distribution of income by its sum: the total of low incomes is relatively small and a very large portion of income is earned by a small number of people with very high incomes:

The classification of income tax payers in Poland in 1936 is shown in Table 6.5. on p. 236.

The calculation of the arithmetic mean in this case is technically impossible because the distribution is very strongly monotonically decreasing, the class intervals are large and the highest class—over 60,000 zlotys—is open-ended. Even if we did calculate the arithmetic mean, it would be too abstract, and not related to the actual distribution. What is the use of saying that the average income is, say, 3–4 thousand zlotys when an overwhelming majority have incomes much lower than the average and a few tax-payers with very high incomes account for one half of the total income? In addition, the measurement of the deviations from the mean also becomes meaningless.

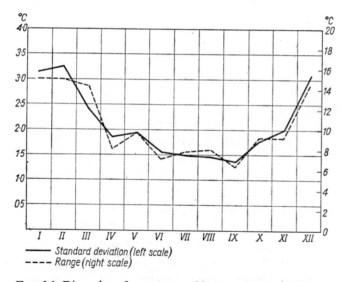

FIG. 6.4. Dispersion of average monthly temperatures in Warsaw in 1826–1910.

For distributions of this kind a notion of the measure of concentration has been devised. *Concentration* here means the massing of a certain portion of all the values in the hands of some of the population. In our example it is the concentration of a considerable portion of total income in the hands of a few tax payers with very high incomes. To understand better the meaning of concentration, and of the

TABLE 6.5. INCOME TAX PAYERS IN POLAND BY SIZE
OF ANNUAL INCOME (in 1936)

| Annual income in thousand zlotys[a] | Number of tax payers |
|---|---|
| *Total* | *385,294* |
| 1·5–2·6 | 193,753 |
| 2·6–3·6 | 67,833 |
| 3·6–6·0 | 64,194 |
| 6·0–12·0 | 39,141 |
| 12·0–24·0 | 13,849 |
| 24·0–36·0 | 3259 |
| 36·0–60·0 | 1858 |
| over 60·0 | 1407 |

[a] Non-taxable income of 1·5 thousand zlotys per annum or less is not included in the table.

measures used to evaluate it, let us consider another example. In Table 6.6 the distribution of farms by size in the country of Kutno is shown from the census of 1921. The class intervals are of unequal length because of the nature of the population. This makes it a little difficult to see the picture clearly at first glance. However, when we look at the first two columns in the table, which together constitute an ordinary frequency distribution, we notice a pronounced irregularity of pattern. The smallest farms are very numerous (especially those from 3 to 4 hectares), the medium-sized farms (from 5 to 10 and from 10 to 20 hectares), are also relatively numerous and there are very few large farms. When we look at the other columns in the table, and particularly at the cumulative frequencies in columns 6 and 7, we can easily see that more than half of all farms are less than 3 hectares, but that their combined area is less than 5 per cent of the total area. On the other hand almost half of the total area is occupied by farms of over 50 hectares, but their number accounts for only 1·2 per cent of the total number of farms. Thus we have established the considerable concentration of land in the hands of a few owners. We have also expressed this fact numerically albeit in a somewhat primitive way. Cumulative series serve as a basis for a special type of graph in which the phenomenon of concentration will appear with particular clarity. Let us take as abscissas the cumulative areas, both in relative values. In this way we obtain Fig. 6.5, a graphical presentation of the data in Table 6.6.

We plot points for the graph using as coordinates pairs of values from columns 6 and 7. Thus the first 3 points are: (20·4, 0·6), (37·3, 1·9), (44·7, 3·2). We join the points either by straight lines, thus obtaining a broken line, or, better, fit a smooth curve by hand or by mathematical interpolation. It should be remembered that the curve has to pass through the points plotted since they represent exact values.

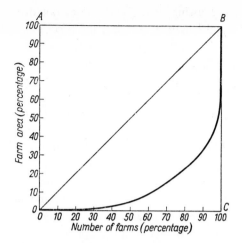

FIG. 6.5. Concentration of farms in the County
of Kutno in 1921.

TABLE 6.6. FARMS IN THE COUNTY OF KUTNO BY TOTAL AREA[64]
(in 1921)

| Size of farm (hectares) | Number of farms | Area of farms (hectares) | Number of farms | Area of farms | Number of farms | Area of farms |
| --- | --- | --- | --- | --- | --- | --- |
| | | | (percentages) | | cumulative series (percentages) | |
| 1 | 2 | 3 | 4 | 5 | 6 | 7 |
| *Total* | *9989* | *88,655* | *100·0* | *100·0* | *100·0* | *100·0* |
| 0·0–0·5 | 2023 | 578 | 20·4 | 0·6 | 20·4 | 0·6 |
| 0·5–1 | 1692 | 1112 | 16·9 | 1·3 | 37·3 | 1·9 |
| 1 –2 | 736 | 1120 | 7·4 | 1·3 | 44·7 | 3·2 |
| 2 –3 | 547 | 1371 | 5·5 | 1·5 | 50·2 | 4·7 |
| 3 –4 | 885 | 3121 | 8·9 | 3·5 | 59·1 | 8·2 |
| 4 –5 | 418 | 1908 | 4·2 | 2·2 | 63·3 | 10·4 |
| 5 –10 | 2173 | 15,335 | 21·7 | 17·3 | 85·0 | 27·7 |
| 10 –20 | 1242 | 16,145 | 12·4 | 18·2 | 97·4 | 45·9 |
| 20 –50 | 140 | 3792 | 1·4 | 4·3 | 98·8 | 50·2 |
| 50 –100 | 15 | 982 | 0·1 | 1·1 | 98·9 | 51·3 |
| 100 –200 | 32 | 4854 | 0·3 | 5·5 | 99·2 | 56·8 |
| 200 –1000 | 84 | 36,194 | 0·8 | 40·8 | 100·0 | 97·6 |
| over 1000 | 2 | 2143 | 0·0 | 2·4 | 100·0 | 100·0 |

*Note:* The area of farms in each size group (column 3 in the table) was given in the original publication. Without this information it would be difficult to estimate the area on the basis of the frequency distribution (columns 1 and 2 in the table) and for the last class it would be impossible. Columns 4 to 7 were calculated on the basis of columns 2 and 3.

---

[64] *Statystyka Polski (Statistical of Poland)*, Warsaw, 1928, vol. XI. No. 2. p. 5.

It is obvious that the drawing of the curve does not depend upon whether the class intervals are of equal length or not, but the precision of the graph will suffer if the intervals are large. The whole graph is drawn within the square *OABC*. We now draw the diagonal *OB*. We thus obtain a curve of a characteristic shape which is called the *curve of concentration* or the *Lorenz curve*. The curve is concave to the abscissa.

We shall now analyse the curve in greater detail and consider two cases: (1) equal division of land where all farms are of the same size, and (2) extreme concentration of land where a great part of the rural population have no land at all, or have only very small plots, and practically all the land belongs to one owner. In the first case, each fraction of the total number of farms will have an equivalent fraction of the total area: 10 per cent of the farms will have 10 per cent of the total area, 20 per cent of the farms will have 20 per cent of the total area, etc. Thus the particular points in the graph will be located along a straight line—the diagonal and instead of a curve we shall have the straight line *OB*. In the case of extreme concentration, where the majority of individuals have very little land, or none at all, the curve will at first be almost horizontal (even for a large number of farms the corresponding percentage of area is nearly zero) and only when far to the right will it start rising rapidly. In the extreme case, when concentration is complete, the curve becomes identical with the sides of the square, and we obtain the broken line *OCB*. In practice the concentration curve is located between the diagonal *OB* which indicates equal distribution and the broken line *OCB* which signifies complete concentration. The more even the distribution the closer the curve will be to the diagonal *OB,* and the greater the concentration the closer the curve will lie to the sides of the square *OCB*.

Let us consider another example: the distribution of farms by size according to the census of 1921 in the counties of Łowicz and Białowieża within their then boundaries. In the county of Łowicz the distribution of land was relatively even. The predominating type was the medium-sized farm: in the class 5–20 hectares there were almost 68 per cent of all farms and over 68 per cent of the total area. In the county of Białowieża, on the other hand, we have an example of almost complete concentration. Indeed, the 7 largest farms, each with an area of over 1000 hectares comprised 137,097 hectares of land out of a total of 156,097 hectares, which constituted 87·8 per cent of the total area (included in this figure were primarily government owned forest administration units): And 99 per cent of all farms occupied less than 10 per cent of the total area.

The degree of concentration can be seen very clearly in the figure, and a comparison of the figures should give a good idea of the situation existing in the counties compared.

However, we shall now also try to find a numerical way of describing concentration. A primitive method was described above (pp. 235–7). We can say that concentration in the county of Łowicz is much smaller than in the county of Kutno; $\frac{3}{4}$ of all farms (of less than 10 hectares) comprised over 40 per cent of the total area. On the other hand in the county of Białowieża 99 per cent of all farms occupied less than 10 per cent of the total area.

TABLE 6.7. FARMS BY AREA IN THE COUNTIES OF ŁOWICZ AND BIAŁOWIEŻA[65]
(in 1921)

| Area of farm (hectares) | County of Łowicz | | County of Biało-wieża | | County of Łowicz | | County of Białowieża | |
|---|---|---|---|---|---|---|---|---|
| | number of farms | area of farms (hectares) | number of farms | area of farms (hectares) | number of farms | area of farms | number of farms | area of farms |
| | | | | | cumulative distribution in percentages | | | |
| Total | 11,888 | 105,634 | 2694 | 156,097 | 100·0 | 100·0 | 100·0 | 100·0 |
| 0·0—0·5 | 560 | 149 | 77 | 24 | 4·7 | 0·1 | 2·9 | 0·0 |
| 0·5—1 | 576 | 390 | 79 | 64 | 9·6 | 0·5 | 5·8 | 0·1 |
| 1 —2 | 537 | 791 | 279 | 406 | 14·0 | 1·2 | 16·1 | 0·3 |
| 2 —3 | 392 | 1022 | 338 | 843 | 17·4 | 2·2 | 28·7 | 0·9 |
| 3 —4 | 703 | 2485 | 389 | 1371 | 23·3 | 4·6 | 43·1 | 1·7 |
| 4 —5 | 814 | 3660 | 346 | 1570 | 30·1 | 8·0 | 56·0 | 2·7 |
| 5 —10 | 5269 | 36,841 | 776 | 5460 | 74·5 | 42·9 | 84·8 | 6·2 |
| 10 —20 | 2773 | 35,450 | 333 | 4324 | 97·8 | 76·5 | 97·1 | 9·0 |
| 20 —50 | 215 | 5319 | 54 | 1516 | 99·6 | 81·5 | 99·1 | 10·0 |
| 50 —100 | 10 | 696 | 7 | 387 | 99·7 | 82·2 | 99·1 | 10·2 |
| 100 —200 | 7 | 1154 | 5 | 705 | 99·8 | 83·3 | 99·4 | 10·7 |
| 200 —1000 | 30 | 12,989 | 4 | 2330 | 100·0 | 95·6 | 99·7 | 12·2 |
| over 1000 | 2 | 4688 | 7 | 137,097 | 100·0 | 100·0 | 100·0 | 100·0 |

However, these more or less arbitrarily selected percentages of the number of farms and of the area are not sufficiently descriptive, since they do not describe the whole distribution in detail. The figure provides a hint of how to seek a better numerical measure of concentration. Such a measure can be found in the ratio of the area $a$ contained between the diagonal $OB$ and the concentration curve to the total area of the triangle $OBC$; or, in other words, the ratio of area $a$ to area $a+b$ if by $b$ we denote the area contained between the concentration curve and the sides $OC$ and $CB$. According to our previous argument his ratio will fluctuate between 0 and 1. When the distribution is even, the concentration curve will become the straight line $OB$ and area $a$ (and consequently the ratio $\frac{a}{a+b}$ ) will be zero.

In the case of extreme concentration, the ratio $\frac{a}{a+b}$ will approach unity. This ratio is called the concentration ratio and is denoted by the Greek letter $\eta$.

[65] *Statystyka Polski*, Warsaw, 1928, vol. XI, No. 2, pp. 5 and 19.

Concentration of farms in 1921

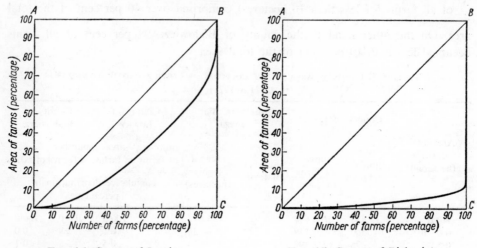

FIG. 6.6. County of Łowicz.                    FIG. 6.7. County of Białowieża.

The calculation of the concentration ratio is not easy. The exact calculation is not even possible. In order to do this, it would be necessary to find a function corresponding to the concentration curve and to calculate its area by integration. It is practically impossible to find a function that exactly fits a particular case. However, there are methods of calculating the approximate area, quite adequate for practical purposes. The calculation can be done by a graphical method. We have to draw as precise a graph as possible on squared paper, or preferably, on profile paper, and count the squares inside the figure *a*, and then, to cross-check, the square inside the figure *b*. The sum of the two areas should equal the area of triangle *OBC* which can easily be calculated since the sides *OC = CB* are known. Half of each square cut by the line *OB* belongs, of course, to the triangle *OBC*. The squares cut by the curve can also be divided half in figure *a* and half in figure *b*, without much error, providing the squares are small in relation to the area of the graph (errors in both directions will cancel out). If the squares are large we can estimate by eye what part of each belongs to one figure and what to another. In spite of being primitive, this sort of calculation is often sufficiently accurate for our purposes.

Better results can be obtained by using a planimeter for measuring area. If we smooth out the concentration curve carefully this would probably be the most precise method available for calculating the concentration ratio.

The graphical calculation gives the following concentration ratios: for the county of Kutno, 0·78, for the county of Łowicz, 0·45, for the county of Białowieża, 0·95. Concentration in the county of Białowieża is almost complete.

There are also other methods of calculating the concentration ratio approximately. We shall describe one of them, devised by Gini, without giving the proof. The calculation is relatively simple, and gives the results perhaps a little more precisely than other approximation methods.

Let $y$ be the number of farms, and $u$ the areas of farms in the cumulative distribution, expressed in relative values (columns 6 and 7, Table 6.6. p. 237) and let us form the auxiliary series:

$$z = y + u \quad \text{and} \quad t = y - u.$$

For the county of Kutno we get the following picture:

TABLE 6.8. CALCULATION OF THE CONCENTRATION RATIO

| Area of farms in hectares ($x$) | Number of farms ($y$) | Area of farms ($u$) | $z = y+u$ | $t = y-u$ |
|---|---|---|---|---|
| | cumulative distributions (percentages) | | | |
| 0·5 and less | 20·4 | 0·6 | 21·0 | 19·8 |
| 1 ,, | 37·3 | 1·9 | 39.2 | 35.4 |
| 2 ,, | 44·7 | 3·2 | 47·9 | 41·5 |
| 3 ,, | 50·2 | 4·7 | 54·9 | 45·5 |
| 4 ,, | 59·2 | 8·2 | 67·3 | 50·9 |
| 5 ,, | 63·3 | 10·4 | 73·7 | 52·9 |
| 10 ,, | 85·0 | 27·7 | 112.7 | 57·3 |
| 20 ,, | 97·4 | 45·9 | 143·3 | 51·5 |
| 50 ,, | 98·8 | 50·2 | 149·0 | 48·6 |
| 100 ,, | 98·9 | 51·3 | 150·2 | 47·6 |
| 200 ,, | 99·2 | 56·8 | 156·0 | 42·4 |
| 1000 ,, | 100·0 | 97·6 | 197·6 | 2·4 |
| Total | 100·0 | 100·0 | 200·0 | 0 |

The figures in series $z$ increase monotonically, to the value 200 for the greatest value of $x$. The figures in series $t$ increase to a certain level (in our case the maximum is richer at $x = 10$) and then decline to zero for the maximum value of $x$.

To proceed further we have to find four values of $t$ corresponding to the following points of the series $z$: $z_1 = 40$, $z_2 = 80$, $z_3 = 120$, $z_4 = 160$. This means that we are dividing the values of series $z$ into 5 equal parts of 40 units each. For $z = 0$ and $z = 200$, $t = 0$, as can be seen from the table. These values of $t$ can be found by interpolation, assuming, for instance, a uniform distribution within class intervals, just as in the calculation of the median and quartiles. In our example $z_1 = 40$ is located between 39·2 and 47·9, and thus $t$ will be located between 35·4 and 41·5, relatively as far from 41·5 as $z_1$ is from 47·9.

Thus we write

$$\frac{47 \cdot 9 - z_1}{47 \cdot 9 - 39 \cdot 2} = \frac{41 \cdot 5 - t_1}{41 \cdot 5 - 35 \cdot 4},$$

or substituting 40 for $z_1$

$$\frac{47 \cdot 9 - 40}{8 \cdot 7} = \frac{41 \cdot 5 - t_1}{6 \cdot 1},$$

Hence

$$t_1 = 41 \cdot 5 - \frac{7 \cdot 9 \times 6 \cdot 1}{8 \cdot 7} = 41 \cdot 5 - 5 \cdot 5 = 36 \cdot 0.$$

In a similar way we calculate $t_2$ for $z_2 = 80$

$$\frac{112 \cdot 7 - z_2}{112 \cdot 7 - 73 \cdot 7} = \frac{57 \cdot 3 - t_2}{57 \cdot 3 - 52 \cdot 9},$$

$$t_2 = 57 \cdot 3 - \frac{32 \cdot 7 \times 4 \cdot 4}{39 \cdot 0} = 57 \cdot 3 - 3 \cdot 7 = 53 \cdot 6.$$

In calculating $t_3$, which is located between $57 \cdot 3$ and $51 \cdot 5$, we should remember that in this segment the values of $z$ increase as the values of $t$ decrease so we have to write

$$\frac{z_3 - 112 \cdot 7}{143 \cdot 3 - 112 \cdot 7} = \frac{57 \cdot 3 - t_3}{57 \cdot 3 - 51 \cdot 5},$$

$$t_3 = 57 \cdot 3 - \frac{7 \cdot 3 \times 5 \cdot 8}{30 \cdot 6} = 55 \cdot 9.$$

Similarly for $t_4$

$$\frac{z_4 - 156 \cdot 0}{197 \cdot 6 - 156 \cdot 0} = \frac{42 \cdot 4 - t_4}{42 \cdot 4 - 2 \cdot 4},$$

$$t_4 = 42 \cdot 4 - \frac{4 \cdot 0 \times 40 \cdot 0}{41 \cdot 6} = 38 \cdot 6$$

We calculate the concentration ratio according to the formula

$$\eta = \frac{25}{144 \times 100} \times [3 \times (t_1 + t_4) + 2(t_2 + t_3)]. \tag{VI.16}$$

After substituting, we get

$$\eta = \frac{25}{14,400} \times [3 \times (36 \cdot 0 + 38 \cdot 6) + 2 \times (53 \cdot 6 + 55 \cdot 9)] = 0 \cdot 769.$$

From the mathematical point of view the calculation consists in the approximate evaluation of the integral.[66]

A graphical solution gives 0·775, or, after rounding off, 0·78. It should be remembered that the computation of the concentration ratio is always approximate, and it is not advisable to retain more than two decimals; even the second decimal place may be inaccurate.

We set out below the results for selected counties.

TABLE 6.9. CONCENTRATION RATIO FOR FARMS IN SELECTED COUNTIES (1921)

| County | Concentration ratio | |
|---|---|---|
| | graphical solution | mathematic solution (formula VI.16) |
| Białowieża | 0·95 | 0·92 |
| Szamotuły | 0·89 | 0·88 |
| City of Poznań | 0·89 | 0·89 |
| Kutno | 0·78 | 0·77 |
| Żnin | 0·74 | 0·73 |
| Radzymin | 0·51 | 0·50 |
| Łowicz | 0·45 | 0·44 |

With the exception of the County of Białowieża the differences between the methods of calculation never exceed one unit in the second decimal place. In any case, these differences are negligible in comparison with the differences among particular counties.

In addition to the concentration ratio, there are other measures of concentration also based on the Lorenz curve. However we shall not discuss them in this book.

By their very nature the measures of concentration are best suited for characterizing extremely asymmetric distributions, with which we often deal in studying the distribution of national income in capitalist countries. However, the method of analysing concentration described above is fairly universal, and can always be used when the measures of dispersion are calculated. It is necessary, though, to have not only the number of events but also the sum of values in particular classes, or some data which enable us to compute these sums fairly accurately.

Let us consider a few more examples of the application of the measures of concentration.

---

[66] A good exposition of the above as well as other calculation methods, logical foundations and different applications of the analysis of concentration was given by S. Fogelson in his work: "Miary koncentracji i ich zastosowanie" (Measures of Concentration and Their Application) in *Kwartalnik Statystyczny (Statistical Quarterly)*, Warsaw, 1933, vol. X, No. 1, pp. 149–97.

S. Fogelson[67] calculated the concentration ratio for farms in different provinces in Poland. According to his calculations, in which Eastern provinces were not included, the values of $\eta$ were smallest for the provinces of Łódź (0·56), Lublin (0·56), Kielce (0·57) and Cracow (0·58), and highest for the provinces of Pomorze (0·77) and Poznań (0·75).

Jan Wiśniewski[68] calculated the concentration of income for different population groups in Poland in 1929. These calculations are partially based on estimates but in general they do reflect the true situation. For income from salaries, wages and pension benefits, the concentration ratio for factory workers was 0·32 and for white-collar workers 0·36. For income other than salaries and wages, outside agriculture the concentration ratio was 0·60. This is much greater, of course, since included in this income category were small merchants and craftsmen with very low incomes as well as businessmen, financiers etc.—whose incomes were high.

TABLE 6.10. INDUSTRIAL ESTABLISHMENTS IN POLAND BY NUMBER OF EMPLOYEES
(1946)

| Number of employees in establishment | Metallurgical industry | | Textile industry | | Clothing industry | |
|---|---|---|---|---|---|---|
| | Number of mills | Total number of workers | Number of factories | Total number of workers | Number of factories | Total number of workers |
| *Total* | *42* | *67,761* | *3549* | *160,444* | *38,110* | *96,824* |
| up to 4 | — | — | 2410 | 4009 | 36,513 | 50,959 |
| 5–9 | — | — | 301 | 1856 | 1088 | 6722 |
| 10–14 | — | — | 122 | 1449 | 158 | 1780 |
| 15–19 | 1 | 18 | 78 | 1315 | 65 | 1077 |
| 20–29 | 2 | 56 | 76 | 1862 | 76 | 1827 |
| 30–39 | — | — | 64 | 2197 | 34 | 1157 |
| 40–49 | — | — | 64 | 2808 | 37 | 1651 |
| 50–74 | 1 | 67 | 104 | 6472 | 24 | 1488 |
| 75–99 | — | — | 64 | 5518 | 24 | 2062 |
| 100–149 | 1 | 114 | 72 | 8599 | 31 | 3737 |
| 150–199 | 3 | 506 | 43 | 7348 | 19 | 3191 |
| 200–249 | 2 | 456 | 20 | 4407 | 1 | 245 |
| 250–299 | 2 | 544 | 25 | 6823 | 11 | 2950 |
| 300–399 | 4 | 1405 | 31 | 10,604 | 7 | 2426 |
| 400–499 | — | — | 16 | 7236 | 7 | 3056 |
| 500–999 | 5 | 3631 | 29 | 20,183 | 10 | 6880 |
| 1000–1999 | 7 | 8268 | 19 | 24,852 | 5 | 5616 |
| 2000–4999 | 11 | 32,355 | 9 | 30,710 | — | — |
| 5000 and over | 3 | 20,341 | 2 | 12,196 | — | — |

[67] Ibid., p. 450 et seq.
[68] Jan Wiśniewski: *Rozdział dochodów według wysokości w roku 1929* (*The Distribution of Income in 1929*), Warsaw, 1934, p. 75.

In *Statystyka Zakładów Przemysłowych i Rzemieślniczych w r. 1946*[69] (*Statistics on Industrial and Handicraft Establishments in 1946*)[69] published by the Central Statistical Office (GUS) there are data on the distribution of industrial establishments according to the number of employees. For this example we have selected the metallurgical, textile and clothing industries. They present the following picture (see Table 6.10 p. 244):

*Concentration of industrial establishments in Poland in 1946*

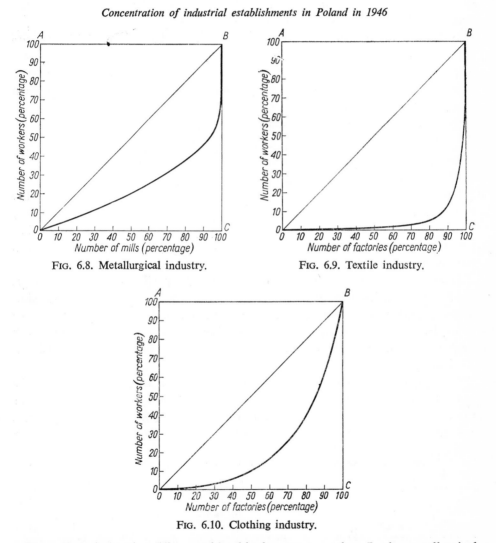

FIG. 6.8. Metallurgical industry.    FIG. 6.9. Textile industry.

FIG. 6.10. Clothing industry.

These three industries differ considerably from one another. In the metallurgical industry there were very large establishments and their average number of workers

[69] *Statystyka Polski,* Series D, No. 5, Warsaw, 1948, pp. XVI–XIX.

was over 160. There were very few employing less than 100 workers, and very large establishments, with 2000 or more workers, employed almost 78 per cent of all workers.

In the textile industry the average number of workers per factory was also fairly large—45·2 (the average for all industries was 9·5 workers per establishment). However, in the textile industry there were many very small factories; almost 68 per cent of all establishments employed fewer than 5 workers; nevertheless, a large portion of all workers were employed in the largest.

In the clothing industry the average number of workers per establishment was only 2·54 and 96 per cent of all factories employed fewer than 5 workers. What is more, these establishments employed almost 53 per cent of all workers. There were very few large factories and the total number of workers employed by them was relatively small.

This situation is reflected in the concentration ratio in the following way:

The metalurgical industry $\eta = 0·56$
The textile industry $\eta = 0·90$
The clothing industry $\eta = 0·72$

Concentration was highest in the textile industry. In addition to a large number of very small establishments there were very large ones employing the majority of the workers. Concentration in the metallurgical industry was much less pronounced: even though large factories predominated, there were no small establishments, and the distribution is more uniform.

The clothing industry occupies the intermediate position.[70] In this example the fact that the intensity of concentration is not related to the size of establishments is very clearly emphasized. In the metallurgical industry in which the establishments ary very large, concentration is relatively small, at any rate much smaller than in the clothing industry in which very small establishments predominate.

S. Fogelson calculated the distribution of population in different parts of the world by areas with different population densities.[71] We give here the figures for Europe and North America. Both in Europe and in North America large areas are very sparsely populated. But, whereas in Europe the areas with the population

---

[70] It is difficult to draw the concentration curve for the clothing industry because the first point that we can plot has an abscissa of 96 per cent (the percentage of establishments employing fewer than 5 workers) and an ordinate of 53 per cent (the percentage of workers employed in those establishments). The shape of the curve between this point and the origin is unknown, and therefore the concentration ratio can be only roughly calculated.

[71] The calculation was based on the data concerning area, population and population density in particular administrative units (provinces, states, departments, etc.) in every major country. Because of great differences in the size of these basic administrative units the picture obtained is not very precise but in general dose not arouse serious reservations. The tables were published in *Encyklopedia Nauk Politycznych* (*The Encyklopaedia of Political Sciences*), Warsaw, 1938, Vol. III. p. 645.

density of fewer than 5 persons per km² constitute 25·5 per cent of the total area, in North America they constitute 73·1 per cent. In Europe the highest portion of the population live in areas with a population density of 50–100 persons per km² (33·6 per cent of the population), and next in areas with a population density of 100–250 persons per km² (24·0 per cent). In these two areas combined live 57·6 per cent of all the inhabitants of Europe. In North America only 7 per cent of all the inhabitants live in areas with these population densities, and the top positions are occupied by areas with the highest density (250 and more persons per km²—29·1 per cent of the population), and by areas with relatively low densities (10–25 persons per km²—29·0 per cent of the population).

TABLE 6.11. POPULATION OF EUROPE AND NORTH AMERICA BY POPULATION DENSITY

| Areas with population density per km² | Percentage of area | Percentage of population | Percentage of area | Percentage of population |
|---|---|---|---|---|
| | Europe | | North America | |
| Less than 1 person | 12·3 | 0·1 | 43·4 | 1·2 |
| 1–5 persons | 13·2 | 0·7 | 29·7 | 6·4 |
| 5–10 ,, | 6·1 | 0·9 | 8·6 | 9·8 |
| 10–25 ,, | 14·0 | 5·3 | 12·9 | 29·0 |
| 25–50 ,, | 22·8 | 17·6 | 4·2 | 17·5 |
| 50–100 | 21·9 | 33·6 | 0·8 | 5·9 |
| 100–250 ,, | 7·9 | 24·0 | 0·1 | 1·1 |
| 250 and more persons | 1·8 | 17·8 | 0·3 | 29·1 |
| *Total* | *100·0* | *100·0* | *100·0* | *100·0* |

After forming the cumulative distributions we get the following concentration curves:

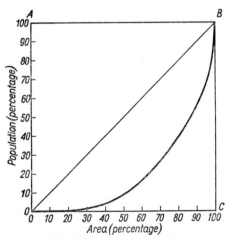

FIG. 6.11. Concentration of population in Europe.

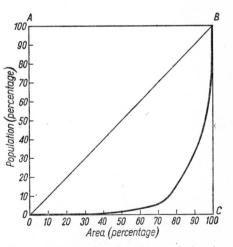

FIG. 6.12. Concentration of population in North America.

The concentration ratio for North America is 0·82 per cent, and for Europe 0·59 per cent, in spite of the fact that the population density in Europe (over 46 persons per km² is much higher than in North America (only 7·2 persons per km²).

The above examples and their explanations should have given a fairly clear idea of the meaning and possible applications of measures of concentration.

# CHAPTER 7

# STRUCTURAL SERIES BASED ON NON-MEASURABLE CHARACTERISTICS

The problems involved in analysing structural series based on non-measurable characteristics cannot be presented as clearly and systematically as the problems involved in analysing frequency distributions.

## 1. ARRANGEMENT OF THE SERIES

Whereas in a frequency distribution the order of arrangement is given by decreasing or increasing values of the variate, and the actual problem consists in determining the class intervals, in the series now discussed the order of arranging the items is, generally, a matter of indifference. Sometimes this order follows a logical sequence warranted by the nature of the classification. When we deal with the colour of eyes or hair it is natural to list the colours from the lightest to the darkest, or the other way around. However, if the order is not maintained the series will not lose much. In other cases even these logical criteria are lacking, and the order can be completely arbitrary. Sometimes we may be guided by the importance of particular parts of the population, for instance, their relative frequencies. In other cases we may arrange the characteristics according to their logical relationship, or list them in alphabetical order, etc.

Much more important is the problem of how far to go into detail. Sometimes the division must be detailed and we may have to deal with each possible alternative separately. This happens when we divide the population by sex, into men and women. The division of government revenues from taxes may be quite detailed if we list all the taxes levied in a given country. However, in many cases the matter is not so simple. Let us consider foreign trade statistics. Even most detailed statements are bound to contain some collective items. For instance "wheat flour" comprises different qualities, different degrees of grinding, etc. The most detailed list comprises several thousand export and import items: such details are published only in very specialized publications. For general purposes, however, a much more abbreviated classification is used. Sometimes only the most important items of the detailed list are selected, say, on the basis of quantities sold or bought, and the remainder is shown as one figure. This method is used with good results in cases where there are a few items of outstanding importance, so that after they are given separately, the remainder is unimportant. This may happen in countries whose imports or exports are very specialized. In such cases the listing of a number of the most important commodities gives a realistic picture, and if we carefully follow yearly changes we can keep abreast of the most important trends. Where the remainder is still significant, after listing of the most important items the report loses in value and usefulness, since important changes may occur in the total of miscellaneous items lumped together.

In the table "Poland's Trade with Selected Countries by Staple Commodities" published before the war in the *Concise Statistical Yearbook 1939* (p. 179), among imports to Poland from Argentina only three commodities were listed, as shown in the table below:

TABLE 7.1. IMPORTS TO POLAND FROM ARGENTINA

| Commodity | 1936 | 1938 |
|---|---|---|
| | in millions of zlotys | |
| *Total* | 27·7 | 36·8 |
| Raw hides | 12·0 | 15·5 |
| Wood and waste | 7·3 | 13·0 |
| Chemical and pharmaceutical products; paints | 7·4 | 7·1 |

In 1936 the above three commodities constituted about 96·4 per cent, and in 1938, 96·7 per cent of our total imports from that country. The listing of these commodities is quite sufficient to establish the fact that imports from Argentina were very one-sided, and that the general increase in that period (by 9·1 million zlotys) was partly due to the increased import of raw hides, but mainly caused by an increase in the import of wool (almost by 80 per cent). The table is quite sufficient to characterize our imports from Argentina. Only in a very special study would we be interested in the data on other imported commodities which in 1936 together constituted only 3·6 per cent, in 1938, 3·3 per cent of the total import. The situation is different as far as our imports from Czechoslovakia are concerned. In the *Yearbook* ten different commodities are mentioned, which in 1938 amounted to only 62·9 per cent of our imports from that country. The remaining 37·1 per cent may contain some items important for characterizing the nature of the turnover with Czechoslovakia.

This method of publishing statistical data may be justified partly by the type of publication (The *Concise Statistical Yearbook* could not very well go into all the details) and partly by the fact that although the ten listed commodities omitted quite a few, none of them separately amounted to very much.

Another way of making a detailed statement a little more general consists in combining certain items into groups based on some general principle of classification.

The difficulty consists in finding the most appropriate principle of classification and its consistent implementation. This is usually very difficult and often impossible without some compromise. Industrial goods in foreign trade may be divided according to (1) the raw materials used, (2) the final use of the product, and (3) the technique employed. Very often all three criteria of division may be used in the same classification. Thus we distinguish between metal, textile, wood and leather industries on the basis of the raw material used. At the same time such groups are formed as food, clothing and musical instrument industries, for which the criterion is the final use of the product. And still another group is, e.g., the chemical industry is distinguished on the basis of the technical production process. This lack of uniformity in selecting according to a universal principle may sometimes be due to inconsistency or untidiness. Sometimes, however, only this kind of approach will best enable us to form groups which are relatively uniform internally.

These examples also show that the classification of the series based on non-measurable characteristics is not exclusively, or even mainly, a statistical problem. For the classification to be good it is necessary to consider first the subject to which the statistical data pertain. A thorough knowledge of the subject and the precision in posing the problem which is to be solved will enable us to choose the most appropriate method of classification in each case. The fact that it is for each given case should be particularly strongly stressed since a change in the objective of the study may cause a change in the criterion of classification.

In foreign trade statistics we can find a good guide to the economic structure of the country in the division of the commodities based on their final use. For instance, the percentages of imported industrial raw materials on the one hand, and production machinery and equipment on the other, are an important indication of the level and direction of economic development of a country.

Apart from the classification according to final use, there is another type of classification based on the degree of processing: raw materials, slightly processed goods, highly processed goods. This division may also throw light on the level of development and studied chronologically it may indicate the trend of development of a country.[72] It is also possible to classify commodities as perishable, i.e. those which perish in manufacturing (e.g. coal, kaolin as a raw material in the production of china), or in consumption (food, ink, etc.), and those which are durable, such as machinery, furniture, etc.

This threefold and overlapping division according to final use, degree of processing, or durability served as a basis for international classification established by

---

[72] This division according to the degree of processing only partly overlaps with the previously used division into raw materials, semi-manufactured goods, finished goods. Yarn in the textile industry is a typical semi-product (cannot be used directly) and is simultaneously a little-processed good. But nails are a finished product, although they are a little-processed good. Milk is neither a raw material nor a semi-product, although in Poland it is sold in a raw state (refrigerated and pasteurized milk is a little-processed good).

the Committee of Statistical Experts at the League of Nations and then accepted by many countries as an auxiliary classification for international comparisons.

From a different point of view it may be worth while to accept classification according to the raw-material used. There are many countries which export wood and its products, metal and metal products, etc.

Sometimes special groups may be singled out if they are important from some point of view. In Polish foreign trade statistics before the war there was a group called "agricultural products and agricultural processed goods of the moderate zone", i.e. those products which could be produced in the country and so could be exported but, perhaps, not imported. The sense of this classification is evident.

The purpose of forming such groups may be a desire to obtain a general picture from which conclusions can be drawn without going into detail. But even when we decide to use detailed classification we have to introduce some sort of order, especially when we deal with a large number of items; obviously we cannot confine ourselves to listing several thousand commodities in alphabetical order and at least some groups must be formed if we want to avoid complete chaos. To do this we have to know the subject and keep in mind the objective. In arranging series based on non-measurable characteristics, criteria outside the formal scope of statistics are always of great importance.

It follows that a change in general conditions may call for a change in the principles of classification. In the capitalist economy of pre-war Poland the criterion for the classification of enterprises was their legal status: joint-stock companies, limited liability companies, partnerships, co-operative societies and privately owned companies. This classification did not give a very good picture of socio-economic relations even at that time and would be completely meaningless today. The classification used in People's Poland until 1949 was by sectors: central government enterprises local government enterprises, co-operative societies, privately owned enterprises (see the *Statistical Yearbook* for 1949, p. 34). An even simpler and clearer classification would be into the socialist sector and the private sector.

We emphasized above that in the final analysis the arrangement of series based on measurable characteristics should also be based on criteria other than statistical (see p.127 *et seq.*). For those series, however, technical statistical considerations are also of importance and may make it desirable to arrange a series in such a way as to facilitate its statistical analysis (e.g. the proper calculation of statistical measures). In arranging series based on non-measurable characteristics this technical statistical consideration plays a much less important role.

Once the problem of classification is settled there should be no major difficulties in designing the table. By simple sorting we find out how many units or what total values there should be in each class. Certain difficulties arise in deciding in which class certain units of the population should be included. For instance, if we classify industrial establishments according to their final product certain doubts may arise when an establishment produces goods which be long to different groups according to the accepted classification. In such cases we can form a group of establishments with mixed product range, and name only typical combinations of products including less common or accidental combinations in a miscellaneous group of "other establishments producing miscellaneous goods". However, this is possible only to a limited extent, and we may often be forced to include an establishment in a certain group on the basis of predominant goods. In this, however, an element of arbitrariness is involved, and the rules for classifying doubtful cases should be unambiguously laid down in appropriate instructions.

All these examples point to the necessity of possessing a good knowledge of the subject for arranging the series properly, for selecting proper criteria of classification and for analysing the data.

## 2. THE TECHNIQUE OF ANALYSING SERIES

In analysing series and especially in a comparative analysis of the structure of different populations we use different computation devices or graphical methods. One of the first preparatory tasks is to computate what is often called relative structural numbers, such as the ratio of the components to the total, or under certain circumstances, the ratios of the components to one another. It is a usual practice to select unity, or some round number like 100 or 1000 in relation to which the ratios are calculated. Certain details of the calculation of relative structural of relative structural numbers will be discussed in the chapter on relative numbers.

In a graphical presentation we use graphs which show the structure: rectangles of the same base and different heights, or vice versa, circles divided into sectors, squares divided into smaller squares, etc. (see above pp. 108 *et seq.*).

Table 7.2 contains the data on foreign trade concerning imports and exports of selected capitalist countries classified according to the final use of the product on the basis of the international classification agreed upon by the Committee of Statistical Experts of the League of Nations. On the basis of this table we shall give an example of a very simple analysis of a statistical and economic type.

In this table the absolute figures do not provide a clear picture of the structure of foreign trade. A much better picture is obtained from the percentages which bring to light quite a few important facts. It can easily be seen that a very important part was played in the foreign trade of the countries shown in the table by production materials; their share was the highest (73·0 per cent) in imports to the United States, and only in exports from Denmark did they play a less important role (16·1 per cent). Consumer goods also important, although here the differences from country to country were much greater. In exports from Denmark they reached 70 per cent, and in imports only 12·2 per cent. Even wider ffluctuations were

TABLE 7.2. FOREIGN TRADE OF SELECTED COUNTRIES ACCORDING TO FINAL USE OF PRODUCT (1936)[73]

| Commodity group | Poland | | England | | Denmark | | United States | |
|---|---|---|---|---|---|---|---|---|
| | import | export | import | export | import | export | import | export |
| | In millions of monetary units of the country | | | | | | | |
| *Total* | *1003·4* | *1026·0* | *782·6* | *426·6* | *1442·2* | *1326·5* | *2397* | *2408* |
| Production materials | 689·3 | 595·4 | 412·2 | 202·3 | 830·9 | 213·6 | 1750 | 1096 |
| Oils and fats | 32·8 | 13·0 | 28·3 | 4·6 | 120·6 | 69·5 | 137 | 22 |
| Fuels, electric power | 7·5 | 167·0 | 37·6 | 38·7 | 206·3 | 1·0 | 57 | 329 |
| Machinery, investment equipment | 120·5 | 16·7 | 23·6 | 74·5 | 108·1 | 117·1 | 27 | 532 |
| Consumer goods | 153·3 | 233·9 | 280·9 | 106·5 | 176·3 | 925·4 | 426 | 429 |
| | In percentages | | | | | | | |
| *Total* | *100·0* | *100·0* | *100·0* | *100·0* | *100·0* | *100·0* | *100·0* | *100·0* |
| Production materials | 68·7 | 58·0 | 52·7 | 47·4 | 57·6 | 16·1 | 73·0 | 45·5 |
| Oils and fats | 3·3 | 1·3 | 3·6 | 1·1 | 8·4 | 5·2 | 5·7 | 0·9 |
| Fuels, electric power | 0·7 | 16·3 | 4·8 | 9·1 | 14·3 | 0·1 | 2·4 | 13·7 |
| Machinery, investment equipment | 12·0 | 1·6 | 3·0 | 17·4 | 7·5 | 8·8 | 1·1 | 22·1 |
| Consumer goods | 15·3 | 22·8 | 35·9 | 25·0 | 12·2 | 69·8 | 17·8 | 17·8 |

noticeable in machinery and equipment. In Poland they accounted for 12 per cent of imports and only 1·6 per cent of exports. On the other hand in the United States the share of machinery and equipment in imports was only 1·1 per cent, and in exports 22·1 per cent.

We can also take particular countries as a starting point for our analysis and say that, for instance, in total imports to Poland the most important part was played by production materials and that goods for direct consumptions as well as machinery and equipment were also quite important. However the share of the latter in exports, was quite negligible, but an important part was played by consumer goods and (in comparison with other countries) fuel. In imports to England the share of consumer goods was particularly high (35·9 per cent). They also played an important part in England's exports, but here machinery and equipment, were more important, the reverse situation to Polands where machinery and equipment were imported, but almost none exported.

This kind of highlighting of the characteristics of different populations is easy if we have properly designed tables of relative numbers. A truly scientific analysis, however, begins anly after the statistical data are commented upon from the economic angle—as in our example—or from some other relevant and pertinent point of view, probing into the nature of the phenomenon.

It should also be remembered that relative numbers are a sort of supplement

---

[73] *The Concise Statistical Yearbook 1939*, p. 174. Table 14.

to absolute numbers, but they are no substitute for the latter. We have to consider not only the relative importance of exports or imports, but also their absolute numbers. In our case a comparison of absolute numbers could be made in monetary units. The difficulty is that the turnover figures are expressed in different currencies and they should be translated into one currency at the prevailing rate of exchange. If we wanted to allow for the purchasing power of money in each country we would have to perform additional and involved calculations.

As we can see from the above discussion of methods of analysing structural series based on non-measurable characteristics the problem is simple from the statistical point of view. This side of it can easily be handled by every statistician familiar with table design. If difficulties arise they are likely to be of a non-statistical nature.

CHAPTER 8

# TERRITORIAL OR GEOGRAPHICAL SERIES

## 1. TERRITORIAL UNITS

Series of this kind are used to present the geographical distribution of events. Such a presentation is possible only on a map of territorial division. Facts relating to each territorial unit are given, or the sum of values corresponding to these facts; sometimes the intensity of a given phenomenon in each territory may be given instead. It may be the number of farms or the total area of arable land in each county, or the number of traffic accidents in different precincts of a city, or the population density in different parts of a country.

Thus the question of selecting the territorial unit and of establishing its size and borders is very important. In principle, each phenomenon may require its own type of territorial unit, the one that is most natural from its point of view. Each unit should be as uniform internally as possible and the contrasts between one and another should appear between particular units. A rigid observance of this principle would lead to as many territorial divisions as there are phenomena to be studied. This is practically impossible, and would create difficulties in comparing the geographical distribution of different phenomena. Another difficulty is that most statistical data, especially in the social field, are published with a break-down by administrative units binding in each State and the administrative division will only in exceptional cases be natural from the point of view of the phenomenon studied statistically.

If, for instance, we are studying the density of population, then, it may happen that the population of county $A$ is not evenly distributed, and the county is composed of two clearly different parts, in one of which the population density is high, and in the other low. It may also happen that the densely populated part adjoins other counties, $B$, $C$ and $D$ which are also densely populated, thus forming a large area with a high population density, whereas the rest of the county, together with the neighbouring counties $K$, $L$ and $M$ forms an area rather sparsely populated. Thus the dividing line cuts across county $A$. If we calculate the population density of the whole county we shall get a meaningless figure. Sometimes even the shape of a teritorial unit may influence its average characteristics. Let us suppose that we have a territory ranging from an uninhabited mountain range to densely populated plains, with a gradual and uniform transition in the whole

256

territory. Let us now imagine the counties as schematic equilateral triangles, some with the apex turned toward the mountain range, some with the bases.

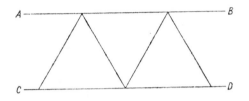

FIG. 8.1. Schematic chart of counties.

If the population density increases evenly across the whole territory from zero in the mountain range (line *AB*) to, say, 60 persons per square kilometer on the plains (line *CD*), the average population density of the counties with the base pointed at the mountains will be 20 persons per square kilometer, and of the counties with apex toward the mountains, 40 persons per square kilometer, i.e. twice as many. Thus for a uniform territory we get different pictures caused by circumstances unrelated to the phenomenon studied—by a variation of the shape of the administrative unit. This kind of systematic shape of administrative units does not occur in real life, but the shapes are occasionally fairly unnatural, and consequently the averages calculated for them may be unreliable.

Sometimes we may be able to choose between larger administrative units and smaller ones. Usually small units are more homogenous than large units. However, when the units are very small the picture obtained may be chaotic. In addition, for most statistical phenomena there is a certain minimum size below which the administrative unit should not go.

Let us return to the example of population density. Let us suppose that we are investigating an agricultural country relatively densely and evenly populated, with population centred in large villages. Disregarding the administrative division, we could calculate the population density for each square kilometer separately. This would be technically feasible if we had sufficiently detailed statistical data, and a large-scale map. In this case there would be many square kilometers completely uninhabited (located between the villages) and beside them large densely populated areas, especially when there appears a very large and compactly built village. The very nature of the notion of population density requires that the administrative units selected be sufficiently large. Their size depends on the type of settlement, and the size and location of the villages. The natural lower limit with regard to the rural areas would be a single settlement, with the territory belonging to it.

If we take a small administrative unit as a starting point, we can transfer to larger units by joining the neighbouring units similar in character, and in so doing we can disregard the administrative division at a higher level. This method was used in publishing the results of the general census in 1931 for major cities: police precincts were combined into "statistical districts". In this way Warsaw was divided into 12 statistical districts, instead of 26 police precincts. At the same time the whole city was divided into 111 much more detailed statistical areas, which were not related to the existing administrative division, but were formed by adding up the data for separate blocks (the houses located within the rectangles formed by neighbouring streets).

It is difficult to form such territorial units of a higher order, unrelated to administrative divisions, because it requires going into the structure of very small administrative units, which is always troublesome, and sometimes impossible. To form them on the basis of intuition is risky, because an erroneous division, instead of providing a basis for proper analysis facilitating the investigation, may lead to wrong conclusions. Nevertheless, the method itself is commendable, since the purpose of geographical analysis is the formation of "natural districts". We shall return to this problem in discussing the preparation of cartograms.

In principle geographical units should be listed in the order of their location, i.e. neighbouring units should be listed next to each other. However, when the number of units is large this is often impossible, and, in addition, it misses the point, because the method does not produce a clear picture of geographical distribution. Such a picture can be obtained only by placing statistical data on a map. In constructing tables, on the other hand, we should always strive to make it easy to find the required unit. This can best be achieved by listing the names of the geographical units in alphabetical order, or, if they are numbered, (e.g. the statistical districts in Warsaw), by listing them in numerical order. In certain cases we may use a conventional order, established once and for all for a given problem.

In the publications of the Central Statistical Office in Poland, and in other official publications, the provinces are listed in a conventional order along a spiral line originating in Warsaw. In this way the provinces are listed next to the adjoining ones. The counties within each province, however, are listed in alphabetical order.

## 2. THE CARTOGRAM AS A TOOL FOR ANALYSING GEOGRAPHICAL SERIES

A cartogram is a map on which the geographical distribution of statistical phenomena is marked. As a base a schematic map is commonly used. All the details that might obscure the statistical picture are usually removed. Very often only the administrative boundaries are marked. Sometimes even these boundaries are removed, with only some essential reference points left on the map: the most important rivers, a few major cities, etc.

a. *The method of symbols*. The distribution of statistical phenomena on the map can be marked in several ways. We can state that a given fact is represented by a certain symbol, and the place these symbols on the map in places where the phenomenon occurs. We see such symbols on ordinary maps in which towns of different sizes are marked by circles or squares of size corresponding to the number of inhabitants within the limits stated on the map.

On the same principle, we can select a number of signs, called *symbols* (or sometimes *hieroglyphs*) to express different phenomena. In this way we can make economic maps in which the location of different economic objects is marked. A hack may denote a mine; a furnace, a foundry, etc. If we want to show not only that the phenomenon appears in a given location, but also the frequency or intensity with which it appears, we can use symbols of different sizes; or, better still, we can repeat the symbol an appropriate number of times, as in the Viennese method (see above, p. 117). In this way we get a clear picture of the geographical distribution. It is desirable that the scale of the map be sufficiently large, to avoid crowding the symbols, and to give a clear picture. When the scale is large, we can also show on the map such geographical details as are necessary to provide the bearings, and to relate the distribution of the events, studied to other geographical factors. This method is particularly appropriate for teaching, and is often used in preparing school maps. It can also be used in scientific research. However, its use is rather limited, since it is quite rigird and not very suitable for presenting complex problems.

b. *The area method*. The area method is a strictly statistical method of presenting facts on the map. It consists of dividing the territory into smaller territorial units, calculating for each of them the relevant values of the phenomenon studied, and shading or colouring the area of each territorial unit in an appropriate way. We usually mark in this way the facts that can be expressed as densities: the number of inhabitants per square kilometer, the output of grain *per capita*, etc. If only one colour is used, we can shade the area using broken or dotted lines, or by points in such a way as to achieve the effect of distinct gradation from rarely placed points, through thin lines more or less densely spaced, to thick lines located close to each other, or even to complete blocking out of the area. The idea is to show gradation from very light areas to very dark ones. The visual effect will convey the frequency of the appearance of the phenomenon. In this way we can use a very broad scale, with up to ten or more units. The shading may be done in black or in any other colour.

The use of colours considerably broadens the scope. When several colours are used, we can reflect subtler variations in intensity. The impression is more pleasing when the whole area is coloured.

Gradation consists in using different shades of the same colour or of different colours. It is more natural to present the intensity of a phenomenon the first way.

We can use brown for population density—pale for sparsely populated areas and dark, almost black, for densely populated ones.

In hypsometric maps, different colours may be used so that, for instance, green is used for lowlands—the lower, the darker the colour—and light yellow to brown for higher regions.

High mountains are usually marked in a special way. In this way the scale may be considerably broadened, and the effect may be pleasing to the eye. In general, however, the effect of contrast between green lowlands and yellow and brown highlands is used on the maps. The use of contrast in making hypsometric maps is justified, because the geographer is interested in distinguishing lowlands from highlands. However, when we want to represent population density on the map, or some other statistical variable, there is no need to resort to contrast. Therefore the statistician is likely to use one colour in preparing cartograms.

The situation is different when we deal with contrasting phenomena. When there are regions in which the production of grains is not sufficient for own needs, and regions in which there is a surplus of grain, we can use two contrasting colours and in each of them the intensity of shade may reflect the intensity of shortage or surplus. In more complex studies we may have to use more colours. The limit is set by the requirement of legibility for the map. An additional consideration is the cost of printing, which increases rapidly as the number of colours increases.

A very important problem in using the area method is the division into territorial units. If the units selected are too large the essential differences between territories may become obscured, and when they are too small we get impression of a medley of colours which renders generalization impossible. For technical reasons the division in a cartogram will almost always be the same as the administrative division, which is often inconsistent with the natural division for a given phenomenon. The mark of the scale in a given area reflects the average level of the phenomenon in areas which are often not uniform. These difficulties are at least partly overcome when we use the isorithmic method (from the Greek words *arithmos* number, and *izos*, equal).

*c. The isorithmic method.* This method is familiar from meteorological charts. It consists of taking two points on the map for which the values of the phenomenon studied are known and finding by interpolation the point for which the value is expressed by a round number. For instance, if one of two neighbouring meteorological stations recorded the average temperature of the month as 6·4° and another at 7·4°, then we assume that between these stations there is a point at which the temperature was 7°. Assuming further that the temperature between the two stations changes evenly in proportion to distance we find this point on the straight line joining these stations at the distance, in this case, $\frac{6}{10}$ of the distance between the stations, measured from the first of them. In the same way we find other points with the temperature of 7° between different stations which recorded a temperature slightly above and slightly below 7°. Continuing in the same way we can plot the points with the temperature of 6, 5, 8, 9°C, etc. Joining points with the same temperature by curves we get lines generally called *isorithms*. In this case, in application to temperature, they are called *isotherms* (lines of equal temperature).

The equivalent of this kind of line on hypsometric maps is the contour line joining points of equal elevation above sea level. On these maps the method of applying different colours to the area between each pair of contour lines is also used, so that on the surface of the map there are belts in different colours corresponding to the elevation above the sea level within the limits indicated by the corresponding contour lines. Using this method in meteorological maps we would get the picture of an area in which the temperature is from 5 to 6°C, from 6 to 7°C, and so on.

In the application of isorithmic maps to statistical problems we also use lines joining the points at which the phenomenon studied appears with the same intensity. We may have the population density lines of 50, 60 or 70 persons per km². The areas between the lines are usually coloured so that we obtain population density belts of 50–60 persons, 60–70 persons per square kilometer, and so on.

However, the application of this method to purely statistical phenomena creates serious difficulties because in most cases these phenomena cannot be directly related to definite points on the map, being expressed by averages corresponding to certain major areas. The population density is the average density, say, of a given county, not of a certain point. The isorithmic method requires plotting on the map the points at which the phenomenon reaches certain definite values. Attempts were made to overcome this difficulty by referring the average intensity of a phenomenon, e.g. the average population density, to a certain point on the map, e.g. the centre of gravity of the county. This does not reflect the actual state of affairs, but it is inevitable if we want to use the isorithmic method, although in this way serious errors may occur, particularly when the geographical units are large and the intensity of the phenomenon within them is not uniform.

In addition to this technical difficulty there are doubts of a more basic nature. The method of interpolation which we use is based on the assumption that the intensity of the phenomenon changes in proportion to distances between two points. This assumption may be correct for meteorological phenomena, for temperature and pressure, but it may not be true for the relations prevailing in demographic or economic statistics. On the contrary, many of these phenomena may change unevenly, or even discontinuously (for instance, next to areas with large population density there may be some sparsely populated). In such cases interpolation gives an untrue picture of smooth transitions which do not exist.

In spite of these reservations, the isorithmic method may be used for many problems dealt with in statistics, but each particular case must be carefully analysed, and the material available must be suitable for our purposes, particularly with regard to territorial division (the units should be of an appropriate size). If the conditions make the use of the isorithmic method possible, the results may be better than those obtained by the area method since the isorithmic method enables us to some extent to disregard territorial divisions, which are often artificial, and it gives a clearer and more systematic picture, thus making generalization easier.

Particularly good results are obtained with the isorithmic methods in drawing cartograms on a very small scale when we are interested in detailed generalization, and in emphasizing only the most essential features.

From a purely practical point of view the isorithms may be useful for comparing several cartograms for the same territory when statistical material about different problems is not available in the same territorial break-down. This happens, for instance, when we want to make a comparison of two periods, and when the boundaries of the counties have been changed. Sometimes, for their own purposes, certain offices use geographical divisions which do not correspond to the normal administrative divisions. By basing our analysis on isorithms and disregarding the boundaries we can make comparisons, at least in general terms.

d. *The point method.* The point method is correct both from the statistical and from the geographical points of view. It is basically the same as the quantitative method discussed earlier (p. 117). It consists of plotting on the map points or other signs, in a quantity proportional to the prevalence of the phenomenon, and in the areas where they appear. Thus in principle we use absolute numbers. In this way we get an accurate picture of the geographical distribution. There may be deviations from the exact location of the point because each point represents, of necessity, a large number of units, which in areas of low density may be distributed over a larger territory. Therefore, the placing of a point at a certain spot is a generalization sometimes far removed from reality. On the other hand, in areas of high density, we may be faced with the difficulty of placing a sufficient number of points next to each other. In such cases, we may have to place the points so that the overlap and form a black spot, which makes it impossible to decipher the number of points but creates the correct impression of great density in this area. We can also use different signs denoting a greater number of units and place them in areas of exceptionally great density; or we can use a point to denote 2000 or 5000 inhabitants in sparsely populated areas, and a square to denote 10,000 or 20,000 inhabitants in large cities.

Apart from these difficulties the point method used for cartograms gives a correct and clear picture, not only of the geographical distribution of events, but also of their intensity in different regions. Since we plot the points in places where the events occur we are not bound by the administrative division, and do not have to be concerned whether this division is appropriate from the point of view of the phenomenon studied. As we can assume that one point represents any number of units, we can easily adapt the proportion to any scale of the map. In general the best results in cartograms are obtained when one point represents the smallest possible number of units that can be reconciled with the scale of the map.

The points may be of the same colour as the map, or of different colours, in which case the clarity of the map is enhanced, and more geographical details (e.g. rivers) may be added. However, all such details affect the clarity of the distribution of the points, with which we are primarily concerned, so it is best to use schematic maps with the minimum number of details.

We can use different colours for points representing different phenomena on one map. Thus we can read off the distribution of the points of different colours representing different phenomena, or consider the distribution of all points disregarding colour, and thus obtaining a picture of the whole situation.

The point method is elastic, and can easily be adapted to different circumstances. Particular care should be exercised in deciding how many units one point should represent. Experience is very helpful, but a trial and error method may be necessary before a correct decision can be reached.

e. *The presentation of the structure of a population on a map.* In certain cases it may be necessary to show on the map not only the geographical distribution of a phenomenon, but also its structure in different areas (e.g. not only the distribution of industrial establishments in the country, but also their relative size). This problem can partly be solved by applying different colours to the point method, or by showing in appropriate places on the map geometric figures (squares, circles) whose total area corresponds to the total frequency of the population in a given area, and whose parts describe its structure. This method is essentially simple and correct. The disadvantage is the necessity of using large territorial units, since otherwise there would not be enough room to draw diagrams. Within each territorial unit the drawing can be placed anywhere, but usually it is in the middle. Thus the exact location of the phenomenon cannot be precisely established. For this reason this method cannot be used for more subtle presentations.

f. *The centrographic method. The location of statistical phenomena.* Just as in a frequency distribution we describe the general level by the average (one of the values of the variable determined in an appropriate way) i.e. by a point on the horizontal axis, so that we can reduce the geographical distribution to one central point appropriately determined. In this way we get the "centre" of population, grain cultivation, etc.

There are different definitions of such a point. It may correspond to the median or the arithmetic mean in a frequency distribution. With reference to population, in the first case we would have to draw across the territory a line from north to south, so that the population east of the line would be equal to the population west of it, and another line from east to west so that the population on both sides of it is the same. The point of intersection of these two lines is the "median point".

In the second case the line would have to be drawn so that the sum of the products of the numbers of persons at different points of the territory and the distances of these points from the line sought, would be equal on both sides of the line. The point of intersection of these lines can be called the centre of gravity of the population of a given territory. This means that if we imagine the territory as a weightless surface on which all the people—all of the same weight—are located where they actually are, and if we support this surface at the central point so determined, the surface would be in a state of equilibrium. (The force with which the people placed at certain points of the surface act on this surface is equal to the product of the number of persons at a given point and the distance between this point and the fulcrum).

The practical importance of such a centre of gravity can be explained in the following way. Let us suppose that we are seeking a place for the administrative centre of the country, and that all citizens would visit it with equal frequency. If we locate it at the centre of gravity of the population the combined distance travelled by all citizens will be shorter than it would be if we located it at any other point (providing, of course, that all the roads lead directly to it). Before we determine the location of this centre, we have to decide whether to consider the area of the territory as a plane or as part of the surface of a sphere. If we decide upon the first, simpler, alternative, the computation will not be as complex as it might at first appear. It is done in a way analogous to the short method of calculating the arithmetic mean of a frequency distribution.

By calculating the centre of gravity for the same phenomenon in different periods we can observe its changes with time. In this way it turns out that in the United States, starting with the first population census in 1790, the centre of gravity of the population has been shifting westward, fairly exactly along one parallel of latitude. It is also possible to compare the centres of gravity of different phenomena (e.g. the population with the production of grain).

The centrographic method was probably first used in the United States toward the end of the nineteenth century. At one time this method was very fashionable. It was commonly used both in Tsarist Russia and in the Soviet Union at the beginning of its existence (in 1926 the Centrographic Institute was set up). Some authors considered the centrographic method as almost ideal for determining the synthesis of the geographical distribution of phenomena. However, the enthusiasm rapidly evaporated, since its virtue was much exaggerated at first. Of course, by finding the centre we have a short of representation, analogous to the representation of a frequency distribution by the arithmetic mean. But the arithmetic mean is also an abstract notion, though useful and necessary, and it is unrelated to reality. The "centre of gravity" of an area is even less related to reality than the arithmetic mean. In a frequency distribution, frequencies are usually grouped around a certain value of the variable; the distribution of phenomena in space is almost always irregular. Sometimes the calculation of the centre of space could be compared to the calculation of an average for an extremely asymmetric series, or even for a series in which only the extreme values are represented.[74]

Nevertheless, the centrographic method should not be rejected altogether. It can be used with care, primarily for phenomena which are distributed over the whole territory and not scattered in loose groups. It should be remembered that the representation of the geographical distribution of a phenomenon of calculating the "centre" is a great simplification. It may be useful as the first approximation, but it is no substitute for a detailed analysis. At least the uniformity of the geographical distribution should be analysed. We can evaluate the situation to some extent with the help of a cartogram: a large spread of scale in an area or isorithmic cartogram or the alternating of the areas with high or low intensity, is proof of a lack of uniformity in distribution. Similar conclusions can be drawn from cartograms based on the point method.

The degree of uniformity of distribution can be presented accurately by methods used for a statistical description of frequency distributions. We divide the whole territory into districts of approximately equal areas and for each district we calculate the intensity of the phenomenon (e.g. the population density). Then we form a frequency distribution treating each district as a unit with a definite intensity of the phenomenon. The series thus obtained will show the number of districts with different population densities. This series, of course, is now not geographical, but we can analyse its dispersion by ordinary methods. We can calculate the quartile, mean, or standard deviation. However, quite often these series are so asymmetric that measures of concentration would be more appropriate. They should be applied as described above in the example of population distribution.

When we analyse dispersion with methods used for an analysis of frequency distributions, we completely lose contact with the territory, and in geographical series we are primarily concerned with geographical distribution. For this reason the calculation of measures of dispersion or concentration is only an auxiliary here, especially we deal with phenomena having uneven geographical distribution with distinct local clusters. Then the problem of localization arises. These clusters can easily be located with the help of a cartogram. When they are distinctly marked it is not difficult to express them numerically, providing the data available are sufficiently detailed with regard to the geographical distribution. When we find out, for instance, that the production of a given commodity is concentrated in several distinctly marked regions we can calculate how much of the total output is produced in each region.

---

[74] The calculation of the centre of gravity of an industry, if its factories are located only at a few points far-apart, would be analogous to the calculation of the arithmetic mean of the age of the inmates of city welfare homes in a case where there are in the city only orphanages for the youngest children and old pople's homes.

The details of this method belong to the field of geography, particularly economic geography.

g. *The analysis of a cartogram.* The preparation of a cartogram is only the first step of a proper analysis of geographical series. The essential step is to relate various events that occur in a territory. We may want to know whether the population density is related to the distribution of rivers, water ways and the transportation system; or we wish to find out whether the cultivation of certain crops is related to the elevation above the sea level, or whether vegetable growing is related to population density.

Thus we may often have to show different phenomena on one cartogram. If we want to make the cartogram easily readable we can use different colours for rivers and the transportation system. If it is impossible to show several phenomena on one cartogram we can make a basic cartogram using as much shading and colouring as possible and we can draw the phenomena that are to be compared with the basic cartogram on transparent material in the same scale. By superimposing one on the other, we can make comparisons.[75] However, the use of this method is very limited. In some cases there may be no way out but to place two cartograms side by side and thus compare them. Sometimes we can use the correlation method (see Part IV of this book) but here again we sever, in a sense, the direct contact between the phenomenon and its geographical distribution.

The analysis of cartograms belongs to geography as much as to statistics and cannot be discussed here in greater detail.

---

[75] It is particularly convenient to place the administrative division and transportation network on transparent paper, because in this way we can eliminate them from the basic cartogram.

CHAPTER 9

# GENERAL PROBLEMS. PRESENTATION AND TECHNIQUE OF THE ANALYSIS OF TIME SERIES

A time series, also called a growth series, presents the order of the appearance of statistical events in time. There are two types of series: those that give the figures at certain definite times, and others that give the number of events which occurred in consecutive periods of time. Intermediate between these two types are series giving the average state during a certain period, e.g. the average number of workers in one year, or the average daily temperature. This distinction is important for certain calculations on such series.

Before we start discussing the methods of analysis of time series, several general problems concerning the technique and substance have to be considered.

## 1. GENERAL PROBLEMS

a. *Uniformity in time.* It is obvious that inference about development in time is possible only when the series always relates the same phenomena presented in the same way. However, the statistical material that we usually have at our disposal is often deficient in this respect, particularly when we are concerned with a long period of time. The scope and reach of the events studied may change (e.g. the number of factories which produce a certain commodity may increase) as well as the approach to the problem (e.g. a switch from f.o.b. prices to c.i.f. prices).

If different parts of a series refer to different populations any conclusions on development in time are as a rule impossible. Only in certain cases is it permissible to perform calculations which enable limited comparisons in time.

Suppose that we are investigating changes in the number of workers employed. We record these changes on the basis of observations on a certain number of industrial establishments (population $A'$). Then, beginning at a certain fixed time we change the scope of our observations by decreasing or increasing the number of establishments studied and thus shift to population $A''$. Let us suppose, further, that at the time at which we change from one population to the other we know the number of workers $a'$ for population $A'$, and the number of workers $a''$ for population $A''$ and that the ratio is

$$\frac{a''}{a'} = s.$$

In this case we can form a series of numbers comparable in time for both periods of observations, multiplying by $s$ the number of workers calculated from population $A'$, or dividing by $s$ the number of workers calculated from population $A''$. This calculation is subject to serious reservations since it is based on the assumption that the ratio $s$ does not change in time, and this is often not true.

If, for instance, up to a certain date the investigation comprised only medium-sized and large establishments, employing from 20 workers upward, and after that date establishments employing from 5 to 19 workers were also included, then it is probable that changes in employment in small establishments are not parallel to those in medium and large establishments (possible changes in the technical and economic structure; in a capitalist economy—different reactions to business cycles, etc.). If we wanted to ascertain whether the developments of the two series are parallel we would have to carry on the calculations on the relationship over several consecutive periods, or to repeat them at certain intervals.

In other cases, re-calculation is subject to less serious reservations. If the position of the thermometer at a meteorological station is changed (the elevation over ground level, the distance from the buildings, or the type of protective equipment) then the recording of temperatures in the old and new set-up over a long period of time will probably provide a basis for re-calculation which may vary depending upon the time of day or year, but which will probably be correct for the following years as well.

The same example from the field of meteorology should draw our attention to another danger. If the environment of a meteorological station changes (for instance large buildings have been erected in the neighbourhood), then the local climate (also called micro-climate) will also change and bring about changes in temperature and other meteorological factors. If these changes are reflected in observations recorded over a period of years we should realize that we are dealing with a transition from one micro-climate to another and not with general climatic changes in this part of the country. Generalizations of this kind may easily lead to serious errors.

The most difficult situation arises when the old and the new series have no points in common. In such cases, is it possible to relate one series to the other only very rarely, and with many reservations. For instance, if prices up to a certain date were given on the f.o.b. basis, and after that date on the c.i.f. basis, then we can switch from one price to another by adding or subtracting the cost of transportation. However, serious doubts will remain, since the differences in price may be due not only to the cost of transportation but also to general market conditions.

Let us now consider a more complex example of the lack of uniformity in time. Suppose that we want to compare the earnings of a certain category of workers before the war and at present. It might seem that a direct comparison should be possible, providing that we allow for the change in the purchasing power of money, i.e. that we express the earnings in both periods in monetary units with the same purchasing power. However, the standard of living of the worker depends not only on his cash earnings but also on various social benefits whose value now is incomparably greater than before World War II. If we do not take the changes in social benefits into consideration we obtain a misleading picture.

To compare the standard of living of a family we must remember that before the war usually one member of the family was employed and now several members can and do work, and their combined income decides the standard of living of the family.

b. *The unit of time.* There is no general rule about the size of the unit of time which constitutes a basis for observations in a time series. In studying general growth trends over a long period the unit is a year, a decade or sometimes even a century. In more detailed studies we shall use months, weeks or even days. In some phenomena we may be concerned with changes over 24 hr; here observations are made hourly. For instance, we may investigate the consumption of electricity at different times of the day or with changes in temperature during the day. For studies in physics we may use a second as the unit of time, and so on.

In a time series the units of time must be of equal length if the investigation of changes in time is to yield meaningful results. Sometimes they are not equal because of a change in statistical reporting from, say, quarterly to monthly reports, or vice versa. Sometimes the cause is a lack of uniformity in the calendar to which the reports must be adapted.

Some calendar units are not of equal length. Even years are not equal since leap years have 366 days instead of 365. However, a difference of one day in relation to the whole year is so small that for practical purposes it does not really count. Differences in quarters are also without any practical consequence there are 90 or 91 days in the first quarter, 91 in the second, and 92 in the third and fourth.

However, the differences in the lengths of months are important. In all but leap years the difference between the month of February and the neighbouring months is about 10 per cent. But even the difference between months with 30 and 31 days may count if we are analysing small fluctuations in time, such as seasonal changes in the number of births. There are two ways of making monthly data comparable. Either we can calculate the daily average in each month, which is simpler, or we can adjust all the months to the same length of 30 days. In the first case we divide the observations by the number of days in the month; in the second we multiply by the fraction whose denominator is the number of days in the month and whose numerator is the number of days to which we wish to change the month. Thus if we wish to have 30-day months, we multiply for January by 30/31, for February by 30/28 or 30/29.

The problem is more complicated when the phenomenon studied depends not upon the number of calendar days, but the number of working days, as is usually the case in analysing industrial production. In such cases we divide the number of events in a given month not by the number of calendar days, but by the number of working days. We have to remember, however, that the number of working days may vary from industry to industry; for instance, in the metallurgical industry, where production is continuous, it may be equal to the number of calendar days.[76]

In certain cases the number of working days may depend upon factors not related to the calendar. For instance, the number of working days of port workers may be reduced in winter months because the port is frozen. Such conditions should be taken into account—for instance by calculating the intensity of port work.

Differences between raw statistical data and data after allowance is made for the number of working days may be considerable, and in such cases they should be taken into account. In some cases, however, these differences are of no importance. To those employers who pay their employees on a monthly basis it does not matter whether there are 28 or 31 days in the month. But it does matter to the employee because expenditures, with few exceptions, depend upon the number of days in the month.

Another difficulty may arise when we shift from one calendar unit to another, particularly when we combine shorter periods into longer ones. There are no difficulties in changing from a monthly to a quarterly or yearly basis, or in changing from days to weeks, months, quarters or years. We can easily shift from a weekly to a quarterly basis (13 weeks = 91 days), or to a yearly basis (52 weeks = 364 days); but it is difficult to change from a weekly to a monthly basis. However, the need for switching from weeks to months arises quite often. In many cases the reporting is on a weekly basis because of the importance of the problem, and the need to watch the events carefully. But weekly reports are sometimes less suitable for characterizing the general trend over a period of time. The difficulty is not only that a month may have from 4 to $4^3/_7$ weeks, but also that the beginning of a week as a reporting period only rarely coincides with the beginning of a calendar month.

These difficulties may be solved in a variety of ways.

(1) The number of events in a week which lies in two months may be divided between them in proportion to the number of days of the week belonging to each of these two months. If the reporting week begins on 29 March, then out of all the events in this week we include $^3/_7$ in March and $^4/_7$ in April. If necessary we can use working days instead of calendar days.

This method is not very precise, and can be used only when we can assume that the distribution of events over the week was uniform. But in some phenomena the distribution is notoriously uneven. Epidemics of certain diseases break out suddenly

---

[76] This method can be used with reference to series which reflect the events that occur within consecutive periods of time. It should not be used for series reflecting the situation at consecutive moments of time. In the latter case the situation at a given moment is presented correctly, regardless of the length of time between the moments with which we are concerned. The differences in calendar units should be taken into consideration, however, in studies of the rate of growth (see below).

and their intensity toward the end of the week may be much greater than at the beginning. The peak may pass just as rapidly as the epidemic passes. This error is somewhat reduced by the fact that always 3 or 4 whole weeks belong to a month. It can also be reduced by a complex interpolation method. This error is avoided in the second method.

(2) In a given calendar month we include those weeks of which a major part (at least 4 days) are in this month. Thus the week starting on March 29 and ending April 4 we include in April, just as we include in April the week starting on April 26 and ending May 2, in this way a month has either 4, or, less frequently, 5 weeks. For these 4 or 5 weeks we calculate the arithmetic mean, and say that, for instance, the average weekly number of new cases of a certain disease was 48 in March, 36 in April, etc. The weekly averages in this case are accurate, but they do not exactly correspond to given months since the weeks partly overlap with the neighbouring months. The most precise method is the third one.

(3) For several (say 4) consecutive weeks we compute the totals, disregarding longer calendar units. This can be done in two ways: (a) by reporting for periods of 4 consecutive weeks: from March 8 to April 4, from April 5 to May 2, etc; (b) by reporting for overlapping periods of 4 weeks: from March 8 to April 4, from March 15 to April 11, etc. These are moving averages which will be discussed later. We can define the periods by giving their starting and ending dates, or by starting only their ending dates (4 weeks ending April 4, etc.). This method is accurate and always uses the same units of time. The main disadvantage is that it is not synchronized with calendar months.

c. *Averages in time series.* It may be necessary to calculate averages (arithmetic means) for a certain number of units of time, e.g. the average weekly production in a given month, the average level of unemployment during a year, etc. We have to distinguish here between the averages of certain events that have occurred during particular periods of time and the averages of certain levels recorded at particular moments of time.

In the first case the matter is quite simple. If the units of time are of equal length we add up the figures for individual periods and divide the total by the number of periods. If they are not of equal length, we have to allow for this variability in an appropriate way. If in a given year we have, for instance, quarterly data for the first 6 months and monthly data for the rest of the year, then by adding them all up we obtain the correct total for the year, but we shall divide them, of course, not by $8(2+6)$ periods, but by 12 or 4; thus we get the monthly or quarterly average. If we calculate monthly averages in consecutive calendar quarters we are also faced with units of unequal lengths: the average length of the month in the first quarter in an ordinary year (not a leap year) is 30 days, and in the third and fourth quarter it is $30\frac{2}{3}$ days. We can usually disregard these minor differences as unimportant. If necessary we can take them into account by adjusting the months to the same number of days. Some institutions use different reporting periods. For instance, if the starting date of the fiscal year changes from January 1 to April 1, or vice versa, the reporting period in the transition period may be 15 months or 9 months. This inequality should be allowed for in calculating, for example, average annual income or expenditure.

A similar situation arises when the units of time are characterized by the corresponding averages. From these averages we can also calculate averages for longer periods. But we have to remember the general rule for calculating averages of averages: they must be weighted averages. In this case the lengths of time will be used as the weights. The averages do not have to be weighted if the periods are of equal length (the weight for each period equals unity).

When a series shows the data at certain moments of time then the accurate calculation of the average level is possible only when the exact dates of changes are known. For instance, if the number of steam engines in operation on January 1 was 3000 and on April 1 another 300 were added, and on both on July 1 and October 1 100 were withdrawn, then we have in operation: 3000 engines during 90 days, 3300 during 91 days, 3200 during 92 days and 3100 during 92 days. The precise calculation of the average number of steam engines in operation is:

$$\frac{3000 \times 90 + 3300 \times 91 + 3200 \times 92 + 3100 \times 92}{365} = \frac{1,149,900}{365} = 3150\cdot4.$$

We arrive at almost the same average assuming that the quarters are of equal lengths and writing:

$$\frac{3000 + 3300 + 3200 + 3100}{4} = \frac{12,600}{4} = 3150.$$

It is rarely possible to make so precise a calculation, since the exact dates of changes are seldom known, particularly when frequencies are high and changes occur often and gradually. In such cases we assume, for calculation purposes, that changes during the reporting period are evenly distributed, and we take as the average level for the whole period the arithmetic mean of the beginning and end values.

For instance if the registered population of Warsaw on 1 January 1948 was 560,510 persons, and on 1 January 1949 it was 578,046 persons, we assume that on the average the population of Warsaw in 1948 was

$$\frac{560,510 + 578,046}{2} = \frac{1,138,556}{2} = 569,278$$

(We always assume that the level at the end of one period is also the level at the beginning of the next period).

This calculation would be precise if the increase, which during the year was 17,536 persons, was evenly distributed over the whole year, i.e. was the same for each unit of time. This assumption, however, is arbitrary and often wrong. If we calculated the average level of unemployment in pre-war Poland as the arithmetic mean of the level on January 1 of two consecutive years, the result obtained would be too high, because unemployment always increased in winter time and decreased during the summer. The error would be smaller if we used shorter periods of time because then the changes would be smaller and more likely to be linear.

But even when we use short periods, e.g. months, systematic errors may occur. For instance, the circulation of the bank notes of the Bank of Poland on 31 December 1936 was 1033·8 milion, and on 31 January 1937 was 999·3 million. The average circulation during the month of January calculated on the basis of these two data would be

$$\frac{1033 \cdot 8 + 999 \cdot 3}{2} = 1016 \cdot 55.$$

But this figure is too high: the circulation on 10 January was only 986·4 million and on 20 January, 957·4 milion. This is not an accident. We know that the circulation of money always increases on the last day of the month. Thus the error in calculation would be repeated from month to month, and always in the same sense, so that it might become quite large. The most accurate results are obtained when the average over a long period of time is based on as frequent recordings of the actual level as possible. For instance, the annual average should be calculated on the basis of monthly recordings, the monthly average on the basis of records for every ten days, etc. In these cases the calculation is done in the following way: first, we calculate the averages for the shortest periods available as arithmetic means of the levels at the ends of periods; then for a longer period we calculate the average of these averages (a simple average if the original, shorter periods are of the same length, and a weighted average if the original periods are of different lengths).

In our example of the circulation of money the calculation is done in the following way:

The average level in the first ten days $\qquad \dfrac{1033 \cdot 8 + 986 \cdot 4}{2} = 1010 \cdot 1,$

„  „  „  „  „  second ten days $\qquad \dfrac{986 \cdot 4 + 957 \cdot 4}{2} = 971 \cdot 9,$

„  „  „  „  „  third ten days $\qquad \dfrac{957 \cdot 4 + 999 \cdot 3}{2} = 978 \cdot 35.$

Hence, the average level during the month is

$$\frac{1010 \cdot 1 + 971 \cdot 9 + 978 \cdot 35}{3} = 986 \cdot 8.$$

This result differs considerably from the result previously obtained. The calculation can be simplified in the following way:

We denote the levels at the beginning of each period by $a_1, a_2, \ldots, a_n, a_{n+1}$. The average for the consecutive periods is

$$\frac{a_1 + a_2}{2}, \quad \frac{a_2 + a_3}{2}, \ldots, \frac{a_n + a_{n+1}}{2}.$$

The number of periods is $n$.

Calculating the average of these averages we obtain

$$\left(\frac{a_1 + a_2}{2} + \frac{a_2 + a_3}{2} + \ldots + \frac{a_n + a_{n+1}}{2}\right)/n$$

$$= \left(\frac{a_1}{2} + a_2 + a_3 + \ldots + a_n + \frac{a_{n+1}}{2}\right)/n. \tag{IX.1}$$

Thus, we have to form the sum containing one half of the level at the beginning of the first period and one half of the level at the end, and the levels on all other dates, i.e. at the beginning of the second, third period, etc., up to the beginning of the last period. This sum is divided by the number of periods. For instance, we take one half of the level on 1 January of a given year, and on 1 January of the following year, and the level on the first of each month from February to December inclusive and we divide the sum thus obtained by 12. It would not be correct to calculate the annual average by adding up the levels at the beginning of each month from January to December inclusive and dividing this sum by 12. This average would not take into account the changes that occurred in December and the weight of the level on 1 January would be too high.

If the dates on which changes in frequencies occur are not known, and they almost never are, this is the only possible procedure. The greater the number of the recorded levels we take into account, the smaller the error. However, before we embark upon our calculations we should analyse the nature of the movement in time of the phenomenon studied. If it turns out for instance, that within the smallest units of time available there appear to exist permanent cyclical changes, then the error may be quite large, even if we use relatively short periods, as we saw in the example of the circulation of banknotes.

If the changes that occur in time are of a continuous nature (e.g. in the case of air temperatures) we should express the curve by an appropriate function, and calculate by integration the area under the curve for a given period of time. We should obtain the same result by calculating with the help of a planimeter the area of the figure outlined at the base by the segment of the horizontal axis corresponding to a given period, at the sides, by the ordinates corresponding to the level at the beginning and the end of the period, and at the top, by the curve representing the changes within this period.[77] The situation is similar when changes are discontinuous, providing that they follow one another frequently, and the particular levels at short intervals are known (a quasi-continuous variable).

If the changes during the period show a regular pattern it is sometimes possible to find a formula which will enable us to calculate the average level fairly accurately on the basis of levels known only for a few moments of time.

The average daily temperature can be calculated fairly precisely if the temperatures are recorded by a thermograph (a device which automatically records the temperature by drawing a curve on a moving paper tape). The calculation would be almost exact if the temperature was recorded at very short intervals, every hour, say. The meteorological stations usually record the temperature three times a day: at 7 a.m., and at 1 p.m. and 9 p.m. A comparison of the averages calculated on the basis of the thermograph recording or hourly recording with the average based on readings three times a day shows that a relatively good result is obtained if the average daily temperature is calculated as a weighted average with the weight of 1 for the readings at 7 a.m. and 1 p.m. and the weight of 2 for the reading at 9 p.m. Denoting the temperatures at 7 a.m., 1 p.m. and 9 p.m. by $t_7$, $t_{13}$, $t_{21}$ we write

$$T = (t_7 + t_{13} + 2t_{21})/4.$$

It is conceivable that similar formulae can be found for calculating averages in some economic series, providing their pattern is fairly regular (e.g. the average level of employment, or the average livestock population during a year, can be calculated on the basis of simple or weighted averages of the levels recorded several times a year). Usually, however, the pattern of economic phenomena is too complex, and such a calculation is too risky.

## 2. ELEMENTARY METHODS OF ANALYSIS OF TIME SERIES

a. *Numerical presentation of changes in time. Index numbers.* In a statistical analysis of time series we use both algebraic and graphical methods.

Changes in time can be looked upon from different points of view. By subtracting from an absolute number in a series the corresponding number in an earlier series we get the absolute increase (or decrease, if the difference has the minus sign). Expressing this difference as a ratio related to the earlier value we get the relative increase, which is usually expressed as a percentage. Finally, by dividing

---

[77] Thus we get an area expressed, for instance, in square centimetres. To calculate the average ordinate (the average level) we have to divide the area by the number of centimetres corresponding to the length of the period measured along the horizontal axis. The quotient will give the average level expressed in centimetres (linear). We should read off from the vertical scale what value corresponds to the resultant number of centimetres.

the absolute figure for the later period by the corresponding figure for the earlier period we obtain the figure expressing the relative difference in the levels.

Since changes in time can be expressed in so many ways, it is imperative to explain exactly which mothod was used in a given case, or else serious misunderstandings may result.

Let us consider an example. The production of steel in Poland was:

| in 1946 | 1,219,000 | metric | tons |
| in 1947 | 1,579,000 | ,, | ,, |
| in 1948 | 1,955,000 | ,, | ,, |
| in 1949 | 2,304,000 | ,, | ,, |

In 1955, according to the 6-year plan, the production was to reach the level of 4,600,000 tons.

Hence we get the following:

| Absolute increase | | Relative increase | |
| from 1946 to 1947 | 360,000 tons | 0·295 or 29·5 per cent | |
| ,,   1947 to 1948 | 376,000 ,, | 0·238 or 23·8 ,, ,, | |
| ,,   1948 to 1949 | 349,000 ,, | 0·179 or 17·9 ,, ,, | |
| ,,   1949 to 1955 | 2,296,000 ,, | 0·997 or 99·7 ,, ,, | |
| (six-year period) | | 1 or 100% after rounding off to nearest hundred or 1% | |

The ratio of levels is:

| 1947 compared to 1946 | 1·295 or 129·5 per cent |
| 1948   ,,   to 1947 | 1·238 or 123·8 ,, ,, |
| 1949   ,,   to 1948 | 1·179 or 117·9 ,, ,, |
| 1955   ,,   to 1949 | 1·997 or 199·7 ,, ,, |
| | (2 or 200 per cent after rounding) |

Indices expressing the ratio of levels are obtained by adding 1 (or 100 per cent) to the figures expressing the relative increases. All three methods of calculating changes in time—the absolute change and relative change, and the ratios of levels—are correct, and each of them gives an answer to different questions.

There is a certain dependence between the relative increase and the relative difference in levels. If from the figure expressing the relative difference in levels we subtract 1 (or 100 per cent) we get the relative increase.

In statistical practice we often use figures of the third kind, expressing the ratio of levels. They are called *index-numbers* and can be calculated either in the way shown above, i.e. the ratio of the figure for a certain period to the corresponding figure for an immediately preceding period, or as ratios of all the figures in the series to one figure selected as a base. Unlike the index numbers with a constant base, index numbers expressing the ratios of figures for two consecutive periods are called chain indices.

The relation between the index numbers with a constant basis and chain indices can be established in the following way.

Let the series $a_1$, $a_2$, $a_3$, ..., $a_{n-1}$, $a_n$ denote the consecutive values which quantity $a$ assumes in consecutive periods from 1 to $n$. The chain indices will be expressed by

$$i_2 = \frac{a_2}{a_1},$$

$$i_3 = \frac{a_3}{a_2},$$

$$\cdots\cdots\cdots$$

$$i_n = \frac{a_n}{a_{n-1}},$$

which we read: "the chain index of period 2 in relation to period 1 is $i_2$, the chain index of period 3 in relation to period 2 is $i_3$, etc."

The index number with the constant base $a_1$ is expressed by

$$I_2 = \frac{a_2}{a_1},$$

$$I_3 = \frac{a_3}{a_1},$$

$$\cdots\cdots\cdots$$

$$I_n = \frac{a_n}{a_1},$$

which we read: "the index-number of periods 2, 3 etc. in relation to period 1 is $I_2$, $I_3$, etc.".

We form the product

$$i_2 \times i_3 \times \cdots \times i_n = \frac{a_2}{a_1} \times \frac{a_3}{a_2} \cdots \frac{a_{n-1}}{a_{n-2}} \times \frac{a_n}{a_{n-1}} = \frac{a_n}{a_1} = I_n \qquad \text{(IX.2)}$$

Multiplying the consecutive chain indices, starting with the index for period 2 in relation to period 1, up to period $n$ in relation to period $n-1$ we get the index number for period $n$ in relation to period 1.

If the indices are expressed as percentages then we have to remember that each ratio $a_2/a_1$, $a_3/a_2$ etc. has been multiplied by 100. Since there are $n-1$ such ratios the final result of multiplying the chain indices must be divided by $100\,(n-1)$ in order to obtain the ratio $a_n/a_1$ (not in percentages), or by $100\,(n-2)$ if the index is to be expressed as a percentage (i.e. with base $a_1 = 100$).

If the index is calculated in relation to a constant base the problem of selecting a base arises. We can choose as a base any expression of a time series. Very often it is the first expression corresponding to the earliest period, but it may also be any other expression. We can also take as a base the average value of the series calculated for a long or a short period of time. It can even be a fictitious value not actually appearing in the series.

To explain the significance of selecting a base we have to be aware of the purpose that index numbers serve. By relating the absolute figures of a given series to the base expressed as a round number, say 100, we facilitate the job of keeping track of the changes occurring in the series. Changes in comparison with the basic period can be read off directly in percentages. Also changes between other periods can be grasped easier than by using absolute figures.

The choice of an poor base may distort the picture and thus, without forging the figures, it may create a wrong impression. If we take as a base the period during which the level of the phenomenon was exceptionally low we obtain a picture of rapid growth which actually took place in relation to the selected base but which has little to do with the dynamics of growth. This will come out with particular clarity when we take as a base the period when the phenomenon was at its beginning stage. In 1925 there were in Poland only 11 anti-trachoma medical centres. Their number increased to 656 in 1937. If we take the year 1925 as a base the index for 1937 will be 5964 which indicates a sixtyfold increase. This increase actually took place. But we have to remember that in 1925 the setting up of medical centres of this type had just started. A similar distortion, but in the opposite direction, will occur if we select as a base a period with a very high level; in this case the decrease would be magnified.

Index numbers are most useful for comparing changes in different series. Comparisons are difficult if the series are expressed in absolute numbers, especially if in the series compared these figures are of different magnitudes. We can make them directly comparable by bringing all the series to a common base. It should be remembered that the index expresses changes only in comparison with the period selected as a base. If one of two indices shows high values, and the other low values, it does not follow that the first of the two original series which served as bases for calculating the indices has higher values than the other: these values are higher or lower only in relation to the starting period and not in absolute terms. For instance, if the price index of bread in one city is 120 and in another 80, it means only that in the first city the price in comparison with the basic period increased by 20 per cent and in the second decreased by 20 per cent, but it does not mean that in one of these cities the price was higher than in the other: this depends upon the ratio of prices in the basic period.

All this is quite obvious, but it is often forgotten that this is how the index number should be understood.

Let us imagine the following price changes of two commodities:

TABLE 9.1. COMPARISON OF CHANGES IN
PRICE ABSOLUTE NUMBERS

| Period | Price of commodity | |
| --- | --- | --- |
| | A | B |
| 1 | 521 | 2580 |
| 2 | 615 | 2300 |
| 3 | 740 | 1900 |
| 4 | 891 | 1650 |
| 5 | 1015 | 1500 |
| 6 | 902 | 1700 |
| 7 | 765 | 1950 |
| 8 | 605 | 2250 |
| 9 | 490 | 2600 |

The prices of commodity $A$ increase rapidly from period 1 through period 5 and then decrease, reaching a level lower in period 9 than in period 1. The prices of commodity $B$ change differently: they reach the highest levels in periods 1 and 9 and the lowest in period 5. Let us calculate their indices taking as a base, first, the prices in period 1 and then the prices in period 5.

TABLE 9.2. COMPARISON OF CHANGES IN PRICES, INDICES WITH DIFFERENT BASES

| Period | Price indices with the bases | | | |
| --- | --- | --- | --- | --- |
| | Prices in period 1 = 100 | | Prices in period 5 = 100 | |
| | Commodity A | Commodity B | Commodity A | Commodity B |
| 1 | 100 | 100 | 51 | 172 |
| 2 | 118 | 89 | 61 | 153 |
| 3 | 142 | 74 | 73 | 127 |
| 4 | 171 | 64 | 88 | 110 |
| 5 | 195 | 58 | 100 | 100 |
| 6 | 173 | 66 | 89 | 113 |
| 7 | 147 | 76 | 75 | 130 |
| 8 | 116 | 87 | 60 | 150 |
| 9 | 94 | 101 | 48 | 173 |

Regardless of what base we choose the indices show what we have already seen from the absolute numbers: the prices of the two commodities change in opposite directions. From period 1 to period 5 the price indices of commodity $A$ show a marked increase and of commodity $B$ a strong decrease; from period 5 to period 9 the situation is reversed: the prices of commodity $A$ decrease and the prices of commodity $B$ increase. This conclusion is correct without reservation. However, looking at the first pair of indices we might be inclined to assume that in period 5 the price of commodity *A* was abnormally low. In period 9 it looks as if the prices of both commodities returned to the normal level. But from the second pair of indices it might appear that in periods 1 and 9 the price of commodity *A* was abnormally low, and the price of commodity *B* abnormally high. Both these contradictory conclusions in the forms stated above are wrong. One of them would be right only if it could be proved that the ratio of prices of the two commodities was normal either in period 1 or in period 5.

The wrong conclusion in this case is not the fault of the indices but is due to incorrect interpretation. However, the impression that we subconsciously accept is very strong. If the basic period for series *A* gives abnormally low values and for series *B* abnormally high values, an increase in indices of series *A* and a decrease of indices of series *B* may simply mean a return to the normal level. It would thus be desirable to select the starting period so that all the quantities compared could be as close to the normal level as possible. However, it is very difficult and sometimes impossible to decide what is a normal level. One remedy is to select as the base of an index number the average over a long period of time in which we can assume that abnormal deviations will cancel out.

After the war in Poland the month of April of 1945 was selected as a base for economic indices, since it was the first month for which reasonably reliable data were available. For the reasons described above this choice was wrong because in the following months different indices showed different tendencies, depending on whether April 1945 was abnormally high or abnormally low for them. Beginning from January 1948 the indices were based on the average for 1947 and later on the average for 1949.

The phenomenon of diverging price indices is known in economics as "price scissors". It consists in movements of the prices of two or more commodities, or groups of commodities, in opposite directions. We then say that prices diverge or that "the scissors" open. These "scissors" may sometimes bring to light facts of great economic importance as far as price movements of important groups of commodities are concerned. For instance, if there is a decrease in the prices of goods produced and sold by a certain population group, e.g. farmers, and a rise in prices of goods bought by this group, e.g. industrial goods used by the farmers, then the purchasing power of this population group will decline. This conclusion is undoubtedly correct. It is not easy, however, to evaluate this fact because one complex economic problem has to be solved first: was the purchasing power of this population group in the starting period normal or excessive from the general, national point of view? If it was normal "the price scissors" would be considered as economically harmful, if it was excessive, "the price scissors" would indicate a return to healthier economic conditions.

If the index stays around the values of the starting period, the differences in the level expressed in points[78] correspond roughly to relative differences. If the index is far removed from the starting point the difference in points does not correspond to a relative difference. The increase from 102 to 104 is approximately 2 per cent (precisely 1·96 per cent). However, when the index increases by 2 points from 50 to 52 this is an increase of 4 per cent; and when the index increases by 2 points from 200 to 202 this is an increase by only 1 per cent. Thus, not only indices with a constant base, but also chain indices are useful because they enable us to make comparisons of two consecutive periods.

b. *Graphs of time series.* Time series are presented in graphs with time as abscissa and frequency as the ordinate. If a series represents the level of a phenomenon at certain times it is natural to locate the corresponding points on the basis of both scales and join them by a broken line. The points at which the line changes direction are on the border of two calendar periods (months); this corresponds to the system of recording the level on the first or the last day of each month. If we deal with events that occurred in particular periods of time it will be natural to present them graphically as rectangles of appropriate height (see Fig. 9.1).

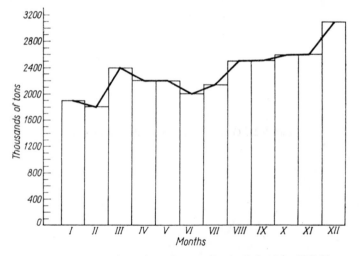

FIG. 9.1. Production of woolen textiles in Poland in 1949.[79]

Of course, there are departures from this method of presentation. A broken line can also be used in the second type of graph, but the points of discontinuity will be in the middle of the segments representing periods of time and not at their end-points, as shown in the same graph. In both cases a smooth curve can be used instead of a broken line.

---

[78] When the index increases from 102 to 104, or from 50 to 52, or from 200 to 202 we say that it has risen two points.

[79] *Wiadomości Statystyczne (Statistical News)*, 1950, No. 3, p. 1.

It is important to select properly both the vertical and the horizontal scale. When the vertical scale is too large in relation to the horizontal, fluctuations in time are artificially magnified; when the horizontal scale is too large the graph is flattened and the fluctuations seem smaller.

The vertical scale should begin from the origin or otherwise we artificially increase the scale of fluctuations and create the erroneous impression that it approaches zero when this does not happen. It is difficult to observe this principle if the whole line remains on a very high level. In such cases even essential fluctuations may be obscured because the vertical scale is too small and moreover the picture does not look very aesthetic. Sometimes the situation can be remedied by breaking the scale at the bottom (as shown in Fig. 9.2b) to draw the reader's attention to the fact that the graph is not drawn in the usual manner.

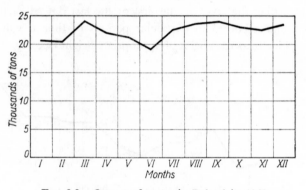

FIG. 9.2a. Output of paper in Poland in 1949.

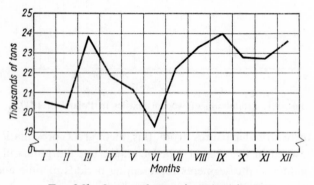

FIG. 9.2b. Output of paper in Poland in 1949.
A break in the vertical scale.[80]

---

[80] *Wiadomości Statystyczne*, 1950, No. 3, p. 3. Diagram IX. 2a is not easy to read; the increase in production is not shown too well. Figure 9.2b gives a much better picture in this respect.

To obtain the correct picture the segments of the horizontal scale must be proportional to the periods of time. If in the graph there are periods of unequal lengths this should be properly allowed for. When we deal with events occurring in consecutive periods a change to longer periods should be allowed for both on the horizontal and the vertical scale. This results from the graphs being related to the area. If we change a segment on the abscissa scale we have to reduce the frequencies correspondingly: in shifting from shorter to longer periods the frequencies should be reduced and in shifting from longer to shorter periods they should be increased in an appropriate ratio (see above pp. 146 *et seq.*, the analogous problem in presenting graphically frequency distributions). In graphical presentations of levels at consecutive times a change in the length of period should be allowed for only on the abscissa.

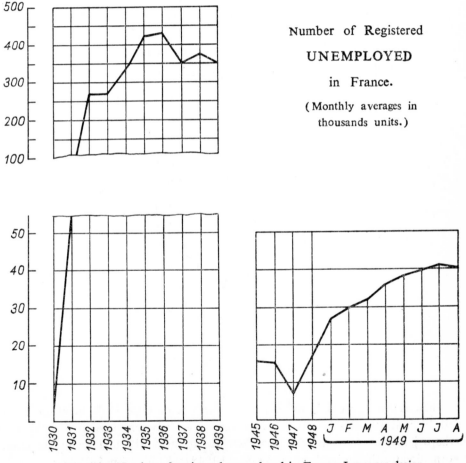

Number of Registered

**UNEMPLOYED**

in France.

(Monthly averages in thousands units.)

FIG. 9.3a. Number of registered unemployed in France. Improper design.

The use of improper scales may completely distort the picture. Fig. 9.3a is
a reprint of a graph that appeared in the Paris edition of the New York Herald
Tribune of 23 September 1949. In the graph the number of registered unemployed
in France is given in thousands, separately for the years 1930–9 and from 1945
to September 1949. The left side of the graph does not arouse any doubts. The
number of unemployed in 1930 and 1931 is of the order of tens of thousands, and
in the following years it is of the order of hundreds of thousands. Therefore the
scale was reduced to one-tenth beginning from 1931 which is correctly marked by
breaking the graph into two parts, the lower for 1930–1 and the higher 1931–9.

Nevertheless the graph so designed diminishes optically the rapid increase in
unemployment during the depression since the eye automatically joins the upper
part of the graph with the lower part which is in a different scale.

But whereas the left side of the graph arouses doubts the right side about to
the post-war period is an outright forgery. It consists in using for months in 1949
the same intervals on the horizontal scale as for years in 1945–8. The impression
thus created is that the rate of increase in unemployment slows down in 1949 in
comparison with the period 1947–48, which is obviously at odds with the facts:
the number of unemployed increased between 1947 to 1948 from 7800 to 17,000,
i.e. by 9200, whereas the increase during the first 8 months of 1949 along was
24,000. A correctly drawn graph gives a completely different picture (see Fig. 9.3b).

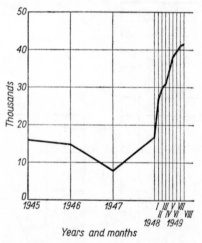

FIG. 9.3b. Number of the registered
unemployed in France. Proper design.

If there is a long break in the series, e.g. after the data for 1938 there is a break
until 1945, it is advisable to interrupt the curve between these two dates and
perhaps join the two ends with a broken line to stress the fact that there is no
information for the period between 1938 and 1945 (see Fig. 9.4 p. 285).

FIG. 9.4. Output of hard coal in Poland
in 1921–38 and 1945–50.

If we want to compare two time series we can put in one graph two or more lines drawn differently: continuous line, dotted line, broken line, or lines in different colours. We can also put two or more bars in different colours or shaded in different ways, in the segments of the horizontal scale corresponding to particular periods, so that each colour or method of shading signifies a different series. In this way, for instance, we can denote births in consecutive years by red bars and deaths by blue. At the same time, the difference in height indicates the excess of births over deaths (or deaths over births).[81]

In studying graphs of time series we have to remember about certain of their properties connected with the drawing technique.

The shape of the curve depends on the pattern of absolute numbers and not on the relative difference in levels. Thus if we have two lines one of which is on a higher level than the other. The same slope in a given segment means that the absolute difference is the same, but the relative difference corresponding to the same absolute difference is smaller in the first case than in the second. And vice versa, the same relative difference is indicated in the first case by a appropriately steeper slope than in the second.[82] Therefore, graphs of this type are not suitable for a proper presentation of relative changes in time.

This inconvenience is particularly noticeable in cases when we want to show in

[81] This method was used in Fig. 3.2 on p. 111, although in that diagram we were concerned with geographical comparison (different countries) and not with comparison in time.

[82] This property was emphasized in discussing indices (see p. 281).

one graph two phenomena on markedly different levels. We face this problem, for instance, in comparing an entire population with a part. Let us take as an example the diagram showing changes in the number of workers insured against illness in 1946–9, both for all the insured (line *A*) and for insured white-collar workers (line *B*). The impression received is that the number of insured white-collar workers increased much more slowly than the number of all workers. This impression is misleading: the number of insured white-collar workers increased by 94·2 per cent and the total number of workers by 74 per cent (see Fig. 9.5a).

The situation is similar when we deal with only one series which displays considerable fluctuations in time; also in this case the same slope of the line in different periods will correspond to different relative changes (see Fig. 9.7a p. 290).

Different methods can be used in the diagram to show properly relative differences in the level as well.

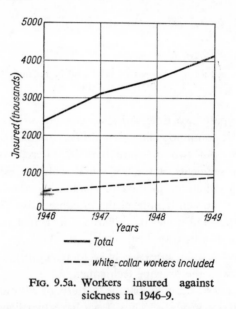

FIG. 9.5a. Workers insured against sickness in 1946–9.

One of these methods consists in showing in the diagram indices instead of the absolute figures of the series. If we want to compare movements of different series in time we can read the changes off directly from the diagram comparing them with a common starting point, and from this point of view, we get the result which is not subject to any reservations. However, as far as the details of fluctuations in time are concerned, it should be remembered that relative fluctuations are shown correctly as long as the indices compared move closely around the starting point. If the deviations from it are considerable—particularly in the opposite directions, when some indices rise and others decline—the situation is almost the same as we wanted to avoid by replacing the absolute figures by the indices. Besides, by presenting a series in the form of indices we lose track of the absolute numbers which may be of importance.

The second method consists in applying different scales to series running on different levels, so that the different lines are approximately on the same level. For instance, if phenomenon *A* is on the level of about 2000 and phenomenon *B* on 10,000 we increase the scale for *A* five times and then both series oscillate around the same level and their fluctuations will be comparable not only with respect to absolute numbers, but also with respect to relative values, with the same reservation as for indices shown on a figure, namely that the fluctuations do not deviate much from the common level. Apart from this reservation the application of this method presents technical difficulties when there are three or more curves. Each line can be shown in a separate diagram, but this makes comparisons more difficult.

However, both the use of curves of indices and the application of different scales fail in the case of one phenomenon whose level changes considerably, as in the case of the growth of the population of Warsaw over a long period of time.

*Workers insured against sickness in 1946–9*

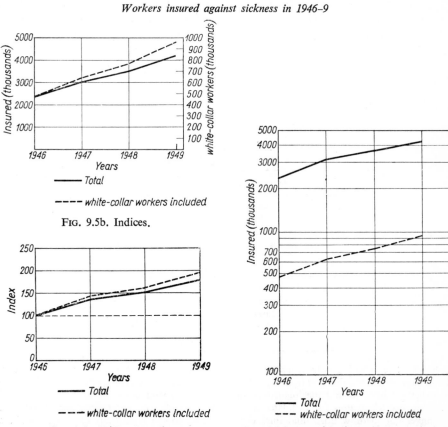

FIG. 9.5b. Indices.

FIG. 9.5c. Different scales.

FIG. 9.5d. Logarithmic scale on vertical axis.

The most correct is the third method: the use of the logarithmic scale on the vertical axis. Then distances in the vertical direction are proportional not to the numbers themselves but to their logarithms. Thus, equal distances on the scale and therefore equal slopes of the line, regardless of the level, always correspond to equal relative deviations. If a segment of the scale 2 cm long corresponds to the difference between 100 and 200 it will also correspond to the difference between 200 and 400, or 1000 and 2000. In this way relative differences in the level will always be shown correctly and will be comparable, whether the curve is in the lower or upper part of the figure.[83] The logarithmic scale also enables us to show on one line the developement of a series even with very wide fluctuations. On the other hand, the logarithmic scale does not give a good and direct picture of the magnitude of absolute numbers. It is true that they can be read off from the scale, but vertical distances do not correspond to the differences of levels.

In Fig. 9.5b, 5c and 5d changes in the number of workers insured against sickness are presented in the three ways discussed above. All three—in contrast to Fig. 9.5a —give correct pictures showing that from 1946 to 1947 the number of insured workers as well as the number of insured white-collar workers increased equally rapidly and then, particularly in the last year, the number of insured white-collar workers increased more rapidly than the total number of insured.

The increase in the population of Denmark, France and the United States during the last century and a half can be shown in a comparable way only with the logarithmic scale.

TABLE 9.3. POPULATION INCREASE IN DENMARK, FRANCE
AND THE UNITED STATES
in 1800–1947

A. Population (thousands)

| Year | Denmark | France | United States |
|------|---------|--------|---------------|
| 1800 | 925  | 27,349 | 5308    |
| 1850 | 1424 | 35,783 | 23,192  |
| 1900 | 2432 | 38,912 | 75,995  |
| 1947 | 4146 | 41,000 | 144,034 |

B. Absolute population increase (thousands)

| Period | Denmark | France | United States |
|--------|---------|--------|---------------|
| 1800—1850 | 499  | 8434 | 17,884 |
| 1850—1900 | 1008 | 3129 | 52,803 |
| 1900—1947 | 1714 | 2088 | 68,039 |

[83] If we have semi-logarithmic paper at hand, since, the figures given for the scale correspond to logarithms, the graph can be drawn as on ordinary graph paper. If we have no such paper we have to find the logarithms of the numbers and draw the graph in the usual way, using the logarithms for ordinates a slide rule is sufficient, for finding the logarithms. It is convenient to draw horizontal lines corresponding to the logarithms of round numbers like 1, 1·1, 1·2, etc.

C. Relative population increase

| Period | Denmark | France | United States |
|--------|---------|--------|---------------|
| 1800—1850 | 53·9 | 30·8 | 336·9 |
| 1850—1900 | 70·8 | 8·7 | 227·7 |
| 1900—1947 | 70·5 | 5·4 | 89·5 |

The absolute increase, of course, is the least in Denmark and the greatest in the United States. If we wanted to show on one diagram the population increase in all three countries and still have a clear picture for Denmark we would have to let at least 1 mm on the ordinate represent 100,000 inhabitants. Thus the curve for Denmark would run on the level between 0·9 cm to 4·15 cm, the curve for France between 24·3 and 41 cm and the curve for the United States between 5·3 and 144 cm. The curve for the United States would be almost vertical. In Fig. 9.6a a much smaller scale was used and therefore it is not 1·5 metres high, but the general picture is not very clear.[84]

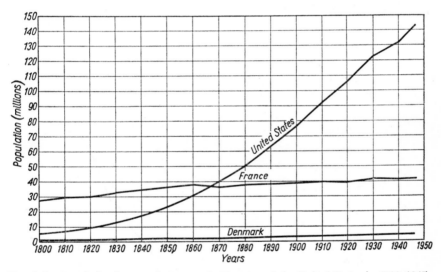

Fig. 9.6a. Population increase in Denmark, France and the United States in 1800–1947. Ordinary scale.

In the logarithmic scale (Fig. 9.6b, p. 290) the population increase of all three countries is quite easy to read. Particularly noticeable is the rapid and uniform

---

[84] It was calculated that during the period of rapid depreciation of money in many European countries after World War I it would be necessary to have a piece of paper of the length of $1/5$ of the distance from the earth to the sun to show graphically a comparison of the fluctuations in the rate of exchange of the dollar in relation to the pound sterling and the German mark.

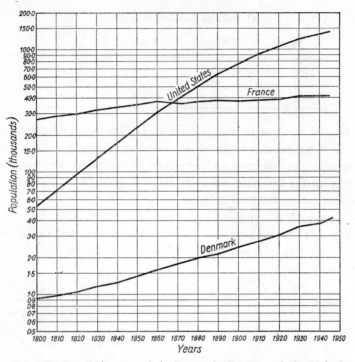

FIG. 9.6b. Population growth in Denmark, France and the United States in 1800–1947. Logarithmic scale.

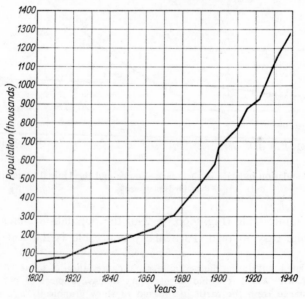

FIG. 9.7a. Population increase in Warsaw in 1800–1939. Ordinary scale.

increase in Denmark, the very slow growth in France (only slightly faster until 1850, and an almost complete stagnation beginning at the end of the 19th century) and the at first rapid and then distinctly slower rate of increase in the United States (toward the end of the curve not any faster than in Denmark).

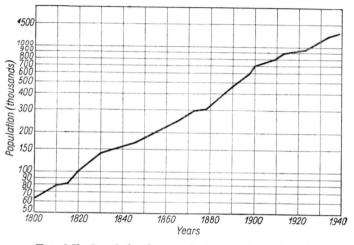

FIG. 9.7b. Population increase in Warsaw in 1800–1939.
Logarithmic scale.

In Fig. 9.7a and 9.7b. the population increase in Warsaw is presented from the beginning of the 19th century to the outbreak of World War II. Here, too, only Fig. 9.7b. in a logarthmic scale, enables us to evaluate correctly the changes in the rate of increase.

As a general rule we should use an ordinary scale when we want to emphasize absolute changes, and a logarithmic scale when we want to have a good picture of general relations. Only in cases when all lines are approximately on the same level and do not show substantial fluctuations can an ordinary scale successfully illustrate relationships.

# CHAPTER 10

# DETAILED ANALYSIS OF TIME SERIES

## 1. TYPES OF CHANGES OCCURRING IN TIME

Changes in time expressed in a time series are often very complex since in the same series fluctuations of different types may occur simultaneously. Consider, for example, economic phenomena which are often analysed from the point of view of their development in time. Fluctuations that occur in them may be of the following types:

(1) Accidental changes from one period to another caused by circumstances unimportant and irrelevant from the general point of view. Temporary stoppages or limitations of production in a large factory caused by damaged machinery may be reflected in a reduced output of the whole industry. On the other hand, one big order, or a resolution of the workers in a socialist factory to complete an important part of production before a set deadline, may lead to a temporary increase in total output. Random fluctuations of this kind may be the subject of a special study, but they are of no consequence in studies of growth in the long run; on the contrary, they confuse the picture and may obscure more important changes. Irregular random fluctuations are more noticeable in short-term studies, although sometimes they may also appear in long-term series. The exceptionally severe winter in 1946–7 not only caused disturbances in the operations of Polish sea ports during the winter months, but could also have affected the annual turnover of these ports.

Somewhat similar to random fluctuations are catastrophic upheavals caused by major cataclysms such as world wars. Their similarity to random fluctuations lies in their irregular nature. Such serious and deep disturbances rarely pass without leaving some permanent trace. However, because of their nature we shall not discuss them further in this book.

(2) Repeated fluctuations may occur as a manifestation of more important and regularly recurring causes. Of particular importance in this group are cyclical fluctuations, in which movements up and down are repeated at approximately regular intervals. Cyclical fluctuations may be of a long-term or a short-term type. For instance, the consumption of electric power in one day shows characteristic changes, within very wide limits: the maximum is reached in the evening and the minimum in the early morning. Accidents at work show a distinct weekly cycle:

they are relatively frequent at the beginning of the week, decline in the middle, and increase again toward the end. The circulation of bank notes, as we already know, displays a monthly cycle. Many natural phenomena, and economic variations apparently have a yearly cycle, with an increase in certain seasons, a decline in others. Fluctuations of this kind with a full cycle of a year's duration are called *seasonal fluctuations*.

In the capitalistic system of production, economic growth proceeds in cyclical waves of up to a dozen years or more: after a period of prosperity and rapidly growing production follows a depression in which production drops rapidly and the whole economic activity declines, to be followed again by a period of enlivened activity. These fluctuations, of a rather indeterminate duration (usually lasting several years), are called business cycles. Similar cyclical fluctuations occur in various fields, even in those seemingly remotely connected with economic activity (e.g. in the number of marriages). Certain facts seem to indicate the existence of very long-term fluctuations, lasting dozens of years, especially in certain natural phenomena.

(3) All these fluctuations may occur around a certain stable level, or they may be accompanied by a general development trend, up or down, permanent or lasting, for a limited but, in comparison to the fluctuations, a relatively long period of time.

It is obvious that the existence of all kinds of fluctuations in time, either accidental or periodical (seasonal or non-seasonal) is very undesirable from the point of view of the national economy. They create periods when the load carried by the productive equipment is excessive, and periods when the existing capacity is not fully utilized. This necessitates the accumulation of substantial reserves relative to the average level, which is economically wasteful. Moreover, the amount of work done by the workers fluctuates, leading to periods of strenuous work or, even worse, to layoffs. These considerations are very important in a socialist economy, although it does not suffer from business cycles which are foreign to the notion of planned economy. However, other types of fluctuations may also be troublesome, such as changing load in electric power plants at different times of the day, uneven distribution of wagon loadings and passenger transport over a year, peaks in city transportation at different times of the day, etc.

A planned economy tries to control this kind of lack of balance in distribution over time. Not all the fluctuations can be eliminated, since some of them are due to natural forces beyond the control of man. The consumption of electric power will always be higher during the evening hours than during the day. Warm clothing will always be more needed in winter time, and light clothing in summer. But in many cases it is possible to eliminate uneven time distribution. Let us consider several examples.

(1) If the demand for a product (e.g. winter clothes) is unevenly distributed over the year, output can be evenly distributed by producing for stock. This requires

properly equipped and enlarged warehouses, and it is possible only if the product does not deteriorate in storage.

(2) If for some reason the existing equipment is not evenly utilized, it can be used for other purposes during the periods of unused capacity. For instance, if railways are overloaded in certain seasons by transporting certain goods which must be shipped at once (e.g. sugar beets in the autumn), the transport of other bulk products not so strictly connected with definite periods can be shifted to other months. One such "slack period" commodity is coal which can be stored. But this again requires larger warehouse space both at the production end and in the distribution network. A characteristic example is passenger transport during the day by city transportation lines. At least partial relief can be achieved by staggering working hours. It is instructive to compare the load carried by city transportation means in Warsaw and in Moscow. In Warsaw the load was very unevenly distributed. About 12·5 per cent of all daily commuters were carried between 7 and 8 a.m., and almost 12 per cent were carried between 4 and 5 p.m. In Moscow the morning peak (from 7 to 8 a.m.) was about 7 per cent and the afternoon peak (from 5 to 6 p.m.) not quite 8 per cent of all pasengers carried during the day. The lowest hourly load in Warsaw was less than 3 per cent (between 10 and 11 a.m.) and in Moscow it dropped to slightly below 5 per cent (between 11 a.m. and 1 p.m.). In this way in Warsaw the peak during the day was more than 4 times as high as the trough (and this without taking into consideration late evening and night hours). In Moscow the highest load compared to the lowest approximately in the ratio of 8 : 5, thanks to staggering the working hours. The situation in Warsaw improved considerably when the staggering of the hours of work began in 1952.

(3) Sometimes a more even distribution in time may be achieved by a change or improvement in technique. For instance, the introduction of new construction methods in the Soviet Union, later also introduced in Poland, to a large extent solved the problem of a "dead season" in construction.

The methods used to eliminate undesirable fluctuations in time may remove the evil, but it may also have some adverse secondary social and economic effects. It is the task of the planning authorities to consider the advantages and disadvantages before reaching a decision. It is obvious, however, that it is imperative to find accurate yardsticks for measuring these fluctuations and for evaluating the consequences of the decisions reached. This is the task of the statistican, and it is not always an easy task.

In a capitalist economy there is the added problem of business cycles. It is not enough to base an analysis on empirical data, since they often obscure the real picture by reflecting the effects of factors of secondary importance.

The problem of growth trends will be discussed separately in section 4 of this chapter.

The various fluctuations described above are by no means limited to economic phenomena. For instance, similar fluctuations affect meteorological phenomena. There are, of course, random fluctuations in the temperature of the air, but temperature is also subject to more or less regular daily fluctuations, and to annual seasonal fluctuations. There are probably also long-term fluctuations, over a period of a dozen years or so, connected with the sun-spot cycle. Another category is that of development trends, i.e. gradual changes taking place over a period of centuries, or of thousands or even hundreds of thousands of years.[85]

Fluctuations of different kinds may be superimposed on one another, with either a cumulative or a neutralizing effect. Seasonal fluctuations may be distorted by simultaneous incidental variations, by a general growth trend, and in a capitalist economy by business cycles. In a similar fashion business cycles may be obscured by general growth trends. A rising growth trend may be damped down or magnified by a simultaneous seasonal rise or decline, or by accidental changes. The net result presents an extremely complex picture.

From this follow some very important postulates, concerning inferences on the basis of time series. It is basically not permissible to base conclusions on observations taken from isolated series of observations. Similarly it is not permissible to infer anything from observations at two arbitrarily selected moments in time. It is almost always possible to choose these times in such a way as to justify any conclusion. Inference from time series must be based on an analysis of the whole development in time of the phenomenon in question.

If a statistical analysis is to constitute a basis for analysing the essence of the problem, it must give answers to two questions:

(1) It must find a correct measure of the changes occurring in time. The problem of seasonality is a good example. If we want to eliminate or reduce seasonal fluctuations in any field, we must first learn about them and understand their nature and dimension.

(2) It must find a method of presenting a time series in such a way as to permit correct reasoning, and to make sure that fluctuations irrelevant from a given point of view are not an obstacle in the process of inference.

We shall discuss the principal methods of analysis by means of an example. It relates to monthly data of the sale of electric power for lighting[86] to private subscribers in Warsaw during the period from January 1923 to December 1939 (see Table 10.1 p. 296). For many reasons this is a very characteristic and even a classic example of change occurring in time.[87]

---

[85] Time series of the kind described here may concern phenomena which begin to appear at certain times, reach their peak and then gradually disappear. This kind of pattern is usually displayed by epidemics. The curve representing this pattern is similar in shape to the frequency curve for frequency distributions but its meaning is completely different.

[86] In pre-war statistics a distinction was made between the sale of electric power (a) to private subscribers for lighting, (b) to private subscribers for power, (c) for street lighting.

[87] An added attraction of this example taken from the period of capitalist economy in Poland is that it enables us to analyse business cycles.

TABLE 10.1. SALE OF ELECTRIC POWER FOR LIGHTING TO PRIVATE SUBSCRIBERS IN WARSAW
in 1923–39ᵃ (in thousands of kWh)

| Year / Month | I | II | III | IV | V | VI | VII | VIII | IX | X | XI | XII | Total |
|---|---|---|---|---|---|---|---|---|---|---|---|---|---|
| 1923 | 2289 | 1938 | 1687 | 1112 | 986 | 980 | 988 | 1280 | 1791 | 2257 | 2777 | 2593 | 20,678 |
| 4 | 2146 | 1810 | 1670 | 1530 | 1143 | 862 | 886 | 1300 | 1548 | 1839 | 2464 | 3028 | 20,226 |
| 5 | 3004 | 2733 | 2150 | 2003 | 1579 | 1238 | 1102 | 1351 | 1820 | 2534 | 2972 | 3449 | 25,935 |
| 6 | 3252 | 2770 | 2463 | 1892 | 1631 | 1235 | 1105 | 1360 | 1912 | 2730 | 3243 | 3737 | 27,330 |
| 7 | 3551 | 3104 | 2638 | 2544 | 1836 | 1523 | 1225 | 1546 | 2257 | 3074 | 3955 | 4432 | 31,685 |
| 8 | 4306 | 3690 | 3066 | 2545 | 2075 | 1822 | 1498 | 1866 | 2634 | 3595 | 4578 | 5354 | 37,029 |
| 9 | 4759 | 4107 | 3310 | 3017 | 2407 | 2030 | 1748 | 1891 | 2436 | 3561 | 4782 | 5205 | 39,253 |
| 1930 | 5271 | 4523 | 3651 | 3326 | 2820 | 2142 | 1780 | 2124 | 2793 | 3895 | 4783 | 5382 | 42,490 |
| 1 | 5352 | 4635 | 3688 | 3457 | 2694 | 1968 | 1769 | 1974 | 2817 | 3745 | 4436 | 5159 | 41,694 |
| 2 | 5152 | 4273 | 3615 | 3001 | 2518 | 2007 | 1601 | 1760 | 2483 | 3488 | 4548ᵇ | 5148ᵇ | 39,594 |
| 3 | 4475 | 4127 | 3530 | 3198 | 2469 | 2130 | 1686 | 1999 | 2708 | 3530 | 4658 | 5060 | 39,570 |
| 4 | 5025 | 4691 | 3744 | 3325 | 2672 | 2157 | 1914 | 2246 | 2900 | 3792 | 5001 | 5720 | 43,187 |
| 5 | 5578 | 4968 | 3992 | 3794 | 3023 | 2519 | 2019 | 2355 | 3123 | 4145 | 5438 | 5889 | 46,843 |
| 6 | 6090 | 5452 | 4295 | 4105 | 3200 | 2822 | 2289 | 2574 | 3603 | 4805 | 5980 | 6417 | 51,632 |
| 7 | 6640 | 5940 | 5069 | 4575 | 3954 | 3049 | 2143 | 3513 | 4083 | 5082 | 6840 | 7604 | 58,492 |
| 8 | 7372 | 6752 | 5970 | 5596 | 4685 | 3964 | 2809 | 4019 | 4822 | 5994 | 7805 | 8448 | 68,236 |
| 9 | 9045 | 8066 | 6938 | 6459 | 5578 | 4929 | 3617 | 4777 | 6554ᶜ | 3059ᶜ | 3278 | 4312 | 66,612 |

ᵃ Statistical Yearbooks of Warsaw to 1937 inclusive—on the basis of the data of Electric Inspection. From January 1938: the data of the Statistical Department of the Warsaw City Council based on the data of the Warsaw Electric Power Station.

ᵇ In the original source 9,696,000 kWh was given as the total for both months. This total has been divided between November and December in the same ratio as prevailed between these two months in 1925–31 and 1933–34.

ᶜ Note in the report for 1939: "The data on the supply of electric power to particular categories of subscribers are not divided between September and October in accordance with the actual charges because payments for September were delayed". The delay was due to the outbreak of World War II which also caused a decline in sales in the following months.

Since we are concerned here with the sale of electric power for lighting, very clearly marked seasonal fluctuations can be expected. Indeed, in each year the figures for the winter months are almost three times as high as the figures for the summer months. On the other hand, business cycles should have a rather weak effect, since depressions do not bring about reductions in the consumption of electricity for household lighting as serious as, for instance, in the consumption of electricity for industrial purposes. Business cycles can be roughly appraised on the basis of yearly totals. These totals increasead rapidly until 1930 inclusive, when 42,490 thousand kWh were sold and then they declined somewhat to 39,570 thousand kWh in 1933, and then increased rapidly again. For comparison it should be noted that the sale of electric power to private subscribers for power showed signs of decline earlier: in 1929 there was practically no increase compared with 1928, in 1930 a slight drop was noticeable and this lasted until 1933, being more marked than the drop in the sale of electric power for lighting (see Table 10.1a).

It should be remembered that neither series in its raw form properly presents the decline in sales due to the business cycle, since this decline is partially camouflaged by the rising growth trend.

The growth trend appears very distinctly. The increase in yearly totals of sales for lighting from 1924 to 1938 is a more than threefold.[88]

There also exist very distinct random fluctuations. These may be related to weather: on cloudy days more electric light is needed than on sunny days. National holidays may also exert some influence. Finally, in this particular case, an important part could have been played by another factor which has nothing to do with the actual pattern of this phenomenon: the consumption of electric power is determined on the basis of meter readings at the home of the subscriber and the months, strictly speaking, are not calendar months, but accounting months. Hence, all distortions in payments are reflected in monthly figures. A particularly striking example of such disturbances are the months of November and December 1932, when because of the strike of payment collectors the sales of electric power were shown for two months together. Other disturbances were caused by war activities beginning with September 1939 (see Table 10.1 Note c).

TABLE 10.1a. SALE OF ELECTRIC POWER FOR POWER TO PRIVATE SUBSCRIBERS IN WARSAW in 1927–34

| Year | Sales in thousands of kWh | Year | Sales in thousands of kWh |
|---|---|---|---|
| 1927 | 30,239 | 1931 | 33,510 |
| 1928 | 36,008 | 1932 | 32,422 |
| 1929 | 36,644 | 1933 | 31,026 |
| 1930 | 36,604 | 1934 | 35,062 |

[88] A rise in electric power consumption is not synonymous with general economic growth. It is a result of technical transformations occurring during this period. From 1928 to 1938

All these peculiarities of the series appear very clearly in Fig. 10.1, p. 299 in which the raw monthly data are given.

In evaluating changes occurring in short time periods the greatest obstacle is seasonal fluctuation. We can eliminate them in a crude way by using an appropriate method of presenting the data.

Let us suppose that we have records for three consecutive months, April, May and June of 1928, in which the sale of electric power for lighting was respectively 2545, 2075 and 1822 thousand kWh. We notice a drop which was mainly caused by seasonal factors. A comparison of the data for these three months gives no indication of the direction of the trend in the sales of electric power. However, certain conclusions can be drawn by comparing these figures with the data for the corresponding month of the preceding year, i.e. 1927 (see Table 10.2).

TABLE 10.2. SALES OF ELECTRIC POWER FOR LIGHTING
(in thousands of kWh)
April, May, June 1927 and 1928

| Year | April | May | June |
|------|-------|------|------|
| 1927 | 2544  | 1836 | 1523 |
| 1928 | 2545  | 2075 | 1822 |

In 1928 there was an increase in these months in comparison with 1927. This increase was considerable in May and June, but negligible in April, which may have been a coincidence. To ascertain that this is so, we can supplement the data for particular months with the totals (or averages) for several months. They can be, e.g. the totals for three months comprising the month reported and the two preceding months (February to April, March to May, etc.), or the totals from the beginning of the year including the month itself. If we choose the last method, it would be natural to show the data for, say, April and May of 1928 in the following form:

TABLE 10.3. SALES OF ELECTRIC POWER FOR LIGHTING
April 1928

| Month — Year | Sales in thousands of kWh |
|--------------|---------------------------|
| IV 1928      | 2545                      |
| III 1928     | 3066                      |
| IV 1927      | 2544                      |
| I–IV 1928    | 13,607                    |
| I–IV 1927    | 11,837                    |

---

the total output of electric power in Poland increased by 52 per cent whereas the general index of industrial production rose only by 19 per cent, the production of steel was unchanged, and the output of pit coal even dropped slightly.

TABLE 10.4. SALES OF ELECTRIC POWER FOR LIGHTING
May 1928

| Month — Year | Sales in thousands of kWh |
|---|---|
| V 1928 | 2075 |
| IV 1928 | 2545 |
| V 1927 | 1836 |
| I—V 1928 | 15,682 |
| I—V 1927 | 13,673 |

The report for June would be similar.

In this way it turns out that in 1928 there was actually a substantial increase in comparison with 1927, and it was probably not a coincidence that it shows in the totals for four and five months. However, the nature of this increase is not explained. It could have been caused by improved economic conditions, or by the general tendency toward greater consumption of electric power. To some extent, however, it may be due to random factors, because there is no guarantee that in the total for four months all random fluctuations have been smoothed out entirely.

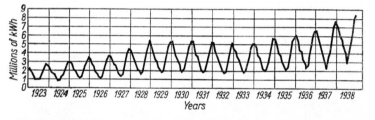

FIG. 10.1. Sales of electric power for lighting to private subscribers in Warsaw
1923–38 (monthly data).

In any case, it is advisable to publish the data on the development of phenomena in time in the way described above.

Good results are also obtained by graphs made in the same way as Fig. 10.2 on p. 300. It depicts the number of workers employed in the construction industry in consecutive months in 1927–30. On the horizontal axis twelve consecutive months have been marked, and the data for each year are represented by a different line, each on a different level. Seasonality is very strongly marked here, with a maximum in winter months and a minimum usually in February; the number of workers employed during the autumn is more than twice or even three times as great as in winter. This is characteristic of the construction conditions in a capitalist economy. (In a socialist economy efforts are made to eliminate seasonality or at least to reduce it considerably). There are also fluctuations of a random nature. But there is something else which is most characteristic. The line for 1927 is on a low level. In 1928 the economic conditions improved suddenly and employment became much higher than in 1927. The line for 1929 is still high, but from the middle of the year it begins to drop below the line for 1928. In 1930 there was a sudden breakdown. In January the level was still high, but from February on the line moves away from the high level of the previous two years, and toward the end of the year it drops considerably below the 1927 level. A severe crisis followed. The conclusions are easy to read from the figure.

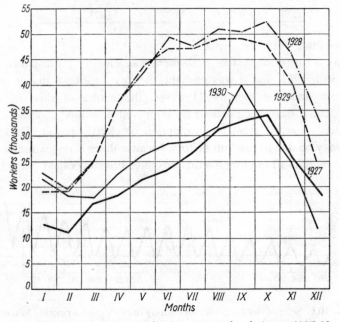

FIG. 10.2. Workers employed in the construction industry 1927–30.

A figure of employment in Poland after the war would be different. Some random fluctuations, of course, remain. Seasonal fluctuations, are also still felt, although to a much lesser extent in recent years. But the lines would not intersect, because each year would be higher than the previous, since in a planned economy there are no depressions.

## 2. THE ELIMINATION OF FLUCTUATIONS. THE MOVING AVERAGE. SMOOTHING THE CURVE BY GRAPHICAL METHODS. OTHER MECHANICAL METHODS.

When we are interested only in changes over long periods of time, and not in random or short-term fluctuations, the simplest way of eliminating the latter is a shift to larger time units. In daily data, changes in the consumption of electric power during the day are not reflected: in the monthly consumption figures shown in the table, differences between different days of the week do not appear. By taking the data for calendar years we eliminate seasonal fluctuations, etc. We can also shift to periods of several years duration, e.g. 1925–7, 1928–30, 1931–3, etc., or of five years duration, e.g. 1925–9, 1930–34, etc., and then random variations between individual years will also disappear completely or in part. However, the use of long periods is often inconvenient, and it makes an analysis of short periods impossible. For this reason we often resort to the smoothing out of series which, in effect, consists in presenting them in the way they would look if changes of no interest to us were eliminated.

A very common method of eliminating fluctuations is by the use of moving averages. These are averages formed of several (e.g. 3, 5, 7 or more) consecutive units of time. For instance, we calculate the average for January, February and March, and then for February, March and April, and so on. Usually the average is ascribed to the middle of the period, e.g. the average for January, February and March is considered to refer to February. For this reason it is convenient to select an odd number of periods. Were we to take, for instance, four consecutive months, such as January to April inclusive, the average would characterize the period from the middle of February to the middle of March. The moving sum has a similar meaning—in this case the total for the three months ending May 31, or June 30, etc.

The calculation of the moving average results in a smoothing of the series, or in other words, in the elimination of certain types of variations in time. Such an elimination may be needed if some of these variations obscure the picture and prevent us from getting a clear ides of the pattern. We shall see later what the essence of such elimination is, and under what circumstances it is permissible. For the time being we shall concern ourselves with problems of a technical nature.

The length of the period selected for calculating the moving average or the moving sum depends on the type of fluctuations that are to be eliminated. If we want to get rid of random fluctuations, the more intense the fluctuations the longer the period that we should select. As a rule, however, we can use relatively short periods for eliminating random fluctuations. If we want to remove periodic fluctuations the number of units to be taken for calculating averages depends strictly on the length of the period of fluctuations, i.e. it has to correspond exactly to the length of the period or to some multiple of this. If this principle is not observed, periodic fluctuations will only be modified and not eliminated; if we calculate averages for periods shorter than the full cycle of fluctuations in certain averages, only the minimum, and in others only the maximum, will be included. If averages are calculated for periods longer than the cycle, but shorter than the two cycles, some averages will have two maxima and one minimum and others two minima and one maximum. A similar situation will arise when the averages comprise more than two but less than three cycles.

The distortions are sometimes considerable. The table below contains seasonal indices computed on the assumption that the yearly average is 100.[89]

TABLE 10.5. SEASONAL INDICES

| Month | Index | Month | Index | Month | Index |
|-------|-------|-------|-------|-------|-------|
| I     | 147   | V     | 76    | IX    | 81    |
| II    | 128   | VI    | 61    | X     | 108   |
| III   | 105   | VII   | 50    | XI    | 137   |
| IV    | 94    | VIII  | 60    | XII   | 153   |

We assume that the pattern of the indices in consecutive calendar years is the same.

From these indices 6-month moving averages were calculated (which might be needed, for instance, to eliminate possible random fluctuations) as well as 18-month averages. A graphical presentation is shown on p. 303, Fig. 10.3.

The 6-month average is smoother and more symmetric than the raw data, it has maxima and minima where the original series does, but its shape is different because the amplitude of the fluctuations is reduced; the minimum is 20 points higher and the maximum 24 points lower than in the raw data.

The 18-month average is even flatter: seasonal fluctuations are still noticeable, shifted by 6 months; the maximum now occurs in the summer and the minimum in the winter; thus the picture is essentially distorted.

A 12-month moving average will, of course, be shown on the diagram as a line parallel to the abscissa at the level 100.

The use of a moving average is permissible if fluctuations of a given type can actually be considered of secondary importance from a given point of view. This will often be the case when we deal with random fluctuations caused by reasons unimportant from the point of view of the general trend. There is also no objection to eliminating periodic fluctuations by using a moving average. For instance, if we want to eliminate seasonal fluctuations then we simply calculate the annual total and the monthly average for the period from January to December inclusive, then for the period from February to January of the next year, from March to February, etc. Each of these totals and averages corresponds to a concrete reality regardless of whether we use a calendar year, from January to December inclusive, or any other fiscal year.

The question arises whether it would not suffice simply to use longer periods comprising the whole cycle of fluctuations, instead of using short periods, or in other words, to use the totals of consecutive calendar years instead of going to all the trouble of calculating moving averages. The answer is that the moving average

---

[89] The data refer to the sales of electric power in Warsaw (see below).

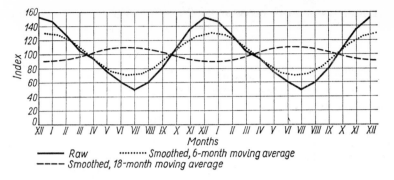

FIG. 10.3. Seasonal indices, raw and smoothed by moving averages.

enables us to follow the development month after month whereas the yearly totals inform us about the development in jumps, in yearly intervals. The advantage of using a moving average can best be shown by an example.

The transportation of goods by the Polish State Railways from January 1946 to December 1950 is shown in Table 10.6.

Since the moving averages are for 12-month periods (an even number) we strictly relate them not to calendar months, but to fiscal months, e.g. the months from the middle of June to the middle of July (in 1946, there were 5,584,000 tons), from the middle of July to the middle of August (in 1946 there were 5,696,000 tons), etc. It is assumed that the arithmetic mean of two consecutive 12-month moving averages corresponds to an appropriate calendar month; thus, in the above example, the arithmetic mean of the numbers 5,584,000 and 5,696,000 (5,640,000) can be considered to correspond to July, etc. The numbers in the last column of Table 10.6 are such averages of two neighbouring 12-month moving averages.

A glance at the annual figures shows that the transportation of goods during this period increases very rapidly, even if we disregard the year 1946, which cannot be considered as normal. The increase from 1947 to 1950 is almost 68 per cent. However, the pattern of the monthly data is very irregular. There are undoubtedly very distinct seasonal fluctuations: a very strongly marked minimum at the beginning of the year, in January of February, and an equally strongly marked maximum at the end of the year, in October or November. The moving average does not reflect these fluctuations, but shows an even, though not quite uniform, growth.

All this is best seen in the diagram, which enables us to grasp certain characteristic features better than the series does. The pattern of the raw data, even when seasonal fluctuations are disregarded, is most irregular. Maxima and minima appear in particular years with various strengths, and there are minor fluctuations in different months. For instance, in one of the spring or summer months there is always a decline in comparison with the preceding month, but this spring or summer minimum appears at different times: in 1950 in April, in 1948 in May, in 1949 in

TABLE 10.6. TRANSPORT OF GOODS BY POLISH STATE RAILWAYS, STANDARD GAUGE
(in thousand tons)[90]

| Year and month | Actual data | 12-month moving average | Year and month | Actual data | 12-month moving average |
|---|---|---|---|---|---|
| 1946 | 67,002 | . | 1948 | . | |
| I | 4415 | . | VII | 9737 | 9553 |
| II | 4158 | . | VIII | 10,051 | 9627 |
| III | 4500 | . | IX | 10,400 | 9710 |
| IV | 4671 | . | X | 11,665 | 9779 |
| V | 4785 | . | XI | 11,759 | 9913 |
| VI | 5223 | . | XII | 9502 | 10,067 |
| VII | 5766 | 5640 | 1949 | 131,715 | . |
| VIII | 5950 | 5706 | I | 8534 | 10,173 |
| IX | 6604 | 5772 | II | 8668 | 10,990 |
| X | 7591 | 5910 | III | 9735 | 10,414 |
| XI | 7336 | 6098 | IV | 9943 | 10,562 |
| XII | 6003 | 6295 | V | 10,825 | 10,725 |
| 1947 | 83,221 | . | VI | 10,550 | 10,890 |
| I | 5761 | 6483 | VII | 11,140 | 11,032 |
| II | 4401 | 6654 | VIII | 11,471 | 11,148 |
| III | 5849 | 6804 | IX | 11,953 | 11,211 |
| IV | 6624 | 6920 | X | 13,666 | 11,400 |
| V | 7344 | 7043 | XI | 13,661 | 11,637 |
| VI | 7397 | 7239 | XII | 11,569 | 11,751 |
| VII | 8108 | 7436 | 1950 | 148,122 | |
| VIII | 7701 | 7656 | I | 9863 | 11,856 |
| IX | 8450 | 7912 | II | 10,128 | 11,952 |
| X | 8537 | 8144 | III | 12,783 | 12,042 |
| XI | 9343 | 8293 | IV | 11,449 | 12,108 |
| XII | 8706 | 8415 | V | 12,000 | 12,217 |
| 1948 | 114,260 | . | VI | 12,100 | 12,320 |
| I | 7794 | 8567 | VII | 12,108 | |
| II | 7628 | 8733 | VIII | 12,804 | |
| III | 8768 | 8912 | IX | 12,792 | |
| IV | 9272 | 9124 | X | 14,402 | . |
| V | 8271 | 9355 | XI | 15,557 | . |
| VI | 9413 | 9484 | XII | 12,136 | . |

June, in 1947 as late as August. All this is incidental to the general growth trend, although, of course, each deviation has its own specific reason. The line of moving everages shows a steady increase, although its pattern is not quite regular: "random" deviations are so strong that they have not been smoothed out even by the 12-month moving average.

In our example a certain technical peculiarity of smoothing the curve by the moving average can be noticed: the first and the last terms of the series have not

[90] *Wiadomości Statystyczne Głównego Urzędu Statystycznego* (*Statistical News, Central Statistical Office*), for the respective years.

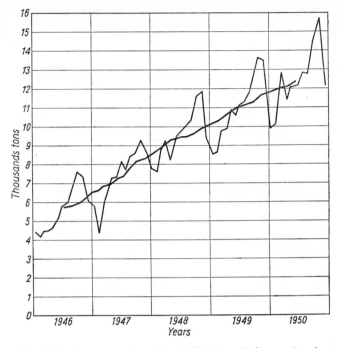

FIG. 10.4. Transport of goods by Polish State Railways, Standart gauge in 1946–50.

been smoothed out. It is easy to determine how many terms will not be smoothed. If we denote by $n$ the number of periods of time constituting the basis for calculating the moving average then there will be $(n-1)/2$ periods—both at the beginning and at the end—which are not smoothed. Thus, for the 3-month moving average this amounts to one month on each side, and the 7-month moving average, three months on each side. If the number of periods is even, we get fractions. They should be understood as meaning that the average obtained corresponds not to some definite period, but, as mentioned above, to the middle "fiscal" period. Calculating the 12-month average, e.g. from January, we get the figure for the fiscal month from the middle of June to the middle of July and there will be $5\frac{1}{2}$ months not smoothed out.[91]

This specific quality of the moving average reduces its usefulness for appraising a situation, because our appraisal is delayed in relation to the last fiscal period.

Besides, the moving average has a certain mathematical property which we have already noticed in Fig. 10.3 on p. 303 and which may result in a biased error. If the curve of a series is convex to the horizontal axis in a certain range the moving

---

[91] In Table 10.6 there are 6 months not smoothed out: in fact, in calculating the average of two consecutive averages we have to consider the thirteenth month.

average gives lower values for all the terms of the series than does the original, and if concave, it gives higher values than the original.[92]

It follows that, for instance, if we eliminate random ffuctuations by means of the moving average comprising a period shorter than one year, seasonal fluctuations in the series will be distorted, i.e. the amplitude of the fluctuations will be dampened. Similarly, the business cycle fluctuations will be distorted after the elimination of seasonal fluctuations by means of the moving average. The same reservations hold, of course, for the moving sum.

This is exactly what we saw in Fig. 10.3 p. 303: the 6-month moving average considerably smoothed out the seasonal fluctuations. Even the 3-month moving average largely smoothed out seasonal fluctuations: it raised the summer minimum by several points and lowered the winter maximum by several points. In the same diagram we saw how an improperly calculated moving average could shift the phase of periodic fluctuations and thus distort the picture.

This property of the moving average considerably limits the scope of its application. Strictly speaking, it may be used to eliminate undesirable fluctuations only in those segments of the series where the basic pattern is represented by a straight line. This is approximately the case in the example of the transport of goods by the Polish State Railways (Table 10.6 and Fig. 10.4).

If we disregard the seasonal fluctuations which were to be eliminated, the growth more or less follows a straight line.

If the basic pattern is represented by a convex or a concave curve, an improper computation of the moving average may result in serious distortion, possibly of the very changes that were to be studied. Therefore the moving average should be used only with great care and after due consideration to all the relevant circumstances.

It appears from the above examples that it may be very dangerous to use the moving average to eliminate short-term random fluctuations in phenomena subject to strong seasonal fluctuations.

The example given in Table 10.7 will show how a moving average may distort the business cycle fluctuations which in this example are very violent. The lowest output which occurred in 1932 constitutes only $24 \cdot 3$ per cent of the maximum output reached in 1929. The second business cycle trough occurs in 1938, immediately after the year of high prosperity. From 1939 there is a sudden climb, obviously caused by the war; in 1944, not shown in the table, the production exceeds 80 million tons.

---

[92] If we denote by $a_1$, $a_2$, $a_3$, $a_4$, $a_5$ five consecutive values of the series the inequality $a_1 > a_2 > a_3 < a_4 < a_5$ ($a_3$ being the smallest) means that within this range the curve is concave to the axis of abscissae. The average $(a_1 + a_2 + a_3 + a_4 + a_5)/5$ is, of course, greater than the middle term $a_3$. If, however, $a_1 < a_2 < a_3 > a_4 > a_5$, (the curve is convex to the axis of abscissae) the average $(a_1 + a_2 + a_3 + a_4 + a_5)/5$ is smaller than $a_3$.

TABLE 10.7. PRODUCTION OF STEEL IN THE UNITED STATES[93]
(millions of tons)

| Year | Actual data | 5-year moving averages | Year | Actual data | 5-year moving averages |
|------|------|------|------|------|------|
| 1924 | 37·9 | · | 1933 | 23·2 | 24·6 |
| 1925 | 45·4 | · | 1934 | 26·1 | 29·0 |
| 1926 | 48·3 | 45·6 | 1935 | 24·1 | 36·4 |
| 1927 | 44·9 | 49·3 | 1936 | 47·8 | 39·4 |
| 1928 | 51·5 | 48·4 | 1937 | 50·6 | 41·6 |
| 1929 | 56·4 | 43·9 | 1938 | 28·3 | 46·7 |
| 1930 | 40·7 | 37·6 | 1939 | 47·1 | 52·0 |
| 1931 | 25·9 | 32·0 | 1940 | 59·8 | · |
| 1932 | 13·7 | 25·9 | 1941 | 74·0 | · |

Since there are also minor fluctuations of a more or less random nature the statistician might deem it proper to calculate a moving average of several years duration. Yet the 5-year moving average shown in the table completely distorts the pattern of the business cycle. Both cyclical maxima have been flattened, the lowest figure (which occurred in 1932) has been almost doubled and the very deep depression of 1938 has disappeared completely. Besides this, the peak of prosperity and the through of the severest depression have been shifted in time. According to the raw data the peak of the first cycle is in 1929, and according to the smoothed out series, in 1927; and the lowest point has been moved from 1932 to 1933. When the 3-year moving average is used these distortions are not so strong, but nevertheless are noticeable.

It is true that the above example is particularly striking since it pertains to the production of a commodity very "susceptible" to business fluctuations in the period of noticeable degeneration of capitalism, but it proves that great care should be exercised in using the moving average to eliminate fluctuations which are considered unimportant. In each case we should begin with an analysis of the pattern of raw data and should not fail to compare them with the smoothed series.

This reservation does not apply, as a rule, to the use of the moving average as a means of eliminating seasonal and other short-term fluctuations, since in the short term a minor part is played in a chronological pattern by possible distortions in the curvature, and periodic fluctuations of a strictly determined duration are eliminated completely by the use of a moving average covering the same length of time.

Sometimes a graphical method of smoothing the curve may be used instead of the moving average. To do this we plot the points as usual on the basis of the actual data and then draw a smooth curve as close as possible to these points; in

[93] *Historical Statistics of the United States,* 1789–1945, Washington, 1949, pp. 187 and 188.

this way we obtain an "ordered" picture of reality. This method is very arbitrary and, depending upon the individual's intuition, different results may be obtained. However, an experienced statistician with a good knowledge of the problem can get better results than might be expected. In this way we can eliminate minor random variations and other, even long-term, fluctuations, if we use a small scale and do not try to be too precise.

Besides the moving average there are other, more or less complicated, computational methods of smoothing. Their usefulness for the analysis of time series is limited, and the danger of reaching wrong conclusions is considerable. The same reservations hold for analytical methods of smoothing, in which we assume that the phenomenon in question develops according to a predetermined function.

Some of these mechanical and analytical methods, as well as the circumstances under which they can be used in statistics, will be discussed in the Appendix.

## 3. MEASURING PERIODIC FLUCTUATIONS

When cyclical fluctuations are of a definite duration the statistician is faced with two tasks:

(1) to find a numerical measure of the cycle,

(2) to eliminate periodic fluctuations in order to make possible a comparison in time.

The second question has already been discussed to some extent, but in addition to the methods described above, there are other methods of smoothing, which under certain circumstances may produce better results.

We shall now discuss primarily the measurement and elimination of seasonal fluctuations, i.e. those which are repeated at yearly intervals. These fluctuations play a very important role in economic phenomena. Similar methods can be applied to other short-term fluctuations: monthly, daily, etc. The problem of the business cycle fluctuations, which also repeat at certain intervals, is more complicated, but the length of the period is not strictly determined and the pattern in time is complex, so that all mechanical methods would of necessity lead to distortions.

The pattern of seasonal fluctuations is seldom very rigid: usually there are deviations from the typical pattern in individual years. Even such a phenomenon as the consumption of electric power for lighting, which seems to depend entirely on the length of the day, shows some variations related to the degree of cloudiness and the number of holidays. A typical example of seasonal fluctuations is sea fishing, which depends upon the appearance of shoals of fish of a given variety in places accessible to fishermen. The appearance of shoals is connected with the annual reproduction cycle of fish: it may be speeded up or delayed, depending upon climatic conditions in a given year. Besides these, weather conditions (the level of the sea) may make fishing difficult or even impossible in certain periods.

A good example of seasonality is the pattern of cod fishing in the Baltic. In 1947 the highest catch occurred between April and June; in February the catch was exceptionally poor (severe winter and the freezing of the Baltic); through the entire second half of the year the catch was high. In 1948 a very distinct maximum occurred in April, the level in the first three months was high and a substantial drop took place toward the end of the year. In 1949, however, the maximum spread over March, April and May, while in 1950 it was in March and April.

Seasonality is often affected by the planned action of man. The annual distribution of the consumption of electric power for lighting may change if daylight-saving time is introduced. In an agriculture strongly orientated toward grain cultivation the work peak will occur at harvest time; when agricultural production is more diversified, and especially when many root crops are grown, work will be more evenly distributed over the whole period of vegetation. A planned effort aimed at the elimination or limitation of seasonal fluctuations, and a uniform distribution of work over the whole year, may have a very great effect.

Thus, the pattern of seasonality may change, the fluctuations may be gradually dampened, or under certain circumstances, may become more severe. Changes in seasonal fluctuations in a capitalist economy may also be connected with the phase of the business cycle: the seasonal pattern may be different during recessions and periods of prosperity.

From the mathematical point of view the following should be noted.

If at certain times of the year the phenomenon studied assumes larger values than at other times, this increase may appear as a component: in the month $i$ there was a certain number of units more than the average for the whole year. This increase may also appear in a different form: in the month $i$ the values are higher than the yearly average by a certain ratio. If we denote by $y$ the monthly average for the year and by $s_i$ the absolute seasonal increase for month $i$, then the value corresponding to month $i$ in the first case may be written as

$$\bar{y} + s_i,$$ (X.1)

and in the second case as

$$\bar{y} \times \frac{\bar{y} + s_i}{\bar{y}}$$

or, if we denote the ratio $\dfrac{\bar{y} + s_i}{\bar{y}}$ by $s_i'$, as

$$\bar{y} \times s_i'.$$ (X.2)

Seasonality is usually calculated according to the second formula: as a factor by which the yearly average should be multiplied in order to obtain the value corresponding to a given period of the year. However, this procedure is not always justified. If a production establishment operates with the same intensity during the whole year, using up a certain amount of electric power to operate the machines, then the additional amount of power used up in certain months for lighting should be expressed as a component, because it does not depend upon the general level of consumption.

Let us now consider a very simple case: stable seasonality, independent of the business cycle and not subject to changes during the period under consideration. We shall also assume that seasonality is expressed by a multiplier, i.e. that to certain periods of the year correspond values higher or lower than the average in a fixed ratio. In this case it is most convenient to express seasonality in the form of an index number based on the yearly average. We shall use the month as a unit of time in analysing seasonality. It is obvious that some other period shorter than one year (a quarter, a week or even a day) can also be chosen.

If we were dealing with a phenomenon not subject to random fluctuations, or any other fluctuations except the seasonal, it would suffice to calculate the monthly average for any year and to relate the figures for particular months to this average. However, since there are other fluctuations we have to use a longer period of time for our calculations.

Returning to our example on the sales of electric power for lighting we shall consider a period of 13 years: 1925-37.

From the basic table (Table 10.1 p. 296) we calculate for each month the arithmetic mean of the 13-year period. We also calculate an overall monthly average for all months (either the arithmetic mean of the above 12 monthly averages, or the total amount of power sold during the 13 years—524,734,000 kWh.—divided by the total number of months, 156).

The monthly averages thus calculated are free from nearly all the minor random variations appearing in every economic series. They are also more or less free from the impact of the business cycle, since the period 1925-37 comprises different phases of the business cycle. Thus, if the averages for particular months differ from the overall monthly average, this is due almost exclusively to the influence of seasonality. Therefore, by dividing the averages for particular months by the overall monthly average we obtain an index number for each month: a relative number expressing seasonal increase or decrease.

The result is shown in Table 10.8.

The figures in the last column are obtained by dividing the figures in column 2 (the average consumption for a given month calculated over a period of 13 years) by 336·7 which is the overall monthly average, and by multiplying the result by 100.

However, in this calculation there is an error caused by the existence of a growth trend. If we have a growing tendency, as is the case here, then the averages for the first months of the year calculated over 13 years have lower values, and those for the months toward the end of the year have higher values compared to the average yearly level. By relating the averages so calculated to the constant yearly averages we obtain indices too law for the first months, and indices too high for the last months of the year. The situation would be reversed if the trends were decreasing. This will be example in Table 10.9 p. 312.

Let us imagine that seasonal fluctuations in the production of a certain commodity are with a stationary general level, those shown in column *a*, i.e. that in January the figure is 47 per cent larger than the monthly average for the year; in February, 28 per cent larger, in July, half as large, etc. These figures are the same as shown in Table 10.5 p. 302.

Let us assume now that we have planned and achieved an increase in production of 2 per cent every month, but that the seasonality factor does not cease to operate.

TABLE 10.8. SALES OF ELECTRIC POWER FOR LIGHTING TO
PRIVATE SUBSCRIBERS
Computation of seasonal indices — method A

| Month | 13-year averages | |
|---|---|---|
| | in thousand kWh | as percentages of the overall monthly average |
| I | 4804·2 | 142·8 |
| II | 4231·8 | 125·8 |
| III | 3477·8 | 103·4 |
| IV | 3137·1 | 93·3 |
| V | 2529·1 | 75·2 |
| VI | 2049·4 | 60·9 |
| VII | 1683·0 | 50·1 |
| VIII | 2043·0 | 60·7 |
| IX | 3736·1 | 81·3 |
| X | 3690·5 | 109·7 |
| XI | 4708·8 | 140·0 |
| XII | 5273·5 | 156·8 |
| *Average* | *3363·7* | *100·0* |

Then if in January the production is 147, as before, in February we shall get not 128 (a seasonal drop) but $128 \times 1 \cdot 02 = 131$, and in March $105 \times 1 \cdot 2 = 109$, etc. The corresponding figures are shown in column *b* of the table.

If we reduce the figures in column *b* so that the monthly average is 100 we get the figures in column *c*. However, they are not correct indices of seasonality: the figures for the first months are too low, and for the last months too high; only the index for July is unchanged. If we eliminated seasonality we would get for January not $132 \times \dfrac{100}{132} = 100$, but $132 \times \dfrac{100}{147} = 89$, and for December not $170 \times \dfrac{100}{170} = 100$,

but $170 \times \dfrac{100}{153} = 111 \cdot 1$ which would correspond to the monthly increase of 2 per cent.

TABLE 10.9. INFLUENCE OF GROWTH TREND ON SEASONALITY

| Month | Seasonality index yearly average = 100 (a) | Seasonality indices modified by monthly increase of 2 per cent | |
|---|---|---|---|
| | | January = 147 (b) | Yearly average = 100 (c) |
| I | 147 | 147 | 132 |
| II | 128 | 131 | 117 |
| III | 105 | 109 | 97 |
| IV | 94 | 100 | 90 |
| V | 76 | 82 | 73 |
| VI | 61 | 67 | 60 |
| VII | 50 | 56 | 50 |
| VIII | 60 | 69 | 62 |
| IX | 81 | 95 | 85 |
| X | 108 | 129 | 115 |
| XI | 137 | 167 | 149 |
| XII | 153 | 190 | 170 |
| Total | 1200 | 1342 | 1200 |

If the empirical data were given as in column *c* and if it were known that the production increased by 2 per cent every month we could calculate proper seasonality indices in the way shown in Table 10.10.

TABLE 10.10. CALCULATION OF SEASONAL INDICES WHEN THERE IS A GROWTH TREND

| Month | Raw seasonality indices (a) | Growth indices (January = 100) (b) | Seasonality indices after the elimination of the influence of growth | |
|---|---|---|---|---|
| | | | $(c) = 100 \, a/b$ | Yearly average = 100 (d) |
| I | 132 | 100·00 | 132·0 | 147 |
| II | 117 | 102·00 | 114·7 | 128 |
| III | 97 | 104·04 | 93·2 | 105 |
| IV | 90 | 106·12 | 84·8 | 94 |
| V | 73 | 108·24 | 67·4 | 76 |
| VI | 60 | 110·41 | 54·3 | 61 |
| VII | 50 | 112·62 | 44·4 | 50 |
| VIII | 62 | 114·87 | 54·0 | 60 |
| IX | 85 | 111·17 | 72·5 | 81 |
| X | 115 | 119·51 | 96·2 | 108 |
| XI | 149 | 121·90 | 122·2 | 137 |
| XII | 170 | 124·34 | 136·7 | 153 |
| Total | 1200 | · | 1072·4 | 1200 |

Column *a* in this table contains raw indices of seasonality, as they were obtained in Table 10.9. In column *b* growth indices of 2 per cent per month are shown (with January = 100). Column *c* contains the quotient obtained by dividing the figures in column *a* by the figures in column *b*. They are thus indices related not to the constant base (the yearly average), as in column *a*, but to a changing base increasing every month by 2 per cent. These are proper seasonal indices, with the reservation that they are not related to the yearly average (100). To obtain proper indices we would have to multiply the figures in this column by the quotient $1200/1072 \cdot 4 = 11,899$. The indices in column *d* were obtained in this way, they are identical with the indices in column *a* in Table 10.9.[94]

In our example of the sales of electric power for lighting the rate of growth is not as great as we assumed in our example in Table 10.9, but there is undoubtedly some growth trend, which must be allowed for if the seasonal indices are to be correct.

In statistics there are several methods of calculating seasonal indices which eliminate the influence of the rate of growth. Each of them is based on certain *a priori* assumptions whose correctness is rather difficult to determine. However, when used with care, some of them give a fairly good approximation, so they can be used for practical purposes.

We shall discuss in greater detail one of them, which is based on relatively few arbitrary assumptions. The starting points are 12-month moving averages calculated for consecutive calendar months in the way described above (see p. 303 *et seq.*).[95] Table 10.11 on p. 314 was obtained in this way.

Moving averages of this kind eliminate the influence of seasonality, and most of the random fluctuations, but they do not eliminate growth trends and business cycles, which should be retained for further calculations.

The pattern of business cycles is somewhat distorted because the moving average smooths out the curve representing the actual data. However, these distortions are not considerable since the 12-month period of which the moving average consists is short in comparison with the business cycle.

---

[94] If the calculations were not made with sufficient accuracy, i.e. if insufficient digits were used, the final result (column *d*) might differ somewhat from the original indices.

[95] The calculation of 12-month moving averages over a long period of time requires a great deal of computation work since each month, with the exception of the first and last months, appears as a component 12 times. However, the calculation can be simplified. We add the figures pertaining to the months from the 1st to the twelfth and write down the total; then we subtract the 1st month and add the thirteenth which gives the total for the months from the second to the thirteenth and repeat this procedure for the following months. The calculation should be checked from time to time by adding up directly the figures for the corresponding 12 months. Then we add each pair of the totals for the consecutive 12 months thus obtained and divide by 24. In this way we obtain the values of the moving average corresponding to calendar months. If we start our computations with January 1925, and end with December 1937, we shall be unable to get the figures for the moving average of the first 6 months of 1925 and the last 6 months of 1937.

TABLE 10.11. SALES OF ELECTRIC POWER FOR LIGHTING TO PRIVATE SUBSCRIBERS
12-month moving averages reduced to calendar months

| Year | I | II | III | IV | V | VI | VII | VIII | IX | X | XI | XII |
|------|------|------|------|------|------|------|------|------|------|------|------|------|
| 1925 | · | · | · | · | · | · | 2171·6 | 2183·5 | 2198·0 | 2206·5 | 2204·0 | 2206·0 |
| 1926 | 2206·0 | 2206·5 | 2210·8 | 2222·8 | 2242·2 | 2265·5 | 2290·0 | 2316·3 | 2337·5 | 2372·0 | 2407·7 | 2428·3 |
| 1927 | 2445·3 | 2458·0 | 2480·1 | 2508·8 | 2552·8 | 2611·5 | 2671·9 | 2727·8 | 2770·0 | 2787·9 | 2797·9 | 2820·3 |
| 1928 | 2844·1 | 2868·8 | 2897·9 | 2935·3 | 2983·0 | 3047·3 | 3104·6 | 3140·9 | 3168·4 | 3198·3 | 3231·8 | 3254·3 |
| 1929 | 3273·3 | 3284·8 | 3277·6 | 3267·9 | 3275·0 | 3277·3 | 3292·4 | 3331·1 | 3362·6 | 3389·7 | 3419·8 | 3441·7 |
| 1930 | 3447·7 | 3458·7 | 3483·3 | 3512·1 | 3526·0 | 3533·5 | 3544·2 | 3552·3 | 3558·5 | 3565·5 | 3565·7 | 3553·2 |
| 1931 | 3545·5 | 3538·8 | 3533·5 | 3528·3 | 3507·5 | 3483·8 | 3466·2 | 3442·8 | 3424·6 | 3402·6 | 3376·3 | 3370·5 |
| 1932 | 3365·2 | 3349·3 | 3326·4 | 3301·8 | 3295·8 | 3300·0 | 3271·3 | 3237·0 | 3227·3 | 3232·0 | 3238·2 | 3241·3 |
| 1933 | 3250·0 | 3263·5 | 3282·8 | 3293·9 | 3300·3 | 3301·2 | 3320·4 | 3366·8 | 3399·3 | 3413·5 | 3427·2 | 3436·8 |
| 1934 | 3447·4 | 3467·2 | 3485·5 | 3504·4 | 3529·6 | 3571·4 | 3622·0 | 3656·5 | 3678·4 | 3708·3 | 3742·5 | 3772·2 |
| 1935 | 3791·6 | 3800·5 | 3814·4 | 3838·4 | 3871·3 | 3896·5 | 3924·9 | 3966·4 | 3999·2 | 4024·8 | 4045·1 | 4065·1 |
| 1936 | 4089·0 | 4109·4 | 4138·5 | 4186·0 | 4236·1 | 4280·7 | 4325·6 | 4368·8 | 4421·4 | 4473·3 | 4524·3 | 4565·1 |
| 1937 | 4568·5 | 4601·5 | 4660·7 | 4692·2 | 4739·6 | 4824·9 | · | · | · | · | · | · |

TABLE 10.12. SALES OF ELECTRIC POWER FOR LIGHTING TO PRIVATE SUBSCRIBERS

Ratio of actual data for each month to 12-month moving averages

Calculation of seasonality — method B

| Year | I | II | III | IV | V | VI | VII | VIII | IX | X | XI | XII |
|------|-----|-----|------|------|------|------|------|------|------|------|------|------|
| 1925 | . | . | . | . | . | . | 50·7 | 61·9 | 82·8 | 114·8 | 134·8 | 156·3 |
| 1926 | 147·4 | 125·5 | 111·4 | 85·1 | 72·7 | 54·5 | 48·3 | 58·7 | 81·8 | 115·1 | 134·7 | 153·9 |
| 1927 | 145·2 | 126·3 | 106·4 | 101·4 | 71·9 | 58·3 | 45·8 | 56·7 | 81·5 | 110·3 | 141·4 | 157·1 |
| 1928 | 151·4 | 128·6 | 105·8 | 86·7 | 69·6 | 59·8 | 48·3 | 59·4 | 83·1 | 112·4 | 141·7 | 164·5 |
| 1929 | 145·4 | 125·0 | 101·0 | 92·3 | 73·5 | 61·9 | 53·1 | 56·8 | 72·4 | 105·1 | 139·8 | 151·2 |
| 1930 | 152·9 | 130·8 | 104·8 | 94·7 | 80·0 | 60·6 | 50·2 | 59·8 | 78·5 | 109·2 | 134·1 | 151·5 |
| 1931 | 151·0 | 131·0 | 104·4 | 98·0 | 76·8 | 56·5 | 51·0 | 57·3 | 82·3 | 110·1 | 131·4 | 153·1 |
| 1932 | 153·1 | 127·6 | 108·7 | 90·9 | 76·4 | 60·8 | 48·9 | 54·4 | 76·9 | 107·9 | 140·4 | 158·8 |
| 1933 | 137·7 | 126·5 | 107·5 | 97·1 | 74·8 | 64·5 | 50·8 | 59·4 | 79·7 | 103·4 | 135·9 | 147·2 |
| 1934 | 145·8 | 135·3 | 107·4 | 94·9 | 75·7 | 60·4 | 52·8 | 61·4 | 78·8 | 102·3 | 133·6 | 151·6 |
| 1935 | 147·1 | 130·7 | 104·7 | 98·8 | 78·1 | 64·6 | 51·0 | 59·4 | 78·1 | 103·0 | 134·4 | 144·9 |
| 1936 | 148·9 | 132·7 | 103·8 | 98·1 | 75·5 | 65·9 | 52·9 | 58·9 | 81·5 | 107·4 | 132·2 | 140·6 |
| 1937 | 145·3 | 129·1 | 108·8 | 97·5 | 83·4 | 63·2 | . | . | . | . | . | . |
| Total[a] 1926—37 (1925—36) | 1771·2 | 1549·1 | 1274·7 | 1135·5 | 908·4 | 731·0 | 603·8 | 704·1 | 957·4 | 1301·0 | 1634·4 | 1830·7 |
| Average[a] for 12 years | 147·6 | 129·1 | 106·2 | 94·6 | 75·7 | 60·9 | 50·3 | 58·7 | 79·8 | 108·4 | 136·2 | 152·5 |

[a] Since the moving average does not smooth out the first and the last 6 months we get the figures for only 12 years: 1926-37 from January to June, 1925-36 from July to December.

The next stage consists of computing the ratio of the actual value for each month to the moving average obtained in the way described above. Thus we obtain seasonal indices not distorted by the general development trend and by the business cycle, because the actual value for each month, subject to these influences, is related to the value smoothed out by the moving average, which also reflects the development trend (slightly distorted), and the business cycle. However, the seasonal coefficients are subject to random variations. Only the average for each month based on whole years to some extent eliminates these random fluctuations.

The results of the calculation are given in Table 10.12 (p. 315).

The advantage of the above method of calculating seasonal indices is that it is not based on any assumptions concerning the pattern of the business cycle or the rate of development.

The question remains: on what number of years should the calculation be based? If the period is too short, random fluctuations will not be eliminated and they may be considerable, as could be seen in our example in Table 10.12. In a very long term, however, the nature of seasonality may change and then we would have an incorrectly calculated average, not based on uniform material. However, changes in seasonality are a different question, and we shall discuss them later.

This calculation may be somewhat simplified. Instead of calculating the ratio of the actual values to 12-month moving averages separately for each month of the 12-year period, and then the arithmetic means of these ratios, we can calculate the ratios of actual absolute sums for each month over the 12-year period to the sum of moving averages also for the 12-year period, which gives the average seasonality indices directly. The calculation is shown in Table 10.13.

Just as in the previous calculation for the first half of the year, the years 1926–37 have been taken and for the second half the years from 1925–36. This explains the drop in the moving averages (and the corresponding decrease in the sums of the actual data) which begins in July; this, however, does not affect the indices. We could possibly reject altogether the second half of 1925, and the first half of 1937, and calculate the totals only for the 11-year period 1926–36.

The simplification in computation compared with method $B$ (Table 10.12) is not so substantial as it might appear. When we apply the ratio method to moving averages the main difficulty is not the computation of 144 indices in Table 10.12, but the computation of 144 values of the moving average (Table 10.11). However, the computation of individual values of the moving average can be avoided and the sums in column $b$ in Table 10.13 can be obtained indirectly. As we can easily check, the sum of all the items from January to December (column $a$ Table 10.13), which amounts to 482,761, is equivalent to 12 times the 12-month moving average for the accounting month from the middle of December to the middle of January. Indeed, the 12-month moving average for the fiscal month from the middle of

December 1925 to the middle of January 1926 is equal to 1/12 of the total for the months from July 1925 to June 1926, the 12-month moving average for the fiscal month from the middle of December 1926 to the middle of January 1927 is equal to 1/12 of the total for the months from July 1926 to June 1927, and so on.

TABLE 10.13. SALES OF ELECTRIC POWER FOR LIGHTING
TO PRIVATE SUBSCRIBERS
Calculation of seasonality — method B′

| Month | Totals for 12 years | | Seasonality indices |
|---|---|---|---|
| | actual (a) | moving averages (b) | $\dfrac{100a}{b}$ |
| I | 59,451 | 40,274 | 147·6 |
| II | 52,280 | 40,407 | 129·4 |
| III | 43,060 | 40,591 | 106·1 |
| IV | 38,778 | 40,792 | 95·0 |
| V | 31,297 | 41,059 | 76·2 |
| VI | 25,404 | 41,394 | 61·4 |
| VII | 19,737 | 39,005 | 50·6 |
| VIII | 23,047 | 39,290 | 58·6 |
| IX | 31,486 | 39,545 | 79·6 |
| X | 42,895 | 39,774 | 107·8 |
| XI | 54,391 | 39,981 | 136·0 |
| XII | 60,935 | 40,155 | 151·7 |

Column a according to Table 10.1 p. 296
Column b according to Table 10.11 p. 314

The sum of all these averages is one-twelfth of the sum for all the months from July 1925 to June 1927. The sum of all the items in column a, Table 10.13 is equal to the total for all the consecutive months for the whole period (in this table the figures from January to June inclusive together comprise the first half of all years from 1926 to 1937, the figures from July to December inclusive, the second half of all the years from 1925 to 1936, as above). Hence the average for the fiscal month from the middle of December to the middle of January is

$$\frac{1}{12} \sum a = \frac{1}{12} \times 482{,}761 = 40{,}230.$$

We get the total of averages for the fiscal month from the middle of January to the middle of February by subtracting from the starting total of 482,761 the sales of electric power in July 1925 and adding the sales for July 1937, according to Table 10.1. Thus we get

$$\frac{1}{12} \times (482{,}761 - 1102 + 2143) = \frac{1}{12} \times 483{,}802 = 40{,}317.$$

By substracting from 483,802 the figure for August 1925 and adding the figure

for August 1937 we get the sum of averages for the accounting month from the
middle of February to the middle of March:

$$\frac{1}{12} \times (483,802 - 1351 + 3513) = \frac{1}{12} \times 485,964 = 40,497.$$

Proceeding in the same way we get the sums of averages for the fiscal months in
the first half of the year up to the accounting month from the middle of June to
the middle of July inclusive.

To calculate the data for the second half of the year we have to start again
from the total of 482,761 and go back, subtracting the sales in June 1937 and
adding the sales in June 1925; dividing by 12 we obtain the sum of averages for
the fiscal month from the middle of November to the middle of December:

$$\frac{1}{12} \times (482,761 - 3049 + 1238) = \frac{1}{12} \times 480,950 = 40,079$$

The sum of the averages for the fiscal month from the middle of June to the
middle of July is thus obtained twice: once going forward (the greater number,
based on the months from January 1926 to December 1937) and the second time
going backward (the smaller number, based on the months from January 1925 to
December 1936). It is necessary to calculate this month twice in order to shift
from fiscal to calendar months.

This transition takes place in the usual ways by calculating the arithmetic mean
of two consecutive accounting months. Thus (see above):

$$(40,230 + 40,317)/2 = 40,274$$

is the sum of 12-month averages for January; and

$$(40,317 + 40,497)/2 = 40,407$$

is the sum of averages for February; and so on.

The results are, of course, identical with those given above in Table 10.13.

This complicated calculation can be made relatively simple by using the calculating machine. The order of operations is as follows:

(1) From Table 10.1 calculate the items in column a, Table 10.13.

(2) Add up these items for all the months from January to December.

(3) Write down the total obtained, 482,761, and enter it in the calculating machine as the multiplicand.

(4) Multiply 482,761 by 0·08333 (which is equivalent to division by 12). Write
down the result (40,230) as the sum of the averages for the fiscal month December–
January.

(5) Transfer the uncancelled number, 482,761, to the carriage, subtract 1102
(July 1925), and add 2143 (July 1937).

(6) Write down the figure obtained 483,802 and enter it in the calculator as
the multiplicand.

These operations will be further repeated (4, 5 and 6) until we reach the fiscal month June–July. Then we again enter the starting figure of 482,761 and going backward, as described above again reach the fiscal month June–July. Finally, we calculate the sums of averages for calendar months in the usual way. Only in this way are the calculations really simplified in comparison with the computations shown in Table 10.12.

The indices thus obtained differ somewhat from the previous ones. The differences can be explained by the fact that previously we calculated the simple averages of index numbers for individual years, and the calculation of indices from sums is tantamount to the calculation of the weighted averages of indices for individual years. It is not immediately apparent whether weighted averages should in this case be given priority over simple averages.[96]

These minor differences are of no importance in studying the nature of seasonality, and no matter which method we consider as theoretically more correct, we can without hesitation use the one that is more convenient. However, from another point of view, the more complex method $B$ is better than the simpler method $B'$. Using method $B$ we get separate seasonality indices for each year. This enables us to: (1) evaluate the dispersion between the indices for the same month in different years (excessive dispersion reduces the accuracy of the final results based on the average); (2) determine whether some indices do not deviate too much from the remaining ones (due to some unimportant reasons) and consequently should be left out in calculating the averages: (3) determine whether during the period under consideration a change in the nature of seasonality has not taken place. We shall return to these questions during the discussion of seasonality indices based on chain indices.

Another method of calculating seasonal indices, which we shall call the method of *chain indices,* is not quite free from certain *a priori* assumptions. The errors that may be committed in using this method are not large. If has certain advantages over the method based on moving averages. It was invented by W. M. Persons, the founder of what is known as the Harvard Method. On the surface, the method of chain indices appears to be very complicated, but in fact it requires much less computational work than do moving averages.

It will be shown here, with certain modifications and simplifications of the original Harvard Method.

---

[96] The differences between indices calculated by methods B and B' are to some extent biased: according to B' they are somwhat higher than according to B in the months from April to July and in February, and somewhat lower primarily in the last months of the year. The reason becomes obvious when we consider that according to Table 10.22 on p. 340, a change in the nature of seasonality took place, and that in calculating a weighted average the final years of the period have greater weights (in the denominator there are 12-month averages which increase owing to the increasing general development trend reflected in the increasing consumption of electric power).

We begin by calculating chain indices of empirical values for each pair of consecutive months: the ratio of February to January, March to February, etc. In our example, the figure for January 1925 is 3004 kWh, for February, 2733 kWh.; the quotient is $\frac{2733}{3004} = 0\cdot910$ which is $91\cdot0$ per cent of the figure for January; the ratio of March to February is $\frac{2150}{2733} = 0\cdot787$ which is $78\cdot7$ per cent of the February figure, and so on. From these indices for each month we calculate the averages for the whole period in our example, 13 years. In this way we obtain Table 10.14 (p. 321).[97]

The values of the ratio of two consecutive months obtained in this way depend—apart from random factors, business cycles and growth trends—on the pattern of seasonality during the year. During the period of a seasonal decline the values for each pair of months in consecutive years will, on average, be less than 100, and during a seasonal growth they will be on average greater than 100. In this case the figures are less than 100 in the first half of the year (with certain deviations in January) up to July inclusive, and greater than 100 in the second half of the year beginning in August.

The average of chain indices with an appropriately selected number of years eliminates the business cycles and some random fluctuations, but it does not eliminate the growth trend.

Looking over the indices in Table 10.14 we can see clear disturbances in the pattern in July, August and September of 1937: in July and September the indices are much too low in comparison with other years and the index for January is much too high ($163\cdot9$, though in no other year does it exceed $126\cdot2$). Not having the detailed reports of the electric power station, we do not know whether these changes were caused by interruptions in cash collections or by other reasons. In any case, it would not be right to use the distorted figures in calculating average chain indices. Therefore, in addition to the averages for 13 years for these months, the averages for 12 years are also given in the table, and the latter are used for further calculations. It may be easier to catch excessive deviations when a frequency distribution of chain indices is made out for each month. It is obvious that the greatest care must be exercised in rejecting extreme deviations; we should reject only those which it is certain cannot be regarded as true.

---

[97] If we stick rigidly to the number of years under study, we have one ratio less for January than for the following months. If we have the required data we can take the ratio of January in the first year to December of the year preceding the period studied, or the ratio of January in the year following to December of the last year in the period studied. In the table both values are given; in further calculations the ratio of January 1938 to December 1937 is used. If we have no data beyond the period studied we have to confine ourselves to one year less for January, which does not rend further calculation impossible but makes it a little less consistent.

TABLE 10.14. SALES OF ELECTRIC POWER FOR LIGHTING TO PRIVATE SUBSCRIBERS

Chain indices

| Year | I | II | III | IV | V | VI | VII | VIII | IX | X | XI | XII |
|---|---|---|---|---|---|---|---|---|---|---|---|---|
| 1925 | (99·2) | 91·0 | 78·6 | 93·2 | 78·8 | 78·4 | 89·0 | 122·5 | 134·7 | 139·2 | 117·3 | 116·0 |
| 1926 | 94·3 | 85·2 | 88·9 | 76·8 | 86·2 | 75·8 | 89·4 | 123·1 | 140·5 | 142·8 | 118·8 | 115·2 |
| 1927 | 95·0 | 87·4 | 85·0 | 96·4 | 72·2 | 83·0 | 80·4 | 126·2 | 146·0 | 136·2 | 128·7 | 112·0 |
| 1928 | 97·2 | 85·7 | 83·1 | 83·0 | 81·5 | 87·8 | 82·2 | 124·6 | 141·2 | 136·5 | 127·3 | 117·0 |
| 1929 | 88·9 | 86·3 | 80·6 | 91·2 | 79·8 | 84·3 | 86·1 | 108·2 | 128·8 | 146·2 | 134·3 | 108·8 |
| 1930 | 101·3 | 85·8 | 80·7 | 91·1 | 84·8 | 76·0 | 83·1 | 119·3 | 131·5 | 139·5 | 122·8 | 112·5 |
| 1931 | 99·4 | 86·6 | 79·6 | 93·7 | 77·9 | 73·1 | 89·9 | 111·5 | 142·7 | 133·0 | 118·4 | 116·3 |
| 1932 | 99·9 | 83·0 | 84·6 | 83·0 | 83·9 | 79·7 | 79·8 | 109·9 | 141·0 | 140·5 | 130·9 | 112·4 |
| 1933 | 87·2 | 92·2 | 85·5 | 90·6 | 77·2 | 86·3 | 79·2 | 118·6 | 135·5 | 130·4 | 131·9 | 108·6 |
| 1934 | 99·3 | 93·3 | 79·8 | 88·8 | 80·4 | 80·7 | 88·8 | 117·3 | 129·1 | 130·8 | 131·9 | 114·4 |
| 1935 | 97·5 | 89·1 | 80·4 | 95·0 | 79·7 | 83·3 | 80·1 | 116·7 | 132·6 | 132·7 | 131·1 | 108·3 |
| 1936 | 103·4 | 89·5 | 78·8 | 95·6 | 77·9 | 88·2 | 81·1 | 112·4 | 140·0 | 133·4 | 124·4 | 107·3 |
| 1937 | 103·5 | 89·5 | 85·3 | 90·3 | 86·4 | 77·1 | 70·3 | 163·9 | 116·2 | 124·5 | 134·6 | 111·2 |
| 1938 | 97·0 | .. | .. | .. | .. | .. | .. | .. | .. | .. | .. | .. |
| Averages | 97·22 | 88·05 | 82·38 | 89·90 | 80·52 | 81·06 | 83·03[a] | 121·09[a] | 135·37[a] | 135·82 | 127·11 | 112·31 |
|  |  |  |  |  |  |  | (84·09) | (117·53) | (136·97) |  |  |  |

[a] The numbers in brackets are the average for the 12 years 1925-36 (cf. p. 322).

These striking deviations from the normal pattern would also appear in calculating the ratio with respect to the 12-month moving average (Table 10.12 p. 315) if it were possible to calculate the moving average for the second half of 1937.

The next stage consists of calculating the index number based on January (=100). Thus we write 100 in January, 88·05 in February, (88·05×82·38)/100=72·54 in March, etc. (see p. 277 *et seq.*). These figures are shown in column 3, Table 10.15.

If the figures of the index reflected only seasonal fluctuations we should expect the figure 100 in January of the next year, as it was in January in the starting year. If we obtain 108·59, this results to some extent from arithmetic reasons, but mainly from the fact that the figures of the index also reflect the influence of the growth trend.

The starting point for further steps is the distribution of the difference which has accumulated during the year during particular months. The difference can be evenly distributed, when we use either the arithmetic mean (the figure for each unit of time is increased by the same amount) or the geometric mean (the figure for each unit of time is increased in the same ratio). The choice between the arithmetic mean and the geometric mean is arbitrary. There is also no basis for contending that changes during the year were uniform; increases can be expressed by other, more complex functions. However, considering relatively small changes caused by the growth trend during one year the choice of the function is of no importance. In Table 10.15 the method of calculation shown is for the case where the arithmetic mean is selected.

TABLE 10.15. SALES OF ELECTRIC POWER FOR LIGHTING TO PRIVATE SUBSCRIBERS
Calculation of seasonal indices — Method C

| Month | Average chain indices | Indices (January = 100) | Correction coefficients | Corrected indices (January = 100) | Reduced indices (average = 100) |
|-------|------|------|------|------|------|
| 1 | 2 | 3 | 4 | 5 | 6 |
| I | ... | 100·00 | 1·0000 | 100·00 | 147·5 |
| II | 88·05 | 88·05 | 1·0072 | 87·42 | 128·9 |
| III | 82·38 | 72·54 | 1·0143 | 71·52 | 105·5 |
| IV | 89·90 | 65·21 | 1·0215 | 63·84 | 94·1 |
| V | 80·52 | 52·51 | 1·0286 | 51·04 | 75·3 |
| VI | 81·06 | 42·56 | 1·0358 | 41·08 | 60·6 |
| VII | 84·09 | 35·79 | 1·0429 | 34·42 | 50·6 |
| VIII | 117·53 | 42·06 | 1·0501 | 40·05 | 59·1 |
| IX | 136·97 | 57·61 | 1·0573 | 54·49 | 80·4 |
| X | 135·82 | 78·25 | 1·0644 | 73·52 | 108·4 |
| XI | 127·11 | 99·46 | 1·0716 | 92·81 | 136·9 |
| XII | 112·31 | 111·70 | 1·0787 | 103·55 | 152·7 |
| I | 97·22 | 108·59 | 1·0859 | (100·00) | (147·5) |
| Total | . | . | . | 813·64 | 1200·0 |

The total deviation for the 12 months from the starting value is 0·0859. Dividing this by 12, we get 0·00716 as the increase in each month. In this way we get the correction coefficient shown in column 4 in Table 10.15. This coefficient is 1 for January, $1 + 0·00716$ or approximately 1·0072, for February, $1 + 2 \times 0·00716$ or roughly 1·0143 for March, etc. Dividing the index by the corresponding correction coefficient we get the "corrected" values of the index with January ($=100$) as a base. The end value in January of the following year is now 100, and every term of the series, beginning with February, will be reduced in the appropriate ratio (column 5).

To obtain the seasonal index all that is now required is to give the "corrected" indices such a form that the monthly average for the year will be 100. Since the sum of indices (column 5) is 813·64 and we should get 1200·0 (since then the monthly average will be 100·0), we should multiply each term of the series by $\frac{1200·0}{813·64} = 1·47485$. Thus we arrive at "reduced indices" (column 6) which are the seasonal indices sought on the basis that the monthly average for the year is 100.

Other methods of calculating seasonal indices are based on first calculating the growth trend. However, this is a different problem which must be first discussed in general terms.

## 4. ANALYSIS OF GROWTH TREND

Elementary methods of the empirical analysis of the dynamics of growth have been discussed above. Now we shall consider more complex methods, which are perhaps not always more precise, but which are necessary in studying economic phenomena in the capitalist system.

Studies on the dynamics of growth are one of the most important tasks of statistics in a socialist system. The checking of planned growth, and the comparison with actual development, the maintenance of the balance between different industries and the detection in time of all signs of developing disequilibrium between industries, constant studies of the impact of growth of particular industries on the whole national economy—these are only a few of the tasks that must be accomplished to create a sound basis for revising the plan and for better planning in the future. To fulfil these tasks it is imperative to have diversified and detailed statistical data, and the skill and knowledge required to use them effectively. To accomplish the tasks facing him the statistician must know the laws governing the development of society, and have the full awareness of the targets set in planning not only for the near future, but also further ahead.

However, even when it is necessary to use complex statistical methods the technical side of a statistical analysis of the dynamics of growth in a socialist economy is usually very simple. We shall discuss this subject in greater detail at the end of this chapter.

A capitalist economy develops spontaneously and its rate of development—increase or decrease—depends upon the interaction of opposing forces and contradictions particularly prominent in the phase of imperialism. Under these conditions more or less violent fluctuations are bound to occur, and their existence must be recognized and studied if the conclusions reached are to be correct.

Business cycles have a particularly disturbing effect. It should suffice to recall that the production of steel in the United States reached 56·4 million tons in 1927 and then dropped to 13·7 million tons in 1932, i.e. by almost 76 per cent. Apart from business cycles, however, a general development trend may underlie fluctuations. In fields in which technical progress takes place, the trend may be upward; elsewhere it may be downward. The measuring of the development trend is very difficult and sometimes impossible.

The moving average cannot be used here, since it eliminates only periodic fluctuations of a definite duration of the cycle. The length of the business cycle is subject to changes in time and may also vary because of secondary random factors, and therefore it is impossible to determine the number of years to be used in calculating the moving average.

Nor would a direct comparison of peak periods of two consecutive cycles give good results because the peaks appear in different cycles with different intensities under the influence of factors of secondary importance. The same reservation applies even more to the low points of recessions.

The best results can be expected from a comparison of averages comprising the whole business cycle so that both the maximum and the minimum are included, preferably so that neither of them is at an extreme point of the cycle for which the averages are calculated. Thus the period could begin several years after a minimum (or maximum) and end several years after the next minimum (or maximum). A comparison of averages would thus show the difference in the levels of two whole cycles: this seems to be as close to reality as it is possible to get.

The length of the periods for which averages are calculated would not be the same, since the lengths of the cycles are different. In order to determine the beginning and the end of the cycle a careful analysis of the whole cycle should be made beforehand. In particular, it should be remembered that the pattern of the cycle may be affected by factors of secondary importance. For instance, in the United States wars also have had a positive effect—of course from the point of view of the industrialist—in increased indices of industrial production during both world wars. An allowance for the effects of secondary factors may seriously change the appraisal of the dynamics of growth based merely on statistics.

In capitalist countries the method of least squares is very widely used for smoothing time series. This and other methods of smoothing series is critically reviewed in the Appendix. The application of this method to economic phenomena is subject to serious reservations which will be discussed later. However, its general outline will be presented here not because it gives a correct picture of growth but because it is most convenient for calculating seasonality indices and is more suitable for presenting business cycle fluctuations than are raw data.

We shall use our example to show how this method works. In Fig. 10.5 the points denote the actual sales of electric power in consecutive years from 1925 to 1937. The straight line drawn among those points goes through some of them; most of the points, however, are located below or above the line. The deviations of the points from the line are measured by segments $y_1-y_1'$, $y_2-y_2'$, etc., parallel to the axis of ordinates. When the line is drawn by the method of least squares the sum of the squares of these deviations, i.e. the sum $(y_1-y_1')^2$, $(y_2-y_2')^2$, etc. is a minimum. Instead of the straight line any other function can be used which reflects the pattern of the phenomenon.

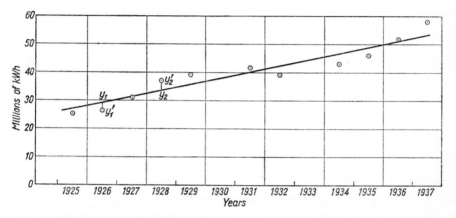

FIG. 10.5. Sales of electric power for lighting to private subscribers Warsaw, 1925–37. The method of least squares.

However, there are some reservations. The choice of a function—and this is a starting point when we use the method of least squares—is almost always arbitrary. Only in exceptional cases is it possible to determine the nature of the function by an analysis of the problem studied. In most cases we can only say generally that a given shape of the curve is more probable or convenient than other shapes.

In practice this is not a very formidable problem. When we are analysing the growth trend for not very long periods the shape of the curve does not much matter, since it affects the results only very little.

To calculate the equation for a long period would usually be an error because it would be tantamount to assuming that during the whole period growth is governed by the same laws, whereas—at least in economic and social phenomena—basic changes often appear and change the conditions of growth. If we deal with a series having such basic turns in the development curve we should confine ourselves to smoothing out by segments using the simplest possible function (e.g. a straight line), instead of trying to fit the whole series artificially to one growth curve.

In 1950 a series of papers (*Die Nachtruhe der Schulkinder*) concerning the sleeping habits of school children in Berlin was published together with mathematical and statistical comments. These papers were sharply criticized by *Statistische Praxis* published in East Berlin (1950, No 10). There were many examples of wrong reasoning of which we shall mention here only two.

(1) To establish a proper norm for hours of sleep for children at various ages, the author establishes the actual number of hours of sleep for children in different types of schools, although the length of sleep may depend on different secondary causes and not only on the physiological need. He assumes that a length of sleep differing from the arithmetic mean for a given age by one mean deviation up or down is within the normal range. This conclusion may be in line with formal mathematic requirements, but it has no real foundation.

(2) The average length of sleep is extended by extrapolation to cover earlier and later ages (up to the age of 50), assuming also that infants after birth must sleep 24 hr. This is ridiculous; it might even happen that, according to this calculation, the length of sleep at the age of 50 is zero, or perhaps even some negative number.

In our example on the consumption of electric power in Warsaw the limitations will be as follows: (1) we cannot go beyond the inter-war period since both world wars affected the phenomenon studied in a decisive way; (2) we should reject the first years after World War I—the years 1922, 1923 and possibly 1924—because conditions then had not yet returned to normal; (3) we should end our analysis with the year 1937 because on 1 January in 1938 new rates for electric power became effective, and they contributed to a sudden increase in consumption, so that the growth line was bound to turn sharply at this point.

As the basis for the calculations presented below, the 13-year period from 1925 to 1937 was taken. In principle, this period should be equal to the length of the business cycle or to its multiple, if we want to avoid distortions. Unfortunately, the length of the business cycle cannot be determined accurately in this case. The period of 13 years is somewhat longer than the business cycle. However, trials have revealed that the length of the period affects the results little in this case. For the smoothing of the series a straight line was used. In the short term the choice of function is of secondary importance and the use of a straight line considerably simplifies the computations. The details of the calculation are shown in the Appendix. Here we shall give only the final result.

Let us denote by $x$ the number of calendar year. It is most convenient to denote by 0 the middle year of the period selected. In this case it is the year 1931. The preceding years from 1931 back to 1925 are denoted by —1, —2, ..., —6, and the following years from 1932 to 1937 are denoted by +1, +2, ..., +6. The sales of electric power in thousands of kWh are denoted by $y$. Solving two simple equations we arrive at the function:

$$y = 40,364 \cdot 15 + 2163 \cdot 165x \qquad (X.3)$$

In this equation $x$ denotes, as before, the consecutive number of the calendar year from —6 to +6 and $y$ is the smoothed value of the sales of electric power in the consecutive years from —6 (i.e. 1925) to +6 (i.e. 1937). Thus, for instance, in 1931, when $x = 0$ the sales after smoothing out would be 40,364 thousand kWh, the annual increase is 2163 thousand kWh so that in 1925 ($x = $ —6) the sales would be 27,385 thousand kWh and in 1937 ($x = $ +6) the sales would be 53,343 thousand kWh, and so on.

These figures differ substantially from the actual values shown in the last column in Table 10.1. This is natural since equation (X.3) is based on the assumption that increases in sales are uniform and amount to 2,163,165 kWh per annum, whereas the actual growth was complicated by the impact of random and business cycle fluctuations. The only justification for smoothing time series is the fact that if there is a trend, up or down, it will show through temporary deviations up or down so that during a depression, for instance, the actual drop when the growth trend is upward is smaller than it would be if there were no such upward trend.

Smoothing of this kind can be applied to phenomena occurring in a capitalist economy in which growth is spontaneous and results from diverse, opposing factors. This kind of smoothing in a socialist economy, where growth is governed by a plan, would be superfluous. Only a very careful elimination of minor deviations in implementing the plan, due to secondary factors is permissible.

The cognitive value of this method in a capitalist economy is relatively small. It only tells us about the existence of a development trend and about its rate of growth. But it disquises the fact that growth in a capitalist economy is not smooth, but is subject to ups and downs due to depressions.

The necessary condition for using analytical methods of smoothing is a qualitative analysis at the beginning and at the end. As a rule, the method of smoothing can be used only for short periods of time, in which the growth trend can be expected to be uniform. In such cases it will also be of little importance whether the smoothing is done by a straight line (which simplifies calculations) or by some more complicated curve. On the other hand the period selected should coincide with the full cycle or cycles, or else the picture obtained will be false (too slight or too steep a slope).

Of course, phenomena can also be studied in the long term, but it would be risky to try to fit the line of actual development into a function selected to depict the "laws" of evolution of the phenomenon. It is far better to analyse the actual development, and perhaps use averages comprising an appropriate number of years for eliminating fluctuations unimportant in long-term growth. Sometimes graphical

methods of eliminating fluctuations may also be used. But the statistician must base
this analysis on actual data and facts, and should determine the conditions which
affected the nature and the rate of development.

On the other hand, analytical methods of smoothing time series within a short
range, in spite of all the reservations, may be a very useful tool in: (1) calculating
seasonal indices for all phenomena showing a growing or declining development
trend; (2) evaluating business fluctuations in a capitalist economy.

Let us consider the second method. As we mentioned above, a reduction in actual
data due to a depression (the last column in Table 10.1 p. 296, and column 2 in
Table 10.16) is partly obscured by the influence of an upward trend; if there were
no tendency to increase the consumption of electric power, the impact of the
depression would have been felt much more strongly. This fact is reflected in
Table 10.16.

TABLE 10.16. COMPARISON OF ACTUAL SALES OF ELECTRIC POWER
WITH THE SERIES SMOOTHED OUT BY A STRAIGHT LINE
(in thousand kWh)

| Year | Actual sales (a) | Smoothed-out series (b) | Difference (a−b) | Ratio $\frac{100a}{b}$ |
|------|------|------|------|------|
| 1 | 2 | 3 | 4 | 5 |
| 1925 | 25,935 | 27,385 | −1450 | 94·7 |
| 1926 | 27,330 | 29,548 | −2218 | 92·5 |
| 1927 | 31,685 | 31,711 | −26 | 99·9 |
| 1928 | 37,029 | 33,875 | +3154 | 109·3 |
| 1929 | 39,253 | 36,038 | +3215 | 108·9 |
| 1930 | 42,490 | 38,201 | +4289 | 111·2 |
| 1931 | 41,694 | 40,364 | +1330 | 103·3 |
| 1932 | 39,594 | 42,527 | −2933 | 93·1 |
| 1933 | 39,570 | 44,690 | −5120 | 88·5 |
| 1934 | 43,187 | 46,854 | −3667 | 92·2 |
| 1935 | 46,843 | 49,017 | −2174 | 95·6 |
| 1936 | 51,632 | 51,180 | +452 | 100·9 |
| 1937 | 58,492 | 53,343 | +5149 | 109·7 |

Fluctuations in differences between the series representing the actual sales and
the smoothed series (a − b, column 4 in the table) and the ratio of the figures in
the empirical series to the figures in the smoothed series (100 a/b, column 5 in the
table) may be due either to random deviations or to the business cycle. We have
a right to think that business fluctuations are decisive here. This view is supported
by their systematic nature: groups of consecutive years with negative differences
and corresponding indices smaller than 100, and groups of consecutive years with
positive differences and indices greater than 100. Random fluctuations can only
be of minor importance here.

This table corrects the conclusions that might be reached on the basis of the actual data. According to these data the decline in the consumption of electric power between 1930 and 1933 was only 2,920,000 kWh, i.e. 6·9 per cent. According to column 4 in the table the actual sales in 1930 were 4,289,000 kWh above the level of the smoothed series and in 1933 the sales were 5,120,000 kWh above that level. In percentages (the last column in the table) the difference is +11·2 per cent in 1930 and 11·5 per cent in 1933. Calculating the percentage decrease according to the last column we get $\dfrac{111\cdot2 - 88\cdot5}{111\cdot2} \times 100 = 20\cdot4$ instead of 6·9 as before. Thus the decrease is three times as great as it appears from the actual data.

In spite of all reservations, it must be conceded that the data concerning business fluctuations based on the smoothed series give a more realistic picture than the actual data which obscure the pattern.

It is interesting to compare business cycle fluctuations in the consumption of electric power in Warsaw for various purposes: (1) for lighting, (2) for power, (3) for street lighting. In Table 10.17 the comparative data for the years 1925–37 are given in thousands of kWh according to the reports of the electric power station and in percentages according to the smoothed line for each of those three series.

The sales of electric power for lighting were analysed above. We shall now discuss the remaining two types of consumption. The three last columns of Table 10.17 are presented graphically in Fig. 10.6.

TABLE 10.17. CONSUMPTION OF ELECTRIC POWER IN WARSAW FOR VARIOUS PURPOSES
in 1925–37

| Year | Actual consumption in thousand kWh | | | Ratio to smoothed-out series (percentages) | | |
|------|----------|-------|--------------------|----------|-------|--------------------|
|      | lighting | power | street lighting | lighting | power | street lighting |
| 1925 | 25,935 | 18,481 | 1284 | 94·7 | 82·4 | 59·0 |
| 1926 | 27,330 | 25,523 | 1972 | 92·5 | 95·5 | 83·8 |
| 1927 | 31,685 | 30,239 | 2385 | 99·9 | 112·7 | 94·3 |
| 1928 | 37,029 | 36,008 | 2825 | 109·3 | 124·1 | 104·4 |
| 1929 | 39,253 | 36,644 | 3775 | 108·9 | 117·4 | 130·8 |
| 1930 | 42,490 | 36,604 | 4627 | 111·2 | 109·5 | 151·1 |
| 1931 | 41,594 | 33,510 | 4437 | 103·3 | 94·1 | 136·9 |
| 1932 | 39,594 | 32·422 | 3395 | 93·1 | 85·8 | 99·3 |
| 1933 | 39,570 | 31,026 | 2780 | 88·5 | 77·6 | 77·3 |
| 1934 | 43,187 | 35,062 | 2568 | 92·2 | 83·1 | 68·1 |
| 1935 | 46,843 | 41,630 | 2643 | 95·6 | 93·8 | 66·9 |
| 1936 | 51,632 | 46,084 | 3752 | 100·9 | 98·9 | 90·9 |
| 1937 | 58,492 | 61,709 | 5683 | 109·7 | 126·5 | 132·0 |

The sales for power (in thousands of kWh) in pre-depression years were highest in 1929; the bottom of the depression was in 1933, and the consumption was lower by 5,618,000 kWh, i.e. by 15 per cent.

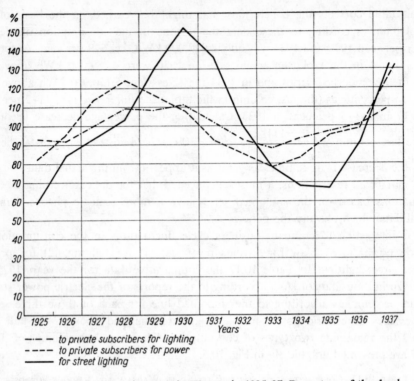

−·− − to private subscribers for lighting
− − − − to private subscribers for power
———— for street lighting

Fig. 10.6. Sales of electric power in Warsaw in 1925–37. Percentage of the development trend.

The largest surplus of the actual sales over the smoothed series (index 124·1) is not in 1929 but in 1928. In 1929 a decline starts (index 117·4), marking the beginning of the depression, although it is obscured in the series of actual sales by a very strong, upward growth trend. The minimum occurs, as before, in 1933, but the index (77·6) is here 37·5 per cent lower than the index at the peak of the cycle. The depression was much more severe than appeared from the data in the original series. In 1936 the actual sales in thousands of kWh were 12·6 per cent higher than in the peak pre-depression year (1929), but the index for 1926 was still somewhat below 100 (98·9) which means that the sales in that year hardly approached the value of the smoothed series.

A very characteristic pattern is displayed by the figures pertaining to the sales of electric power for street lighting. The pattern reflects not so much the effect of the depression as the economic policy of the city authorities dictated by this depression. The index drops by 55·7 per cent between 1930 and 1935, which shows how radically street lighting had to be reduced. The policy of economizing was continued even when economic conditions began to improve.

In spite of all the reservations concerning the correctness of the method used, there is no doubt that a comparison with the smoothed series essentially enriches our knowledge of the depression. However, it should be remembered that in this way we use only the empirical data relating to the depression.

A more penetrating analysis should be based on the Marxist theory of crises, and should take into consideration all the factors affecting the pattern of the depression in a given case. Statistical data only supply the basis for such an analysis.

Another application of a series smoothed by an analytical method is in the calculation of seasonal indices. It consists in comparing actual data (in our example in Table 10.8 p. 311 covering the period of 13 years) for each month with the corresponding values of the smoothed series. If, as in our example, the number of years is odd, the monthly averages for the whole period represent, in a sense, consecutive months of the middle year (1931). According to the smoothed series the sales of electric power in 1931 should amount to 40,364,150 kWh and the monthly average for this year is 3,363,700 kWh, of course, in accordance with the monthly average calculated on the basis of actual sales over the 13-year period (see above). We can assume that this average represents the middle month of 1931, i.e. the fiscal month from the middle of June to the middle of July. In calculating the data for the consecutive calendar months we should take into account the increases in sales before and after, beginning with this fiscal month.

The increase in the annual sales during the year, according to formula X.3 (p. 327) is 2,163,165 kWh. Thus the increase in monthly sales over the year is approximately 180,000 kWh (1/12 of the annual increase) and the increase in monthly sales during one month is 1/12 of 180,000 kWh, i.e. 15,022 kWh.

Now we have to shift from fiscal to calendar months. We can assume that the sales in June are by $0 \cdot 5 \times 15,000 = 7,500$ kWh less than in the middle fiscal month, i.e. 3,356,200 kWh, and the sales in July are by 7,500 kWh higher, i.e. 3,371,200 kWh. By subtracting from these figures consecutively 15,022 kWh we get the value for January and by adding consecutively the same amount we get the value for December. Thus we arrive at column $b$ in Table 10.18.

This calculation differs from that in Table 10.8 (p. 311) in so far that in the latter we divided all monthly figures by the same general average, and here we divide the actual sales for each month by changing (increasing) values of the smoothed series. The result is that in comparison with the previous calculation the indices for the first half of the year increase and for the second half decrease, which is correct considering that the general growth trend in this case is rising.

The calculation based on the smoothed series is very simple. Smoothing by the method of least squares and using a straight line is quite easy.

In this case we could also calculate the ratio of the actual values to the smoothed values for each of the 156 months of the period from 1925 to 1937. We should—

TABLE 10.18. SALES OF ELECTRIC POWER FOR LIGHTING TO PRIVATE SUBSCRIBERS
(in thousands of kWh)
Calculation of seasonality indices — Method D

| Month | Actual monthly average over 13 years (a) | Monthly sales according to the smoothed-out series (b) | Ratio 100b/a |
|---|---|---|---|
| I | 4804·2 | 3281·1 | 146·4 |
| II | 4231·8 | 3296·1 | 128·4 |
| III | 3477·8 | 3311·1 | 105·1 |
| IV | 3137·1 | 3326·1 | 94·3 |
| V | 2529·1 | 3331·2 | 75·7 |
| VI | 2049·4 | 3356·2 | 61·1 |
| VII | 1683·0 | 3371·2 | 49·9 |
| VIII | 2043·0 | 3386·2 | 60·3 |
| IX | 2736·1 | 3401·3 | 80·5 |
| X | 3690·5 | 3416·3 | 108·0 |
| XI | 4708·8 | 3431·3 | 137·3 |
| XII | 5273·5 | 3446·3 | 153·0 |
| Average | 3363·7 | 3363·7 | 100·0 |

continuing series b in Table 10.18 showing monthly figures smoothed for the middle year 1931—subtract consecutively 15,022,000 kWh until we get to January 1925 and add 15,022,000 kWh until we get to December 1937; and we should enter in column a the values of actual sales in each month from Table 10.1. p. 296. However, the advantage of this procedure would not compensate for the effort involved; the indices would be subject to violent business fluctuations, and therefore it would be very difficult, if not impossible, to find deviations of secondary importance, as in methods B and C.

## 5. CONCLUSIONS AND COMMENTS ON THE CALCULATION AND ELIMINATION OF SEASONALITY

Let us now compare the results of calculating by different methods the seasonal indices of the sales of electric power for lighting to private subscribers, and the indices of the sales of electric power for power and for street lighting (see Table 10.19 on p. 333).

It follows from Table 10.19 and from Fig. 10.7 that, if we disregard method A (which is wrong), the calculation of seasonal indices of the sales of electric power by the methods B′, C and G gives similar results. The only difference is that methods B′ and C give slightly higher results in the first months of the year and slightly lower results in the last months than method D.

However, there are essential differences among all these indices and the indices of the sales of electric power for power and for street lighting.

The type of seasonality in the sales for power differs essentially from the type of seasonality in the sales for lighting.

First of all, seasonality in the sales for power is relatively weak. In summer there is a slight minimum and a maximum appears in October, November or December, but never in January. The seasonal indices of the sales of electric power for street lighting are surprising. One would expect that they would be analogous to the indices of the sales for lighting to private subscribers. Indeed, the general type of seasonality is the same: an obvious summer minimum and an equally pronounced winter maximum. But in the consumption of electricity for street lighting the contrasts between summer and winter are much sharper; the summer minimum shifts to the earliest months of the year; the indices for April, May and June are much lower and for August and September much higher than the indices of the sales for lighting to private subscribers. From the point of view of the Electricity Authority this matter would warrant further study.

TABLE 10.19. COMPARISON OF SEASONAL INDICES OF THE CONSUMPTION
OF ELECTRIC POWER IN WARSAW

| Month | Sales for lighting | | | | Sales for power | Sales for street lighting |
|---|---|---|---|---|---|---|
| | method A | method B' | method C | method D | method D | method D |
| I | 142·8 | 147·6 | 147·4 | 146·4 | 96·6 | 140·0 |
| II | 125·8 | 129·4 | 129·1 | 128·4 | 97·8 | 112·1 |
| III | 103·4 | 106·1 | 105·5 | 105·1 | 100·5 | 102·9 |
| IV | 93·3 | 91·1 | 94·6 | 94·3 | 97·5 | 77·1 |
| V | 75·2 | 76·2 | 75·8 | 75·7 | 95·3 | 64·5 |
| VI | 60·9 | 61·4 | 61·1 | 61·1 | 93·8 | 45·4 |
| VII | 50·1 | 50·1 | 49·9 | 49·9 | 90·1 | 55·1 |
| VIII | 60·7 | 58·7 | 60·2 | 60·3 | 95·5 | 83·1 |
| IX | 81·3 | 79·6 | 80·2 | 80·5 | 103·0 | 99·5 |
| X | 109·7 | 107·8 | 107·6 | 108·0 | 109·2 | 116·8 |
| XI | 140·0 | 136·0 | 136·5 | 137·3 | 112·6 | 142·1 |
| XII | 156·8 | 151·7 | 152·1 | 153·0 | 107·1 | 159·7 |

*Method* A. The ratio of the actual average for each month over the full 13 years to the overall monthly average (p. 331).

*Method* B'. The ratio of the actual average for each month over 12 years to the average of moving averages for the same month over the 12 years (p. 317).

*Method* C. This method is based on the chain indices of 13-year averages for individual months (p. 322).

*Method* D. The ratio of the actual average for each month over 13 years to the values smoothed by a straight line (p. 332).

The results of the calculations by method B' and C were obtained by using the most simplified versions discussed above.

From the statistical point of view it should be stated that the calculation of seasonal indices by each of the above methods produced results sufficiently accurate to determine the type of seasonality. Thus they can be used in spite of all the reservations raised above.

There remain a few more problems to be considered. One of them is the effect of the unequal lengths of the months on the values of seasonal indices. As a result, in February and for all months numbering 30 days the indices obtained in the way described above are diminished, and for all months numbering 31 days are increased. To eliminate the effect of the unequal lengths of the months we should reduce appropriately either the absolute numbers from which we compute the indices, or the indices themselves. This matter has already been discussed in a different context (see p. 269 *et seq.*). Such reduced indices are compared with the raw indices in Table 10.20 on p. 335. The differences in comparison with the original series are considerable, particularly for February, for which the adjusted index is 138·1 instead of 128·4 as previously obtained.

Only indices adjusted in this way give the correct picture of the pattern of seasonality. Therefore, adjustment should be made to the proper lengths of the months if the object is to present seasonal changes.

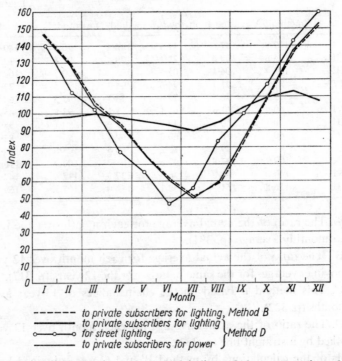

FIG. 10.7. Comparison of seasonal indices of the consumption of electric power.

The question remains whether it can be assumed that the seasonal pattern does not change over the whole period under consideration: only if it does not can the calculation of averages for the whole period be justified. If it does change, it must be determined how it changes. These changes may be of different kinds: (1) a general development trend, a gradual transition from one type of seasonality to another; (2) sudden jumps caused by changes in the factors behind seasonal fluctuations; (3) changes due to business cycle fluctuations (it is not impossible that the pattern of seasonal fluctuations differs in periods of prosperity and recession). There may be minor accidental causes which produce strong effects. In the case of the consumption of electricity for lighting, seasonal fluctuations may be affected by the introduction of daylight-saving time, which should result in a reduction in the consumption in summer.

The methods of calculating changing seasonality will not be discussed here in detail, but we shall try to discover in an elementary way whether in our example a change did take place. For this purpose 3-year averages of seasonal indices have been calculated according to Table 10.12. (p. 315) for the first three years (1926–28) and for the last three years (1934–36). The results are shown in Table 10.21 p. 336.

TABLE 10.20. ADJUSTMENT OF SEASONAL
INDICES TO A STANDARD LENGTH OF MONTH
Sales of electric power for lighting

| Month | Indices | |
| --- | --- | --- |
| | Raw[a] | Adjusted |
| I | 146·4 | 143·4 |
| II | 128·4 | 138·1 |
| III | 105·1 | 102·9 |
| IV | 94·3 | 95·4 |
| V | 75·7 | 74·2 |
| VI | 61·1 | 61·8 |
| VII | 49·9 | 48·9 |
| VIII | 60·3 | 59·1 |
| IX | 80·5 | 81·5 |
| X | 108·0 | 105·8 |
| XI | 137·3 | 139·0 |
| XII | 153·0 | 149·9 |

[a] Calculated by method D (Table 10.19. p. 333)

A similar calculation, which requires more work, could be made on the basis of chain indices (Table 10.14 p. 321). The results leave no doubt: the seasonality indices increased in summer months and decreased in winter months; particularly toward the end of the year the intensity of seasonal variations in the sales of electric power for lighting were noticeable. In consequence, in the years 1926–8 the seasonal index for December was 3·3 times as great as the seasonal index for July, and in the years 1934–6 the ratio of January to July (in these years the index for January was higher than the index for December) was only 2·8. There is no doubt that these changes are not accidental, and that the systematic pattern of negative and positive differences should be suficiently convincing. The only exception is the month of February.[98]

The explanation of the reasons for such changes in seasonality is not the task of statistical technique, but it should be given if statistics are to play the role of a means of analysing reality.

TABLE 10.21. SALES OF ELECTRIC POWER FOR LIGHTING COMPARISON OF
AVERAGE SEASONALITY INDICES
in 1926–8 and 1934–6

| Month | Indices | | Difference | Ratio |
|---|---|---|---|---|
| | 1926–8 $a$ | 1934–6 $b$ | $b—a$ | 100 $b/a$ |
| I | 148·0 | 147·3 | — 0·7 | 99·5 |
| II | 126·8 | 132·9 | + 6·1 | 104·8 |
| III | 107·9 | 105·3 | — 2·6 | 97·6 |
| IV | 91·1 | 97·3 | + 6·2 | 106·8 |
| V | 71·4 | 76·4 | + 5·0 | 107·0 |
| VI | 57·5 | 63·6 | + 6·1 | 110·6 |
| VII | 47·5 | 52·2 | + 4·7 | 109·9 |
| VIII | 58·3 | 59·9 | + 1·6 | 102·7 |
| IX | 82·1 | 79·5 | — 2·6 | 96·8 |
| X | 112·6 | 104·2 | — 8·4 | 92·5 |
| XI | 139·3 | 133·4 | — 5·9 | 95·8 |
| XII | 158·5 | 145·7 | —12·8 | 91·9 |

Once seasonal indices have been calculated, the elimination of seasonality[99] is simple. The actual figure for each month should be divided by the seasonal index for this month (the actual figure multiplied by 100 if the indices are in percentages, as in our examples). In this way we reduce the empirical values in those months for which seasonal indices are higher than 1 (100) and increase them in the months for which seasonal indices are less than 1 (100).

The sales of electric power in the first four months of 1938 were 7372, 6756, 5970 and 5596 thousand kWh respectively (see Table 10.1 p. 296). Multiplying by 100 and

---

[98] The reason for the increase in the seasonality index for February in 1934–6 in comparison with 1926–8 could be, for instance, greater cloudiness in 1934–6. Meteorological observations do not support this contention. The influence of secondary factors is most probable in this case.

[99] The elimination of seasonality in this case is understood not as the removal of real seasonal changes but the presentation of the data for different periods of the year as though seasonal changes did not exist; this, as we know, is a necessary condition for the correct presentation of the process of evolution.

dividing consecutively by the indices 146·4, 128·4, 105·1, and 94·3 we get 5036, 5259, 5680, and 5934 thousand kWh. These figures show a rapid increase, whereas the raw data showed a strong decline, but, as it turns out, it was only a seasonal decline. An increase in sales may be due to many causes, and a further analysis would bring to light the underlying factors. There is, as we know, a general rising trend, but this is not a sufficient explanation of such a rapid growth; the increase caused by the growth trend amounts to only about 15,000 kWh per month (Table 10.16 p. 328).

The increase could be accidental, but its stability (it does not peter out in the following months) and its intensity disproved this contention. Thus the only alternatives left are the influence either of improved business conditions or of some new factors which essentially modify growth. In this case it is undoubtedly due partly to improved business conditions and, to an even greater extent, to the change in the rates for electric power which was bound to result in increased consumption.

A completely different picture is obtained from a comparison of the months of September, October and November of 1931. The sales in these months, according to the reports of the electric power station (see Table 10.1), were respectively 2817, 3745 and 4436 thousand kWh, showing a rapid growth in consumption. Dividing by the corresponding seasonal indices we get for these months 3499, 3468 and 3231 thousand kWh. These figures show a distinct decline caused by the developing depression.

The elimination of seasonality is a necessary condition for a correct analysis of time series, especially those pertaining to economic phenomena, in which seasonality may be very pronounced. The methods now discussed which lead to direct elimination are in this case more convenient than elementary methods, which are mere comparisons of the data for a given period with the corresponding data in the preceding year. Thus the data for the whole year were needed before a comparison could be made, whereas the new methods enable us to compare each month with the preceding month as soon as the data become available, provided that we have seasonal indices for both months.

When seasonal fluctuations are eliminated by the 12-month moving average described above, the six final months are not smoothed, so that we have to wait half a year before an appraisal of the situation can be made. On the other hand the superiority of the moving average over the method of eliminating seasonality by seasonal indices is that the former also eliminates most random and periodic—other than seasonal—fluctuations of duration of less than one year, if they exist at all.

In published statistics the absolute figures are usually given in the raw state, so that the elimination of seasonality is left to the user of the data. But different types of time indices are often given after seasonal fluctuations have been eliminated. This is a useful practice provided that the institution responsible for the preparation of the indices uses correct seasonal indices. In any case, in all publications it should be clearly stated whether or not seasonality has been eliminated, and if so, what method was used.

The principal methods of calculating and eliminating seasonal fluctuations were presented above in application to examples from economic statistics. Of course, these methods can also be applied to the analysis of other types of series in which seasonal fluctuations exist.

*

*          *

Analogous methods can be used in analysing other types of periodic fluctuations, not only seasonal ones. For instance, we can analyse in a similar way the daily consumption of electric power and the daily variations in air temperature, or variations in the temperature of the human body.

The calculation in these cases will probably be simpler than the calculations involved in eliminating seasonal fluctuations in economic series. For instance, in analysing the fluctuations of temperature it is not necessary to take into account the impact of a growth trend, and it suffices to use as a basis the average over a period sufficiently long to eliminate random fluctuations. In most cases, however, an analysis of the nature of the phenomenon should be made first to avoid possible errors.

It can be seen from the above exposition that the analysis of time series is fairly complicated, and even so it does not lead to very accurate results. However, the methods described above are in most cases good enough for answering the questions with which we are usually faced in statistical practice.

*

*          *

In analysing time series in a socialist economy the emphasis is usually placed on aspects different from those in a capitalist economy. Skill in correctly presenting business cycle fluctuations is needed only for the analysis of economic conditions in capitalist countries. In a planned economy there are no business cycle fluctuations. But there is the problem of the dynamics of growth as expressed in the plan and as realized in its implementation. An important part is also played by studies of seasonality which must be made if we are to control it.

The question arises whether in studying the dynamics of growth in a socialist economy it is necessary and permissible to use the complicated methods of smoothing required in a capitalist economy. The answer to this question is, in principle, that it is not. In studies of a capitalist economy even such risky methods as smoothing by the method of the least squares may produce good results, since growth there is a result of diverse and often opposing forces, and is expressed in averages. In a socialist economy the figures of the plan are real and they need not be changed by smoothing.

The implementation of the plan is a different matter. The figures on the execution of the plan may not only differ from the plan (slightly, if the plan was made correctly) but are also subject to random fluctuations. Let us take agriculture as an example. Plans are made—and carried out—to raise crops the output of which fluctuates in particular years, in consequence, first of all, of changing weather conditions whose influence can be somewhat controlled but not completely eliminated. In such cases it is necessary to adjust the data for particular years. This can usually be done in a very simple way: graphically or by moving averages covering medium length periods.

The calculation of seasonal indices in a socialist economy is not so complicated as in a capitalist economy, because in the former there are no business cycle fluctuations. Nevertheless it would be an intolerable practice to calculate indices on the basis of the raw data for one year. This is intolerable for two reasons: (1) seasonality is almost always subject to random changes from year to year, and (2) it is almost always affected by growth trends, which in a socialist economy appear with greater force than in a capitalist economy. Therefore average seasonality should be calculated for a number of years, and one of the methods described above should be used to eliminate the influence of trend. However, averages should not be based on too long a period for the following two reasons: (1) in a planned economy the rate of growth may change considerably; (2) the nature of the seasonality may change.

Let us now consider two simple examples starting with the data in Table 10.6 (p. 304) which relate to the transportation of goods by the Polish State Railways in 1946–50. From the analysis of this table and of Fig. 10.4 which is based on it, we know that during the period studied: (1) the transport of goods showed a stable growth trend, basically uniform although not quite regular; (2) seasonal fluctuations were very pronounced; (3) there were strong disturbances both in the seasonal pattern and in the growth trend. It follows that: (1) seasonal indices must be calculated as averages for a number of years; (2) in calculating them, the upward development trend must be taken into account.

In our calculation only the years 1948–50 have been included, since in the data for the preceding years there are very strong fluctuations not essentially related to the seasonal fluctuations. Particularly in 1947 a very severe winter caused disturbances in railway traffic, and therefore the total volume of transport in February (and to a lesser extent in March) dropped much more than could be expected on the basis of a normal seasonal decline for these months.

To calculate indices the method D (described on p. 332 et seq.) was used. As we know, it consists of dividing the actual average for each month (in this case over the 3-year period) by the figures adjusted by a straight line, on the assumption that growth is expressed by an arithmetic progression. To calculate the monthly increase a comparison was made of the total volume of transport in the last quarters of 1950 and 1947, i.e. in the quarters ending and immediately preceding the period studied. The monthly increase in transport obtained in this way is 143,600 tons. The overall monthly average for the 3-year period 10,947,100 tons, when a straight line is used for smoothing, the average corresponds to the fiscal month from the middle of June to the middle of July. This is how Table 10.22 was drawn up.

TABLE 10.22. CALCULATION OF SEASONAL INDICES OF THE TRANSPORT OF GOODS BY THE POLISH STATE RAILWAYS in 1948—50

| Month | Actual monthly averages over the 3-year period _a_ | Monthly transport according to the adjusted series _b_ | Seasonality indices | |
|---|---|---|---|---|
| | | | method A | method D |
| | in thousand tons | | | |
| I | 8730·3 | 10,157·3 | 86 | 80 |
| II | 8808·0 | 10,300·9 | 86 | 80 |
| III | 10,428·7 | 10,444·5 | 100 | 95 |
| IV | 10,221·3 | 10,588·1 | 97 | 93 |
| V | 10,365·3 | 10,731·7 | 97 | 95 |
| VI | 10,687·7 | 10,875·3 | 98 | 98 |
| VII | 10,995·0 | 11,018·9 | 100 | 100 |
| VIII | 11,442·0 | 11,162·5 | 103 | 105 |
| IX | 11,715·0 | 11,306·1 | 104 | 107 |
| X | 13,244·3 | 11,449·7 | 116 | 121 |
| XI | 13,659·0 | 11,593·3 | 118 | 125 |
| XII | 11,069·0 | 11,736·9 | 95 | 101 |

Method A. The ratio of the figures in column _a_ to the overall monthly average.
Method D. 100 _a_/_b_.

Method D makes possible a clear determination of the nature of seasonality. In the first two months of the year there is a clearly marked minimum, and a definite maximum occurs in October and November. In December the index is slightly lower than the annual average and the indices for the remaining months from March to July and even to September are very close to the average.[100]

As we know, this seasonal increase in transport toward the end of the year poses a difficult problem for the railways. To solve it, all the resources and all the reserves must be employed, and therefore it is a harmful phenomenon from the point of view of railway economics.

The seasonal indices obtained by method A (see p. 310 _et seq._ and Table 10.8) are highly distorted: too low at the beginning and too high at the end of the year.

---

[100] An attempt was also made to use the ratio to the moving average (method B′) and the results were almost identical with those obtained by method D. This is understandable since the moving average shows almost a linear increase in transport. (See Fig. 10.6 p. 330).

It is also true that in planning transport, not only seasonal fluctuations should be taken into account, but also the expected normal increase; and then it may be much more important to know that the volume of transport in November is greater than in January and February in the ratio of 125 to 80, i.e. greater by almost 56 per cent (by method A), than to know that the seasonal increase in November in relation to January and February is expressed by the ratio of 118 to 86, i.e. greater by 37 per cent (by method D). It depends upon the technique of planning which piece of information will be more useful, but both are needed.

We also attempted to calculate seasonal indices for transport in 1946 and 1947. The results were not satisfactory because of the disruptions in normal railway operations in the first months of 1947. We can say, however, that apart from lower indices in February and March the nature and intensity of seasonal fluctuations in 1946 and 1947 did not differ much from the nature and intensity of seasonality in 1948–50. It would be interesting to repeat the same calculations at some later date.

Serious changes in the nature and intensity of seasonality were found in the production of cement in Poland both in comparing the post-war with the pre-war period, and in comparing the years 1949 and 1950 with the first years after the war. The results are very interesting. The production of cement always decreases in winter for technical reasons. But before the war production in January and February ceased almost altogether, in 1946 the winter decline was much smaller and in 1950 it was smaller still. At the same time the summer maximum is lower, and less marked. It should be added that the pattern of seasonality in 1947 was similar to that in 1946; in 1950 the pattern was similar to that in 1949; the year 1948 occupied the intermediate position.

TABLE 10.23. PRODUCTION OF CEMENT IN POLAND
in 1938, 1946 and 1950
(thousands of tons)

| Month | 1938 | 1946 | 1950 |
|---|---|---|---|
| I-XII | 1721 | 1399 | 2512 |
| I | 7 | 50 | 125 |
| II | 32 | 53 | 162 |
| III | 102 | 88 | 182 |
| IV | 136 | 92 | 228 |
| V | 162 | 124 | 248 |
| VI | 182 | 149 | 244 |
| VII | 201 | 150 | 237 |
| VIII | 211 | 153 | 236 |
| IX | 193 | 154 | 227 |
| X | 198 | 147 | 231 |
| XI | 168 | 107 | 208 |
| XII | 129 | 132 | 184 |
| *Monthly averages* | *143* | *117* | *209* |

We can save ourselves the trouble of computing precise seasonal indices because the facts are so obvious. The calculation would be difficult because of the uneven rate of growth in those years. To get a general idea it is enough to calculate for selected years raw indices expressed as ratios of production in a given month to the general monthly average for the whole year.

TABLE 10.24. MONTHLY PRODUCTION OF CEMENT IN POLAND AS PERCENTAGE OF THE MONTHLY AVERAGE FOR THE YEAR[a]

| Year | Highest production | Lowest production |
|------|--------------------|-------------------|
| 1938 | 148(VIII) | 5(I) |
| 1946 | 132(IX) | 43(I) |
| 1950 | 119(V) | 60(I) |

[a] The months in which production was the highest or the lowest are shown in brackets.

The lowest monthly production in 1938 was one-twentieth of the monthly average, and in 1950 it was lower by only 40 per cent. The monthly peak in 1938 was 48 per cent higher than the average and in 1950 it was 19 per cent higher. Real progress had been made in eliminating seasonality.

# PART III

*Relative Numbers. Composite
Index-Numbers. Elimination Tables*

CHAPTER 11

# RELATIVE NUMBERS

## 1. DEFINITION AND TECHNIQUE OF CALCULATING
## RELATIVE NUMBERS

In statistics a relative number is the ratio of two statistical quantities. These quantities may be compared by subtracting ("*a* is greater or less than *b*" by a certain number of units), or by dividing ("*a* times a certain multiplier equals *b*"). The second method is the basis of the concept of a relative number.

In 1947–8 there were 5000 regular teachers and 267,395 students in rural elementary public schools of the province of Warsaw and 5217 teachers and 223,581 students in the rural elementary public shools of the province of Poznań. Although these numbers are interesting in themselves, from the point of view of the school system the relationship between them is also important. We can see that in the province of Warsaw there were more students and fewer teachers that in the province of Poznań. Thus we may conclude that in 1947–8 the school system was better organized in the province of Poznań than in the province of Warsaw.

But a direct comparison of absolute numbers seldom leads to such clear conclusions, and even in this example, while it is unquestionable, the conclusion is not stated in terms of a yardstick that permits is numerical comparison. Such a yardstick, for instance, might be the ratio of one of the numbers to the other. If these ratios are to be compared they should have a common denominator.

In our example this can be done in two ways: either by relating the number of students in each province to some round number like 1000, so that we could say that in the province of Warsaw, there were on the average 18·7 teachers per 1000 students and in the province of Poznań 23·3 teachers per 1000 students; or we can say that on the average there were 53·5 students per teacher in the province of Warsaw and 42·9 students in the province of Poznań. In the first case we divided the number of teachers by the number of students and added three zeros to the quotient (so that it is "per 1000 students") and in the second case we divided the number of students, by the number of teachers. These two methods of calculation answer different questions. The first is: How adequate was the ratio of teachers to students in the two provinces? (The answer is that it was better in the province of Poznań than in the province of Warsaw). The second is: What was the burden carried by the teachers? (The answer: It was greater in the province of Warsaw than in the province of Poznań). Both these methods answer essentially the same problem.

These two methods of computation are almost always feasible. Either we relate one of the figures—usually but not necessarily the greater—to 100 or 1000 (or a higher power of ten), and each of the others we express as a percentage of this; or one of the figures, usually the smaller, we relate to unity and express the others as multiples of it (or less frequently as fractions of it). From a strictly formal point of view, if we treat these numbers as fractions in which the numerators are the numbers of teachers and the denominators the numbers of students, we can say that either we reduce to fractions with some power of ten as common denominator ("there are $18 \cdot 7$ teachers per 1000 students")—or we reduce to the common numerator of one ("there are $53 \cdot 5$ students per teacher").

In statistical practice we may question which method of expressing the ratio to choose. For instance, to determine the relationship between the area and the population of a country, on the one hand, and the number of cars, post offices, radios, etc. on the other, we can either say that there are, on average, $x$, $y$ or $z$ of each, per 100 km² or per 1000 persons; or that, on average, there is one car, radio, or post office for $w$ km² or $w$ persons.

In many cases statistical usage is completely standardized. Births, deaths, marriages are always given per 1000 inhabitants. But even here different usage was once common. In studies by demographers in the eighteenth century, and even later in Quetelet's studies, we find calculations in which one birth or death is given in relation to a certain number of inhabitants. Sometimes the prevailing statistical usage leads to peculiar inconsistencies. Speaking of the number of men and women in a population census we may say that in a given country there are $107 \cdot 6$ women to every 100 men. But speaking of births of boys and girls we may say that there are $105 \cdot 3$ boys born to every 100 girls. In both cases we refer to 100 but in one case it is a hundred males and in the other a hundred females. As we can see, usage is arbitrary.

Which of the above methods of expressing the ratio we decide to choose is more or less a matter of indifference. The point is to use the more convenient one. But consistency is by no means a matter of indifference. Once a certain usage has been established it is better not to change it without good reason, in order to avoid misunderstandings.

## 2. GENERAL CLASSIFICATION OF RELATIVE NUMBERS

There are several types of relative numbers, depending upon the logic of the relationship between the dividend and the divisor. We shall now discuss briefly these types in general terms, and the nwe shall analyse some related problems in greater detail.

(1) First of all, there are numbers expressing the relationship of statistical quantities of equal importance, for instance, the ratio of the price of a commodity to its price at some other time or place, or the ratio of the population of a given country to its population 10 or 50 years ago or to the population of some other country. Usually, as in the examples just mentioned, we are concerned with values of to one phenomenon at different times or at different places. However, the relationship may also be of a different kind; the price of one commodity to the price of some other related commodity, e.g. the price of wheat, etc., or the number of persons at the age of 15–19 to the number of persons at the age of 45–49, etc. The essential point is that in all these instances we deal with ratios of quantities of equal importance.

Relative numbers of this type are called *index numbers*. We calculate them by taking a certain starting point in time or space which we call the *base* of the index number. The base is a round number, usually 100, 1000, or even 1. By dividing another number in this series by the base and multiplying by 100 (or 1000, etc.), we obtain the index number for this number in relation to the chosen base. For instance, if in the budget for 1953 the expected number of university students was 136,000 and in 1937 there were only 48,000 students, the index number for 1953 (with 1937 equals 100) is $(136,000/48,000) \times 100 = 283$. This means that the number of students in 1953 was expected to show an increase of 183 per cent (283–100) relative to 1937.

The base of the index number is sometimes 1, especially when the figures compared with it are not large. The prices at the foundation of People's Poland can be expressed in this way in relation to pre-war prices, since in consequence of the devaluation they increased considerably. In this case the index number shows how many times the price increased in relation to the base price. Were the base price expressed as 100 in this case it would result in expressing the index number by a number 100 times as great, which would only lead to confusion. In general, care should be taken not to attempt to be too precise in calculating index numbers and other relative numbers. Especially when the quantity selected as a base is small, say, a two-digit number, an index number with the base of 100 to one or two decimal places gives a fallacious appearance of accuracy. Since the main task of relative numbers is to facilitate understanding of the relations between phenomena we should be satisfied with the minimum degree of accuracy required.

Certain problems related to the calculation of index numbers have already been discussed in the chapter on time series. What has been said there should suffice to provide a general idea of how to use index numbers in other types of series, e.g. in geographical series. The notion of chain indices and index numbers with a fixed base has also been explained, together with the method of changing chain indices into index numbers with fixed base. A completely different and a very complicated is the calculation of composite index numbers: we shall discuss them later.

(2) The second type of relative numbers are structural numbers which correspond to structural series. Structural numbers were discussed earlier as one of the tools of analysis of structural series in the context of some basic problems. We shall supplement this discussion here by mentioning certain aspects of a formal statistical nature.

Structural relative numbers are obtained by relating the whole population to 1 or, more frequently, to 100 or 1000 (or some larger power of ten), and expressing the components as parts of this. Here, as with index numbers, superfluous accuracy should be avoided.

From the formal point of view, the sum of the components of the whole population usually is a round number like 1, 100, 1000, etc. In consequence of rounding off sometimes there is a difference of one or even two units in the last digit, e.g. 100·1 or 99·8 instead of 100. In such cases we correct, or strictly speaking round off, so as to arrive at the correct figure. We should be guided by two rules: (1) to alter the rounding off of numbers in which the next rejected number is close to 5 e.g. 35·66 we round off, if necessary, to 35·6 instead of to 35·7 as is usual; (2) to introduce corrections in large numbers rather than small; it is better to round off 75·47 to 75·4 than to round off 0·26 to 0·2 instead of 0·3, since in the first case the inaccuracy does not much matter and in the second it makes a big relative difference.[101]

However, it is not absolutely necessary for the components to be calculated as parts of the whole population. The ratio of any one component to another may also be a structural number. In such cases, not the total but one of the components is expressed as a round figure and other components are related to it. This method is often used when the population is divided into only two parts. For instance, when we state the number of men and women that the census has revealed, we almost always give the number of women per 100 men instead of expressing the number of men and women as percentages of the total. This makes no essential difference, but gives a clearer picture, because the two numbers are closer to one another, as in the above example in which the number of men is almost equal to that of women.

This method is used not only when the population is divided into two parts, but also when the number of components is larger. For instance, instead of calculating the percentage of different age groups to the total population we can denote one age group by 100 (e.g. the population at the age 10–15 years) and express the frequencies of other age groups as ratios to the frequency of this group. Such

---

[101] The principle of adjusting the total to 100 or 1000 is a matter of taste rather than substance. From the latter point of view we could leave the total as it happens to be after correct rounding off even if there is a difference of one or two units in the last digit, but a table with such totals might appear untidy, especially to readers not too familiar with statistical technique.

relative numbers also provide a picture of the structure of the population, some-times even more convenient than the more common methods. Table 11.1 presents the structure of the populations of Poland and France in 1931 in two ways. In the first part of the table the total population of each country is denoted by 100, and in the second part the population at the age 20–59.

In the first case we see that in Poland the younger groups were more numerous than in France, particularly those below 20, and in France the older groups were (40–59 and 60 years and over).

TABLE 11.1. POPULATION OF POLAND AND FRANCE BY AGE
in 1931

| Age group | Poland | France | Poland | France |
|---|---|---|---|---|
| | total population = 100 | | population aged 20–59 = 100 | |
| *Total* | *100·0* | *100·0* | . | . |
| 0–19 years | 42·9 | 30·4 | 87 | 54 |
| 20–39 | 33·0 | 31·4 | } 100 | } 100 |
| 40–59 ,, | 16·3 | 24·3 | | |
| 60 years and over | 7·8 | 13·9 | 16 | 26 |

In the second case the population at the working age was denoted by 100. In relation to this group the group of children and teen-agers below 20 who had not yet reached the full working age constituted 87 per cent in Poland, and only 54 per cent in France. The oldest group, aged 60 and over, of whom a great majority have already lost full ability to work, constituted only 16 per cent in Poland and 26 per cent in France. When the problems are formulated and answered in the way shown above the second method of presenting the structure of the population is more expressive than the first. In this way we obtain the "measures" of the burden that the people at full working age must carry by providing full or partial livelihood for those who are not able, or are only partly able, to work.

From a formal point of view structural relative numbers of this kind related to one of the components can be regarded as coefficients. This, incidentally, does not affect the essence of their interpretation.

Both index numbers and relative numbers are used to facilitate understanding of the relations existing among the quantities on the basis of which they were cal-culated, but, as a rule, they do not lead to the formation of new concepts. For this purpose we use two other types of relative numbers, which we shall describe pres-ently.

(3) The third type of relative numbers are numbers expressing the relationship of events to the population to which they refer. An example of such a relationship is the ratio of the number of births or deaths during one year to the population to which those births or deaths refer. Thus we arrive at the concepts of the birth

rate and the death rate.[102] In comparison with the number of births or deaths they are new concepts, and express the intensity of occurrence of births or deaths. Relative numbers of this kind are called measures of intensity. They are measures in the strict sense of the word.

By definition, a measure of intensity is a fraction with the number of events as numerator and the total population as denominator. This ratio is called the coefficient, or in some cases the probability.[103]

If we want to compare coefficients we can reduce them to the common numerator 1. However, it is more usual to reduce them to a common denominator: the total population to which the events are related is equated to 100 or 1000, etc. For instance, the general death rate is calculated per 1000 inhabitants; the death rates due to different diseases are computed per 10,000 or 100,000 inhabitants, since the number of deaths caused by some diseases is so small that it is difficult to express it per thousand population.

Since in calculating relative numbers of the third type we introduce the notion of intensity the logical correctness of the relationship between the numerator and the denominator becomes very important. We must therefore make sure that the figure in the denominator corresponds strictly to the population of the events numerically expressed as the numerator. Though obvious, this rule may sometimes be difficult to apply.

To calculate the death rate for a city, we divide the total number of deaths in the city during the year by the average population of the city for the year. However, the category deceased always includes visitors, especially thos who came to the city for medical treatment and died in hospitals, clinics, etc. When we include them in the numerator of the ratio, we inflate the number of deaths in the city by the deaths of persons who are not strictly speaking a part of its population. An artificial inflation also takes place even when these visitors are included in the population of the city, because the death rate among those visitors is much greater than that of the population proper. It would be more correct to include only the deceased inhabitants of the city without the deceased visitors. But even this is not quite correct, because a certain number of the inhabitants of the city probably died outside the city. A fully correct calculation can be made only within the framework of national statistics and not on the basis of statistics of particular cities. The cities usually limit their statistics to subtracting from the total number of deaths the deaths of persons visiting the city. The error committed by disregarding the rule

---

[102] A note on terminology is in order here. The birth rate is the ratio of births to the total population in distinction to the fertility rate which is the ratio of births to the number of women at the child-bearing age. The death rate is the ratio of the number of deaths to the total population in distinction to mortality rate which is the ratio of deaths from that some disease to the total number of cases of this disease. Thus the typhus mortality rate is the ratio of those who died of typhus to the total population.

[103] The notion of "coefficient" and "probability" will be discussed in later chapters.

mentioned above may sometimes be quite large. In large cities with a great many hospitals and clinics, the number of deceased visitors in hospitals and clinics may constitute a high percentage of the deceased, and therefore the inclusion of all the deaths may considerably increase the death rate. On the other hand if the deaths of the inhabitants of the city outside the city are not included, the resultant error is usually not large, since the number of such deaths is rather small.

Much more complicated is the calculation of the death rate among infants: the ratio of the number of deaths of infants less than 1 year old to the number of all births. If the births are evenly distributed in time it is sufficient to take the ratio of infants who died during the calendar year to the number of births in the same year. If births fluctuate considerably, the population expressed by the denominator of the ratio will not strictly correspond to the number of events shown in the numerator, since the children who died before reaching the age of 1 during the calendar year could have been born either in the same year or in the preceding year. We cannot go into the details of the complicated calculations made in such cases. A similar difficulty arises in calculating the mortality rates for different diseases in short periods of time, particularly during epidemics. Those who died in a given month could have contracted the disease either in the same month or in the previous month, or even earlier; and some of those who contracted the disease in a given month may die either the same month or in the following months. When epidemics are spreading or dying out, the ratio of deaths in a given month to those who contracted the disease during that month will not give a proper mortality rate: when the epidemic is spreading the figure will be too low and when it is dying out it will be too high.

We should be particularly careful when the statistical data and the population to which they relate come from different sources, since they may be based on different notions. For this reason it is difficult to calculate the death rates for different professions. Occupation statistics are very difficult and the correct classification of the population by occupations requires great skill and consistency.

What is more, the difficulties that may appear can be solved in different ways. When the processing of the census data is centralized, precise and uniform classification by occupations is relatively easy; but it is very difficult to ensure consistency in the classification of deaths since information on the occupation of the deceased is given by those notifying the registrar of the death. We cannot control consistency in any classification by occupations based on such sources of information.

The general rule is that we should exclude from the figure in the denominator of the ratio that part of the population which should not be taken into account in calculating the intensity of a given phenomenon, i.e. that part of the population in which the events studied cannot occur. For this reason in detailed studies of births, in addition to the birth rate (the ratio of births to the total population) we also introduce the notion of fertility, which is the ratio of the number of births to the number of the population that can bear children, i.e. women of childbearing age. We could go even further and exclude women who had children within approximately a year before the beginning of the study, since within that time they could not have babies again. On the same principle, in calculating the crime rate as the ratio of convicted criminals to the population we take into consideration not the whole population but only that part which could be convicted by law. Thus we subtract from the total population the number of children who cannot be convicted, and possibly also the armed forces and other population groups which are under the jurisdiction of special courts.

For the same reason we also exclude from the population studied those sections in which the events in question must necessarily occur. For instance, in studying illiteracy we allow for the fact that small children are bound to be illiterate. Were we to include all those who cannot read we would obtain an unfair picture by artificially increasing the percentage of the genuine illiterate. (In this way a considerable degree of illiteracy would appear to exist even in countries in which the principle of compulsory education is strictly observed, and the general level of educations is high). Even more important is the fact that this might change the comparative relationship of different populations from the point of view of illiteracy, since the percentage will increase more in populations in which there are many small children than in those with relatively few children. It is more appropriate to calculate the intensity of illiteracy with respect only to the population above a certain age e.g. to take into account the number of the illiterate and the population from 10 years of age and over.

In discussing the question of excluding certain parts of the population in calculating intensity we have touched upon a more general problem: what to do when the population is heterogeneous with respect to the prevalence of certain events. We shall discuss this problem later on.

(4) Relative numbers of the fourth type express the relationship of populations related in logic but foreign in conception. These are, for example, the ratio of the number of teachers to the number of students, the ratio of the number of cars to the population or area of a country, the ratio of the population to the area of a country, the ratio of railway personnel to the length of the railway system or to the intensity of traffic, etc. The field of application of ratios of this kind is very wide, and the procedure involved cannot be uniquely determined. This is a new notion in comparison with the ratio expressed in absolute numbers. Here also the basic problem is how to choose appropriate populations for comparison. Only in this case it is not a problem of statistical technique but one of substance, and the procedure depends upon the requirements of the subject. We are dealing here with yardsticks that must be so designed as to provide a valid measure of the phenomenon. The formal (and also the essential) concern of statistics is to see that the populations shown in the numerator and the denominator of the ratio have the

some coverage, e.g. that the reported number of teachers in elementary schools is actually the number of teachers who teach in elementary schools.

Difficulties of a completely different kind are encountered when we have to decide whether the cars should be counted in relation to the population or to the area of the country. Each of these ratios answers a different question. Similar problems arise, for instance, in the analysis of railway personnel. The number of the railway personnel, and especially of the traffic personnel is of course related to the mileage of the railway system in a district. But it is also related to the intensity of traffic, which can be expressed by the number of trains run. If we want to compare two districts, to find out in which one the personnel is better utilized, or in which one there is a surplus or shortage of workers, none of the above-mentioned criteria will suffice separately. We shall have to take both into consideration, and possibly also some other circumstances, e.g. the relative importance of passenger and freight traffic, the kind of goods carried, etc. The next question is whether it would not be possible to derive from these ratios some kind of average which would characterize the whole problem with a single value.

The above examples should suffice to explain the gist of the problem. Relative numbers of the fourth type—in our listing—are often fluid, and cannot be strictly defined. The correct choice of populations to be compared can only be made after an analysis comprising the complexity of problems related to the phenomenon studied. These measures answer certain definite questions and this should be remembered in drawing conclusions so as to avoid misinterpretation.

The fact that we devote less space to the discussion of the relative numbers of the fourth type does not mean that they are less important. On the contrary, as typical measures they are very important. But relatively little can be said about them from the formal statistical point of view. The difficulties that may arise are not of a statistical nature: they consist in a proper selection of quantities whose ratio will best answer the problem posed. The construction of proper measures is the concern of specialized statistics (e.g. statistics on industry, transport, culture, etc.).

So far we have been discussing general problems involved in the calculation of relative numbers. Now we shall consider special cases.

CHAPTER 12

# COMPOSITE INDICES

## 1. INTRODUCTION TO THE PROBLEM

It often happens that we need an index number relating not only to one series of events, but to a whole group of events. For instance, we may want an index which expresses quantitative changes in the production not only of one commodity, but of many commodities; or an index expressing changes in the prices not of one commodity but, say, of all manufactured goods. In contrast to simple or individual indices which express the ratio of two specific quantities we shall call these indices composite index numbers. They may characterize a certain entity, e.g. the price movements of all manufactured goods, or of certain groups of these goods, e.g. raw materials, semi-processed goods of finished products. Thus we shall distinguish between general composite index numbers (characterizing certain entities), and composite group index numbers.

Only in a few cases is it possible to compute a composite index number directly from the totals or from the averages of absolute numbers. If we have the volume of the output of different varieties of coal (clod, briquette, dust) we can add up the output of these varieties (although not without certain reservations) and on the basis of the total tonnage produced we can compute the composite index number of coal production. We can conceivably add up the output of the four staple grains (wheat, rye, barley and oats) to obtain a basis for calculating the composite index number of grain production. But we cannot add to the total weight of grain the weight of potatoes, or to the total weight of coal the weight of oil, not to mention such products as machinery, textiles, etc. By the same token, only in very exceptional cases—when we are dealing with very similar commodities—can we calculate average prices of different commodities, and then the composite index number on the basis of everage prices. In most cases we have to proceed differently. We may have to calculate first individual index numbers and then compute their average index number. The problem is to decide which average to use. It may be a simple arithmetic mean the sum of all indices divided by their number. Some statisticians also suggest the use of the geometric or even the harmonic mean. All averages can be simple or weighted.

The choice of a proper average is essential. As we know, of three "classical" averages the arithmetic mean gives the greatest value, and the harmonic mean the

354

smallest. The greater the differences in the terms from which we calculate the average, the greater the differences in the averages. Sometimes they are considerable. The three averages will produce identical results only when all the terms are equal, but then the calculation of any average is superfluous.

In the chapter on averages (see p. 170 *et seq.*) we have given the criterion for choosing the average, namely, that under the conditions defined by the problem the average, when substituted for any value from which we calculate this average, should leave the final results unaltered. This criterion cannot be applied to the calculation of the average index number from individual index numbers, without additional assumptions about the conditions of the problem.

Suppose the price of commodity $A$ has doubled and the price of commodity $B$ dropped by one half. The question is: How did the price of these combined commodities change? Our first reaction might be to say: The price did not change. However, this answer would be correct only with certain specific assumptions.

If we denote by 100 the price of each commodity at the start, then during the period studied the price index of commodity $A$ will rise to 200 and of commodity $B$ will drop to 50.

The arithmetic mean of these indices is:

$$(200 + 50)/2 = 125,$$

the geometric mean

$$\sqrt{200 \times 50} = 100$$

and the harmonic mean

$$2/\left(\frac{1}{200} + \frac{1}{50}\right) = 80$$

Which of these three very different results (a rise of 25 per cent, no change in price, and a drop of 20 per cent) is true? We have to determine exactly the changes that the composite index number is to reflect. From the point of view of the buyer (or seller) of these goods the correct index is the one such that, if the price of each commodity changed in the ratio determined by the average index number, the amount paid (or received) for both commodities together would be the same as if the price of the first of them doubled and that of the second was reduced by half.

Let us suppose that we bought one unit of each commodity. This assumption or a similar one is necessary to a solution of the problem.

Let us suppose that:

(1) In the base period[104] the prices of the two commodities were the same, say 20 zlotys each, and during the period studied the price of $A$ rose to 40 zlotys, and the price of $B$ dropped to 10 zlotys. Altogether we pay 40 zlotys in the base period,

---

[104] The starting (base) period is the period in relation to which the index numbers are calculated. The reporting period is the one for which the index numbers are calculated.

and 50 zlotys in the period studied, which is an increase of 25 per cent, as shown by the arithmetic mean.

(2) If the price of commodity $A$ increased from 10 to 20 zlotys, and the price of commodity $B$ decreased from 40 to 30 zlotys (the prices of both being the same in the period studied) this means a decline in the amount paid from 50 to 40 zlotys, i.e. by 20 per cent, as shown by the harmonic mean.

(3) If the price of $A$ increased from 20 to 40 zlotys, and the price of $B$ dropped from 40 to 20 zlotys (i.e. the price of $A$ in the base period was the same as the price of $B$ in the period studied, and the price of $B$ in the base period was the same as the price of $A$ in the period studied) then we would pay, for the two commodities combined, 60 zlotys both at the start and in the period studied, and the combined prices for the buyer or seller would not change, as shown by the geometric mean.

It is easy to show why this is so. We are dealing here with the average of ratios which, as we know, must be calculated as a weighted average. The weights in the case of the arithmetic mean should be the divisors, and in the case of the harmonic mean, the dividends. In the first case the amounts paid in the base period (the divisors) are the same, and therefore the simple arithmetic mean gives the correct results: in the second case the dividends (the prices in the period studied) are the same and therefore the simple harmonic mean should be used.

Similarly, it could be shown mathematically why the geometric mean gives the correct result when the prices change in opposite directions. We shall not discuss this here, because the geometric mean is artificial in a calculation of the average index number, and its use cannot be justified.

Some statisticians maintain that the geometric mean should be calculated in this case because we deal with ratios. This argument is a complete misunderstanding of the problem. In fact the geometric mean should be used only when we deal with the product of ratios. For instance if production increases from one period to another in the ratios $p_1, p_2, ..., p_n$ then the average increase during one period is

$$G = \sqrt[n]{p_1 \times p_2 \,...p_n.}$$

In the above example of the average price index the individual indices cannot be multiplied.

The harmonic mean can always be replaced by the arithmetic mean properly weighted, so that in effect we can confine ourselves to a discussion of the arithmetic mean.

If the composite index is to reflect the ratio in which the amount paid changes, the use of the simple arithmetic mean (i.e. weights equal to one) is in order if in the base period the amounts paid for each commodity were equal. If they were not equal the weighted arithmetic mean should be used,[105] and the weights should be numbers proportional to the amounts paid for particular products.

---

[105] In the above example (case 2) we have: 2 and 0·5 are the individual price indices for commodities $A$ and $B$: 1 and 4 are the weights proportional to the amounts paid (10 and 40 zlotys). The proof will be given later.

This is the way the composite index number should be used when it is intended that it should reflect changes in the amounts paid. For different needs other solutions should be sought.

Generally speaking the composite index number may be calculated as the arithmetic mean of the individual indices, if appropriate weights are given to those indices. The difficulty lies in finding appropriate weights. This problem cannot be solved in a general way, and specific solutions cannot usually be properly justified if we do not approach the problem in a different way.

## 2. AGGREGATE INDICES

The logical meaning of composite indices can best be shown by discussing a special case—the aggregate index. We shall return later to composite indices calculated as averages of individual indices.

The starting point for the aggregate index is the transformation of quantities that cannot be added into ones that can be added. This can be done in a variety of ways.

We cannot compare directly the number of wagon-loadings in different periods because a wagon is not a uniquely defined notion: its loading capacities is not always the same. However, if we express the loads of all wagons in terms of standard loadings (e.g. 15 tons) then we may add and compare without reservation the number of wagons loaded in different periods.

If we have doubts about whether we may add different varieties of coal produced because of their different heating qualities, we can convert them into numbers of calories and then add and compare without reservation.

If in one slaughter-house different kinds of animals are slaughtered (oxen, cows, pigs, etc.), then the numbers of animals cannot be added. However, if their utilitarian ratios (such as the weights) are known we can value all the animals in standard units (e.g. hypothetical oxen), which can be added and compared.

In order to make data comparable it is most common practice to value them in monetary terms. In this way we can add and compare the production and sales of different commodities.

The above examples have different interpretations. Without reservation in the first example (wagon-loadings), and with few reservations in the second (coal), we deal with a constant conversion ratio. After conversion and addition we may calculate the indices as if they were individual indices. But in the third example the ratio of the weights of different kinds of animals may change with time and may be different in different regions. Even greater differences may exist in valuing in monetary terms, because the conversion is based on prices. This method of expressing different items in units which can be added, adding them and dividing the totals, gives indices which are called aggregate indices. However, many difficulties may arise.

Let us consider a problem from manufacturing. Let $q$ be the quantity of a commodity produced and $p$ its price. The subscript (0, 1, 2, etc.) denotes the period, e.g. $q_0$ and $p_0$ are the quantity and the price in the starting or base period, $q_1$ and $p_1$ in the period studied, to be compared with the starting period. Thus $q_1/q_0 = i_q$ and $p_1/p_0 = i_p$ are the individual indices of production and price. The product $qp$ expresses the value of the commodity produced and the quotient $q_1 p_1/q_0 p_0 = i_w$ is the individual index of the value of the commodity produced.

The quantities $q$ and the price $p$ cannot be added. But the product $pq$, being expressed in monetary terms, can be added and the sum $\sum qp$ expresses the total value of the production of all commodities or of a group of them. Therefore the quotient

$$\frac{\sum q_1 p_1}{\sum q_0 p_0} = I_w \qquad \text{(XII.1)}$$

is the composite index number of the total value of production during the reporting period in relation to the total value of production in the starting period.[106]

However, the value of the quotient $\sum q_1 p_1/\sum q_0 p_0$ depends upon changes in two factors: quantities produced and prices. And we may be interested in finding out how the quantity produced changed regardless of changes in prices, or how the prices changed regardless of changes in quantities produced. Thus we have to find an index whose value would depend only on changes in quantities produced, or only on changes in prices. We obtain such an index by assuming constant prices $p_c$ for each commodity when we want to calculate the index of the quantity produced, and assuming constant quantities $q_c$ when we want to calculate the price index of the produced commodities. Then we write

$$I_q = \frac{\sum q_1 p_c}{\sum q_0 p_c} \qquad \text{(XII.2)}$$

and

$$I_p = \frac{\sum q_c p_1}{\sum q_c p_0}. \qquad \text{(XII.3)}$$

Subscript $c$ with the letter $p$ here means, as assumed, that the price of each commodity in period 1 is the same as in period 0, and subscript $c$ with the letter $q$ means, as assumed, that the quantity of each commodity produced in period 1 is the same as in period 0.

These are aggregative indices. They are expressed as quotients of the sums of products, which in this example are expressed in monetary terms so that they can be added. They can also be converted into other quantities that can be added. The

---

[106] Thus we denote individual indices by $i$ and composite indices by $I$. The subscript denotes the type of index: the quantity index ($q$), the price index ($p$) or the value index ($w$).

essential thing is that we take constant values of one factor and change only the values of the factor whose changes are to be expressed by the composite index.

However, if the prices of quantities are to be fixed, we have to decide at what level. We shall show below the composite index of the quantities produced (the reasoning will be analogous to that of the price index). In this case we can fix prices either at the starting level or at the level in the period studied. We take these prices as examples: we could, of course, fix them at different levels.

Thus we obtain two indices

$$I'_q = \frac{\Sigma q_1 p_0}{\Sigma q_0 p_0},$$
(XII.4)

$$I''_q = \frac{\Sigma q_1 p_1}{\Sigma q_0 p_1}.$$
(XII.5)

From now on we shall denote by $I'$ the indices of quantities or prices based on the structure of prices or quantities in the base period, and by $I''$ indices based on the structure of prices or quantities in the period studied.

The first index ($I'$) in the denominator is the actual value of the combined production of all commodities in the base period, and in the numerator it is the quantity artificially created by calculating the value of production on the basis of the quantities produced in the period studied, but at the prices prevailing in the base period. In the second index ($I'_q$) we have the reverse situation: in the numerator are the actual quantities of the combined production of all commodities in the period studied, and in the denominator the fictitious value of production based on the quantities produced in the base period, but at the prices of the period studied.

In both cases the value of the quotient depends entirely on changes in quantities produced and not on prices, which are constant for each commodity. In spite of this, the two indices can give the same results only by coincidence.

To prove this basic theorem let us convert the indices so that in the numerator of each of them there is the individual index $i_q = q_1/q_0$. This can be achieved by dividing and multiplying the products in the numerator by $q_0$. Thus we obtain

$$I'_q = \frac{\Sigma \dfrac{q_1}{q_0} \times q_0 p_0}{\Sigma q_0 p_0} = \frac{\Sigma i_q \times q_0 p_0}{\Sigma q_0 p_0},$$
(XII.4')

$$I''_q = \frac{\Sigma \dfrac{q_1}{q_0} \times q_0 p_1}{\Sigma q_0 p_1} = \frac{\Sigma i_q \times q_0 p_1}{\Sigma q_0 p_1}.$$
(XII.5')

Now we have the weighted arithmetic means (see p. 190 *et seq.*) of the individual indices with the weights: in $I'_q$ the actual value of the production of a given commodity in the base period, and in $I''_q$ the value calculated on the basis of the quantity produced in the base period, and the prices in the period studied. The weighted averages calculated for the same quantities with different weights must, of course, produce different results.[107] This means that the value of the aggregate index number depends upon how we fix one of the components. In our example of the index of the quantity produced the value of the index depends upon whether the prices are fixed at the level of the base period or of the period studied. Once the level of prices has been fixed, however, the value of the index depends only on changes in the quantities of commodities produced.

Analogous formulae can be obtained for the price index by fixing the quantities produced. The general form of such an index is

$$I_p = \frac{\sum q_c p_1}{\sum q_c p_0}. \tag{XII.6}$$

Hence, fixing the quantities at the level either of the starting period or of the period studied, we have

$$I_p' = \frac{\sum q_0 p_1}{\sum q_0 p_0}, \tag{XII.7}$$

$$I_p'' = \frac{\sum q_1 p_1}{\sum q_1 p_0} \tag{XII.8}$$

or, in the form of the weighted arithmetic means of the individual indices

$$I_p' = \frac{\sum q_0 p_1}{\sum q_0 p_0} = \frac{\sum \dfrac{p_1}{p_0} \times q_0 p_0}{\sum q_0 p_0} = \frac{\sum i_p \times q_0 p_0}{\sum q_0 p_0}. \tag{XII.7'}$$

$$I_p'' = \frac{\sum q_1 p_1}{\sum q_1 p_0} = \frac{\sum \dfrac{p_1}{p_0} \times q_1 p_0}{\sum q_1 p_0} = \frac{\sum i_p \times q_1 p_0}{\sum q_1 p_0}. \tag{XII.8'}$$

Note that the weights in formula (4') are the same as in formula (7'): in formula (5') the weights are the products $q_0 p_1$—the quantities in the base period multiplied by the prices in the period studied, and in formula (8') the weights are the products $q_1 p_0$—the prices of the base period multiplied by the quantities of the period studied.

These formulae can be also presented as harmonic means:

$$I_q' = \frac{\sum q_1 p_0}{\sum \dfrac{q_0}{q_1} \times q_1 p_0}, \tag{XII.4''}$$

---

[107] The results may be identical: (1) if the prices of particular goods did not change between the base and the current period, or (2) if the prices of all goods changed in exactly the same ratio.

$$I_q'' = \frac{\sum q_1 p_1}{\sum \dfrac{q_0}{q_1} \times q_1 p_1}, \qquad\qquad \text{(XII.5'')}$$

$$I_p' = \frac{\sum q_0 p_1}{\sum \dfrac{p_0}{p_1} \times q_0 p_1}, \qquad\qquad \text{(XII.7'')}$$

$$I_p'' = \frac{\sum q_1 p_1}{\sum \dfrac{p_0}{p_1} \times q_1 p_1}. \qquad\qquad \text{(XII.8'')}$$

Of course, $q_0/q_1$ and $p_0/p_1$ are the reciprocals of the individual indices of quantities and prices, and the composite indices are identical with the previous ones denoted by the same symbols $I_q', I_q'', I_p', I_p''$.

The possibility of presenting aggregate indices in the form of a weighted average of the individual indices facilitates the analysis of the indices, and in certain circumstances may simplify calculations.

The logical meaning of the aggregate indices can best be grasped by discussing the cost-of-living index. It is the price index designed to represent all the needs of a family of a definite type. We calculate it as a typical aggregate index according to formula (XII.6).

$$I_p = \frac{\sum q_c p_1}{\sum q_c p_0},$$

where the $q_c$ are the items of the family budget—the quantitative norms of goods and services needed by the family and assumed to be constant, and the $p$ are the prices of these goods and services: the product $qp$ is the money expended on a given commodity or service and the sum $\sum qp$ is the total expenditure for the upkeep of the family. The logical meaning of this index varies, depending on whether the budget is fixed at the level of the base period, or at the level of the period studied. If we make the calculation according to formula (XII.7).

$$I_p' = \frac{\sum q_0 p_1}{\sum q_0 p_0},$$

then we answer the question: how would the amount needed for the living expenses of the family in period 1 change in relation to period 0 if the family lived in period 1 on exactly the same budget as in period 0? Using formula (XII.8)

$$I_p'' = \frac{\sum q_1 p_1}{\sum q_1 p_0},$$

we answer the question: What would be the expenditures for the living expenses of the family in period 1 in relation to the expenditures in period 0 if the family lived in period 0 on exactly the same budget as if lived in period 1?[108]

The next example is from a different field, but the problems are related. Suppose that we want to calculate the price index building materials. We use formula (XII.6) and take as $q_c$ a set of building materials needed, say, for the building of a 5-storey apartment house in a large city. If the index applies to a long period of say fifty years or more, then $q_0$—the set of building materials in the base period—will apply to the type of house that was built at that time: of full brick with lime mortar, perhaps with wooden beam ceiling, a large amount of wood and a small amount of steel, with tiled stoves and probably with gas piping, but without electric wiring, etc. Set $q_1$ would apply to a house with a reinforced concrete construction made of hollow brick and with insulation boards, with a large quantity of steel and small quantity of wood a large amount of cement, equipped with central heating, gas, electricity, etc. Calculating $I'_p$ by formula (XII.7) we answer the question in what ratio the expenditures for building materials needed for constructing the house of the type built in 1893 would change in 1953 in comparison with 1893. Calculating $I''_p$ by formula (XII.8) we answer an analogous question in relation to building materials used for houses of the type built in 1953. Both questions are unrealistic. In 1893 houses were not built of reinforced concrete because the technique then was not advanced enough. In 1953 large houses were not built of brick the way they were 60 years earlier, because it was uneconomical. It is not impossible, by any means, that $I_p$ might show higher costs in 1953 (because, for instance, in 1893 certain materials needed for building a house of the 1953 type might have been scarce; even if they were theoretically known they would have to be made to order—e.g. hollow brick, insulation boards—and therefore would be very expensive).

There is no need to seek artificial examples. W. S. Nyemtchinov[109] gives an aggregate index of yields per hectare for the main crops in the Soviet Union in comparison with the United States.

We are quoting this example in full because we want to show, first of all, how to make calculations and secondly to point out why and how absurd are the results sometimes obtained.

In the table the averages for the second 5-year plan period (1933–37) in the Soviet Union are shown together with the averages for the same period in the United States. The first four columns show the actual areas under crops, and the actual yields per hectare in both countries, and the last four, the total crops

---

[108] It should be noted that in calculating the aggregate index we assume that the structure of the budget does not change but we do not assume that the quantities consumed are the same. If, in the period studied the family consumes an even 20 per cent more of all goods and services then the structure of the budget does not change and the two indices $I'_p$ and $I''_p$ will give the same results.

[109] W. S. Nyemtchinov: *Syelskokhaziaystviennaya Statistika*, Moscow, 1945, pp. 262–4.

calculated as indicated by the letters $q$ and $u$ with their subscripts: $q_0 u_0$ denotes the actual total crop in the Soviet Union and $q_1 u_1$—the actual total crop in the United States, $q_1 u_0$ —the total crop calculated according to the yields per hectare in the Soviet Union and the area sown in the United States, and $q_0 u_1$—the total crop calculated according to the yields per hectare in the United States, and the area sown in the Soviet Union. We assume that different crops expressed in metric quintals can be added.

We now have the complete material for calculating in different ways the aggregative indices of yields per hectare with the aggregates expressed in units of weight and not in monetary units.

TABLE 12.1. YIELDS PER HECTARE AND TOTAL CROPS OF GRAINS IN THE SOVIET UNION AND THE UNITED STATES

| Crops | Area under crops in million hectares | | Yield in quintal per hectare | | Total crop in millions of quintals | | | |
|---|---|---|---|---|---|---|---|---|
| | U.S.S.R. $q_0$ | U.S. $q_1$ | U.S.S.R. $u_0$ | U.S. $u_1$ | $q_0 u_0$ | $q_1 u_1$ | $q_1 u_0$ | $q_0 u_1$ |
| Winter wheat | 12·3 | 15·6 | 10·9 | 8·8 | 134·07 | 137·28 | 170·04 | 108·24 |
| Spring wheat | 24,9 | 5·2 | 8·0 | 6·9 | 199·20 | 35·88 | 41·60 | 171·81 |
| Rye | 23·2 | 1·2 | 9·6 | 6·7 | 222·72 | 8·04 | 11·52 | 155·44 |
| Barley | 8.6 | 3.8 | 10.0 | 10·4 | 86·00 | 39·52 | 38·00 | 89·44 |
| Maize | 3·4 | 31·2 | 11·6 | 14·2 | 39·44 | 443·04 | 361·92 | 48·28 |
| Oats | 17·7 | 14·1 | 9·9 | 8·9 | 175·23 | 125·49 | 139·59 | 157·53 |
| Rice | 0·14 | 0.36 | 21·2 | 24·6 | 2·97 | 8·86 | 7·63 | 3·44 |
| Total | 90·24 | 71·46 | · | · | 859·63 | 798·11 | 770·30 | 734·18 |

Denoting by 100 the yields per hectare in the Soviet Union we get two indices for the United States

$$I'_u = \frac{\sum q_0 u_1}{\sum q_0 u_0} \times 100 = \frac{734 \cdot 18}{859 \cdot 63} \times 100 = 85 \cdot 4,$$

$$I''_u = \frac{\sum q_1 u_1}{\sum q_1 u_0} \times 100 = \frac{798 \cdot 11}{770 \cdot 30} \times 100 = 103 \cdot 6.$$

Thus, depending upon whether $q$—the area under crops—is fixed at the level prevailing in the Soviet Union or in the United States, it turns out that yields per hectare are in the United States either 14·6 per cent lower or 3·6 per cent higher than in the Soviet Union.

Transposing the numerators and the denominators, i. e. calculating the indices for the Soviet Union with yields in the United States as 100, we also obtain two indices

$$I'_u = \frac{\sum q_0 u_0}{\sum q_0 u_1} \times 100 = \frac{859 \cdot 63}{734 \cdot 18} \times 100 = 117 \cdot 1,$$

$$I_u'' = \frac{\sum q_1 u_0}{\sum q_1 u_1} \times 100 = \frac{770 \cdot 30}{798 \cdot 11} \times 100 = 96 \cdot 5.$$

And again depending upon the method of calculation it turns out that the yields per hectare in the Soviet Union are either higher or lower than in the United States.

We shall find the explanation by looking closely at the first four columns with data in the table. It appears from columns 3 and 4 that for most crops the yield per hectare is higher in the Soviet Union than in the United States. The exceptions are barley (in which the difference is negligible), rice (in which the difference is considerable, but which plays a minor part in cultivation in both countries), and finally maize (in which the yield is much higher in the United States—24·2 against 21·6 quintals—and which is cultivated on a small area in the Soviet Union and on a very large area in the United States—43·6 per cent of the area under all crops). On the other hand, the area under the four ear crops (winter and spring wheat, rye and oats) in which the yields per hectare were much higher in the Soviet Union than in the United States there were in the Soviet Union 78·1 million hectares i.e. 86·5 of the total area under the crops considered here and in the United States only 36·1 million hectares i.e. 50·5 per cent of the total.

This means that if we calculate total crops according to the area sown in the Soviet Union, a much more important part will be played by those crops in which the yield per hectare is much higher in the Soviet Union, and if we calculate them according to the area under different crops in the United States a more important part will be played by crops in which the yield per hectare is higher in the United States (primarily maize).

Analysing the results obtained by the two indices, we must remember the assumption on which they are based: either we assume that areas under different crops are in the same ratio as in the Soviet Union, or in the same ratio as in the United States.

Let us now return to the cost of living index. Here things are apparently not so obvious as in the case of home construction. But the budget that serves as a basis for calculating the cost of living index is subject to a slow process of transformation; and not only the individual budget of a specific family, but the average budget of the families of a given backround. The state of the market changes, as do the price ratios, customs, etc. After a long time these changes may completely transform the structure of the budget, even under normal conditions, to say nothing of periods of radical changes. Let us consider the situation during the war or immediately after: then the calculation by the aggregate method as in formula (XII.7) would answer the question: How much more would the family have to spend during the war in comparison with the pre-war period to be able to live in the same way as before the war? Or according to formula XII.8 the question would be: How much less would the expenditures be before the war if the family were to live before the war in exactly the same way as during the war? The posing of the problem in this way is absurd.

Similar nonsense may sometimes be arrived at in geographical comparisons. An international comparison of the cost of living is very important. If we have to compare two countries, $A$ and $B$, which differ considerably from one another with respect to their way of life, it would be absurd to ask the question how much would one have to spend in country $B$ to live in exactly the same way as in country $A$, or vice versa. Under these conditions it will probably turn out either that in country $B$ it is impossible to live as in country $A$ because certain goods and services are not available, or that to arrange life in the same way as in country $A$ would be abnormal and would result in unnecessary expense. The same would be true if we wanted to arrange life in country $A$ in the same way as in country $B$.

The situation is analogous in calculating the indices of quantities. Index $I'_q$ is a measure of changes in total quantities when the price structure (i.e. the ratios of the prices of different goods) in the period studied remains the same as in the starting period; index $I''_q$ is a measure of changes in total quantities calculated on the assumption that the price structure in the period studied has been transferred to the starting period.[110] When changes in the price structure are considerable, the two calculations may give very different results. The discrepancy in the results of calculating indices when the differences in the structure of prices or quantities are considerable will be discussed later in "Generalizations and Conclusions" (p. 366). Compare also the example on the calculation of the index of the volume of production in the Soviet Union (p. 372 *et seq.*).

Under certain conditions it can be shown that indices of the $I'_q$ and $I'_p$ type based in the structure of prices or quantities in the starting period will, as a rule, give higher values than indices of the $I''_q$ and $I''_p$ type based on the structure of prices or quantities in the period studied. As far as the economic phenomena are concerned, generally quantities will decline (or increase slightly) as prices rise (or decline slightly); and they will increase (or decrease slightly) as prices decrease (or increase slightly). In a similar way changes in quantities will bring about changes in prices. The point is that the commodities whose prices decline or rise but less than the prices of other commodities are generally in greater demand than the commodities which became more expensive and vice versa, the commodities which are supplied to the market in greater quantities usually become cheaper and the prices of the commodities which are scarce on the market rise. We can put it in this way: There is a negative relation between the volume of production, turnover and consumption and the prices.

If we now consider formulae (4') and (5') in which indices $I'_q$ and $I''_q$ were

---

[110] More strictly we should say that the index shows in what proportion the combined value of all goods changes for a given price structure.

presented as weighted indices of the individual indices, then on the basis of the above statement we can conclude: (1) for those commodities for which the individual index $i_q$ has a relatively high value (which corresponds to a relatively large increase or a relatively small decrease in quantity) the product $q_0 p_1$, i.e. the weight in index $I_q''$ is relatively smaller than the product $q_0 p_0$, i.e. the weight in index $I_q'$, because $p_1$ is small in comparison with $p_0$; and (2) and vice versa, for those commodities for which $i_q$ is relatively small the weight $q_0 p_1$ is relatively large in comparison with the weight $q_0 p_0$. Since in the weighted index $I_q''$ relatively small weights correspond to relatively large values of the individual index, and vice versa, the weighted average

$$I'' = \frac{\sum i_q q_0 p_1}{\sum q_0 p_1}$$

is usually smaller than the weighted average.

$$I'' = \frac{\sum i_q q_0 p_0}{\sum q_0 p_0}$$

The same reasoning also applies to price indices in formulae (7') and (8').

It should be remembered, however, that the above reasoning is correct on the assumption of the existence of negative interdependence between quantities and prices. This assumption may be justified under certain economic conditions and not justified under others, and may also assume a different form with reference to problems of a different kind.

To avoid possible misunderstandings the following should be added. If between periods 0 and 1 a purely quantitative change took place in the budget (i.e. all the quantities of goods and services increased or decreased in the same proportion) then it is a matter of complete indifference whether we base our calculation on the quantities in period 0 or in period 1. If a change in the structure accompanied changes in quantities, e.g. if in consequence of a rise in the standart of living the quantitative relations between particular goods and services changed, then calculation by formula (8) will give different results than that by formula (7), but we cannot say in advance which formula will yield a higher walue of the index unless quantities depend on prices.

## 3. GENERALIZATIONS AND CONCLUSIONS

We can now make certain generalizations on the composite indices in general, and aggregate indices in particular.

(1) The aggregate indices are always based on certain strictly defined assumptions, and are a precise measure only so long as these assumptions are valid. It follows that:

(2) Every aggregate index expresses changes only in relation to those specific

conditions on the basis of which it was constructed. The cost of living index based on the budget of a worker's family of four expresses changes in the prices of goods and services only from the point of view of just this kind of family: for measuring other sets of prices other indices should be constructed.

(3) If serious changes occur in the structure of quantities or prices that formed the basis for calculating the index it ceases to be a proper measure of changes: when changes in the structure are considerable it may even become a misleading measure.

(4) Difficulties connected with a change in the structure could be overcome if the fixed structure could be replaced by a structure which changes with the circumstances but is equivalent. In theory such a notion of equivalence can be developed. We could imagine a quantitative family budget as changing but still satisfying the same needs to exactly the same degree, both from the objective and subjective points of view: then the formula for calculating the cost of living index would assume the following form:

$$I_p = \frac{\sum q_1' p_1}{\sum q_0 p_0},$$

where $q_1'$ would denote the quantitative budget of the type that existed in the period studied, but with such a selection and such quantities of goods and services as to satisfy the needs—objectively and in the subjective interpretation of the members of the family—to the same extent as in budget $q_0$. Unfortunately, we can design such an equivalence as a theoretical model but we cannot give it real substance. Nevertheless, it is along these lines that we shall have to seek solutions to difficulties arising in comparisons in time and space when the structure changes essentially.

(5) To find out to what extent changes in the structure have diminished the usefulness of an index, we can compute the index for the starting period twice: according to the structure in the base period, and the structure in the period studied. If these calculations show considerable discrepancies the old index should be abandoned and a new base should be found.

(6) Composite indices based on the weighted averages of individual indices may sometimes be reduced to aggregate indices of the weights can be reduced to an expression of the $qp$ type. Then the above remarks will apply to these indices as well.

Indices based on weighted averages which cannot be converted into aggregate indices are usually without real content and in this sense are rather misleading. If we cannot convert an index based on the weighted average of individual indices into a corresponding aggregate index we should try to give the individual indices weights proportional to the importance of the objects (e.g. commodities) to which these indices refer. It is usually difficult to find a sufficiently appropriate measure to express numerically the importance of these objects; then the weights must be fixed more or less arbitrarily, according to intuition. This is not as bad as it sounds, because the intuition of a person familiar with the problem may lead to correct results.

It is important to realize—and this follows from our considerations so far—that the assigning to the index of definite weights is tantamount to filling it with a real and strictly defined content.

For instance, if for a price index we accept as weights the value of the turnover in particular goods in the base period this is tantamount to the acceptance of formula (XII.7, p. 360)

$$I'_p = \frac{\sum q_0 p_1}{\sum q_0 p_0},$$

which, in turn, is equivalent to assuming that a proper measure of changes in prices are changes in the amounts paid by the buyer (or received by the seller) who in all the periods compared buys goods in the same quantitative proportions as he bought them in the starting period.

It also follows that all the reservations concerning aggregate indices in the case of a basic change in relations apply also to all indices based on weighted averages. In particular the original meaning of indices concerning growth changes with changes in the structure of the phenomena; if these changes are of a basic nature even an index correct at the start may become meaningless.

Some wholesale price indices in capitalist countries are published for long periods of time without any change in the method (e.g. the index published in England in *The Economist* since 1869, the index designed in 1886 by Sauerbeck and continued by *The Statist*).

The calculation of an index in the same way is supposed to have an advantage which offsets the imperfection of the method (both indices are based on simple average of individual indices). In the light of our arguments this reasoning is wrong. The very lack of change in the structure of the index makes it lose its economic meaning in the course of time, regardless of whether the method used is correct or not.

Out of many composite indices constructed at different times and still in use some are based on simple averages of individual indices. The two indices mentioned above are in this category. It should be noted, however, that these indices are only seamingly not weighted.

A really "non-weighted" or simple index would be the average of the individual price of all the goods on the market or the average of the price indices of a sufficiently large number of goods selected by random sampling. In fact, all the non-weighted indices are based on a conscious and careful selection of goods whose indices enter into the composite index. This selection of goods is actually a sort of weighting, especially when as sometimes happens, the commodities considered as being of greater importance are quoted more than once (e.g. on several different markets or in several different varieties). Therefore "non-weighted" indices should often be treated as weighted indices with hidden and sometime elusive weights. Other conclusions concerning composite indices will be given later.

## 4. SOME PROPERTIES OF INDIVIDUAL AND AGGREGATE INDICES

We shall now discuss certain properties of composite indices, and especially those of aggregate indices, and compare them with corresponding properties of individual indices.

The following can be said about individual indices:

(1) The index for period 0 in relation to period 1 is the reciprocal of the index for period 1 in relation to period 0, which is obvious, because the ratio $q_0/q_1$ is the reciprocal of the ratio $q_1/q_0$.

(2) The product of consecutive chain indices gives, in effect, the index for the last period covered by chain indices in relation to the starting period. If we denote by $i_{1/0}$, $i_{2/1}$, etc. the consecutive chain indices expressing the ratio of period 1 to period 0, of period 2 to period 1 etc., then

$$i_{1/0} \times i_{2/1} \ldots i_{n/n-1} = i_{n/0},$$

because, of course

$$\frac{q_1}{q_0} \times \frac{q_2}{q_1} \ldots \frac{q_{n-1}}{q_{n-2}} \times \frac{q_n}{q_{n-1}} = \frac{q_n}{q_0}$$

(3) By changing the base of individual indices we change the absolute values of the indices, but we do not change their ratios. The ratio

$$i_{1/0} : i_{2/0} : i_{3/0} \ldots = i_{1/k} : i_{2/k} : i_{3/k} \ldots$$

If instead of $q_0$ we take as a base any other $q_k$ this means, in effect, that we have just multiplied all the previous indices $i_{1/0}, i_{2/0}, i_{3/0}, \ldots$ by the ratio $q_0/q_k$.

$$\frac{q_m}{q_0} \times \frac{q_0}{q_k} = \frac{q_m}{q_k}$$

or, reversing the problem, we shift to a new base by dividing the previous indices by the number expressing the ratio of the new base the old base: $q_k/q_0$.

(4) An individual quantity index multiplied by the corresponding individual price index gives the individual value index, and vice versa the value index divided by

the quantity index gives the price index, and the value index divided by the price index gives the quantity index, because, of course

$$\frac{q_1}{q_0} \times \frac{p_1}{p_0} = \frac{q_1 p_1}{q_0 p_0},$$

and therefore

$$\frac{q_1 p_1}{q_0 p_0} : \frac{q_1}{q_0} = \frac{p_1}{p_0},$$

$$\frac{q_1 p_1}{q_0 p_0} : \frac{p_1}{p_0} = \frac{q_1}{q_0}.$$

None of these simple properties applies to aggregate indices.

*Property 1.* For this property to be applicable to aggregate indices the indices of the $I_q''$ and $I_p''$ types (formulae (XII.5) and (XII.8) would have to be identical with the indices of the $I_q'$ and $I_p'$ types formulae (XII.4) and (XII.7)).

The quantity index in period 1 in relation to period 0 can be expressed by the formula

$$Iq_{1/0} = \frac{\sum q_1 p_0}{\sum q_0 p_0} :$$

Then, analogously, the index in period 0 in relation to period 1 is

$$Iq_{0/1} = \frac{\sum q_0 p_1}{\sum q_1 p_1}.$$

In accordance with the accepted notation the first of these indices is $I_q'$ and the second is the reciprocal of $I_q''$. Were $I_{q0/1}$ to be the reciprocal of $I_{q1/0}$ then $I_q'$ would have to equal $I_q''$. We know that

$$I' \neq I''.$$

*Property 2.* It is obvious that

$$\frac{\sum q_1 p_0}{\sum q_0 p_0} \cdot \frac{\sum q_2 p_1}{\sum q_1 p_1} \neq \frac{\sum q_2 p_0}{\sum q_0 p_0} \neq \frac{\sum q_2 p_1}{\sum q_0 p_1}$$

The same applied to the price index

*Property 3.* By changing the starting period by which we establish the structure (of quantities or prices) in the agregate index, we change not only the absolute values of particular indices but also their relations. The ratio

$$I_{i/m} : I_{m/k}$$

will vary depending upon whether we calculate by formula

$$I_{i/m} = \frac{\sum q_i p_m}{\sum q_m p_m}, \quad I_{m/k} = \frac{\sum q_m p_m}{\sum q_k p_m},$$

or

$$I_{i/m} = \frac{\sum q_i p_k}{\sum q_m p_k}, \quad I_{m/k} = \frac{\sum q_m p_k}{\sum q_1 p_k}.$$

This is tantamount to saying that if we change the structure (of quantities or prices) which forms the basis for calculating the aggregate index, the new index will not be a continuation of the old, and a chain-relation will lead to results different both from those that would result from continuing the old index and from the new index recalculated back over the period covered by the old index.

It should be stressed, however, that the choice of a new starting period on which to base the structure is not tantamount to equating this period to 100 as the base of the index. So long as we do not change the starting period according to which the structure is determined we can change at will the base of the index denoted by 100, just as in individual indices, and we can shift by the chain method from one base to another.

This means that is, for instance, in calculating the index (quantitative) of industrial production we base it on constant prices of 1937, we can denote by 100 either the value of production in 1937 or in any later year (e.g. 1947) without disrupting the continuity of the index. Through such changes the figures will change but their ratios will remain the same, as in the individual index. The continuity will be disrupted only when we substitute some other prices for the constant prices of 1937.

*Property 4.* Aggregate indices of values, quantities and prices are interdependent but this interdependence among aggregate indices is of a specific nature, namely, dividing the value indices by prices indices we obtain

$$\frac{\sum q_1 p_1}{\sum q_0 p_0} : \frac{\sum q_0 p_1}{\sum q_0 p_0} = \frac{\sum q_1 p_1}{\sum q_0 p_1} = I_q'',$$

$$\frac{\sum q_1 p_1}{\sum q_0 p_0} : \frac{\sum q_1 p_1}{\sum q_1 p_0} = \frac{\sum q_1 p_0}{\sum q_0 p_0} = I_q',$$

i.e. dividing a value index by the price index of the $I_p'$ type based in the quantities structure of the starting period we get the quantity index of the $I_q''$ type based on the price structure of the period studied, and dividing by the price index of the $I_p''$ type we get the quantity index of the $I_q$ type. The same applies to the price index as a quotient of the value index by the quantity index. Thus

$$I_q' \cdot I_p'' = I_q'' \cdot I_p' = I_w,$$

but

$$I_q' \cdot I_p' \neq I_w,$$
$$I_q'' \cdot I_p'' \neq I_w.$$

This specific property of aggregate indices may be of practical importance. As we shall see, we sometimes calculate quantity indices by dividing value indices by price indices.

## 5. EXAMPLES OF THE APPLICATION OF COMPOSITE INDICES IN THE SOVIET UNION AND IN PEOPLE'S POLAND

### A. IN THE SOVIET UNION[111]

When we speak of the practical application of composite indices we have to distinguish between the Soviet Union and the people's democracies on the one hand and the capitalist countries on the other. A characteristic feature of indices used in socialist countries is that they are generally based on aggregate formulae.

We shall discuss now selected indices used in the Soviet Union[112] and in Poland.

The volume index of production in the Soviet Union is calculated on the basis of the formula

$$I_q = \frac{\sum q_1 p_0}{\sum q_0 p_0},$$

i.e. the calculation is based on the prices of the starting period. Not only is the index expressed in relative numbers important but also the difference (in absolute numbers) between the numerator and the denominator of the index: this difference expresses the absolute increase during the period studied.

The report on the results of the first five-year plan period states that in 1925 the annual increase in production was 66 per cent, and in absolute figures somewhat over 3000 million roubles, which is 45 million roubles increase per per cent. In 1931 the annual increase was 22 per cent, which is one third of the increase in 1925, but in absolute figures it was over 5600 million roubles, i.e. 250 million roubles per per cent of the increase which is six times as much as in 1925. This indicates that in studying the rate of growth of production we should not confine ourselves to considering the total percentage increase but should also know what each percent of the increase in production represents and what the total annual increase is.

Speaking of constant prices ($p_0$) in the index the authors of the *Kurs Economichyeskoy Statistiki* note that they should be the prices of a period which from the point of view of basic economic factors differs little from the conditions of the current period. Otherwise "we would bring production in the current period to the conditions prevailing in a period in which the production of the current period could not be produced at all, or could be produced only in part, or could be

---

[111] Since this book was written studies on indices have developed considerably, and the methods of calculating some indices have been changed.

[112] The examples from the Soviet Union are mainly taken from the collective study edited by Professor A. I. Pietrov: *Kurs economitchyeskoy statistiki*, Moscow, 1952.

produced with a completely different composition of labour and with different price ratios of particular products."[113]

It follows that the constant prices $p_0$ must be changed from time to time when there is a basic change in economic conditions.

In the Soviet Union the volume indices of production have been calculated since 1919–20. Originally the prices of 1912 were accepted—as the last pre-war year for which relatively detailed price quotations were available. However, the records were not sufficiently complete and besides they pertained to an economic structure that was foreign to a socialist economy.

The next stage was the acceptance of the prices of 1926–27 as a base. This base was first introduced in 1927–28 for the appraisal of the implementation of the plan and after 1928–29 it was used for the indices of the growth of total production compared with the preceding years. However, it took several years before the prices of all commodities had been established.

Now the calculations are based on wholesale prices put into effect on 1 January 1952.[114]

The index of the volume of production can also be obtained directly by dividing the value index of production by the price index in the form generally accepted in the Soviet Union:

$$I_p = \frac{\sum q_1 p_1}{\sum q_1 p_0}.$$

Of course

$$\frac{\sum q_1 p_1}{\sum q_0 p_0} : \frac{\sum q_1 p_1}{\sum q_1 p_0} = \frac{\sum q_1 p_0}{\sum q_0 p_0} = I_q, \qquad \text{(XII.9)}$$

just as by dividing the value index of production by the volume index we would obtain the price index

$$\frac{\sum q_1 p_1}{\sum q_0 p_0} : \frac{\sum q_1 p_0}{\sum q_0 p_0} = \frac{\sum q_1 p_1}{\sum q_1 p_0} = I_p. \qquad \text{(XII.10)}$$

As we have already explained (p. 371) the calculation is correct only on the assumption that the volume index is based on a formula of the $I'$ type, the price index is based on formula $I''$, (or vice versa); the results obtained on the basis of this assumption are identical with direct calculations since we assume that the total production of all goods and all prices have been taken into consideration.

In a socialist economy a very important part is played by the index of productivity of labour. The productivity of the production of one commodity can be

---

[113] *Ibid.*

[114] Since this book was written the system of constant prices has been changed several times.

measured by the number of units produced per unit of working time (e.g. per man-day).

The productivity of labour can also be determined by the lenght of time required to produce a unit of the product. Denoting by $t$ the length of time used for the production of one unit (one piece, one ton, etc.) of a given commodity and by $q$ the number of units produced we can write the following formula for the labour productivity index

$$I = \frac{\sum q_1 t_0}{\sum q_1 t_1}. \tag{XII.11}$$

The calculation of indices in this form is not only difficult, but almost impossible, because it is almost impossible to calculate individual labour productivity indices for all commodities produced.

For this reason the following index in terms of money value at constant prices is generally used:

$$I = \frac{\sum q_1 p_c}{\sum T_1} : \frac{\sum q_0 p_c}{\sum T_0}. \tag{XII.12}$$

$T_1$ denotes the number of workers or the combined working time of all the workers in the period under consideration, and $T_0$ denotes the same in the base period. It is thus the ratio of the total value of production in both periods at constant prices per worker.

This index is considered to be less precise because the price of the commodity is not always proportional to the amount of labour consumed.

The index of the dynamics of average income is expressed by the formula

$$I = \frac{\sum p_1 T_1}{\sum T_1} : \frac{\sum p_0 T_0}{\sum T_0}. \tag{XII.13}$$

where $p_1$ and $p_0$ denote the individual earnings of the worker, $T_1$ and $T_0$ the number of workers receiving the given earnings in periods 1 and 0, respectively $\sum p_1 T_1$ and $\sum p_0 T_0$ the total earnings of all workers. Dividing the total earnings of all workers by $\sum T_1$ and $\sum T_0$, i.e. by the total number of workers, we obtain the average earnings per worker. We can obtain the same result, of course, by adding up directly the earnings paid out in all establishments in both periods, and dividing the result by the total number of workers employed.

This index in the form of the ratio of weighted arithmetic means reflects changes in the average earnings of the worker in both periods: its value is influenced both by changes in individual earnings ($p$) and by changes in the relative frequencies of workers in different earning brackets.

For instance, if in period 1 the number of workers with higher earnings increases in relation to the number of workers with lower earnings, this will result in an increase in average earnings just as increased rates will raise average earnings.

An index which eliminates the influence of the structure of the population of workers according to wage rate can be obtained by establishing the same structure for both periods, say, on the level of period 1. We then have

$$I = \frac{\Sigma q_1 T_1}{\Sigma T_1} : \frac{\Sigma p_0 T_1}{\Sigma T_1} = \frac{\Sigma p_1 T_1}{\Sigma p_0 T_1}, \qquad (XII.14)$$

analogous to other aggregate indices.

This index also loses its meaning, as to other aggregate indices, if the structure between period 0 and period 1 undergoes a basic change.

Analogously to the above the cost index per unit of product is expressed by the formula

$$I = \frac{\Sigma q_1 z_1}{\Sigma q_0} : \frac{\Sigma q_0 z_0}{\Sigma q_0}, \qquad (XII.15)$$

where $z$ denotes the unit cost of production and $q$ the quantity of the product. This index can be used only when we are concerned with one product (e.g. in different factories) because the $q$ cannot be summed when other products are involved. The general index of changes in production costs of different goods, assuming that the structure is the same in both periods, is expressed in the form of the aggregate index:

$$I = \frac{\Sigma q_1 z_1}{\Sigma q_1 z_0}. \qquad (XII.16)$$

We shall not elaborate further on the price index discussed above

$$I_p = \frac{\Sigma q_1 p_1}{\Sigma q_1 p_0}$$

or on the volume of consumption index corresponding to it:

$$I_q = \frac{\Sigma q_1 p_0}{\Sigma q_0 p_0}.$$

The latter is identical with the volume of production index, the volume of sales index,[115] and so on.

The index of real wages in the U.S.S.R. takes into account: (1) money wages, (2) pensions, scholarships and other cash benefits, (3) changes in the purchasing power of money caused by changes in prices (owing to the policy of lowering retail prices in the Soviet Union the purchasing power of the rouble steadily increases), (4) free benefits granted by the State in the field of culture and welfare.

---

[115] If prices are systematically lowered, as in the Soviet Union, the difference between the numerator and the denominator of the fraction of the $I_p''$ index type $q_1 p_1 - q_1 p_0$, expresses the total savings of the worker due to lower prices.

If should be noted that in capitalist countries the index of real wages is obtained by dividing the crude wage index by the cost of living index, thus allowing for changes in average earnings and changes in the purchasing power of money. Since there are no benefits to speak of in the field of culture and welfare the index of real wages thus constructed could be considered as correct if the indices on which it is based were correct. It should be remembered, however, that at best this index correctly reflects changes in earnings of the employed workers, but it does not reflect fluctuations in the earnings of the working class as a whole since it does not allow for unemployment.

## B. IN PEOPLE'S POLAND[116]

We shall now discuss certain indices used in People's Poland. The history or these indices is a story of the struggle with the remnants of capitalism on the one hand, and of the efforts to overcome the difficulties in the manner of application of correct statistical methods on the other.

The first volume index of industrial production was based on the records of the production of 20 "staple commodities" calculated at 1937 prices with the base 1937 = 100. The index was first published in *Wiadomości Statystyczne* (*Statistical News*) in September 1945, but it covered the period from April 1945 onwards. The representativeness of the selected commodities would have been obviously inadequate were the index to be treated as a general index of industrial production and not as "the production index of staple commodities", in accordance with its name. Up to a certain time it could play its planned role. In any case, immediately after the war there was no possibility in Polish statistics of expanding the range of commodities included in the index. In 1949 the Central Statistical Office decided to switch to an index based on the total production of all commodities. Before the index was designed the range of commodities included had been increased more than threefold. The new, expanded, "temporary" index replaced the old one. It was published from October 1949 to April 1950 with the same base (1937 = 100). From May 1950 the index based on the value of total industrial production at 1937 prices was published. The base of the new index was at first, also 1937 and, at the same time, 1947 = 100, and later only 1949 = 100. The 1937 prices were also partly revised. The revision was necessary because the list of prices for 1937 was incomplete, and not all the prices listed were correct. The list of "constant" prices in effect was published and it constitutes a basis for industrial establishments to report: the value of production is supplied by the establishments both in current and in constant prices. The latter are used for calculating the index.[117]

In Table 12.2 a comparison is made of all three indices for those periods for which it was possible, i.e. during which all three indices were published. They

---

[116] Since this book was written, studies on indices have developed considerably, and the methods of calculating some indices have been changed.

[117] Since this book was written the system of constant prices was revised several times.

TABLE 12.2. COMPARISON OF THE INDICES OF INDUSTRIAL
PRODUCTION

| Year | Index | | |
|------|-------|---|---|
| Month | 1 | 2 | 3 |
| 1937 | 100 | 100·0 | 100·0 |
| 1947 | 121 | 108·2 | 105·8 |
| 1948 | 153 | 141·3 | 145·7 |
| 1949  I | 161 | 162·2 | 160·7 |
| II | 154 | 157·2 | 158·1 |
| III | 169 | 175·8 | 182·1 |
| IV | 163 | 169·7 | 176·0 |
| V | 170 | 175·2 | 183·5 |
| VI | 161 | 166·3 | 177·8 |

Index 1: Index of the production of staple commodities.
Index 2: Expanded, temporary index of industrial production.
Index 3: General index based on the total value of industrial
production at constant prices.

are annual averages for 1947 and 1948, and indices for particular months of the first half of 1949.

The differences between the indices are considerable. They are caused not only by different ranges of goods—from about 20 in index 1 to the total production in index 3. The dicrepancies are also due to differences in the price structure and there are other reasons which we shall not elaborate here. The differences are so great that it would be inconceivable to treat the indices as possible substitutes for each other in economic analysis. Even more important, however, is the fact that changes in the short run, from month to month, are not uniform. For instance the increase in production in March in comparison with February 1949 was 10 per cent according to the first index, 11·8 per cent according to the second, and 15·2 per cent according to the third. Of course, if we interpret the first index exactly as we should, namely that it is "the index of the production of staple commodities", then for the commodities listed it correctly presents changes in total output.

Lower production indices in the even months (February, April, June) as compared with odd months 1949 is noticeable. This is caused by fewer working days in even months. Later the Central Statistical Office began the additional publication of "the index adjusted to the average number of full working days", at first only for the heavy and medium State industries (beginning with No. 5 of *Wiadomości Statystyczne*, 1951). In these "adjusted" indices no drop in production in even months is noticeable.[118]

The cost of living index for Warsaw and Łódź was published for the first time in *Wiadomości Statystyczne* No. 4/5 (1945) with the note: "Preliminary calculations until detailed data based on family budget studies can be obtained from the Central Statistical Office. Calculations are based on the pre-war system adapted to present conditions and with approximately the same standard of living". The

[118] See p. 269 *et seq.*

cost of living in April 1945 was denoted by 100. The cost of living based on 1938 = 100 (later equal 1) was also calculated.

The index based on the pre-war budget, even with certain adjustments, could not give correct results because of basic changes in the structure of the family budget. However, family budget studies on which a new and more correct index could be based took longer than expected, and therefore the old index had to be continued December, 1947.

Starting with No. 13 of *Wiadomości Statystyczne, 1948* the cost of living index has published under the changed title: "The retail price index of goods and services bought by a worker's family in Warsaw", with the note: "The indices now published differ in structure from the cost of living indices published up to now." Simultaneously the index with the base 1947 = 100 and the index with the base 1938 = 1 were also published. It appears from the explanatory notes[119] that the index with the base 1947 = 100 was based on consumption studies after the war and the index with base 1938 = 1 was based in the arithmetic mean of the quantities of goods and services purchased before and after the war.

Both the new and the old indices were first based on free market prices without an allowance for food rationing and from April 1950 they were based on "prices in the socialized and private sectors".

In June 1951 the publication of the index in *Wiadomości Statystyczne* was discontinued.

We shall now describe other composite indices used in Poland.

These indices were published either by the Central Statistical Office or by the Government Committee for Economic Planning in reports on the realization of the national economic plan.

They are primarily volume indices calculated by the aggregate method on the basis of constant prices, and thus based mainly on formulae of the $I'_o$ type (see p. 358). Here belong, first of all, the indices of total industrial production described above. Indices on the implementation of the production plan are calculated in the same way. Bulletins on the realization of the national economic plan, the indices of the realization of the plan by particular ministries are published in addition to the general indices of the implementation of the plan. In this category belong the indices of the total value of assembly and construction work, the indices of postal and telecommunication services, the indices of retail sales in the socialized sector together with group catering. The data on exports from and inports to Poland "at 1937 prices" were published in the *Statistical Yearbook* for 1949, for the years 1937, 1947 and 1948. The results were given in thousand of zlotys, but in fact those are the figures which should constitute a basis for calculating the aggregate index of the type mentioned above.

---

[119] *Statistical Yearbook* 1949, p. 108.

Another type of index number is the calculation of the reduction in the cost of production and labour productivity indices based on the value of total production per employee in the industrial sector.

In the first post-war period economic indices were calculated and published not only by the Central Statistical Office but also by the National Economy Institute. They published the index of industrial production and the index of free market prices in Warsaw. These indices were based on similar formulae but in details they differed considerably from the indices published by the Central Statistical Office, and of course the results were consequently different. After the incorporation of the National Economy Institute into the Central Statistical Office in 1949 these indices were discontinued.

## 6. COMPOSITE INDICES IN THE STATISTICS OF CAPITALIST COUNTRIES

In the statistics of the capitalist countries it is impossible to calculate indices based on the total production or sales, on the prices of all goods, etc. Indices in these countries are always based on selected items which are assumed to be representative of the whole. Thus, depending upon whether the selection was right or wrong, these indices may represent a phenomenon more or less correctly, or may be completely unrealistic. The latter is more often the case when the designer of the index is not very familiar with the problem: in such cases it is usually a matter of coincidence whether or not he designs a correct index. If he knows the problem involved the index may be correct and may properly reflect the changes that have occurred. However, even in using the correct indices published in capitalist countries a critical evaluation of their applicability from the point of view of Marxian theory is advisable.

However, it is also possible that a skilled statistician familiar with the problem involved may construct an index especially designed to give misleading information, to present only one side of the problem, to be an apology for capitalism, or to promote the interests of a group of capitalists.

The general public is usually not familiar with the technique of calculating indices and may be inclined to take them at their face value, having faith in apparently simple data and in the learned statisticians who produced them.

In section 3 of this chapter several examples were given of indices with a completely faulty structure and nevertheless very popular and commonly accepted. We shall give a few more examples of such indices.

Before we do so, however, a few words should be said about the most popular book on index numbers in capitalist literature. We refer to Irving Fisher's *The Making of Index Numbers* (Boston and New York, 1922 and later editions). The author presents 56 different simple formulae of composite price indices and over 120 combined formulae (i.e. those obtained by combining different formulae). Although he adds that the actual number of formulae is smaller because some of them differ only in their algebraic form and can be derived from one another it should be stressed that out of the approximately 180 formulae only 24 were ever used in practice.

The book by Fisher is undoubtedly a discouraging example of statistical formalism. The author is not interested in the logic of the formulae but is seeking by mathematical combination formulae which would meet certain tests, without worrying whether there is any sense in them. To test empirically the usefulness of different formulae Fisher considers only one example: the prices and sales of thirty six different commodities in the United States in 1913–18 and rejects those formulae which do not satisfy the requirements of the tests.

After considering all possible types of indices the author finally arrives at the index that he calls "ideal". This is the geometric mean of the indices that we denoted above by $I'$ and $I''$. From the formal point of view it is true that this index satisfies the reciprocal condition $I_{q1/0} = 1/I_{q0/1}$

Taking as an example the price index we write

$$\sqrt{\frac{q_0 p_1}{q_0 p_0} \times \frac{q_1 p_1}{q_1 p_0}} \qquad \text{(XII.17)}$$

and

$$\sqrt{\frac{q_1 p_0}{q_1 p_1} \times \frac{q_0 p_0}{q_0 p_1}}. \qquad \text{(XII.18)}$$

The first of these it the index for period 1 in relation to period 0 and the second is the index for period 0 in relation to period 1. It is obvious that these indices are reciprocals of each other: the same terms that are in the numerator of one are in the denominator of another and vice versa.

However, the aggregate indices $I'$ and $I''$ have a logical meaning which the geometric mean of $I'$ and $I''$ lacks. The calculation of the average would be justified only if it were true that each of the indices $I'$ and $I''$ is only an approximation to the same ratio occurring in reality, and each deviates from this ratio, one up and another down: then we would be justified in seeking some average, possibly the arithmetic or geometric mean, on the assumption that in this way we come closer to reality. However, indices $I'$ and $I''$ are not approximations, and each of them corresponds strictly to the accepted assumptions.

Having established the formula for the "ideal" index, on the basis of selected prices and sales of 36 commodities Fisher calculates the indices according to each of over one hundred formulae for years 1914–18 with the base 1913 = 100.

He evaluates the usefulness of each formula according to how much particular indices deviate from the "ideal" index. On the basis of this analysis the author divides the indices into several groups: useless, unsatisfactory, satisfactory, good, very good, perfect and superlative. At the end of the list there is his "ideal" index. The amount of work involved in these calculations is staggering, but its usefulness is practically nil.

The oldest indices known in the West come from the 18th century (France, Italy, England). They were calculated as ratios of simple sums of the prices of selected commodities, or, at best, as simple averages of individual indices.

In 1780 in Massachusetts (then an English colony) a law was passed concerning the payment of debts. This was the period of the depreciation of paper money. The law read: "Both the principal and the interest are to be paid in the currency of the State to a greater or less amount, depending upon whether 5 bushels of wheat, 68 4/7 lb of beef, 10 lb of sheep wool and 16 lb of sole leather cost at current prices more or less than 130 "currency" pounds.[120]

This apparently complex calculation is, in fact, quite simple, and in spite of the primitive wording it may be more correct than it seems. If we assume that the sum of £130 is the cost of the specified goods at the time when the law was passed, which is likely the calculation is reduced to the computation of the aggregate index of the type.

$$I'_p = \frac{\Sigma p_1 q_0}{\Sigma p_0 q_0},$$

where $\Sigma p_0 q_0 = 130$. This may be the first aggregate index number in history. The correctness of the formula depends upon whether the selected commodities and their quantities correctly reflected the state of the market at the time, i.e. whether they were really the staple commodities which influenced the flow of money to the farmers. We cannot determine whether this was true, but considering the primitive level of the economy of the British colonies in America at that time, this alternative does not appear impossible.

About a century and a half later another index became very popular in the United States. It was Bradstreet's wholesale price index and it cannot be considered anything but queer. It is based on the formula

$$\Sigma p_1 / \Sigma p_0 \qquad\qquad\qquad (XII.19)$$

It is the ratio of the sum of the unit prices of the commodities included in the index in the current period to the sum of the prices of these commodities in the base period. To say the least, it is a very dubious practice to sum up the unit prices of particular goods, but the main error lies elsewhere.

This index may be presented as the weighted average of individual indices

$$\frac{\Sigma p_1}{\Sigma p_0} = \frac{\sum \frac{p_1}{p_0} \times p_0}{\Sigma p_0} \qquad\qquad (XII.19')$$

---

[120] Cited from I. Fisher: *The Making of Index Numbers*, Boston and New York 1922, p. 458. It is possible that a similar index was already designed in 1747.

The weights are the unit prices of particular commodities, which in itself is odd. To this Bradstreet adds something equally strange: he calculates prices not in units customary in trading with the product concerned, but recalculates all prices in terms of price per 1b, regardless of whether this commodity is customarily sold in tons, ounces, gallons, dozens or yards. If the author wanted to give the same weight to all commodities by this conversion he made a serious error. In this case the weight of the commodity is its unit price (according to formula XII.19′). If we take the same units weighing one pound each, we are giving greater weights to the commodities whose price per pound is higher. If we realize that when the aggregate index is properly constructed, the weights should be the values of the sales of the commodities, i.e. the products of the prices and the sales, then we see how nonsensical Bradstreet's calculation is.

Goods as important as grain, coal or cement would affect the movements of the index very little. If, by chance, two very expensive commodities were included in the index their price movements would decisively affect the whole index.

In spite of such unrealistic assumptions the index did not give obviously ridiculous results. Before World War I the movements of this index did not differ much from the movements of the best American price index published by the Bureau of Labour Statistics and based on the aggregate method with a large number of commodities. However, this was not because of, but in spite of, the accepted method of weighting, and was due to the fact that the designer of the index, undoubtedly familiar with the commodity market, had introduced hidden weighting by the selection of goods, thus preventing the appearance of startling anomalies (cf. p. 368).

Price indices were the earliest indices in the capitalist economy. The variety of price index known as the cost-of-living index has also been known for a long time. In this case correct aggregate formulae were derived very early. In 1864 Laspeyres came out with the formula of the type $I_p' = \dfrac{\sum q_0 p_1}{\sum q_0 p_0}$, and in 1874 Paasche used the formula of the type $I_p'' = \dfrac{\sum q_1 p_1}{\sum q_1 p_0}$.

Both these formulae (in the capitalist economy particlarly the $I_q'$ type) are commonly used in constructing cost of living indices, and if the results are often incorrect it is not the fault of the formulae.

Cost of living indices are well suited for demonstrating more important errors that can be committed in designing indices, even those based on proper formulae.

First of all it should be remembered that every composite index gives correct results only insofar as it is used under the circumstances for which it has been designed. Let us consider from this point of view the Polish cost of living index before the war, as well as immediately after the war at the time when it was used.

Before the war the Central Statistical Office published two cost of living indices, one for the physical worker's family. Let us remember first of all what the cost of living index is supposed to express. It is a price index designed from the point of view of the needs of a certain type of family. The cost-of-living index for the physical worker's family was based on studies of worker's family budget in 1927. Families with different levels of expenditures were included and a "typical" family of four with the average level and structure of expenditures was formed. The family budget of the white-collar worker was calculated on the basis of family budget studies in 1932. Each of these cost indices was a proper measure only for those two clearly defined population groups. This is so not because the level of expenditures is higher in the white-collar worker's family—the level of the index does not depend upon the level of expenditures—but because different types of families have different types of expenditures. For instance, in worker's families expenditures on food constituted 66·9 per cent of the total, on rent 0·7 per cent, miscellaneous items 5·8 per cent, and in the white-collar worker's families these expenditures were 44·0, 13·6 and 13·1 per cent respectively.

In the following years the prices of food were relatively low but rents and "miscellaneous" prices were fairly high in comparison with the starting period. In consequence the cost of living index for white-collar workers was higher than for physical workers. The cost of living index for the "typical" worker's family could differ considerably both for the worker's family with the lowest expenditures (less than 600 zlotys per annum per consuming unit) and for one with the highest expenditures (1200 zlotys and more); this again is due to the fact that in families with different levels of expenditures the share of different expenditure groups varies.[121] None of these budgets, of course, can be used as a basis for calculating the cost of living index for a well-to-do bourgeois family.

After the war the Central Statistical Office used the family budget of 1927 with minor changes caused by the state of the market and other circumstances (see p. 377). In the first years after the war this was unavoidable: nevertheless, the results were misleading and the publication of this index was discontinued at the end of 1947 in favour of a index based on post-war family budgets.

This does not mean that for each type of family a separate cost of living index should be designed. This would be obviously impossible. The index can and should be applicable to similar circumstances, but it cannot be used under basically different conditions. Then it ceases to be a measure because the structure on which it is based (in this case the structure of the budget) has changed significantly.

Other reservations stem from the fact that frequently the data needed for calculating a full aggregate index are not available. In such cases various simplifying devices may be employed.

---

[121] Worker's family budgets will be discussed again in Chapter 22.

(1) If all the data needed for the calculation of the complete index are not available some items may be left out (the prices of some goods). This is tantamount to assuming that changes in the prices of all goods and services are proportional to the changes in the prices of goods and services included in the index. Such omissions are sometimes inevitable, both because all prices may not be available and because the calculations would be too involved if too many commodities were included. If the goods omitted are of lesser importance and few the risk of a major error is negligible.

(2) A certain number of components can be selected on purpose, assuming that they also represent other items not included in a given group. This practice is quite common in calculating certain indices. In capitalist countries this method is of necessity used very often. The justification is the assumption—which should be proved in each particular case—that the prices of the whole group move in unison with prices of the components included in the index.

On the use of this method in designing the cost of living index J. Wojtyniak[122] writes: "It is necessary to simplify the typical budget, and to confine it to the most essential items by selecting them so that they represent certain groups of expenditures and that their prices are available".

However, if a commodity is to represent a whole group it must be included in a properly increased ratio so that the total amount spent on this commodity is equal to the amount actually spent on the whole group. For instance, the budget which was used as a basis for calculating the cost of living index in Warsaw from 1945 to 1947 lists among "Household equipment" the items: pots, glasses, towels and wicker chairs, obviously only some of the items in this group. But the annual norms were set at: 3·55 pots, 12 glasses, 3 towels and 0·96 chairs per consuming unit, which means that for one family (which has 3·25 consuming units) the norms were: 11·5 pots, 39 glasses, almost 10 towels and over 3 chairs, which is obviously more than the actual needs. In the "Miscellaneous" group were such cultural expenditures as 36 schools copy-books per consuming unit, i.e. 117 copy-books per family in which there is only one child of school age. Such inflating of the quantities of one commodity may increase the error if the commodities selected do not properly "represent" the price movements of the whole group.

(3) In calculating composite indices it may sometimes be necessary to replace, permanently or temporarily, certain selected items by other items. This may happen when a commodity disappears from the market, or a new product is introduced and cannot be left out. Such substitution or supplementing of the list of goods require particular care, and should be done so as not to affect the general structure of the index.

---

[122] J. Wojtyniak: Metoda obliczania wskaźnika kosztów utrzymania (The Method of Calculating the Cost of Living Index), *Wiadomości Statystyczne Głównego Urzędu Statystycznego* (*Statistical Information from the Central Statistical Office*), 1947, Special Issue III, p. 3.

(4) In some cases, notably in capitalist countries, it may be necessary to replace information concerning a given commodity directly, by information on other commodities only indirectly related to the commodity. In this case the underlying assumption is that the movements of the prices of these commodities are parallel to the movements of the price of the commodity which is left out. This situation is, in a sense, analogous to the choice of "representative" goods discussed in section 3, but the problem reaches deeper and the practice is subject to more serious reservations. This may happen in designing price indices but it is more common in designing the index of industrial production. For instance, in calculating the index of industrial production in Poland before the war partly the number of persons employed, and partly the man-hours worked, were used instead of the actual data on production in a given industry. The building activity index was based on new permits for the construction of houses or on the railway transport of lime. Instead of a cotton production index, data on the cotton imported were used. Such "symptomatic" indices have been and are used and not only in Poland. They enable us to allow in the general index for items which cannot be measured directly, but they may also lead to considerable errors. For instance, the number of man-hours worked reflects changes in production in a given industry only as long as there is no change in labour productivity. Although the cotton industry in Poland uses only imported cotton, it does not follow that the production of cotton goods in a given year is based on the import of cotton for the same year. It is possible that the stocks from the previous year are used, or that only a part of the cotton imported in a year is used up in that year.

Of course, what was said in the above four points on the cost of living and production indices also applies to all other composite index numbers.

The number of index numbers now in use in particular capitalist countries is very large. They differ in many resepects from the ones previously published.

(1) Old indices were designed and published by private persons or organizations, often by firms for which they were a source of profit (e.g. by copyright). The more important index numbers are now published by government organizations. This has resulted in a considerable increase in the number of items included and in improved efficiency in the calculations. Some indices of industrial production include over 1000 items, which of course reduces the magnitude of certain errors.

The same is true with respect to general price indices. Similarly, in cost of living indices the prices of several hundred goods and services are included, which is a great deal for this type of index.

(2) The knowledge of the theory and technique of calculating index numbers is now more widespread. This has led to formally more correct methods of design and to a better understanding of the real meaning of the results obtained, and consequently to the limitation of the use of each index to the circumstances for which it has been designed. Hence the crop of specialized indices, e.g. price or

production indices of especially selected groups of commodities, price indices for exported or imported goods, construction costs indices, foreign trade volume indices (volume indices at constant prices).

The indices of the prices of "sensitive" commodities are often published. They are indices of a few selected commodities particularly sensitive to business cycles. It should be remembered that one of the main objects of using index numbers in the capitalist economy is to provide quick warning signals of changes in business activity.

(3) In consequence of a more widespread knowledge of the construction of indices, aggregate formulae or their derivatives are frequently used.

There is no significant improvement in the real value of the indices now published by government agencies in comparison with the old ones published by private persons or organizations. With very few exceptions both are clearly attuned to the needs of the capitalist economy and therefore should be used with caution.

Nevertheless, there is now a wealth of material on which to draw for studies of capitalist countries. The limitations and scope of each index should be kept in mind, however, and the basis of its construction should be carefully analysed. Only very rarely are sufficiently detailed explanatory notes published on the construction of indices. They are usually available in special issues of statistical publications or in those issues in which the publication of a new index begins. One general rule should be observed: indices should not be used without checking on the details of their construction, and they should be taken from publications in which they appear in the most detailed form. Sometimes it may be difficult but it is certainly worth while, as can be seen from the example on pp. 39–41 in which it was shown what revealing results can be obtained by substituting detailed for general data.

# CHAPTER 13

# COEFFICIENTS AND PROBABILITIES
# IN HETEROGENEOUS POPULATIONS.
# STANDARDIZATION OF COEFFICIENTS

## 1. COEFFICIENTS IN HETEROGENEOUS POPULATIONS

In discussing the example on illiteracy we concluded (p. 353) that it is more correct to calculate the ratio of the illiterate from the age of 10 upwards to the population of the same age, than to calculate the ratio of all the illiterate to the total population. But the exclusion of children less than 10 years old does not solve all problems in measuring the intensity of illiteracy.

In the central provinces of Poland in 1921 the illiterate aged 10 or more constituted 31·7 per cent of the population. In 1931 the figure dropped substantially, to 22·3 per cent. However, a proper view of the problem can be obtained only after calculating the percentage for each age group separately.

TABLE 13.1. ILLITERACY IN POLAND BEFORE
WORLD WAR. CENTRAL PROVINCES,
1921 and 1931[123]

| Age | Percentage of illiterate | |
|---|---|---|
| | 1921 | 1931 |
| 10 years and over | 31·7 | 22.3 |
| 10–14 | 25·1 | 3·7 |
| 15–19 | 20·6 | 7·4 |
| 20–24 | 22·3 | 11·3 |
| 25–29 | 25·1 | 15·1 |
| 30–39 | 31·4 | 22·6 |
| 40–49 | 38·8 | 32·5 |
| 50–59 | 47·6 | 41.6 |
| 60 and over | 56·2 | 54·2 |

We see from the table that both in 1921 and in 1931 illiteracy was undoubtedly greater in old age than youth (a result of the partitions, low level of education

---

[123] *Concise Statistical Yearbook,* 1939, p. Table 23.

particularly in earlier times). In 1931 we notice a considerable decline in illiteracy at early ages in comparison with 1921: at 10–14 years of age it dropped from 25·1 to 3·7 per cent, at 15–19 from 20·6 to 7·4 per cent. However, if we consider that the law making education compulsory for all children from 7 to 14 years of age was passed in February 1919, then we have to conclude that the percentages for 1931 are still very high. If the principle of compulsory education had really been observed the precentage of the illiterate should not have exceeded 0·7 per cent, at least for those less than 20 years old, since they should have benefited from the law. If the percentage of the illiterate was 3·7 per cent at 10–14 and 7·4 per cent at 15–19, this means that the then government of Poland was not able to enforce this law. In the later age groups an increase in illiteracy is noticeable: in 1931 for the age group 40–49 it was 32·5 per cent whereas in 1921 for the corresponding age group 30–39 it was 31·4 per cent; In 1931 for the age group of 50–59 it was 41·6 per cent and in 1921 for the corresponding age group of 40–49 it was 38·8 per cent. This means that the then government of Poland had done nothing to eliminate illiteracy among adults.

This example enables us to formulate the first general rule: when we deal with a population of which we know or have reason to believe that it is heterogeneous we should divide it into parts as homogeneous as possible and should calculate the coefficient for each of them separately. Sometimes it may suffice to divide it into several large groups, but sometimes a more detailed breakdown may be necessary.

We have here, in a sense, a reverse problem to the one with which we were faced in calculating composite indices: there we were concerned in combining individual items into one entity which would enable us to make comparisons, and here we have an entity which because of its heterogeneity cannot be compared with other entities of the same type, but of a different structure. We have to consider this problem in greater detail since the breakdown into smaller parts, as in the example on illiteracy, solves only a part of the problem.

The general coefficient is the weighted arithmetic mean of partial coefficients. If we denote by $p$ partial coefficients and by $f$ the frequencies of the groups corresponding to particular value of $p$ then the general coefficient $P$ is expressed by the formula

$$P = \frac{\Sigma pf}{\Sigma f}.$$

(XIII.1)

Of course, the value of $P$ depends both on the values of the partial coefficients and on the structure of the population, i.e. on the relative frequencies of particular classes expressed by $f$.

Weighted averages of this kind often lead to peculiar paradoxes. Let us consider several examples, partly based on direct observations and partly artificially constructed.

In Table 13.2 the number of children of age 2–4 per thousand inhabitants[124] is given according to the 1931 census.

TABLE 13.2. RATIO OF THE NUMBER OF CHILDREN TO THE TOTAL POPULATION IN THE PROVINCES OF KIELCE AND LUBLIN in 1931

| Province | Total | In towns with population of | | In rural areas |
|---|---|---|---|---|
| | | over 20,000 | 20,000 and fewer | |
| Kielce | 79·2 | 62·4 | 73·1 | 83·9 |
| Lublin | 79·5 | 60·0 | 72·3 | 82·3 |

What stands out in the table is that in both large and small towns, as well as in the rural areas, the ratio of the number of children to the total population was smaller in the province of Lublin than in the province of Kielce, i.e. fertility was lower in the province of Lublin than in the province of Kielce. The difference is small but definite. But for the total population of the provinces the figure is larger for the province of Lublin: 79·5 as compared to 79·2 for the province of Kielce.

This can be explained. The coefficient in the "Total" column is the weigted average of the coefficients in the following columns and the weights are the population figures for urban and rural areas.

In the province of Kielce as compared with the province of Lublin the urban population was relatively large (25·5 per cent as against 17·6 per cent in the province of Lublin) and its coefficients are large. In consequence the general coefficient for the province of Lublin is relatively high.

If we had only the totals for each province without the division by areas we would have reached completely erroneous conclusions concerning fertility since thes existing differences to the disadvantage of the province of Lublin are obscured by different degrees of urbanization in the two provinces.

The next example is even more striking and the resultant paradox is seemingly more difficult to explain.

In Fig. 13.1 the probability of death for German men aged 22–29 is given according to the German Life Table for 1924–26[125] with a breakdown by bachelors, married men and the total. As we can see in the period under consideration the death rate for the bachelors rapidly increases, the death rate for the married men, which is much lower than for the bachelors, also increases, though slightly, whereas the total death rate declines very distinctly.

The numerical data are as follows:

---

[124] The ratio of the number of children to the total population according to the census is calculated to get a general idea about the fertility of different population groups.

[125] *Statistik des Deutschen Reiches*, Vol. 360, pp. 176 and 180.

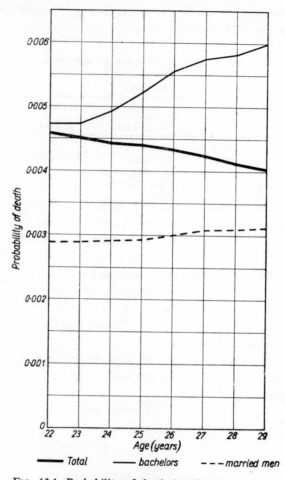

FIG. 13.1. Probability of death for German men by
family status. Ages 22—29.

TABLE 13.3. PROBABILITY OF DEATH WITHIN ONE YEAR
ACCORDING TO THE GERMAN LIFE TABLE
for 1924–26

| Age (years) | Bachelors | Married men | Total |
|---|---|---|---|
| 22 | 0·00473 | 0·00286 | 0·00457 |
| 23 | 474 | 286 | 450 |
| 24 | 491 | 286 | 443 |
| 25 | 523 | 289 | 439 |
| 26 | 552 | 299 | 433 |
| 27 | 575 | 308 | 423 |
| 28 | 583 | 306 | 411 |
| 29 | 595 | 309 | 404 |

In the original table there is one more column for "widowers and divorced" with a very high death rate, which remains on the same level between the ages of 25 and 29 (a probability of 0·00756). No calculations were made for the widowed and divorced aged less than 25, because the number is negligible.

Life tables by family status were calculated only in a few countries, but wherever such a breakdown was available the results were almost identical with those in Table 13.3: a much smaller death rate for the married men than for bachelors, a drop (or at least some slowing down) in the rate of increase in the death rate for all men between the ages of 21 and 30.

Similar results appear in the tables on Poland calculated by E. Vielrose.[126] According to them the probability of death within one year is 0·0062 for bachelors aged 22 and 0·0084 aged 29; for married men the values are 0·0033 and 0·0043, respectively, and for all men, 0·0058 and 0·0055, respectively. The diagram shows the data for Germany where the decline in the death rate for all men is more pronounced.

To explain the apparent paradox two things should be taken into account: (1) the death rate for married men is much smaller—in the examples shown here about half as great—than the death rate among bachelors;[127] (2) at earlier ages of about 20, a great majority of men are not married, and at the age of about 30 most of them are married. In other words most men at the age of about 20 are bachelors for whom the death rate is high, and most of those aged about 30 are married, and their death rate is low. In the following example the full calculation for the ages from 20 to 29 is shown; although it is somewhat simplified, it is generally in line with the observations (see Table 13.4).

We assume for the sake of simplicity that the death rate for bachelors for each age is twice as high as the death rate for married men and that the death rate in both groups increases evenly with age: for bachelors from 4.4 per thousand at the age of 20, to 6·2 at the age of 29; and for married men from 2·2 to 3·1. We also assume that all men at the age of 20 are bachelors, and that each year 10 per cent of the original number get married, so that at the age of 29 there are only 10 per cent bachelors and 90 per cent married men. For simplicity we assume further that the total number of those living does not change.

The figures according to the above assumptions are shown in the first part of Table 13.4. The last three columns contain the results of the calculations based on the above assumptions: first the number of the deceased bachelors and married men separately, then the death rate for all men. We can see that the death rate for all men drops from 4·4 per thousand at the age of 20 to 3·41 at the age of 29. The results are in full conformity with the observations.

---

[126] E. Vielrose: Umieralność według stanu cywilnego w Polsce 1931–32, (Death Rates by Family Status in Poland in 1931–32) *Studia i Prace Statystyczne (Statistical Studies and Papers)* 1951, No. 2–3, p. 15–22, and Polish Life Tables 1931–32, *Statystyka Polski,* Series C, No. 41, Warsaw, 1938.
[127] The lower death rate among married men is mainly due to a more regular life.

TABLE 13.4. NUMBER OF DECEASED AT THE AGE OF 20–29

| Age | Deaths per 1000 of the living | | The living in percentages | | Number of deceased | | |
|---|---|---|---|---|---|---|---|
| | bachelors $p_1$ | married $p_2$ | bachelors $l_1$ | married $l_2$ | bachelors $p_1 l_1$ | married $p_2 l_2$ | total per 1000 of the living $\dfrac{p_1 l_1 + p_2 l_2}{100}$ |
| 20 | 4·4 | 2·2 | 100 | 0 | 440 | 0 | 4·4 |
| 21 | 4·6 | 2·3 | 90 | 10 | 414 | 23 | 4·37 |
| 22 | 4·8 | 2·4 | 80 | 20 | 384 | 48 | 4·32 |
| 23 | 5·0 | 2·5 | 70 | 30 | 350 | 75 | 4·25 |
| 24 | 5·2 | 2·6 | 60 | 40 | 312 | 104 | 4·16 |
| 25 | 5·4 | 2·7 | 50 | 50 | 270 | 135 | 4·05 |
| 26 | 5·6 | 2·8 | 40 | 60 | 224 | 168 | 3·92 |
| 27 | 5·8 | 2·9 | 30 | 70 | 174 | 203 | 3·77 |
| 28 | 6·0 | 3·0 | 20 | 80 | 120 | 240 | 3·60 |
| 29 | 6·2 | 3·1 | 10 | 90 | 62 | 279 | 3·41 |

The above example reveals another possible paradox. Let us take somewhat different figures: let the death rate for the married for all ages be 20 per cent lower than rates for the single (such ratios sometimes exist between the death rates for single and married women). Let us consider a longer age range, say from 20 to 39: during these years let the death rate for single women increase uniformly from 5·0 to 8·8 per thousand and let their numbers decrease evenly from 100 to 10; let the death rate for married women increase evenly from 4·0 to 7·04 (with the preservation of the ratio 4 to 5 in relation to the death rate for single women), and let their number increase from 0 to 90. If, by the method shown in Table 13.4, we now calculate the joint death rate for both groups for the ages 20–39, then for single women we have 6·28 deaths per thousand, and for married women 6·07. The difference is very small and in any case very far from favouring married women by 20 per cent. Figures can easily be selected in such a way as to obtain higher death rates for married than single women. All we have to do is to assume that most single women get married upon reaching the age of 20.

Here also we can support theoretical reasoning with an example. In the text book on medical statistics by Prinzing[128] the death rates of 4·1 per thousand are given for both married and single women aged 20–39 in Germany. But from the table on the next page in which the probabilities of death for the same age range are given according to life tables, it appears that the death rate for married women is much lower than for single women. The probabilities at the age of 25 are 4·14 per thousand for single women, and 3·60 for married women; at the age of 30 they are 4·80 and 3·87; at the age of 35, 5·20 and 4·29; and at the age of 40,

---

[128] Prinzing: *Handbuch der medizinischen Statistik*, Jena, 1931, 2nd ed., p. 417.

6·77 and 4·98, respectively. Only at the age of 20 is the ratio reversed: 3·30 per thousand for single women and 3·55 for married women. In calculating the joint coefficient for the whole group 20–39 it is of decisive importance that in this group there are many single women aged about 20, with a low death rate, and few single women closer to 40 with a high death rate. The situation is reversed with regard to married women.

This disqualifies comparisons of death rates by family status as so often given in international statistics—in large age groups of 20–39, 40–59, 60 and over, etc. Within such large groups the structure is completely different for different status groups, and this affects the coefficient significantly.

The habit of breaking down these statistics into 20-year age groups originated, it appears, in the French Statistical Office in its publication: *Statistique internationale du mouvement de la population. Résumé rétrospectif* (Paris, 1907). A great deal of valuable material is given in this publication, going back to beginning of the organization of registry offices in various countries. The same 20-year breakdown in maintained in later publications of the same kind. Demographic yearbooks published so far by the United Nations Organization do not contain data on deaths by family status, nor, in the classification by the causes of death, is the breakdown by age sufficiently detailed (from the age of 25 up the groups are of year range: 25–44, 45–64 and over). Statistics of this kind are of little values, and may be misleading.

At one time it appeared from the statistics published in the United States that the percentage of persons serving prison sentences was twice as high for those born outside the United States as for native Americans. The Census authorities concluded that the crime rate among the immigrants was twice as high as among those born in the America. However, an honest and inquisitive American undertook a detailed analysis. It turned out that among those born abroad a higher percentage were of the ages at which the crime rate is the highest than there were native Americans of this age. The author therefore concluded that the accusation was a great injustice to the immigrants. When the difference in the age structure was allowed for, the reverse turned out to be true: the crime rate among the native population was higher than among those born abroad.[129]

In the 1928 *Rocznik Statystyczny Warszawy (Statistical Yearbook of Warsaw)*[130] a table was published with the following data for some professions: (1) the total number of deceased, (2) the number of deaths from tuberculosis, and (3) the percentage ratio of deaths due to tuberculosis to the total number of deaths. This percentage was the highest for the school-age group of over 15, and amounted to 47·2 per cent when the percentage of deaths due to tuberculosis among those at the working age was only 20·3 per cent. The conclusion that learning makes

---

[129] The example taken from the paper by H. E. Chaddock: "Age and Sex in Population Analysis", published in the joint study: The American People, Studies in Population, p. 183 (in *Ann. Amer. Acad. Polit. Soc. Science*), November 1936.

[130] *Rocznik Statystyczny Warszawy (Statistical Yearbook of Warsaw)*, 1928, p. 50.

one susceptible to tuberculosis would be completely wrong. If we analyse the relative frequency of deaths due to tuberculosis for different age groups it turns out that the percentage of deaths caused by tuberculosis in relation to all deaths was the highest at the age 15–19 (41·4 per cent) and 20–29 (44·9 per cent) i.e. at the age of high school and university studies.

But up to one year of age the percentage of deaths due to tuberculosis was only 3·2, at the age 50–59 it was 14·5 per cent, at the age 60–69, 7·7 per cent, at the age 70 and over, 3·1 per cent. The relatively high percentage of deaths due to tuberculosis at school age is caused by the fact that at this age other causes of death play a minor part. It should be remembered that the percentage of deaths due to tuberculosis in different professions depends, to a large extent, upon the ages of those working in these professions.

Let us consider another example in which the apparent paradox is particularly striking, and the explanation is more involved.

*Agricultural Statistics* for 1937[131] gives data for various provinces on yields in quintals per hectare on large private farms over 50 hectares and on those of less than 50 hectares. From these data we have calculated yield indices for farms of over 50 hectares taking the yields on farms of less than 50 hectares as 100. We also give the percentage of the area under barley in particular provinces in relation to the total area under barley in Poland, separately for these two groups of farms.

The paradox shows in the indices of yield per hectare. These indices are over 100 in all provinces, and everywhere the yields of the large private farms are higher than on the small farms. The differences between provinces are substantial. The surplus harvest is least in the province of Tarnopol (index 102·8), and largest in the province of Kielce (index 138·3). And yet the general index for the whole country is 138·5, larger than for any of the provinces. This is a surprise and at first there appears to be an error since one is inclined to believe that the overall index for Poland is an average of the indices for the provinces and the average can never be greater than the largest individual item. However the overall index is not an average index, but an index idependently calculated on the basis of average yields in Poland on farms of over 50 hectares, and less than 50 hectares. These averages are obtained either directly, by dividing the total crop of barley in Poland by the total area under barley, or as weighted averages of yields per hectare in the provinces and the weights are numbers proportional to the areas under barley in the provinces. These figures are given in the last two columns in the table. It appears that for large private farms there is a very strong positive correlation between yields per hectare and the area under barley: 63·5 per cent of the total area under barley on large farms is concentrated in the four provinces in which yields

---

[131] *Statystyka Polski (Statistics of Poland)*, Series C, No. 92, Warsaw, 1938, Table 7, p. 17.

TABLE 13.5. BARLEY YIELDS IN QUINTALS PER HECTARE IN 1937

| Province | Yields in quintals per hectare | | | Area under barley in percentages on farms of | |
|---|---|---|---|---|---|
| | farms of | | indices (yields on farms of less than 50 hectares = 100) | | |
| | 50 hectares and over | less than 50 hectares | | 50 hectares and over | less than 50 hectares |
| Poland | 14·4 | 10·4 | 138·5 | 100·0 | 100·0 |
| Warsaw | 14·8 | 12·2 | 121·3 | 15·1 | 5·9 |
| Łódź | 13·9 | 11·1 | 125·2 | 4·5 | 2·0 |
| Kielce | 13·0 | 9·4 | 138·3 | 3·6 | 10·0 |
| Lublin | 10·1 | 9·3 | 108·6 | 4·5 | 10·5 |
| Białystok | 7·4 | 7·1 | 104·2 | 2·5 | 5·8 |
| Wilno | 8·1 | 7·1 | 114·1 | 2·5 | 5·2 |
| Nowogródek | 9·0 | 8·5 | 105·9 | 2·2 | 5·7 |
| Polesie | 7·3 | 6·4 | 114·1 | 0.8 | 3·4 |
| Wołyń | 13·9 | 12·8 | 108·6 | 2·7 | 12·8 |
| Poznań | 16·7 | 15·2 | 109·9 | 33·0 | 5·9 |
| Pomorze | 16·8 | 15·0 | 112·0 | 14·2 | 4·1 |
| Silesia | 18·2 | 14·2 | 128·2 | 1·2 | 0·3 |
| Kraków | 12·5 | 10·0 | 125·0 | 1·6 | 5·9 |
| Lwów | 11·3 | 9·6 | 117·7 | 3·6 | 8·6 |
| Stanisławów | 9·7 | 8·5 | 114·1 | 1·4 | 2·6 |
| Tarnopol | 11·2 | 10·9 | 102·8 | 6·6 | 11·3 |

per hectare are highest: Poznań, Pomorze, Silesia and Warsaw, so that the weighted average for Poland is large—14·4 quintals per hectare, whereas the simple average is only 12·1. On the other hand, on the small farms there is no noticeable correlation between yields and the area under barley so that the weighted average gives the same results as the simple average (10·4 quintals per hectare).

What we see here is more than a striking example of statistical paradox, on the surface, quite difficult to explain. What conclusions can be drawn from the table? In 1937 barley yields per hectare in Poland on large private farms were indeed 38·5 per cent higher than on smaller farms. However, in particular provinces where both types of farms operated under similar conditions the differences were much smaller. The large difference for the whole country was due to the fact that on large private farms barley was cultivated where yields were high (or that large private farms existed where yields were high). Then, if we want to know to what extent yields on the large private farms increase in consequence of better cultivation, better fertilizing, better seed grain, then the overall figure for the whole country will not give us the answers. Do the indices for particular provinces answer these questions? It is doubtful. In any case, the result obtained is a forcible reminder of the obvious principle: we can compare only comparable phenomena under the same conditions.

There are many examples of this kind. We have quoted quite a few, and from various fields, to emphasize the danger of basing conclusions on comparisons of coefficients calculated for populations with different structures.

It is important to understand the point well. Let us consider some further examples. It is undoubtedly true that both in Poland and in Germany the death rate was smaller for men 29 years old than for men 22 years old. But it is also true that for men living in the same conditions (the same family status) the death rate increased with age and the above result—of a decline in the death rate with age for all men—was a consequence of more and more men improving their living conditions by getting married. It is undoubtedly true that in the province of Kielce as a whole there were relatively fewer children than in the province of Lublin which leads to the conclusion (if we disregard differences in the death rates) of lower fertility, However, it is also true that under identical environmental conditions (urban or rural) in the province of Kielce there were more children than in the province of Lublin and the opposite general result is due to differences in environment: relatively more people living in towns in the province of Kielce and relatively more living in the country in the province of Lublin.

If in society $A$ the birth rate (the ratio of births to population) is higher than in society $B$ then we state the obvious fact that in society $A$ births affect an increase in population in relation to the existing situation to a greater extent than in society $B$. But if we conclude that fertility in $A$ is higher than in $B$—ignoring the fact that in $A$ there are fewer births in relation to the number of women at the child-bearing age than in $B$, and the birth rate in $A$ is higher only because there are relatively more women there of child-bearing age than in $B$—then we commit an unforgivable error, by using a measure not appropriate to the problem.

Similar errors in drawing conclusions on the basis of general coefficients are very common, particularly among people not too familiar with statistics, and inclined to draw conclusions on the basis of information obtained accidentally. However, such errors also occur among trained statisticians, either because they are not sufficiently aware that the population was not homogeneous, or because there is not enough material available to draw proper conclusions.

The first condition of a proper analysis is the division of a heterogeneous population into more or less homogeneous parts and the calculation of the intensity of the events studied for each part separately. It is always difficult and sometimes impossible to divide a population into homogeneous parts. However, if we assume that differences in death rates are related to living in settlements of different sizes then the problem becomes relatively simple.

If the factor disturbing homogeneity is the geographical location as in the case of yields per hectare, then the question arises whether the districts are uniform under the available territorial division, e.g. whether the provinces are sufficiently uniform, whether we should consider the smaller counties instead, or whether we should combine counties. It should be remembered that the prevalence of certain events is usually related not directly to the geographical location, but to other factors which are, in turn, related to the geographical location. In our example these factors may be the general level of agricultural technique, the fertility of the soil, the climate, and so on.

It should also be noted that we are dealing with statistical populations for which lack of uniformity is an essential characteristic. We should try to make the parts into which we divide a population as homogeneous as possible with respect to the characteristic relevant to the problem. It is usually impossible to achieve complete homogeneity, or unnecessary to do so.

It is hard to tell in advance how far one should go in breaking down a population, because this depends upon the circumstances and on what is feasible, and it should be left to the research worker's intuition.

The problem should be properly stated, and the proof schould not be open to doubt.

Under certain circumstances greater precision may be achieved, e.g. in correlation calculus which will be discussed later. Greater precision can also be achieved in designing elimination tables (Chapter 14).

However, in most cases the procedure is rather simple: we divide the whole range into classes according to the relevant characteristic and compute the class frequencies. Depending upon the circumstances, class intervals may be large or small. For instance, for those ages at which the death rate in relation to age changes little, we can use large intervals and calculate coefficients, say, for decades, particularly when it can be assumed that in the populations compared there are no substantial differences in the age structure. But for those years at which the death rate is strongly related to age the intervals should be smaller, perhaps even as small as one year or one month. For the calculation of death rates the following division is generally considered sufficient: 0–1 year, 1–5 years, 5–10 years and so on in 5-year age groups until the age of 20 or 25, and from then on in 10-year age groups. When we compare the death rates of bachelors and married men the division for the range from 20 to 30 years should be very detailed, not because the death rate changes rapidly with age, but because in both groups the number of those exposed to death changes rapidly with age and, what is more, these changes go in the opposite direction: the number of bachelors decreases and the number of married men increases.

It should be stressed once again that a problem of great importance in all statistical studies is the availability of sufficiently detailed statistical data which can, if necessary, be further divided into smaller groups. This is the responsibility of the institutions compiling and processing statistics. It is not always possible with respect to current reporting in which speed is essential, and which should not be too much of a burden on the reporting units. For this reason, current reporting must be supplemented by general censuses and other special studies, including sample surveys, which will be discussed in Part V.

Current statistical reporting is, of course, a necessary prerequisite for a planned economy. But it is equally obvious that planning, especially long-term planning, cannot be based only on current and past statistical reports. Current reports represent reality correctly only as long as there are no basic structural changes which are not a direct object of these reports. Current reporting may sometimes draw the planner's attention to certain difficulties which have arisen in connexion with the appearance of new phenomena, possibly in completely different fields.

The task of the planner, however, is not only to state the existence of a problem or difficulty but to foresee that it may appear and to prevent its undesirable consequences. This is possible only with the help of special studies which are outside the scope of current reporting.

## 2. STANDARDIZING COEFFICIENTS

The division of a population into groups, if done properly, usually clarifies the situation, and makes possible comparisons of populations with different structures. However, this method also has certain disadvantages, becauses instead of characterizing each population by one coefficient we have as many coefficients as there are parts into which the population has been divided. This creates considerable difficulties in making comparisons, particularly when we compare not two, but many more series of coefficients. There is therefore a natural tendency to design one numerical measure to characterize the intensity of the events in the whole population in such a way that in making comparisons differences in the structure will not interfere.

This problem first arose in relation to deatch statistics in making comparisons of the general mortality in population groups with different age structures (e.g. between urban and rural population, between different occupations).

In principle we are faced here with a typical problem of composite coefficients. However, in population statistics usage went at first in a different direction, which led to misunderstandings in spite of the fact that the method used was essentially correct. Both because of these misunderstandings and because of the broad application of this method we shall discuss the problem in greater detail.

The values of general death rates, which are ratios of the total numbers of deaths to the total population, depend both on partial death rates in particular population groups and on the structure of the population. Here the factor disturbing the homogeneity of the population is primarily the age structure of the population because of the tremendous differences in death rates at different ages. These disturbances in homogeneity appear with particular force in death statistics broken down by occupations, since the age structure varies considerably between different occupations. For this reason, many years ago attempts were made in England to eliminate the disturbing impact of the age structure in computing death rates for different occupations. In 1870 the Hungarian statistician J. Körösi independently pointed out the difficulties which arise for the same reason in geographical comparisons of death rates, particularly in comparing urban with rural areas.

In towns there are many young and middle-aged people for whom the death rates are low and in the country thtere are relatively many very young children and old people. In calculating general death rates, this results in seemingly low urban rates and relatively high rural rates. But even differences in the age structure between different countries alone are sifficiently large to cause misunderstandings.

Körösi should be credited with posing the problem on the international forum: he delivered a paper at the *Third Conference of the International Institute of Statistics* (Vienna, 1891) which provoked a likely discussion both at the Institute and outside. This discussion led, at least in theory, to a full clarification of the situation.

We give here the example of death rates in two different occupations where paradoxes of the kind mentioned appear with particular force (see Table 13.6).

TABLE 13.6. DEATH RATES IN ENGLAND IN 1930–2

| Age (years) | Anglican clergymen | | | Waiters | | | |
| | Number of the living according to census $l_1$ | Number of deaths $d_1$ | Deaths per 10,000 living $m_1$ | Number of living according to census $l_2$ | Number of deaths $d_2$ | Deaths per 10,000 living $m_2$ | Index 100 $m_2$ / $m_1$ |
|---|---|---|---|---|---|---|---|
| 20–25 | 236 | 1 | 14·1 | 5022 | 70 | 46·5 | 320 |
| 25–35 | 2318 | 19 | 33·9 | 7066 | 96 | 45·3 | 134 |
| 35–45 | 3620 | 48 | 44·2 | 4357 | 109 | 83·4 | 189 |
| 45–55 | 4906 | 83 | 56·4 | 2902 | 123 | 141·3 | 251 |
| 55–65 | 5303 | 283 | 177·9 | 1803 | 167 | 308·7 | 174 |
| 65–70 | 2486 | 304 | 407·8 | 552 | 86 | 520·0 | 128 |
| 70–75 | 1875 | 356 | 632.9 | 300 | 87 | 967·0 | 153 |
| 75 and over | 1999 | 804 | 1341·0 | 193 | 109 | 1883·0 | 140 |
| Total | 22,743 | 1898 | 278·2 | 22,195 | 847 | 127·1 | 46 |

In this table columns $d_1$ and $d_2$ (the number of deaths) denote the total number of deaths in a given occupation and age group in the three years 1930–2. Columns $l_1$ and $l_2$ (the number of the living) denote the population in a given occupation and age group according to the census of 26 April 1931. It follows that in order to calculate the death rates (columns $m_1$ and $m_2$) $d_1$ and $d_2$ should be divided by the numbers $l_1$ and $l_2$ multiplied by 3.

It turns out that the death rates for waiters (see indices in the last column) are in each age group much higher than the death rates for clergymen, sometimes more than twice as high; but the general death rate for waiters is less than half the general death rate for clergymen. The explanation is simple: the death rate rapidly increases with age and among the clergymen are relatively few young people, and on the other hand there are very few old waiters.

The table was published in England in the *Registrar-General's Decennial Supplement, England and Wales 1931, Part IIa. Occupational mortality* (London, 1938). Such supplements have been published every ten years since the middle of the nineteenth century, and contain a detailed analysis of population movements. Only those subjects are dealt with which require detailed data on population, which can therefore only be studied in conjunction with general population censuses.

The death rates in particular occupations are given in this publication in great detail. For about a hundred occupation groups the number of deaths is given in nine age groups divided into fifty causes of death. For each age group the number of the living is shown according to the census and the death rates are calculated as well as the ratios of the death rates in each age group to the average death rates for the total population in England. Moreover, composite indices are calculated at the fixed age structure both for the total population in each occupation and for each cause of death in a given occupation.

In addition, similar although much less detailed information (also by age and cause of death) is provided for several hundred additional occupations.

Such detailed material is, of course, valuable and may provide a basis for very important conclusions, but a tremendous amount of work must be done before proper generalizations can be arrived at. In using this material, however, one should be on guard against possible errors due to the faulty classification into "classes" within particular occupations.

Several general observations can be made with regard to this material. The differences in the death rates in particular occupations are considerable. Very strong contrasts are noticeable in Table 13.6. (p. 399) containing the data on the clergymen and waiters. The death rate is very high not only among waiters, but in almost all occupations connected with the tavern, restaurant and hotel business. Characteristic of very bad working conditions in the capitalist system is a very high death rate among longshoremen and other outdoor workers with strenuous jobs. Work in tin and copper mines is deadly; the death rate among the tin and copper miners is $3 \cdot 4$ times as large as the average for England. It is all the more striking that the death rate for coal miners does not differ much from the average. Lower than the average are the death rates for white-collar workers, certain "professions", farmers and farm workers.

Returning to the example in Table 13.6 we find that after reducing both occupational groups to the same age structure we obtain for the waiters in relation to the clergymen the index of 166 instead of the directly calculated index of 46. We use the formula

$$\frac{\sum m_2 l_c}{\sum m_1 l_c},$$

(XIII.2)

where $m_2$ and $m_1$ are the death rates for the waiters and the clergymen in different age groups, $I_c$ denotes the population in those age groups on the assumption of the constant "standard" structure. What values have been assumed for $I_c$ will be discussed later (p. 404). The formula is identical with the formulae for aggregate indices discussed above; they are used in the statistics on price, volume, and so on.

A misapprehension that lingered in statistics for dozens of years, and which can occasionally be met with even today, consists in calculating the indices not directly according to formula (XIII.2) but as weighted death rates according to formula

$$\frac{\sum m_1 l_c}{\sum l_c}, \quad \frac{\sum m_2 l_c}{\sum l_c} \text{ etc.} \qquad (XIII.3)$$

The coefficients thus calculated were called "standardized" or even "adjusted" coefficients. This, of course, is muddled thinking, since there is no real meaning behind these coefficients. The numerator does not represent a real number: it is the total number of deaths that would occur if the death rates in each age group were $m_1, m_2$, etc., and the populations in these age groups were as assumed for the standard population.[132] This is obviously fictitious, and the only link with reality is the denominator: the total population is assumed to be standard.

Only indices which can be expressed as quotients of standardized coefficients are real quantities, e.g. for:

$$\frac{\sum m_2 l_c}{\sum l_c} \bigg/ \frac{\sum m_1 l_c}{\sum l_c} = \frac{\sum m_2 l_c}{\sum m_1 l_c} \text{ as in formula (XIII.2)}$$

or, if by $m_c$ we denote the death rate in the standard population,

$$\frac{\sum m_1 l_c}{\sum l_c} \bigg/ \frac{\sum m_c l_c}{\sum l_c} = \frac{\sum m_1 l_c}{\sum m_c l_c}, \qquad (XIII.4)$$

for:

$$\frac{\sum m_2 l_c}{\sum l_c} \bigg/ \frac{\sum m_c l_c}{\sum l_c} = \frac{\sum m_2 l_c}{\sum m_c l_c}, \qquad (XIII.4')$$

i.e. the ratio of the number of deaths in different groups, or in other words, an aggregative composite index in the sense described above. "Standardized" coefficients as such are fictitious quantities, and the result depends upon the structure of the population that we choose as "standard".

Bourgeois statisticians were not too quick to understand the situation. Standardized coefficients were used by Körösi and their theory was developed by the Danish statistician Westergaard in the study: *Die Lehre von der Mortalität und*

---

[132] Of course, the product $ml$ is the number of deaths in each group and $\sum ml$ is the total number of deaths.

*Morbilität* (Jena, 1882).[133] Even after it had been theoretically established that the method of standardization is identical with the method of composite indices, "standardized" coefficients still appeared in various statistical publications, e.g. in recent statistical yearbooks in the Netherlands and New Zealand in comparing death rates at different periods of time.

In the English publications mentioned above the statistics on death rates by occupation now always relate the indices to the average death rate of the whole population, which is denoted by 1000 or 100.

In statistical practice the following cases may be encountered:

(1) Both for population *c* (taken as standard) and for the population groups 1, 2, etc. which are to be compared with it, all three relevant quantities are known: the number living (*l*) the number of deaths (*d*), and the death rate based on them ($m = d/l$), all three with an appropriate division by age.

(2) All three quantities are known only for the standard population *c*; for populations 1, 2, etc. only the age structure (1) and only the total number of deaths is known, without a breakdown by age; it is thus impossible to calculate death rates for age groups of populations 1, 2, etc.

(3) As in point (2), all three quantities are known for population *c*; for population 1, 2, etc., the number of deaths by age is known, but only the total number of living is known, without a breakdown by age; thus, as in point (2), it is impossible to calculate death rates by age groups for populations 1, 2, etc.

The first case is typical and formulae (XIII.4), already derived, apply only to this case. From the formal point of view these formulae are identical with those used for calculating industrial production indices at constant prices. In both of them the base denoted by round figure (100, 1000) can be changed without changing the ratio between the composite indices for population 1, 2, etc. because of course,

for:
$$\frac{\sum m_2 l_c}{\sum m_1 l_c} = \frac{\sum m_2 l_c}{\sum m_c l_c} \bigg/ \frac{\sum m_1 l_c}{\sum m_c l_c} = \frac{\sum m_2 l_c}{\sum m_1 l_c}.$$

In the second case, as in the first, we also convert the death rates which cannot be added into absolute numbers of deaths ($ml = d$) which can, but with different subscripts:

$$\frac{\sum m_1 l_1}{\sum m_c l_1}, \quad \frac{\sum m_2 l_2}{\sum m_c l_2}, \quad \text{etc.} \qquad\qquad \text{(XIII.5)}$$

In the numerators of these fractions $m_1$, $m_2$, etc. are not known and therefore the products $m_1 l_1$, $m_2 l_2$, etc. are not known either, but according to the assumption in point (2) the sums of the products $\sum m_1 l_1$, $\sum m_2 l_2$, etc. (i.e. the total numbers of deaths in populations 1, 2, etc.) are known.

---

[133] *Die Lehre von der Mortalität und Morbilität*, Jena, 1882.

In the third case we can obtain population figures which can be added considering that $l = d/m$, i.e. that the population is equal to the number of death divided by the death rate (because by definition $m = d/l$). Since when $d$ is given a larger population corresponds to a smaller death rate and vice versa, we can write the formula

$$\frac{\sum \dfrac{d_1}{m_c}}{\sum \dfrac{d_1}{m_1}}, \qquad \frac{\sum \dfrac{d_2}{m_c}}{\sum \dfrac{d_2}{m_2}}, \qquad \text{etc.} \qquad \text{(XIII.6)}$$

Here, too, in accordance with the assumption, the particular values of the quotients in the denominator: $d_1/m_1$, $d_2/m_2$ are not known but their sums are.

The formulae obtained in the second and third cases differ from the formula in the first case in that they have no common denominator; the denominator varies from case to case, is different for populations 1 and population 2, etc. This means that we are comparing here the death rates populations 1, 2 etc. with the death rate for the standard population, but we compare them in pairs and not the death rates for population 1, 2, etc. with each other. There is no exchangeable base here, as there was in the first case.

These somewhat complicated conditions for calculating indices will come out more clearly if we present the above aggregate formulae in the form of the weighted averages of individual indices.

We shall show this for population 1. Of course, the situation is analogous for population 2, 3, etc.

The first case is

$$\frac{\sum m_1 l_c}{\sum m_c l_c} = \frac{\sum \dfrac{m_1}{m_c} \times m_c l_c}{\sum m_c l_c} = \frac{\sum \dfrac{m_1}{m_c} \times d_c}{\sum d_c}. \qquad \text{(XIII.7)}$$

The weights are always the products $m_c l_c$, i.e. the absolute numbers of deaths in particular age groups in the standard pupolation.

The second case is

$$\frac{\sum m_1 l_1}{\sum m_c l_1} = \frac{\sum \dfrac{m_1}{m_c} \times m_c l_1}{\sum m_c l_1}. \qquad \text{(XIII.8)}$$

The weights are also the absolute numbers of deaths in age groups, although not in a constant population, but calculated on the assumption that in each age group the death rate is the same as in the standard population, and the number of the living the same as in population 1, 2, etc. The weights are different for all pairs of indices.

This also applies to the third case:

$$\frac{\sum \dfrac{d_1}{m_c}}{\sum \dfrac{d_1}{m_1}} = \frac{\sum \dfrac{m_1}{m_c} \times \dfrac{d_1}{m_1}}{\sum \dfrac{d_1}{m_1}} = \frac{\sum \dfrac{m_1}{m_c} \times l_1}{\Sigma l_1} \qquad \text{(XIII.9)}$$

The weights are the actual numbers of the living in populations 1, 2, etc., different again for all pairs of indices.

For the second case the accepted name is "indirect standardization". The same name should be used (if we agree to accept the word "standardization") with reference to the third case.

It follows from the above that satisfactory results in calculating indices can be obtained only in the first case which, incidentally, is the most common.

We should still consider the problem of choosing the standard population on which the calculation of indices is to be based.

In certain respects the situation here is worse than it is in calculating composite aggregate indices in economics where it is usually possible to determine the logical meaning of the indices before choosing the structure. In calculating composite death rates this possibility does not exist.

But technically the situation for the death rate is easier, because there is a dependence between the rates calculated for different age groups: if in society $A$ the death rate in certain age groups is smaller than in society $B$, it is almost always also smaller in the remaining age groups, and therefore for every reasonably chosen standard the order of the values of composite indices will be the same or almost the same. But the differences between indices may vary because the differences in death rates in different age groups vary.

With respect to the whole population the differences in death rates are greatest at the early ages, smaller for middle age, and least for old age. Therefore, if in the standard chosen the values for early age groups are relatively large, the indices will show a greater spread than when older groups are relatively more numerous in the standard population. But, if we agree that the essential thing is the order of composite indices and not their magnitude or spread, we can regard this reservation as being of little importance.

In practice the structure of the whole population of a country is usually accepted as standard in making comparisons within the country. For international comparisons different standard populations have been suggested, e.g. the average structure of the population of all European countries, or the structure of the population of Sweden. The latter proposal was not very convincing because it was based on the fact that population statistics have existed longest in Sweden. Reasonable results have been obtained with an artificially determined standard in which it is assumed that the population at age 0–5 is 16, at age 5–10 is 15, and so on, or one unit less for each 5-year period. The lowest number 1 is at age 75–80. The death rate above the age of 80 is ignored. The advantage of this standard is the simplicity of calculations since small numbers are used.[134]

We refer here to the first case of the calculation of composite indices. Of course, if we know the death rate for each population 0, 1, 2, etc., in further calculations according to formulae (XIII.4) and (XIII.4') we have only to take into account the age structure of the standard population.

It should be remembered that age groups should not be too large. Generally 5-year age groups suffice for the first 20–30 years of age (perhaps singling out infants less than 1 year old), and then 10-year age groups can be used. Smaller groups increase accuracy, but also increase the amount of computation. In any case the division into 20-year groups suggested at the conference of the International Institute of Statistics in 1895 in Berne is definitely insufficient. In the statistics on death rates by occupations in England only ages from 20 to 65 are considered in calculating indices. The exclusion of elder groups is explained, on the one hand, by the insufficient reliability of the statistical material, and on the other hand, because the people involved have already ceased to work and therefore their death rate is now more affected by general than by occupational factors. This last explanation warrants checking. The working conditions in different occupations significantly affect the general state of health of those retiring. Besides, occupation undoubtedly affects the living conditions after retirement.

In recent English publications, besides the age group 20–65, the age group 35–65 years is sometimes singled out.

It is argued that the age group 20–35 years, being at the beginning of occupational work is still little affected by working conditions and the impact of the latter on the death rate is negligible.

It is obvious that the method of calculating composite indices that we have used for death rates can also be used in other fields when we deal with heterogeneous populations such as those in Table 13.1 and 13.2 (pp. 387 and 389). If these populations can be divided into homogeneous groups, composite indices can also be calculated on the assumption of a common structure for them all. If several factors simultaneously affect the intensity of a given phenomenon, e.g. age, sex social class, or occupation, all of them may be fixed at a certain level and the indices may be calculated from two, three, or more points of view, assuming of a constant structure. It should be remembered, however, that an analysis from the point of view of technique and substance should be made for each case because a purely mechanical application of the method may lead to serious errors.

The methods of "standardization" discussed here differ from the method of calculating aggregate composite indices described in Chapter 12 in so far that

---

[134] This standard was used for comparing death rates of clergymen and waiters (see pp. 400–1).

in the latter we had individual values (e.g. of production, or prices of different products) of which we constructed composite indices by reduction to a common structure (e.g. constant prices or constant quantities of consumed goods) and here we start with heterogeneous populations which must first be split into relatively homogeneous parts, and then transformed to the common structure. The difference is strictly formal, and the method is essentially the same in both cases.

CHAPTER 14

# ELIMINATION TABLES

## 1. GENERAL DESIGN OF ELIMINATION TABLES. LIFE TABLES. RELATIONS BETWEEN BIOMETRIC FUNCTIONS

Composite indices and the method of standardization discussed above do not as a rule enable characterization of a phenomenon in precise terms but give only a general idea about the relationships that exist under certain assuptions. The method that we are to discuss presently is one of the most precise in statistics. We shall first present it using an example from demography—life tables. However, as we shall see, it may also be used in other fields.

Let us imagine a population composed at time $t_x$ of $l_x$ units. With time a certain number of these units is eliminated from the population under the influence of certain factors, so that at time $t_{x+1}$ the number of remaining units is $l_{x+1} < l_x$. A table giving the consecutive values $l_{x+1}$, $l_{x+2}$, etc. diminishing because of elimination, as well as the numbers of units eliminated, the measures expressing the intensity of elimination, and other related quantities, is called an elimination (or outflow) table.

It is also possible that the number of units increases with time, and we then obtain an inflow table designed in the same way as the outflow table. However, they are not as common as the elimination tables.

A more appropriate general name would probably be "outflow and inflow tables", but in this chapter we are primarily concerned with elimination tables.

More complex tables are also encountered when two or more factors affect outflow. We come across such tables, for instance, in studying the number of unmarried persons; their number diminishes with time in consequence of deaths and marriages. The number of married men diminishes in consequence of their deaths, the deaths of their wives (married men become widowers) and divorces, and it increases in consequence of the marriage of the bachelors, widowers and divorced men. By presenting all the changes in the number of married men we would have an example of the combined influence of three factors affecting outflow, and three factors affecting inflow.

A classical example of elimination tables are life tables, sometimes called mortality tables. We shall use this example to discuss the design of elimination tables.

Let us imagine a certain number of persons who begin life simultaneously. In

407

consequence of deaths, a certain proportion of these people is eliminated with time, so that in subsequent age groups their number is smaller. The rate of elimination depends upon the death rate at a given age. After a sufficiently long time the whole generation dies out.

Bringing the number of persons to an arbitrary round figure, say 10,000, we can present the relationship existing here in the following table.

TABLE 14.1. POLISH LIFE TABLE FOR 1931–32[135]

| Age (years) | Number of survivors (order of dying out) | Number of deaths during the year | Probability of death within one year | Probability of surviving one year | Total number of years to be survived | Further life expectation |
|---|---|---|---|---|---|---|
| $x$ | $l_x$ | $d_x$ | $g_x$ | $p_x$ | $T_x$ | $e_x$ |
| 0 | 10,000 | 1552 | 0·1552 | 0·8448 | 497,681 | 49·8 |
| 1 | 8448 | 251 | 0·0297 | 0·9703 | 488,457 | 57·8 |
| 2 | 8197 | 111 | 0·0135 | 0·9865 | 480,135 | 58·6 |
| 3 | 8085 | 67 | 0·0083 | 0·9917 | 471,993 | 58·4 |
| 4 | 8019 | 47 | 0·0058 | 0·9942 | 463,940 | 57·9 |
| 5 | 7972 | 36 | 0·0045 | 0·9955 | 455,945 | 57·2 |
| 10 | 7832 | 20 | 0·0026 | 0·9974 | 416,467 | 53·2 |
| 15 | 7731 | 24 | 0·0031 | 0·9969 | 377,556 | 48·8 |
| 20 | 7581 | 39 | 0·0051 | 0·9949 | 339,246 | 44·7 |
| 25 | 7378 | 41 | 0·0056 | 0·9944 | 301,844 | 40·9 |
| 30 | 7171 | 42 | 0·0058 | 0·9942 | 265,469 | 37·0 |
| 35 | 6954 | 46 | 0·0066 | 0·9934 | 230,150 | 33·1 |
| 40 | 6718 | 50 | 0·0074 | 0·9926 | 195,962 | 29·2 |
| 45 | 6457 | 57 | 0·0088 | 0·9912 | 163,012 | 25·2 |
| 50 | 6141 | 74 | 0·0120 | 0·9880 | 131,486 | 21·4 |
| 55 | 5719 | 102 | 0·0178 | 0·9822 | 101,779 | 17·8 |
| 60 | 5156 | 131 | 0·0254 | 0·9746 | 74,537 | 14·5 |
| 65 | 4419 | 173 | 0·0391 | 0·9609 | 50,515 | 11·4 |
| 70 | 3485 | 208 | 0·0596 | 0·9404 | 30,687 | 8·8 |
| 75 | 2407 | 218 | 0·0907 | 0·9093 | 15,927 | 6·6 |
| 80 | 1356 | 187 | 0·1376 | 0·8624 | 6569 | 4·8 |
| 85 | 556 | 114 | 0·2057 | 0·7943 | 1928 | 3·5 |
| 90 | 140 | 42 | 0·3002 | 0·6998 | 338 | 2·4 |
| 95 | 16 | 7 | 0·4259 | 0·5741 | 26 | 1·7 |
| 100 | — | — | 0·5831 | 0·4169 | — | — |

This Polish life table is based on the 1931 population census and the number of deaths in 1931 and 1932.[136]

All the columns in the table are functionally related, and can be calculated one from another. We shall now discuss their meaning and relationship.

The letters under the heading of each column are internationally recognized notations commonly used in the same sense as here.

---

[135] *Statystyka Polski (Statistics of Poland)*, Series C, No. 91, Warsaw, 1938.
[136] The Polish life table for 1948 will be discussed later.

The first column, $x_1$ list consecutive years of age. Life tables usually are broken down by single years: "abbreviated" tables use longer intervals, as we did for the age of over 5 years (in the original table 1-year intervals are used throughout).

Sometimes shorter periods, such as months, are used for the early period of life. In special tables, e.g. on the elimination of married persons, the table begins from some later age, say 20 years, and the number of those living at that age is denoted by some round figure (10,000 or 100,000). $x$ may take all values from zero to the age at which there are no survivors. This final age is denoted by the Greek letter $\omega$ (omega).

In the second column, $l_x$ the gradual dying out of the generation is shown. It should be understood that the numbers shown here give the number of persons from the generation studied who have survived to the age shown in the first column. In our table, out of 10,000 infants 7972 survived to the age of 5, 3485 survived to 70 years, etc.

The third column, $d_x$, shows the number of the deceased within a given year of life. According to the table 1552 children died in infancy, i.e. before reaching 1 year of age, 251 died between the age of 1 and 2, etc. Of course, the consecutive figures in column 3 are obtained by subtracting consecutive figures in column 2. The relationship between $l_x$ and $d_x$ can be expressed by formula

$$l_x - l_{x+1} = d_x \qquad \text{(XIV.1)}$$

or

$$l_x - d_x = l_{x+1}. \qquad \text{(XIV.2)}$$

It follows from the definition of $l_x$ that these figures form a diminishing sequence: $l_0 > l_1 > l_2 \ldots$ . This sequence ends with zero since it is continued until the last member of a generation dies.

It is easy to see that the total number of the deceased from the first to the last year of life is equal to the number of those beginning life, $l_0$, i.e.

$$\sum_{x=0}^{\infty} d_x = l_0 \qquad \text{(XIV.3)}$$

and generally, the number of the deceased from any age $l_k$ to the end of life equals the number of persons who survived to the age $l_k$:

$$\sum_{x=k}^{\infty} d_x = l_k. \qquad \text{(XIV.4)}$$

Similarly, the number of the deceased from the age $x$ to $x + n$ is equal to the difference between the numbers of the suvivors to the age $l_x$ and the survivors to the age $l_{(x+n)+1}$. For instance, the number of deceased between the ages of 5 and 10 is

$$d_5 + d_6 + d_7 + d_8 + d_9 = l_5 - l_{10}. \qquad \text{(XIV.5)}$$

The fourth column $q_x$ contains the probabilities of death within one year, i.e. the ratio of the deaths within a given year of life to the number of those who survived to this year, that is those who were exposed to death. Thus we write

$$q_x = \frac{d_x}{l_x} \tag{XIV.6}$$

or

$$q_x = \frac{l_x - l_{x+1}}{l_x}. \tag{XIV.7}$$

In our table the probability of death of an infant within one year is expressed by the ratio $1522/10{,}000 = 0 \cdot 1552$, and the probability of death within one year of a child one year old is $251/8448 = 0 \cdot 0297$, etc.

The next column, $p_x$, gives the probability of a person aged $x$ surviving a further year. This is the ratio of the number of persons who have survived to the age of $x + 1$ years to those who survived to the age of $x$. The probability of surviving a year is, of course, 1 minus the probability of death (one can only either die within a given year or survive it), so that

$$q_x + p_x = 1, \tag{XIV.8}$$

just as

$$p_x = 1 - q_x, \tag{XIV.9}$$

$$q_x = 1 - p_x. \tag{XIV.10}$$

$p_x$ can be expressed directly by the ratio of two consecutive values of $l_x$

$$p_x = \frac{l_{x+1}}{l_x} \tag{XIV.11}$$

The probability of death can, of course, be calculated not for one year of age, but for several years, say five, i.e. instead of the ratio $\frac{l_x - l_{x+1}}{l_x}$ the ratio $\frac{l_x - l_{x+5}}{l_x}$ is calculated. Similarly, the probability of surviving not one but several years can be calculated, say, $\frac{l_{x+5}}{l_x}$. According to our table the probability of death within 5 years is expressed for the 10-year-old by the ratio

$$\frac{7832 - 7731}{7832} = \frac{101}{7832} = 0 \cdot 0129,$$

and the probability of surviving 5 years for the 10-year-old is expressed by the ratio

$$\frac{7731}{7832} = 0 \cdot 9871.$$

Of course,

$$0 \cdot 0129 + 0 \cdot 9871 = 1$$

Especially characteristic is the term of the $\dfrac{l_x}{l_0}$ type. It expresses the probability of surviving to the age of $x$. In our example, the probability of reaching the age of 60 is $0 \cdot 5156$ (and therefore the probability of dying before that age is $0 \cdot 4844$). Since in life tables $l_0$ is expressed by a number composed of unity with a certain number of zeros the probability of surviving can be read off directly from the table by treating $l_x$ as a decimal.

The last two columns of the table, $T_x$ and $e_x$, should be discussed in greater detail.

In column $T_x$ the total number of years yet to be lived by the generation is given. In other words, $T_x$ denotes the number of years to be lived by the generation from the age $x$ to the time when the whole generation dies out. Strictly speaking $T_x$ is the integral of the function expressing $l_x$. Since this function cannot be expressed by a mathematical formula, and in any case cannot be expressed simply, this method of calculating cannot be used, and the only method is to calculate by approximation. This can be done in the following way. The table shows that out of 10,000 infants who were born, 8448 survived to the next year of life, and 1552 died within the year. Thus the total number of years lived by the generation within the first year of life is 8448 plus a certain number of years lived by the 1552 children who died within this year. If we assume that the deaths were evenly distributed over the year the children lived on average half a year each and the total number of years lived within the first years is

$$8448 + \frac{1552}{2}, \quad \text{i. e.} \quad 9224,$$

which can also be written as

$$\frac{10{,}000 + 8448}{2} = 9224$$

$\Bigg($10,000 is composed of $8448 + 1552$ and therefore

$$\frac{10{,}000 + 8448}{2} = \frac{8448 + 8448 + 1552}{2},$$

or, as above, $8448 + \dfrac{1552}{2}\Bigg).$

Similarly, we obtain the number of years lived during the second year:

$$8197 + \frac{251}{2} = \frac{8448 + 8197}{2} = 8322 \cdot 5.$$

Using letters and summing up we can write, starting with the age 0

$$T_0 = \frac{l_0 + l_1}{2} + \frac{l_1 + l_2}{2} + \dots + \frac{l_{\omega-2} + l_{\omega-1}}{2} + \frac{l_{\omega-1} + l_\omega}{2}$$

$$= \frac{l_0}{2} + l_1 + l_2 + \dots + l_{\omega-2} + l_{\omega-1}. \qquad \text{(XIV.12)}$$

The last term is $l_{\omega-1}$ because $l_\omega = 0$.

This calculation is analogous to that used for calculating averages in time series (see formula IX.1 p. 274).

We can also start calculating from any other age. We can calculate the number of years lived within a certain interval, from $l_x$ to $l_{x+n}$, say from 10 to 20 years. This is only an approximate calculation. It would be exact if the function $l_x$ was linear within the limits of each year, from 0 to 1, from 1 to 2, etc.—i.e. if the functions were represented by linear segments. Since normally the function $l_x$ represents a smooth curve we overestimate the number of years lived where the curve is convex to the $x$-axis and underestimate where it is concave.

Since the curve is convex within certain ranges and concave others the errors will partly cancel out over the whole range (but not within particular segments). Besides, by calculating in relatively small yearly intervals we avoid lerge errors.[137]

The calculation of $e_x$, the life expectation at each age, is simple. It is the total number of years to be lived divided by the surviving number of the generation, i.e. by $l_x$. Thus $e_x$ is the life expectation of a person aged $x$.

$$e_x = \frac{T_x}{l_x} = \left( \frac{l_x}{2} + l_{x+1} + l_{x+2} \dots + l_{\omega-1} \right) / l_x$$

$$= \frac{1}{2} + (l_{x+1} + l_{x+2} + \dots + l_{\omega-1}) / l_x. \qquad \text{(XIV.13)}$$

This quantity can also be calculated both for infants and for any other age. In the first case it is the average age that can be reached by a person under the prevailing death rate; in the second it is the life expectation at a given age. According to our table an infant lives, on the average, 49·8 years, for a person 30 years old the life expectation is 37 years, etc.

---

[137] The greatest error occurs in the part of the curve within which the slope changes most rapidly, i.e. particularly in the first year. In some life tables the values of $l_x$ within this range are given in monthly intervals which makes possible a more exact calculation of the years lived. According to the German table of 1932–4 the average length of time lived by one person at the age from 0 to 1 is 0·934 years when calculated by months and 0·957 years when calculated by years; the difference is only 0·023 years. Undoubtedly, children who die within the first year of life live on the average for less than half a year (because many die shortly after birth). The same, although to a lesser extent, applies to other years. This can be allowed for in calculations in a variety of ways: it will result in decreasing the life expectation of an infant by several tenths of a year.

The death rate is expressed in the life table by the probability of death. We could also calculate death rates. In contrast to the probability of death the death rate is the ratio of the number of deaths in a given period to the average number living in this period.

In the terminology used for life tables it is the ratio of those who died at age $x$—$(x+n)$ to the number of years lived by the generation from the age $x$ to the age $(x+n)$.

$$m = \frac{l_x - l_{x+n}}{T_x - T_{x+n}}. \qquad \text{(XIV.14)}$$

For yearly intervals, if we assume, as we did in calculating $T_x$, that deaths are evenly distributed in time and if we denote by $m_x$ the death rate at the age from $x$ to $x+1$, we can write

$$m_x = \frac{d_x}{(l_x + l_{x+1})/2} = \frac{2d_x}{l_x + l_{x+1}} \qquad \text{(XIV.15)}$$

or

$$m_x = \frac{d_x}{(l_x + l_x - d_x)/2} = \frac{d_x}{l_x - \dfrac{d_x}{2}}, \qquad \text{(XIV.15')}$$

(because $l_{x+1} = l_x - d_x$).

Dividing both the numerator and the denominator of the fraction on the right-hand side of this equation by $l_x$ we obtain

$$m_x = \frac{q_x}{1 - \dfrac{q_x}{2}}, \qquad \text{(XIV.16)}$$

$\left(\text{because by definition } \dfrac{d_x}{l_x} = q_x\right)$.

From this equation we can calculate the death rate $m_x$ if we know the probability of death.

Solving equation (XIV.16) with respect to $q_x$ we get

$$q_x = \frac{m_x}{1 + \dfrac{m_x}{2}} \qquad \text{(XIV.17)}$$

which enables us to calculate the probability of death on the basis of the death rate. These formulae are not exact since the assumption of an even distribution of death is not correct, but the error is insignificant within small age intervals (see comments on the computation of the number of years lived, on p. 412). If the death rate refers to a long period of time, say 5 years, the time lived should be calculated by single years.[138]

It is easy to prove that for the whole period from age $x$ to the end of life the death rate is the reciprocal of the life expectation of a person aged $x$. As we know, life expectation is the quotient of the number of years to lived by the generation from the age $x$ to the end of life, divided by the number of persons who have survived to the age $x$

$$e_x = \frac{T_x}{l_x}.$$

The reciprocal of this term is

$$\frac{1}{e_x} = \frac{l_x}{T_x}. \qquad (XIV.18)$$

But $l$ is also the sum of death from the age of $x$ to the end of life (because all survivors must die), so that

$$\frac{l_x}{T_x} = \frac{\sum d_x}{T_x}, \qquad (XIV.19)$$

where we add up $d_x$, from the age $x$ to the end of life.

This follows directly from formula (XIV.14) (p. 413) where, if we calculate to the end of life, we have to assume that both $l_{x+n}$ and $T_{x+n}$ equal zero.

In particular the death rate for the whole generation counting from birth is the reciprocal of the life expectation of the infant.

$$m_0 = \frac{1}{e_0}. \qquad (XIV.20)$$

This rate is equivalent to the death rate in a stationary population, i.e. an isolated population with a constant order of dying out, and of numbers of births.

Besides the average length of life, the probable length of life is sometimes calculated. The average length of life is an arithmetic mean, and the probable length of life is a median. It is the age at which the number of survivors is reduced by half. For infants it is the age at which the number of those living is one half of the number of all born. In other words the probable length of life is the age before which one half of the whole generation die and after which the other half die. In our table the probable length of life is 61·2 years.

As an approximation, this age can also be read off from the table on the basis

---

[138] If we know $T_x$ and $T_{x+n}$, i.e. the number of years that the generation still is to live on the average from the age $x$ and from the age $x+n$ to the end, and if we know $l_x$ and $l_{x+n}$, i.e. the number of survivors at the ages of $x$ and $x+n$ we can calculate $m$ directly by formula (XIV.14) p. 413. We can also calculate $T_x$ as the product $l_x e_x$, and $T_{x+n}$ as the product $l_{x+n} \times e_{x+n}$.

of the shape of the function $l_x$; for a more accurate calculation interpolation should be used. In a similar way the probable further length of life can be calculated for a person at any given age. Quartiles—the ages before which one-quarter or three-quarters of the original population will die and the other quartiles — can also be calculated (see p. 209). Quartiles may sometimes be useful supplements to the arithmetic mean of the age (i.e. to the average number of years that remain to be lived).

Since all the columns in the table are functionally related, the calculation of the table from the material available can be started from any function: the order of dying out, the probability of death or the probability of survival. The most frequent starting point in general tables is the probability of death, which is calculated on the basis of appropriate data on the age of the living (on the basis of the census) and on the age of those who died during the period close to the time of the census (on the basis of vital statistics). The complicated details of the calculation cannot be expounded here, similarly as there is no room in a general statistical textbook for a discussion of the calculation of actuarial tables based on the data from life insurance companies.

It should be noted, however, that the probability of death calculated directly from actual data does not have a smooth pattern, either because the number of observations is usually too small, or because there are errors in the data on the living and the dead.

Therefore the probability of death is usually smoothed out before other functions are calculated, so that unwarranted kinks in the pattern of $q_x$ can be removed.[139]

From the practical point of view another question is more important. When life tables are calculated by strict "classical" methods the amount of work involved is tremendous. Besides this until quite recently the death rate fluctuated considerably from year to year, so that it was rightly considered that for a life table to be correct it had to be based on averages over a long period of about ten years or so.

In consequence, tables were rarely calculated and appeared with great delay so that they were usually obsolete by the time they were published. Today much more simplified methods of approximate calculation of life tables are in common use. The tables calculated in this way are perhaps not so precise in detail as the older ones, but they are quite sufficient and present a correct general picture.

Since medical science has reduced the fluctuations in the death rate from year to year, data for several years or sometimes even one year usually suffice for calculating the life table. They can thus now be calculated and published without delay.

---

[139] General information about the calculations involved in smothing out is given in the Appendix at the end of the book.

## 2. ANALYSIS OF BIOMETRIC FUNCTIONS OF THE LIFE TABLE

The life table is the most perfect tool for analysing the death rate in human societies, since it isolates the problem and presents the changes that occur in a society under the influence of only one factor—the death rate.

For this reason measures based on such tables are free from the disadvantages of other measures which were discussed above (see Chapter 13, Coefficients and Probabilities in Heterogeneous Populations, particularly Section 2 of this chapter on the standardization of coefficients).

From among different measures based on the life table, the most synthetic is the measure of life expectation denoted by $e_x$. With only one number it characterizes the final effect to which a given situation leads. In particular $e_0$, i.e. the life expectation of an infant, gives the average age that can be reached under the given circumstances. This measure is fully correct since it is free from disturbances caused by secondary factors.

However, this measure by itself does not suffice since the same life expectation can be obtained under different circumstances. If out of 10,000 infants 100 die every year, the whole generation will die out after 100 years and the life expectation will be 50 years. But the same life expectation of 50 years would be obtained if nobody died before the age of 50 and then all died at one time, or of all those born half died immediately after birth and the other half lived exactly 100 years. Even though such extreme cases do not occur in actual life, somewhat similar situations may arise, and therefore life expectation as a measure by itself does not suffice, and other functions of the life table should also be taken into consideration, particularly the order of dying out, the pattern of the probability of death and the number of deaths.

A short analysis of these functions will be made on the basis of Fig 14.1, 2 and 3. The graphs present the pattern of the three functions mentioned above: the probability of death, the order of dying out, and the number of deaths by age for four countries. These functions represent the full range of death rates known today: from an extremely high death rate in India in 1901–11 to the very low death rate in the Netherlands in 1947–49. The two remaining countries, Bohemia and Moravia (an old table from 1899–1902) and Poland (1948), occupy intermediate positions.

In this cotext Poland's position appears very good although we know that there is much to be done before we reach the level made possible by medical science.

All the graphs relate to death rates among women, but this does not matter, since death rates of men have a similar pattern, with the difference that rates are somewhat higher than for women.

The average length of life of a female infant in the four countries considered shows a very large range: 23·3 years in India, 40·3 in Bohemia and Moravia,

61·5 in Poland, and as high as 71·5 in the Netherlands. The spread between the functions shown in the graphs is much wider.

Let us begin with the probability of death (Fig. 14.1). The general pattern is similar in all curves: a relatively very high probability of death in infancy, a very rapidly declining probability in the next dozen years or so with a distinct minimum between the ages of 10 and 15, and then a probability that increases af first slowly and then more rapidly. In the last year of life the probability of death is, of course, unity, because by then everybody will die.

The probability of death in the neighbourhood of the minimum (age 10–15) is smaller than in infancy: in India about one-twentieth, in Poland one-eighty-fifth, in the Netherlands less than one seventieth. The highest probabilities of death are in India, the lowest in the Netherlands. The probabilities of death in India are greater than those in the Netherlands—over ten times as great in infancy, about thirty and more in childhood (from 1 to 10 years). Later the differences gradually diminish, but even at the most advanced age shown in the diagram the death rate in India is $2\frac{1}{2}$ times that in the Netherlands.

A quite different picture is displayed by the order of dying out in the four

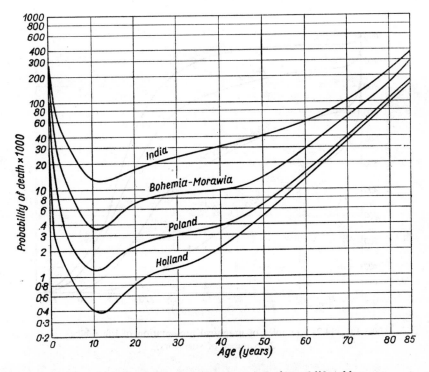

FIG. 14.1. Examples of graphical presentation of life tables.
1. Probability of death. Logarithmic scales.

countries studied (Fig 14.2) but the general similarity of the patterns is also very distinct. The similarity consists in: (1) a rapid decline in the number of the living after birth, (2) a slow decline over a longer or shorter period in the following years, (3) an increasingly rapid decline afterwards, (4) during the last period of life the rate of decline slows down again and approaches the horizontal axis almost asymptotically. India is an exception in so far as the curve representing the order of dying out is almost straight over a long segment.

The pattern of the order of dying out as reflected by the first three lines is characteristic of human societies at the stage of civilization. This is not the only possible pattern for living organisms. We shall return to this subject later.

The horizontal line in the middle of the diagram enables us to read off approximately the median age. The probable length of life—the median—is in India about 12·3 years, in Bohemia and Moravia about 49·9 years; in Poland about 71·9 years, and in the Netherlands about 76·1 years.[140]

These figures differ considerably from the figures expressing the average length of life of an infant, and their spread is much wider. Even more striking is that in India almost 30 per cent of the infants die before their first birthday whereas in the Netherlands 90 per cent live to the age of 50.

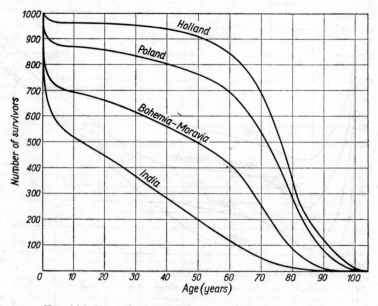

FIG. 14.2. Examples of graphical presentation of life tables.
2. Number of survivors.

---

[140] These figures are not quite exact since they have been interpolated on the basis of 5-year age groups.

The number of the deceased during one year can be obtained as the product of the number of survivors by the probability of death. It follows that as the probability of death increases the number of deaths increases as long as the number of survivors decreases slowly: when the decline in the number of survivors is large the number of deaths during the year declines: in other words, the curve representing the number of deaths should have a maximum. It will occur, of course, within the segment of age in which the slope of curve expressing the order of dying out is the steepest.

This situation is shown in Fig 14.3. The three curves relating to Bohemia–Moravia, Poland and the Netherlands have clearly marked maxima toward the end of life, and the lower the death rate in the country the more clearly marked is the maximum, and the further it is shifted toward old age. In India a maximum also appears, but it is so weak that it is hardly visible in the graph; it occurs at a much earlier age, below 40. The number of deaths in very early years of life is large, but in the Netherlands the number of deaths in the first year of life is smaller than the number of deaths during any one year between the ages of 70 and 85. In other countries the number of deaths in infancy is so large that it goes beyond the diagram: in India this is also true of the age 1–2.

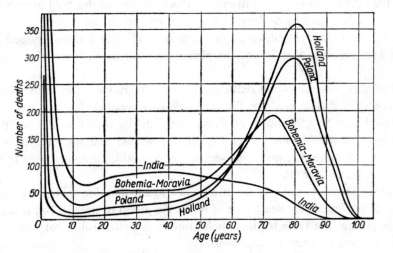

FIG. 14.3. Examples of graphical presentation of life tables.
3. Number of deaths in one year.

Apart from India the distribution of deaths by age is typical of human societies at this stage of civilization.

On the basis of the analysis of life tables and medical research, deaths by basic causes can be divided into three categories: (1) Deaths due to causes which have their origin in the pre-natal period. These deaths usually occur in the earliest infancy, in the first year, or even in the first few weeks. (2) Deaths due to the normal aging process of the human organism. They are reflected in the maxima in Fig. 14.3. From a clearly marked maximum there are greater or smaller random deviations in both directions. (3) A great number of deaths from early infancy to old age. They are what might be called premature deaths caused by general living conditions in the society, primarily by contagious diseases. A very large proportion of these premature deaths can be eliminated by the provision of proper living and working conditions and by the development of medical science.

The age at which deaths from old age are most common can be considered as the normal limit of human life. However, this is not a mode of the death series, since the curve of premature deaths is superimposed on the curve of normal deaths, which results in shifting the maximum to the left, toward the earlier years. Therefore the fact that the maximum moves further to the right cannot be considered as a direct proof that within the period to which the data refer the normal limit of human life has been extended. It should be stated that life tables give no clear indication of this effect and the extension of the average length of life $e_0$ usually means a decline in the number of premature deaths.

This does not preclude the possibility of extending the normal limit of human life in the future, but so far no dramatic improvements in this field are noticeable.

From this short and by no means exhaustive analysis it can be seen how valuable life tables are in studying demographic relations. The are a necessary and precise tool of analysis since they isolate the phenomenon of death from other disturbing influence.

Besides this, life tables are indispensable in actuarial science, especially in life insurance studies. The need for life tables was so pressing that the first traces of concepts similar to "the order of dying out" can be found in Roman times in the writings of the famous lawyer Ulpian (the second and third centuries A.D.). In more recent times the first, and very imperfect, tables are attributed to Graunt (1662) and Halley (1693).

To avoid misunderstanding we stress once again that life tables are and ideal method of presenting the death rate of a specific group of people. But it is obvious that one general life table for the whole country is quite insufficient, since it offers only an average of diverse components.

In this case the population should first be divided into classes, and not one but several different types of life tables should be calculated. At the present stage of development of statistics in capitalistic countries this is an almost unmanageable task. However, it should be undertaken by Marxist studies.

A penetrating analysis, even of general life tables in their geographical and historical differentiation, may lead to valuable results. But this belongs to the field of demography and not to statistics.

## 3. ELIMINATION TABLES FOR LOWER ORGANISMS AND FOR TECHNICAL EQUIPMENT

The pattern of dying out represented by the functions $q_x, l_x$ and $d_x$, characteristic of human societies at the present stage of civilization, differs from the pattern of dying out for other living beings. American research workers have calculated a number of elimination tables for lower organisms: certain insects, mice, etc. From the data provided by R. Pearl[141] it appears that for living organisms of a lower order the order of dying out of the kind known for human beings does not occur at all. For many of them death soon after birth is a very rare occurrence; only after some time does the curve of survivors begin to decline, at first slowly, then more rapidly, and then slowly again. For some lower organisms the pattern of dying out is uniform in time so that the number of survivors is represented by an almost straight line. In one case the decline in the number of the living was at first a very rapid decrease, then rapid and uniform i.e. from a certain age on it was represented by an almost straight line.

In the United States many elimination tables have been calculated for technical equipment[142]—telephone installations, eletric bulbs, railway track sleepers, railway wagons, passenger wagons, etc. In all there are sixty-five tables in this publication.

On the basis of these tables we can study all kinds of "order of elimination". In some cases elimination starts amlost at once and is fairly uniform throughout, to the end of the life of the object; the order of elimination curve is in such cases almost a straight line and runs diagonally from upper left to lower right. This kind of order of elimination is observed, for instance, in old-fashioned motor cars. It can be due to the elimination being caused by random factors, e.g. mechanical defects, accidents, etc. which occur uniformly from beginning to end. Modern cars and many other objects are represented by a different curve which declines slowly at first, then bends downward, the steepest slope being in the middle part (the greatest rate of elimination) whence it slowly declines again (less repid elimination).

In other cases the curve may first be horizontal for quite a long time, and then drop suddenly and very rapidly. This happens with railway track sleepers, which may be in order for years and then begin to deteriorate rapidly, and which must all be replaced within a short period of time. To these different types of the order of elimination correspond different distributions of the units being eliminated. If the curve of the order of elimination approximates a straight line the number of units eliminated is almost the same throughout the period of use of the object. In other cases the number of eliminated units may be distributed symmetrically with

---

[141] R. Pearl: *Introduction to Medical Biometry and Statistics*, Philadelphia and London, 1941, 3rd edition, p. 239 *et seq.*

[142] R. Winfrey and E. B. Kurtz: *Life Characteristic of Physical Property*, Ames, Iowa, 1931.

a maximum in the middle. When the line resembles the case of the railway sleepers, the concentration of eliminated units occurs toward the end of the period of use.

In addition to these typical curves there are other intermediate types, or indistinct curves. It is worth noting that none of these curves resembles the order of dying out for man.

Similar tables may be used for representing elimination for many other objects, buildings, etc.

Elimination tables for technical equipment may be used as a basis of calculating amortization or as a starting point for forecasting the time and rate of replacement of worn out units by new ones, which is of particularly great importance in a planned economy.

# PART IV

# *Correlation Analysis*

# CHAPTER 15

# THE CORRELATION COEFFICIENT
# AND REGRESSION LINES

## 1. THE PROBLEM STATED

In our considerations of time series thus far we have discussed the structure of the population from the point of view of each of its characteristics separately. The problem with which we shall now deal is whether these characteristics are related to each other, and if so, how and by what means.

TABLE 15.1. YIELDS IN QUINTALS PER HECTARE IN POLAND
in 1948[143]

| Province | Wheat | Oats |
|---|---|---|
| 1. Rzeszów | 7·7 | 10·7(1) |
| 2. Lublin | 8·7 | 11·4(2) |
| 3. Białystok | 9·1 | 11·7(3) |
| 4. Kielce | 9·9 | 12·5(4) |
| 5. Kraków | 10·5 | 13·3(6) |
| 6. Warsaw | 10·6 | 13·6(7) |
| 7. Szczecin | 11·2 | 12·8(5) |
| 8. Łódź | 11·8 | 14·4(9) |
| 9. Olsztyn | 12·3 | 13·8(8) |
| 10. Wrocław | 13·3 | 14·9(10) |
| 11. Gdańsk | 14·0 | 15·2(11) |
| 12. Pomorze | 14·4 | 15·5(12) |
| 13,5. Silesia | 14·7 | 15·7(13) |
| 13,5. Poznań | 14·7 | 16·0(14) |

We are analysing here two characteristics of each province: the yield of wheat and the yield of oats.

The provinces are ordered and numbered according to increasing yields of wheat. In the last column the yields of oats are given; the figures in brackets denote the order of the provinces according to increasing yields of oats.[144]

---

[143] *Statistical Yearbook,* 1949, p. 64.

[144] The provinces of Silesia and Poznań have the same yields of wheat; they have the same position number—the arithmetic mean between the numbers 13 and 14. The same values of characteristics and therefore the same position numbers appear nuch more frequently in Table 15.2 (p. 426).

We can see that the orderings agree very well. The order of the yields of oats in comparison with the yields of wheat is transposed only for the provinces of Szczecin, Kraków and Warsaw, and also for the provinces of Olsztyn and Łódź. Apart from these five provinces the order is the same. This fact—the consistency of the orders of the provinces in the yields of wheat and oats—is an indication that there is a relation between the yields of these two crops, namely that in general higher yields of oats correspond to higher yields of wheat. This is to be expected because the yields of all crops depend upon soil, climate and the level of agricultural technique. A change of order in some cases may indicate that for oats the requirements for soil or climate are different than those for wheat or it may indicate the existence of special conditions which affect the yields of oats and wheat differently.

When the order of the second characteristic is the reverse of the order of the first we also have a relationship: to increasing values of the first characteristic correspond decreasing values of the second, and vice versa.

The picture obtained in the second example (Table 15.2) on average annual barometric pressures and average annual temperatures in Warsaw during the 5-year period from 1923 to 1937 is less clear. The years are arranged in order, from the lowest to the highest barometric pressure. The numbers denote, as before, the order of years according to each characteristics. If the same pressure or the same temperature occurred in different years, these years were given the same number. In this case the numbers according to the temperature (the last column) do not appear to display a distinct order. In any case no direct relationship is apparent between the order of years according to the barometric pressure and the order

TABLE 15.2. AVERAGE ANNUAL BAROMETRIC PRESSURE AND AVERAGE
ANNUAL TEMPERATURES IN WARSAW IN 1923–37

| Years | Pressure | | Temperature | |
|-------|----------|-------|-------------|-------|
|       | (mm)     | order | degrees centigrade | order |
| 1925 | 752·5 | 1 | 8·5 | 11 |
| 1923 | 752·7 | 2 | 7·8 | 6·5 |
| 1935 | 752·8 | 3 | 8·0 | 8 |
| 1936 | 752·9 | 4 | 8·7 | 12·5 |
| 1930 | 753·0 | 5 | 8·7 | 12·5 |
| 1926 |       | 7 | 8·4 | 9·5 |
| 1931 | 753·2 | 7 | 7·5 | 4 |
| 1937 |       | 7 | 8·8 | 14 |
| 1927 | 753·5 | 9 | 7·6 | 5 |
| 1928 | 753·9 | 10 | 7·8 | 6·5 |
| 1934 | 754·0 | 11 | 9·5 | 15 |
| 1933 | 754·2 | 12 | 6·6 | 1·5 |
| 1924 | 754·4 | 13 | 6·9 | 3 |
| 1932 | 754·8 | 14 | 8·4 | 9·5 |
| 1929 | 755·4 | 15 | 6·6 | 1·5 |

according to the temperature. We can see whether the picture becomes clearer if we combine particular years into groups according to the order of the barometric pressure, and calculate for each of these groups average ordinal numbers of years according to temperature.

In combining into groups we must remember that certain years have the same barometric pressure, and therefore the same ordinal number. Such years cannot be included in different groups because this would be completely arbitrary, and average numbers according to the temperature would be different depending upon the method of divisions into groups according to the pressure. Let us divide all the years into four groups.

It now becomes clear that lower temperatures generally correspond to higher pressures, although, as can be seen from Table 15.2 there are substantial deviations from this general rule.

TABLE 15.3. AVERAGE ANNUAL BAROMETRIC PRESSURE
AND AVERAGE ANNUAL TEMPERATURES IN WARSAW
Groups of years

| Position by barometric pressure | Average position by temperature |
|---|---|
| 1–5 | 10·1 |
| 7 (three years) | 9·17 |
| 9–12 | 7 |
| 13–15 | 4·67 |

Generalizing, we can say that when the number of units in a population is small, the existence of non-existence of a relationship between characteristics can be established by arranging the observations according to increasing or decreasing values of one characteristic, and writing down numbers representing the positions of the observations according to the second characteristic beside those representing the first. If the correlation is strong this will be immediately and clearly visible; if it is weaker we can form groups of neighbouring values of the first characteristic (and it should be remembered that the observations with the same position must not be included in different groups), and calculate the average of the position numbers of the second characteristic. For technical reasons this cannot be done when the population is large. The question remains open whether the conclusion concerning the existence or non-existence of correlation is sufficiently proved when it is weakly marked. Another open question is the intensity of the correlation.

The observations could also be arranged as a frequency distribution according to the first characteristic, and the average values of the second characteristic could be calculated for each class of the series. In this case, if we confine ourselves to four classes, and use more or less even class intervals we obtain the result shown in Table 15.4.

28*

TABLE 15.4. AVERAGE ANNUAL BAROMETRIC PRESSURE
AND AVERAGE ANNUAL TEMPERATURES IN WARSAW
Grouped according to barometric pressure

| Barometric pressure (mm) | Average temperature (centigrade) |
|---|---|
| 753·0 and less (1–5) | 8·34 |
| 753·2 and 753·5 (7–9) | 8·075 |
| 753·9–754·4 (10–13) | 7·7 |
| 754·8 and 755·4 (14 and 15) | 7·5 |

ᵃ Numbers in brackets correspond to the order according to increasing barometric pressure (see Table 15.2 p. 426)

A clear and steady, although small, decline in the temperature with increasing barometric pressure is visible. However, this is an essentially different approach to the problem. We shall discuss it by means of other examples with a greater number of observations, and we shall also explain certain basic notions on statistical dependence.

## 2. THE NOTION OF CORRELATION AND REGRESSION

The example that we are now going to discuss relates to the yields per hectare of two crops—oats and barley—not in one province but the average in all 241 counties of Poland in 1928–37.[145] The data are plotted in the system of co-ordinates used in Table 15.1, with the yields of oats as abscissae, and the yields of barley as ordinates. The arrangement of the points is very characteristic: they are located close to the diagonal from the lower left-hand corner, which, corresponds to low yields of both crops, to the upper right-hand corner, which corresponds to high yields per hectare of both oats and barley. In the areas of the diagram corresponding to low oat yields and high barley yields or high oat yields and low barley yields there are no points at all. Although the points are located around the diagonal, they are not on one line—they are scattered around one line. Different yields of one crop may correspond to one yield of the other. Thus there are three counties in which the yield of oats per hectare was 6·4 quintals; in one of these counties the yield of barley was 5·5, and in another 6·0, and in the third 7·0 quintals per hectare. But the dispersion of the yields of barley for specific yields of oats is much smaller than the dispersion of the yields of barley itself. The yields of barley fluctuate within the limits 5·5–20·0 quintals per hectare. Thus the range is 20·0 − 5·5 = 14·5 quintals, whereas the yields of barley, for yields of oats amounting to, say, 13·8 quintals, per hectare, fluctuate only between 12·0 and 14·8

[145] The example is from before the war since after it no data were published on yields by counties. Besides, we are dealing here with averages for the 10-year period owing to which we can study strong relationships, not disturbed by accidental factors in each particular year.

quintals, and the range is $14 \cdot 8 - 12 \cdot 0 = 2 \cdot 8$ quintals. The same is true of the dispersion of the yields of oats for specific yields of barley. If we calculated average yields of barley for specific yields of oats, or vice versa, we would find that average yield of one crop distinctly increases with increasing yield of the other.

We have thus arrived at a basic definition of correlation in contrast to a functional relationship. We speak of a functional relationship when to specific values of one magnitude correspond definite values of another magnitude. We speak of correlation when to specific values of one magnitude correspond certain average values of another magnitude.

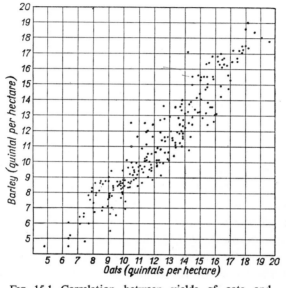

FIG. 15.1. Correlation between yields of oats and barley.

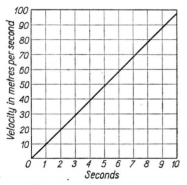

FIG. 15.2. Velocity of body falling in a vacuum.

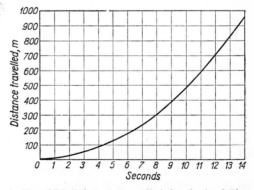

FIG. 15.3. Distance travelled by body falling in a vacuum.

If in physics we consider, say, the formula expressing the velocity of a body falling in a vacuum in relation to time:

$$v = gt,$$

then this velocity after the lapse of a definite number of seconds, for a given $g$, will have a strictly defined value. In this formula $t$ stands for the number of seconds, $g$ is the gravitational acceleration which in our latitude is $9 \cdot 81$ m per second.

From Fig. 15.2 we read off, for instance, that the velocity after 3 sec of falling is approximately $29 \cdot 4$ m per sec and after 10 sec it is $98 \cdot 1$ m per sec.

The distance travelled by a body falling in a vacuum in relation to time is expressed by the formula

$$h = \frac{gt^2}{2}$$

where $g$, as before, is the gravitational acceleration, $t$ is the time of fall in seconds.

From Fig. 15.3 we can see that within the first second the body travels the distance of $4 \cdot 9$ m, in 3 sec, $44 \cdot 1$ m, and in 14 sec, 961 m.

The function in this case is represented by a curve, but here also the distance travelled is strictly determined by the time of fall of a body.

In case of a correlation we cannot determine what specific value of $y$ will correspond to a given value of $x$, since the values of $y$ fluctuate within certain limits; we can only tell what average value of $y$ corresponds to a given value of $x$.

Of course, in statistical practice correlation is not presented in the form of points plotted in a coordinate system, but in the form of a numerical table with horizontal rows giving the values of one characteristic arranged in classes and vertical columns the values of the other characteristic. At the intersections of appropriate columns we write the number of observations in which a given combination of characteristics appears. Such tables are called contingency tables.

The example presented in the form of points in Fig. 15.1 (p. 429) is shown here in the form of a numerical table (Table 15.5 p. 431).

In this table the totals at the bottom are the frequencies of the frequency distribution of oat yields in particular counties in Poland, and the totals on the right-hand side are the frequencies of the frequency distribution of barley yields. Both series give a characteristic picture of heterogeneous populations in which there are two or three maxima, or at least the high frequencies are spread over a longer range than could be expected in a normal frequency distribution. This is a consequence of differences in the quality of soil, and in the level of agricultural technique in different parts of the country.

The general nature of correlation between the two characteristics—the yields of the two crops in individual counties—is just as visible in the table as in the point diagram. Low yields of barley correspond to low yields of oats, and vice versa;

TABLE 15.5. CORRELATION BETWEEN YIELDS OF BARLEY AND OATS IN QUINTALS PER HECTARE

Yields by counties in 1928–37[146]

| Barley (y). Yield in quintals per hectare | Oat (x). Yield in quintals per hectare | | | | | | | | | | | | | | | | Total number of counties |
|---|---|---|---|---|---|---|---|---|---|---|---|---|---|---|---|---|---|
| | 4–4·9 | 5–5·9 | 6–6·9 | 7–7·9 | 8–8·9 | 9–9·9 | 10–10·9 | 11–11·9 | 12–12·9 | 13–13·9 | 14–14·9 | 15–15·9 | 16–16·9 | 17–17·9 | 18–18·9 | 19–19·9 | |
| | Number of counties | | | | | | | | | | | | | | | | |
| 20–20·9 | | | | | | | | | | | | | | | 1 | | 1 |
| 19–19·9 | | | | | | | | | | | | | | | 2 | 1 | 3 |
| 18–18·9 | | | | | | | | | | | 1 | | 1 | 5 | 2 | 1 | 10 |
| 17–17·9 | | | | | | | | | | | | 3 | 8 | 3 | | | 14 |
| 16–16·9 | | | | | | | | | | | 3 | 7 | 2 | 1 | | | 13 |
| 15–15·9 | | | | | | | | | | | 1 | 4 | 3 | | | | 8 |
| 14–14·9 | | | | | | | | | 1 | 6 | 6 | 5 | 2 | | | | 20 |
| 13–13·9 | | | | | | | 1 | 4 | 2 | 6 | 4 | 3 | | | | | 20 |
| 12–12·9 | | | | | | | 2 | 3 | 6 | 13 | 1 | | | | | | 25 |
| 11–11·9 | | | | | | | 1 | 11 | 9 | 3 | 1 | | | | | | 25 |
| 10–10·9 | | | | | | 3 | 9 | 11 | 5 | | | | | | | | 28 |
| 9–9·9 | | | | 2 | 6 | 16 | 14 | 3 | | | | | | | | | 41 |
| 8–8·9 | | | | 2 | 5 | 9 | 1 | | | | | | | | | | 17 |
| 7–7·9 | | | 1 | 4 | 2 | 2 | 1 | | | | | | | | | | 10 |
| 6–6·9 | | | 2 | 1 | | 1 | | | | | | | | | | | 4 |
| 5–5·9 | 1 | | 1 | | | | | | | | | | | | | | 2 |
| *Total number of counties* | *1* | *0* | *4* | *9* | *13* | *31* | *29* | *32* | *23* | *28* | *17* | *22* | *16* | *9* | *5* | *2* | *241* |

medium yields of barley correspond to medium yields of oats, high yields of barley to high yields of oat. However, for specific values of the yields of one crop the yields of the other do not assume strictly defined values but fluctuate within limits. Sometimes these fluctuations are considerable; for instance, for oat yields of 10–10·9 quintals per hectare the yields of barley fluctuate between 7 and 13·9 quintals per hectare, for barley yields of 13–13·9 quintals per hectare the yields of oats are 10–15·9 quintals per hectare. However, the dispersion in each column or row is much smaller than the general spread of the yields per hectare of oats or barley: for instance, the standard deviation of the barley yields (the frequencies of the frequency distribution on the right-hand side of the table) is 3·26 quintals and the standard deviation of the barley yields in the 17 counties in which the yield of oats is 14–14·9 quintals per hectare is only 1·64 quintals (judging by eye

---

[146] Statystyka rolnicza 1937 (Agricultural Statistics), *Statystyka Polski,* No. 92, Series C, Warsaw 1938, pp. 119–21.

the dispersion of the yields of barley is greatest in this column). In the 32 counties in which the oat yield is 11–11·9 quintals per hectare the standard deviation of the barley yield is even smaller—only 1·13 quintals. A similar picture is obtained when we analyse the dispersion of the yield of oats (in the horizontal row) for specific yields of barley.

The next example pertains to the correlation between the yields per hectare of potatoes and wheat. The figure and the table (p. 432 and p. 433) are based on the same source and are arranged in the same way as Fig. 15.1 and Table 15.5.

The scatter pattern of the points in the figure and of the data in the table is similar to that of the oat and barley yields: small values of one crop correspond to small values of the other and large values of one to large values of the other; the opposite corners corresponding to high yields of potatoes for low yields of wheat and low yields of potatoes for high yields of wheat are empty. In spite of this the picture does differ from the previous one; the points are scattered more chaotically, and over a larger area. Taking at random any column in which the range of variations of the wheat yields is neither too large nor too small, e.g. the column corresponding to potato yields of 135–139 quintals per hectare, we obtain

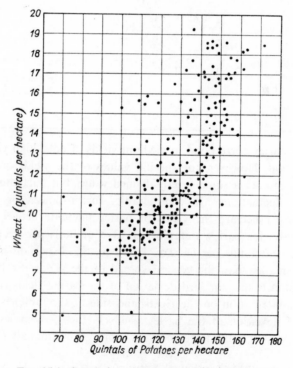

Fig. 15.4. Correlation between yields of potatoes and wheat.

TABLE 15.6. CORRELATION BETWEEN YIELDS OF POTATOES AND WHEAT IN QUINTALS PER HECTARE YIELDS IN PARTICULAR COUNTIES IN 1928-37

| Wheat (y) yields (quintals per hectare) | Potatoes (x). Yields in quintals per hectare — Number of counties | | | | | | | | | | | | | | | | | | | | | Total number of counties |
|---|---|---|---|---|---|---|---|---|---|---|---|---|---|---|---|---|---|---|---|---|---|---|
| | 160-164 | 155-159 | 150-154 | 145-149 | 140-144 | 135-139 | 130-134 | 125-129 | 120-124 | 115-119 | 110-114 | 105-109 | 100-104 | 95-99 | 90-94 | 85-89 | 80-84 | 75-79 | 70-74 | 65-69 | 60-64 | |
| 19-19.9 | | | | | | | | 1 | | | | | | | | | | | | | | 1 |
| 18-18.9 | 1 | | 2 | | 1 | 4 | 2 | | | | | | | | | | | | | | | 10 |
| 17-17.9 | | | 1 | 3 | 1 | 2 | 1 | 2 | 1 | | | | | | | | | | | | | 11 |
| 16-16.9 | | | | 1 | 1 | 3 | 3 | 1 | | 1 | | | | | 1 | | | 2 | | | | 10 |
| 15-15.9 | | | | | 4 | 3 | 2 | 2 | 1 | | | 1 | 2 | 1 | | | | | | | | 17 |
| 14-14.9 | | | | 2 | 4 | 4 | 1 | | 2 | | | | | | | | | | | | | 13 |
| 13-13.9 | | | | | 2 | 2 | 6 | 1 | 2 | 2 | 3 | 1 | 1 | 1 | | | | | | | | 20 |
| 12-12.9 | | | | | | 1 | 4 | 1 | 4 | 2 | 2 | 2 | 2 | 2 | 1 | | | | | | | 17 |
| 11-11.9 | | | | | | 1 | 4 | 3 | 5 | 2 | 4 | 6 | 4 | 1 | 2 | | | | | | | 25 |
| 10-10.9 | | | | | 1 | | 1 | 6 | 5 | 9 | 3 | 5 | 3 | 4 | 6 | 2 | | | | | 1 | 43 |
| 9-9.9 | | | | | | | | 1 | 1 | 6 | 7 | 2 | 5 | 6 | 2 | 2 | 1 | | 1 | | | 33 |
| 8-8.9 | | | | | | | | | | 2 | | 2 | 1 | 6 | | | 1 | | | 2 | | 26 |
| 7-7.9 | | | 1 | | | | | | | | | | | 2 | | | 2 | 2 | | | | 9 |
| 6-6.9 | | | | | | | | | | | | | | | | | | | | | | 4 |
| 5-5.9 | | | | | | | | | | | | | | 1 | | | | | | | | 1 |
| 4-4.9 | | | | | | | | | | | | | | | | | | | | | 1 | 1 |
| Total number of counties | 2 | 2 | 1 | 4 | 4 | 12 | 24 | 18 | 19 | 19 | 24 | 21 | 18 | 24 | 20 | 14 | 6 | 4 | 0 | 1 | | 241 |

the standard deviation of 2·04 quintals per hectare where the general standard deviation of the yield of wheat is 3·14 quintals, whereas before, in the apparently least favourable case, the standard deviation of the barley yields was only 1·64 quintals, and the general standard deviation of the barley yields was 3·37 quintals. Also the horizontal dispersion of the potato yields is large for given yields of wheat.

We reach the same conclusions about Fig. 15.4. Here the points are also located approximately along the diagonal, but are more widely scattered than in the case of oats and barley.

In the third example, the distribution of the data is still different. This example is from meteorology, and relates to the correlation between average temperatures of two months of the year—July and September. The question is which temperature in the month of September corresponds to a given temperature in July of the same year? The observations pertain to the temperatures in 1826–1910 in Warsaw.[147] (See Table 15.7).

TABLE 15.7. CORRELATION BETWEEN AVERAGE TEMPERATURES IN JULY AND SEPTEMBER IN WARSAW IN 1826–1910

| September (y). Average monthly temperature, centigrade | July (x). Average monthly temperature, centigrade | | | | | | | | Total number years of |
|---|---|---|---|---|---|---|---|---|---|
| | 14–14·9 | 15–15·9 | 16–16·9 | 17–17·9 | 18–18·9 | 19–19·9 | 20–20·9 | 21–21·9 | |
| | Number of years | | | | | | | | |
| 16–16·9 | | | 1 | 1 | | | 1 | | 3 |
| 15–15·9 | | | 3 | 2 | | | 3 | | 8 |
| 14–14·9 | | 1 | 1 | 2 | 6 | 6 | | 1 | 17 |
| 13–13·9 | | | 3 | 3 | 7 | 7 | 1 | 1 | 22 |
| 12–12·9 | | 2 | 5 | 2 | 7 | 6 | 2 | 1 | 25 |
| 11–11·9 | 1 | | | 1 | 3 | 1 | 1 | | 7 |
| 10–10·9 | | | | | 2 | | 1 | | 3 |
| *Total number of years* | 1 | 3 | 13 | 11 | 25 | 20 | 9 | 3 | 85 |

The figures are scattered chaotically all over the table. For relatively low temperatures in July (say 16–16·9°C) there occur relatively very high temperatures in September, and for very high temperatures in July (e.g. 20–20·9°) temperatures in September may be very high or very low. The dispersion in particular columns and rows is—judging by eye—probably somewhat smaller than the general dispers-

---

[147] The two months considered here are not adjacent since if they were an accidental correlation might appear due to the fact that cold and hot spells usually last a long time and may spread from one adjoining month to another. Our problem is to find out whether high temperatures in one month correspond to high temperatures in another month of the same year, or vice versa, or whether there is no correlation.

ion in temperatures in September and July, but it is considerable.[148] It is hard to judge by eye whether there is any correlation between the temperatures in the two months, but we might be inclined to think that there is none.

The three tables shown here give a clear idea of what the essence of correlation is. They also enable us to estimate roughly whether correlation is strong (Table 15.5) or weak (Table 15.6), or whether there is no correlation at all (Table 15.7). Now we shall have to find statistical yardsticks for measuring the intensity and the nature of this relationship.

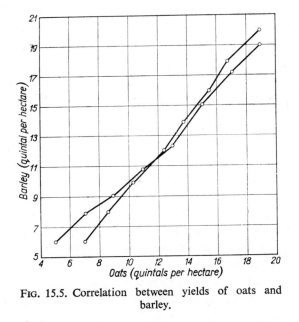

FIG. 15.5. Correlation between yields of oats and barley.

The simplest approach is to calculate the average values of one characteristic corresponding to specific values of the other. The corresponding data are shown[149] in Fig. 15.5, 6 and 7.

Before we start analysing the diagrams we shall make a few general comments on the shape of the curve in a functional relationship and in correlation.

If there is a functional relationship between two quantities the shape of the

---

[148] In some cases the dispersion of temperatures in September corresponding to specific temperatures in July is equal to or greater than the general dispersion of temperatures in September. For instance, for the temperature in July of 17–17·9° the standard deviation for September is 1·44°, and for the temperature in July of 20–20·9° it is even 1·99°, whereas the general standard deviation of temperatures in September is only 1·35°.

[149] In the diagrams the class intervals have been increased in comparison with the intervals in the tables in order to reduce a random deviation of the line from a smooth pattern that could have been caused by a small number of observations.

curve is determined by corresponding values of the two variables. There is only one curve in the rectangular system of coordinates; if the function is linear it is a straight line.

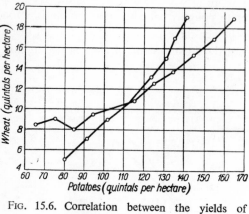

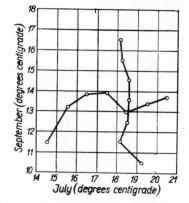

FIG. 15.6. Correlation between the yields of wheat and potatoes.

FIG. 15.7. Correlation between average temperatures in July and September.

For correlation the curves represent average values of one characteristic corresponding to changing values of the other. Even if the correlation is strong, as in Table 15.5, to the lowest values of one variable, say the yields of barley, correspond very low values of the other variable, the yields of oats; but they are not the lowest values, since as averages they must be somewhat higher than the lowest possible values. Similarly, very high, but not the highest possible values of the yields of oats correspond to the highest yields of barley. The same applies to average yields of barley for specific yields of oats. Thus we have two curves in the diagram. If they are straight lines we can say intuitively that the weaker the correlation between the variables, the less acute the angle, and vice versa. If there is no dependence between the characteristics, the average values of characteristic $y$ do not depend upon the values assumed by characteristic $x$ and consequently, when the number of observations is sufficiently large, in each vertical column the average values of $y$ are the same, and they are equal to the general average value of $y$; the line representing the average values of $y$ for specific values of $x$ is horizontal. Similarly, the average values of $x$ do not depend upon specific values of $y$, and the corresponding line is vertical. Thus we obtain two lines intersecting at right angles.

The lines in Fig. 15.2 and 15.3 (p. 429) represent a functional relationship—one linear and one non-linear. Each of them can be read in both directions; for instance in Fig. 15.2 we can read off speed $v$ after $t$ sec of falling, or the time of falling for a given value of $v$.

In Fig. 15.5, 6 and 7 which correspond to Tables 15.5, 6 and 7 there are two curves in each of them. One of these curves represents the average values of characteristic $y$ for changing values of characteristic $x$, and the other the average values of $x$ for changing values of $y$. These curves are called regression curves. They are not straight lines, at least not in Fig. 15.5 and 6, but it can be assumed that deviations from the straight line are accidental, and are caused by the fact that the number of observations in particular columns and rows is small. We can see that shape of the "lines" corresponds to the findings of our previous analysis of the table. For the yields of oats and barley, the two lines are so close together that they almost coincide; for the yields of potatoes and wheat they are a little more apart but the angle is still acute; and for temperatures they intersect almost at right angles.

Considering the shape of these regression "lines" we can state one more thing. If the kinks in a line are accidental then we can try to draw lines which also represent the pattern of the average values of one characteristic for specific values of the other, but which are smooth and without random kinks. They can be smoothed either graphically or mathematically by finding an appropriate function. This kind of determination of correlation may be of great practical value. Let us take an example from agriculture. By increasing the amount of fertilizer we generally raise the yields per unit of area, although the same increase in the amount of fertilizer may not always result in the same increase in the yield. Sometimes the yield may even decrease with an increase in fertilizer. This is a clear case of correlation. A considerable increase in the amount of fertilizer may increase the yield but to a diminishing extent until finally excessive increases may lead to a lowering of the yield. Therefore, in order to establish to what extent it is advisable under given economic conditions, to increase the amount of fertilizer it is necessary to find a function—either in the form of a mathematical equation or a graph—representing the relationship between average yields and the amount of fertilizer used.[150] In capitalistic countries, in which profit is the main criterion, given the prices of fertilizers and crops, this is the way limit to which it is profitable to increase the amount of fertilizers is determined.

As we mentioned before, sometimes—for example, in correlation between the yield of oats and barley—regression lines are straight lines, if we disregard random kinks. In the case of the yields of potatoes and wheat there may be certain doubts as to the shape. Regression curves are clearly not lines when the correlation is between the yield and the amount of fertilizer used: when the amount of fertilizer is increased the yield increases—at first rapidly, then more slowly, and eventually further increases in the amount of the fertilizer lead to a decrease in the yield. Thus, regression may be linear or non-linear, similarly as a functional relationship

---

[150] We are talking here about increasing the quantity of one fertilizer; if the quantities used are excessive the result must be a decline in the yield. However, by changing not only the amount of one fertilizer, but all the conditions affecting the crop we can influence the yield in a different way.

may be represented by a straight line or a curve. This distinction between linear and non-linear regression is important not only from the point of view of its cognitive value, but also from the point of view of calculation, which is much simpler in cases of linear regression than in cases of non-linear regression. Fortunately, in many problems with which we deal in statistics, regression curves can be presented with sufficient approximation as straight lines.

The second basic matter we have to settle is whether or not the correlation between two characteristics is strong. We can settle it either on the basis of the pattern of the figures in the correlation table or on the basis of the shape of the regression curves. However, a numerical expression of the degree of correlation should be found.

For linear correlation the numerical measure of the degree of correlation and the function expressing average values of one characteristic in terms of the other characteristic can be found jointly. The measure of the degree of correlation in this case is the correlation coefficient.

## 3. DERIVATION OF FORMULAE. A CASE OF LINEAR REGRESSION

We shall derive the formulae for calculating the regression line equations and the correlation coefficient using the contigency table for the heights and the weights of young men enrolling for university studies in Warsaw in 1946.

The numerical results of the investigation are presented in Table 15.8 (p. 440).

We denote the height in centimetres by $x$, the weight in kilogrammes by $y$, the difference between the height and the arithmetic mean of heights ($X = x - \bar{x}$) by $X$, the difference between the weight and the arithmetic mean of weights ($Y = y - \bar{y}$) by $Y$, the number of young men of a specific height by $f_x$ (the totals shown at the bottom of the table), the number of a specific weight by $f_y$ (the totals on the right-hand side of the table), the number with a specific combination of weight and height by $f_{xy}$ (the totals shown in the panels of the table), and the total number of observations by $F$ (the figure at the bottom right corner).

Of course

$$\Sigma f_x = \Sigma f_y = \Sigma f_{xy} = F.$$

Finally, $\bar{y}(x)$ is the mean weight for a specific height (the figures at the bottom of the table) and $\bar{x}(y)$ is the mean height for a specific weight (the figures on the right-hand side of the table). The average weight of all the students regardless of their height is 67·9 kg, and the average height of all the students regardless of their weight is 173·0 cm.[151]

---

[151] Stefan Szulc: Wzrost i waga młodzieży szkół wyższych w Warszawie w 1946 (The Height and Weight of University Students in Warsaw in 1946), *Przegląd Statystyczny (Statistical Review)*, 1949, No. 1–2.

The values of the mean height and the mean weight are shown in Fig. 15.8 below. The points in the diagram express average weights for a given height (e.g. 46·5 kg for a height of 146·5 cm), and average heights for a given weight (e.g. 155·2 cm for a weight of 46·5 kg). By joining the neighbouring points with straight lines we obtain empirical regression lines of weight on height (the more horizontal line), and of height on weight (the more vertical line). These lines are not quite regular, especially at the ends. We can assume that this irregularity is caused by the insufficient number of observations, and that therefore it is random; since there is correlation between height and weight, there is no reason to suppose that the average weight will change in leaps as we move from a smaller to a greater height, or that the average height will change in leaps as we move from a smaller to a greater weight. It thus is justified to look for such lines (or such numerical functions) whose pattern would express the most probable relationship between height and the average weight, and between weight and the average height.

Let us assume (as in this case is fully justified by the actual location of points in the middle segments) that this line is a straight line, and that if the points deviate from it such deviations are accidental.

Thus we can smooth out both regression lines by the method of least squares which we described briefly during the discussion of smoothing the development trend (see p. 324 *et seq.*).

In certain cases it may turn out that an empirical regression line is a straight line over a certain range, and that its extreme segments deviate clearly from the straight line. In such cases it may be advisable to calculate the measures of correlation only on the basis of the segments which are closest to a straight line. The results obtained are, of course, applicable only to these segments and cannot be extrapolated. We should not forget to include a note to this effect in giving the results. Fig 15.8 also creates the impression that the extreme

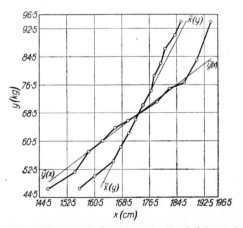

FIG. 15.8. Correlation between the height and weight of male university students.

TABLE 15.8. CORRELATION BETWEEN THE HEIGHT AND WEIGHT OF MALE UNIVERSITY STUDENTS IN WARSAW IN 1946

| Weight in kilogrammes (y) | Height in centimetres (x) | | | | | | | | | | | | | Total | x̄(y) |
|---|---|---|---|---|---|---|---|---|---|---|---|---|---|---|---|
| | 146·5 | 150·5 | 154·5 | 158·5 | 162·5 | 166·5 | 170·5 | 174·5 | 178·5 | 182·5 | 186·5 | 190·5 | 194·5 | | |
| | Number of students | | | | | | | | | | | | | | |
| 94·5 | | | | | | 1 | | | | 3 | | 4 | 1 | 9 | 185·6 |
| 90·5 | | | | | | | | | 1 | 3 | 1 | 1 | | 6 | 183·8 |
| 86·9 | | | | | | | | 3 | 5 | 5 | 3 | 1 | | 17 | 181·1 |
| 82·5 | | | | | | 2 | 4 | 8 | 13 | 20 | 8 | 2 | | 57 | 179·9 |
| 78·5 | | | | | | 4 | 18 | 25 | 42 | 34 | 8 | 1 | | 132 | 177·9 |
| 74·5 | | | | | | 7 | 40 | 80 | 67 | 46 | 13 | 2 | | 255 | 176·9 |
| 70·5 | | | | | 4 | 38 | 102 | 136 | 96 | 30 | 6 | 2 | | 414 | 174·4 |
| 66·5 | | | | 4 | 13 | 67 | 121 | 129 | 66 | 8 | 3 | | | 411 | 172·4 |
| 62·5 | | | | 6 | 39 | 82 | 129 | 85 | 30 | 9 | | | | 380 | 170·4 |
| 58·5 | | | | 13 | 28 | 49 | 55 | 24 | 3 | 2 | | | | 174 | 168·0 |
| 54·5 | | | 4 | 10 | 12 | 18 | 14 | 6 | 1 | 1 | | | | 66 | 165·8 |
| 50·5 | | | 7 | 6 | 7 | 4 | 1 | | | | | | | 25 | 160·3 |
| 46·5 | 2 | | 1 | 1 | 2 | | | | | | | | | 6 | 155·2 |
| Total | 2 | — | 12 | 40 | 105 | 272 | 484 | 496 | 324 | 161 | 42 | 13 | 1 | 1952 | ... |
| ȳ(x) | 46·5 | — | 51·5 | 57·4 | 60·2 | 64·0 | 66·2 | 68·7 | 71·4 | 75·2 | 76·9 | 83·7 | 94·5 | | |

Note: y(x) denotes the average weight for a given height, and x(y) denotes the average height for a given weight. Instead of the class limits the centres of the classes are shown in the table. The class limits for height are. 144·5–148·5, 148·5–152·5, etc. and for weight: 92·5–96·5, 88·5–92·5, etc.

segments of both regression lines deviate from the straight line. If we considered all the values this could lead to: (a) a change in the slope of the regression line of weight on height; (b) a parallel shift of the regression line of height on weight. In this case, however, the changes would be unimportant since the extreme observations are few. For this reason the calculation is based on the whole contingency table.

The equation of the regression of weight on height is

$$Y = aX + b.$$ 

(XV.1)

For determining the parameters $a$ and $b$ we have the equations:[152]

$$a\sum X + b\sum f = \sum Y,$$

(XV.2)

$$a\sum X + b\sum X = \sum XY.$$

(XV.3)

However, since quantities $X$ and $Y$ appear with various frequencies we have to modify these equations by introducing frequencies $f_x$ and $f_y$:

$$a\sum f_x X + b\sum f = \sum f_y Y,$$

(XV.2′)

$$a\sum f_x X^2 + b\sum f_x X = \sum f_{xy} XY.$$

(XV.3′)

Since $X$ and $Y$ are counted from the arithmetic means, $\sum f_x X = 0$, and $\sum f_y Y = 0$. $\sum f$ of course, is equal to $F$.

Thus, from equation (XV.2′) we obtain

$$Fb = 0,$$
$$b = 0,$$

and from equation (XV.3′)

$$a\sum f_x X^2 = \sum f_{xy} XY,$$

$$a = \frac{\sum f_{xy} XY}{\sum f_x X^2}.$$

Dividing the numerator and denominator by $F$ we have

$$a = \frac{\frac{1}{F}\sum f_{xy} XY}{\frac{1}{F}\sum f_x X^2} = \frac{\frac{1}{F}\sum f_{xy} XY}{\sigma_x^2}$$

(see the formula for the standard deviation, p. 217 formula VI.8).

In this way the equation of the regression of weight on height assumes the form

$$Y = \frac{\frac{1}{F}\sum f_{xy} XY}{\sigma_y^2} X$$

(XV.4)

---

[152] We accept this without proof. See the Appendix at the end of the book.

and, similarly, the equation of the regression of height on weight is

$$X = \frac{\frac{1}{F}\Sigma f_{xy}XY}{\sigma_y^2} \; Y. \tag{XV.5}$$

It follows from equations (XV.4) and (XV.5) that if $X = 0$ then $Y = 0$ (and vice versa), which means that the two regression lines intersect at the point corresponding to the arithmetic means of both characteristics.

The expressions

$$a_1 = \frac{\frac{1}{F}\Sigma f_{xy}XY}{\sigma_x^2} \tag{XV.6}$$

$$a_2 = \frac{\frac{1}{F}\Sigma f_{xy}XY}{\sigma_y^2} \tag{XV.7}$$

are called the coefficients of the regression of weight on height (XV.6) and of height on weight (XV.7).

As we can see in both regression coefficients the numerators are the same and the only difference is in the denominators ($\sigma_x^2$ and $\sigma_y^2$).

The coefficients $a_1$ and $a_2$ are measures of the slopes of the straight line $\overline{y}(x)...\overline{y}(x)$ with respect to the horizontal axis and of the straight line $\overline{x}(y)...\overline{x}(y)$ with respect to the vertical axis; thus $a_1 = \tan \alpha$, $a_2 = \tan \beta$.

Let us now introduce the notation

$$r_{xy} = \pm \sqrt{\tan\alpha\cdot\tan\beta} = \sqrt{\frac{\frac{1}{F}\Sigma f_{xy}XY}{\sigma_x^2} \; \frac{\frac{1}{F}\Sigma f_{xy}XY}{\sigma_y^2}} = \frac{\frac{1}{F}\Sigma f_{xy}XY}{\sigma_x\sigma_y} \tag{XV.8}$$

$r_{xy}$ is called the correlation coefficient of $x$ and $y$.

The plus and minus signs before the square root sign here have a definite meaning, and are given by the last part of formula (XV.8).

Considering that

$$\sigma_x = \sqrt{\frac{\Sigma f_x X^2}{F}}, \quad \sigma_y = \sqrt{\frac{\Sigma f_y Y^2}{F}},$$

and therefore

$$\sigma_x\sigma_y = \frac{1}{F}\sqrt{\Sigma f_x X^2 \times \Sigma f_y Y^2},$$

we can write formula (XV.8) in the following form:

$$r_{xy} = \frac{\dfrac{1}{F}\Sigma f_{xy}XY}{\dfrac{1}{F}\sqrt{\Sigma f_x X^2 \times \Sigma f_y Y^2}} = \frac{\Sigma f_{xy}XY}{\sqrt{\Sigma f_x X^2 \times \Sigma f_y Y^2}}. \qquad (XV.8')$$

Calculation by this formula is somewhat simpler than that by formula (XV.8), but the standard deviations are not thereby calculated.

If the various products $XY$ appear only once each (thus, if we do not calculate according to the contingency table but according to individual observations), the factor $f_{xy}$ in the numerator of formula (XV.8) will be equal to one and the formula for the correlation coefficient will assume the form

$$r_{xy} = \frac{\dfrac{1}{F}\Sigma XY}{\sigma_x \sigma_y} \qquad (XV.8a)$$

or

$$r_{xy} = \frac{\Sigma XY}{\sqrt{\Sigma X^2 \ \Sigma Y^2}}. \qquad (XV.8'a)$$

The correlation coefficient is a measure of the degree of the correlation between the two characteristics. If the regression lines coincide then $r_{xy} = 1$ because $\beta = (90 - \alpha)$ and $\tan \alpha (90 - \alpha) = 1$.

To make it clearer we shall show this in the diagrams.

*Case 1:* The regression lines concide, $r_{xy} = 1$ (Fig. 15.9).

By definition

$$\tan \alpha = \frac{ED}{OE}, \quad \tan \beta = \frac{CD}{OC}, \quad ED = OC, \quad OE = CD.$$

$$\tan \alpha \tan \beta = \frac{ED}{OE} \times \frac{CD}{OC} = \frac{ED}{OE} \times \frac{OE}{ED} = 1.$$

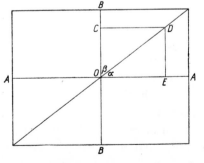

FIG. 15.9. Schematic presentation of regression lines.
Case 1: $r_{xy} = 1$.

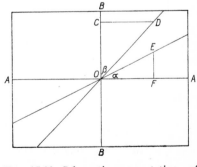

FIG. 15.10. Schematic presentation of regression lines.
Case 2: $r_{xy} < 1$.

*Case 2:* The regression lines do not coincide, $r_{xy} < 1$; (Fig. 15.10)

$$\tan \alpha = \frac{EF}{OF}, \quad \tan \beta = \frac{CD}{OC}.$$

We assume that $OF = CD$.

Then $EF < OC$.

$$\tan \alpha \cdot \tan \beta = \frac{EF}{OF} \times \frac{CD}{OC} = \frac{EF}{OF} \times \frac{OF}{OC} = \frac{EF}{OC} < 1.$$

*Case 3:* If any angle (and therefore the tangent of any angle) equals 0, then $r_{xy} = 0$, but if $\tan \alpha = 0$ then also $\tan \beta = 0$ because an expression of the type

$$\frac{\frac{1}{F} \Sigma f_{xy} XY}{\sigma^2}$$

can equal zero only if $\Sigma f_{xy} XY = 0$.

Thus the correlation coefficient may vary between zero and one. When it equals zero, there is no correlation between the characteristics $x$ and $y$. As we have shown by examples, when there is no correlation the regression line of $y$ on $x$ is horizontal, and the regression line of $x$ on $y$ is vertical. In other words, the regression lines intersect at right angles and, of course, both tangents equal 0.

If the regression lines coincide, i.e. when we deal with a linear functional relationship, then $r_{xy} = 1$.

Values of $r_{xy}$ between zero and one indicate that there is correlation; the closer $r_{xy}$ is to unity, the stronger the correlation.

The expression $\dfrac{\frac{1}{F} \Sigma f_{xy} XY}{\sigma_x \sigma_y}$ may be positive or negative depending upon whether $\Sigma f_{xy} XY$ is positive or negative (the denominator $\sigma_x \sigma_y$ is the product of two positive quantities).

The sum of products $XY$ is positive when on average large values of $y$ correspond to large values of $x$ and vice versa; it is negative if on average small values of $y$ correspond to large values of $x$, and vice versa.[153]

A positive sign for the coefficient $r_{xy}$ is interpreted as meaning that an increase in the average values of $y$ corresponds to an increase in the value of $x$ and that an increase in the average values of $x$ corresponds to an increase in the value of $y$. A negative sign for the coefficient $r_{xy}$ means that an increase in the value of $x$ is accompanied by a decrease in the average values of $y$ and an increase in the value

---

[153] The product of the tangents under the square root sign is always positive because the numerators are the same, thus having the same sign.

of $y$ is accompanied by a decrease in the average values of $x$.[154] It follows from the formula that it is impossible that, for example, an increase in the value of $x$ be accompanied by an increase in the average values of $y$ and that simultaneously an increase in the value of $y$ be accompanied by a decrease in the average values of $x$.

It should be remembered that the above formulae and considerations are strictly correct only with reference to linear regression. Non-linear regression will be discussed later.

If the correlation coefficient $r_{xy}$ is known, there is no need to determine the shape of the regression line by smoothing the abservations by the method of least squares since the regression coefficients can be expressed in the function $r_{xy}$.

Multiplying the correlation coefficient (formula XV.8) by $\dfrac{\sigma_y}{\sigma_x}$ we obtain

$$r_{xy} \cdot \frac{\sigma_x}{\sigma_y} = \frac{\dfrac{1}{F} \Sigma f_{xy} XY}{\sigma_x \sigma_y} \cdot \frac{\sigma_y}{\sigma_x} = \frac{\dfrac{1}{F} \Sigma f_{xy} XY}{\sigma_x^2}; \tag{XV.9}$$

multiplying by $\dfrac{\sigma_x}{\sigma_y}$ we obtain

$$r_{xy} \cdot \frac{\sigma_x}{\sigma_y} = \frac{\dfrac{1}{F} \Sigma f_{xy} XY}{\sigma_x \sigma_y} \cdot \frac{\sigma_x}{\sigma_y} = \frac{\dfrac{1}{F} \Sigma f_{xy} XY}{\sigma_y^2}. \tag{XV.10}$$

However, the expression on the right-hand side of equation (XV.9) is the regression coefficient of $y$ on characteristic $x$ ($a_1$, equation (XV.6)) and the expression on the right-hand side of the equation (XV.10) is the regression coefficient of $x$ on $y$ ($a_2$, equation (XV.7)). Therefore we can write the regression equations as

$$Y = \frac{\sigma_y}{\sigma_x} r_{xy} X, \tag{XV.11}$$

$$X = \frac{\sigma_x}{\sigma_y} r_{xy} Y \tag{XV.12}$$

This is the form in which the regression equations are most convenient for calculating the regression coefficients, provided that we have previously calculated the correlation coefficient.

These expressions require some further explanation. The meaning of $X$ and $Y$ is not the same on both sides of the regression equation. $X$ and $Y$ on the right-hand

---

[154] This interpretation is conventional in so far as algebraically the root of the product of the tangents may have either a plus or the minus sign. However, if we compute $r_{xy}$ by the last part of formula (XV.8), or formula (XV.8') the plus or minus sign is uniquely determined.

side denote specific values of the characteristics, and on the left-hand side they denote the average values of these characteristics corresponding to given values of $X$ and $Y$.

The correlation coefficient $r_{xy}$ is an abstract number—the geometric mean of the tangents which themselves are abstract numbers. But $X$ and $Y$ in the regression equations are numbers with dimensions, and they can be expressed in the same units (e.g. centimetres when we are studying the correlation between the heights of parents and children or in different units, as in the example above in which $X$ stands for height in centimetres and $Y$ for weight in kilogrammes.

For a functional relationship, in which $r_{xy} = \pm 1$ the expressions (XV.11) and (XV.12) are simplified. We then obtain

$$Y = \pm \frac{\sigma_y}{\sigma_x} X,$$

$$X = \pm \frac{\sigma_x}{\sigma_y} Y.$$

Moreover, if $\sigma_y = \sigma_x$, then

$$Y = \pm X,$$

$$X = \pm Y,$$

which means that when $X$ changes the average values of $Y$ increases or decreases by the same number of units (no matter how measured) by which the value of $X$ has changed; the same applies to the average value of $X$ when $Y$ changes.[155] It does not follow, however, that $\bar{y} = x$ and $\bar{x} = y$, because $X$ and $Y$ are measured from the arithmetic means of both characteristcs, which can equal one another only by coincidence.

In addition the standard deviations of the two characteristics can only be equal by coincidence. If $\sigma_x \neq \sigma_y$ then $\frac{\sigma_y}{\sigma_x} > 1$ wherever $\frac{\sigma_x}{\sigma_y} < 1$, and vice versa; in other words one of the regression coefficients is greater than one, and the other is less than one. If the average value of $Y$ increases faster than $X$ then the average value of $X$ will increase more slowly than $Y$, and vice versa. For a correlation in which $|r_{xy}| < 1$, at least one regression coefficient must be less than one and the other may be either less or greater than one.

For instance, if $\sigma_y < \sigma_x$ then $a_1$ is always less then one because both $\frac{\sigma_y}{\sigma_x}$ and $a_2$ are less than one; $a_2$ may be greater than one, less than one or equal to one,

---

[155] Then the tangents of both $\alpha$ and $\beta$ equal one, which means that both are 45° angles.

depending upon whether $\dfrac{\sigma_y}{\sigma_x}$ is less than, greater than, or equal to the absolute value of $r_{xy}$.[156]

In regression equations the magnitudes $x$ and $y$ are measured from their arithmetic means. In practice we usually need the values of both variables measured from zero.

Substituting $(y - \bar{y})$ for $Y$ and $(x - \bar{x})$ for $X$ in equation (XV.11) we get

$$y - \bar{y} = \frac{\sigma_y}{\sigma_x} r_{xy} (x - \bar{x}),$$

and hence

$$y = \frac{\sigma_y}{\sigma_x} r_{xy} x - \frac{\sigma_y}{\sigma_x} r_{xy}\bar{x} + \bar{y} = a_1 x + (\bar{y} - a_1\bar{x}). \qquad (\text{XV.13})$$

In this expression

$$a_1\bar{x} = \frac{\sigma_y}{\sigma_x} r_{xy}\bar{x}$$

is constant; it is the product of the arithmetic mean of characteristic $x$ multiplied by the regression coefficient of $y$ on $x$; this quantity may be greater than or less than $y$. Therefore, in order to calculate the average value of characteristic $y$ corresponding to a given value of characteristic $x$ we should multiply $x$ by the regression coefficient of $y$ on $x$ and add to the result the constant quantity (positive or negative)

$$\bar{y} - a_1\bar{x}.$$

Similarly we transform equation (XV.12)

$$x = \frac{\sigma_x}{\sigma_y} r_{xy} y - \frac{\sigma_x}{\sigma_y} r_{xy}\bar{y} + \bar{x} = a_2 y + (\bar{x} - a_2\bar{y}). \qquad (\text{XV.14})$$

## 4. EXAMPLES OF CALCULATING CORRELATION COEFFICIENTS AND OF DETERMINING REGRESSION LINES

The method of calculation will be shown first by using the example on the yield per hectare of wheat and oats in Poland in 1948, shown in Table 15.1 (p. 425).

---

[156] For instance, if $r_{xy} = \pm 0.64$ and $\dfrac{\sigma_y}{\sigma_x} = 0.4 \left( \dfrac{\sigma_y}{\sigma_x} < |r_{xy}| \right)$, then $a_1 = \pm 0.64 \times 0.4 = \pm 0.256$ and therefore $a = \pm 0.256\,X$. But $a_2 = \pm 0.64 \times \dfrac{1}{0.4} = \pm 1.6$; thus $X = \pm 1.6\,Y$. If $r_{xy} = \pm 0.64$ and $\dfrac{\sigma_y}{\sigma_x} = 0.64$ then

$$a_1 = \pm 0.64 \times 0.64 = \pm 0.4096$$

$$a_2 = \pm 0.64 \times \frac{1}{0.64} = \pm 1.$$

There are 14 provinces, and therefore 14 pairs of observations. Since we are concerned here not with the contingency table but with individual observations, we use formula (XV.8a) (p. 443). The calculation may be set up as in Table 15.9.

TABLE 15.9. CALCULATION OF CORRELATION BETWEEN THE YIELD OF WHEAT AND OATS IN POLAND IN 1948

| Province | Yields (quintals per hectare) | | $X = x - \bar{x}$ | $Y = y - \bar{y}$ | $X^2$ | $Y^2$ | $XY$ |
|---|---|---|---|---|---|---|---|
| | wheat | oat | | | | | |
| | 1 | 2 | 3 | 4 | 5 | 6 | 7 |
| Rzeszów | 7·7 | 10·7 | −3·94 | −2·98 | 15·524 | 8·880 | +11·741 |
| Lublin | 8·7 | 11·4 | −2·94 | −2·28 | 8·644 | 5·198 | + 6·703 |
| Białystok | 9·1 | 11·7 | −2·54 | −1·98 | 6·452 | 3·920 | + 5·029 |
| Kielce | 9·9 | 12·5 | −1·74 | −1·18 | 3.028 | 1.392 | + 2·053 |
| Kraków | 10·5 | 13·3 | −1·14 | −0·38 | 1·300 | 0.144 | + 0·433 |
| Warsaw | 10·6 | 13·6 | −1·04 | −0·08 | 1·082 | 0.006 | + 0·083 |
| Szczecin | 11·2 | 12·8 | −0·44 | −0·88 | 0.194 | 0.774 | + 0·387 |
| Łódź | 11·8 | 14·4 | +0·16 | +0·72 | 0.026 | 0.518 | + 0·115 |
| Olsztyn | 12·3 | 13·8 | +0·66 | +0·12 | 0.436 | 0.014 | + 0·079 |
| Wrocław | 13·3 | 14·9 | +1·66 | +1·22 | 2·756 | 1·488 | + 2·025 |
| Gdańsk | 14·0 | 15·2 | +2·36 | +1·52 | 5·570 | 2·310 | + 3·587 |
| Pomorze | 14·4 | 15·5 | +2·76 | +1·82 | 7·618 | 3·312 | + 5·023 |
| Silesia | 14·7 | 15·7 | +3·06 | +2·02 | 9·364 | 4·080 | + 6·181 |
| Poznań | 14·7 | 16·0 | +3·06 | +2·32 | 9·364 | 5·382 | + 7·099 |
| Total | 162·9 | 191·5 | ... | ... | 71·358 | 37·418 | +50·539 |

$$\bar{x} = \frac{162 \cdot 9}{14} = 11 \cdot 64, \quad \bar{y} = \frac{191 \cdot 5}{14} = 13 \cdot 68,$$

$$\sigma_x = \sqrt{\frac{71 \cdot 358}{14}} = \sqrt{5 \cdot 097} = 2 \cdot 258,$$

$$\sigma_y = \sqrt{\frac{37 \cdot 418}{14}} = \sqrt{2 \cdot 673} = 1 \cdot 635,$$

$$r_{xy} = + \frac{\frac{1}{14} 50 \cdot 539}{2 \cdot 258 \ 1 \cdot 635} = + \frac{3 \cdot 610}{3 \cdot 691} = + 0 \cdot 98.$$

Calculating by formula (XV.8′a) we obtain the same result:

$$r_{xy} = + \frac{50 \cdot 539}{\sqrt{71 \cdot 358 \times 37 \cdot 418}} = + 0 \cdot 98.$$

The arithmetic means of the yields of wheat and oats have been calculated with the same weight for all provinces. While this is not quite correct, it does not cause a substantial error.

The sums of the $X$'s and $Y$'s, being sums of deviations from the arithmetic mean, should be 0; small differences are the result of rounding off. For this reason dots have been placed in appropriate columns in the row for the totals. The technique of computation does not require any additional explanation.

The value of the correlation coefficient is close to one, which means that the correlation is very strong. Thus our intuitive conclusion to the same effect (p. 425) has been confirmed.

The next example (Table 15.10) relates to the annual averages of barometric pressure and temperature in Warsaw in the years 1923–37. (See Table 15.2 p. 426).

TABLE 15.10. CALCULATION OF CORRELATION BETWEEN ANNUAL AVERAGE BAROMETRIC PRESSURE AND AVERAGE TEMPERATURE IN WARSAW IN 1923–37

| Year | Average pressure (mm) $(x)$ | Average temperature (°C) $(y)$ | $X=x-\bar{x}$ | $Y=y-\bar{y}$ | $X^2=$ $(x-\bar{x})^2$ | $Y^2=$ $(y-\bar{y})^2$ | $XY=$ $(x-\bar{x})\times$ $\times(y-\bar{y})$ |
|------|------|------|------|------|------|------|------|
| | 1 | 2 | 3 | 4 | 5 | 6 | 7 |
| 1925 | 752·5 | 8·5 | −1·080 | +0·513 | 1·1664 | 0·2632 | −0·5540 |
| 1023 | 752·7 | 7·8 | −0·880 | −0·187 | 0.7744 | 0·0350 | +0·1646 |
| 1935 | 752·8 | 8·0 | −0·780 | +0·013 | 0.6084 | 0·0002 | −0·0101 |
| 1936 | 752·9 | 8·7 | −0·680 | +0·713 | 0·4624 | 0·5084 | −0·4848 |
| 1930 | 753·0 | 8·7 | −0·580 | +0·713 | 0·3364 | 0·5084 | −0·4135 |
| 1926 | 753·2 | 8·4 | −0·380 | +0·413 | 0·1444 | 0·1706 | −0·1569 |
| 1931 | 753·2 | 7·5 | −0·380 | −0·487 | 0·1444 | 0·2372 | +0·1851 |
| 1937 | 753·2 | 8·8 | −0·380 | +0·813 | 0·1444 | 0·6610 | −0·3089 |
| 1927 | 753·5 | 7·6 | −0·080 | −0·387 | 0·0064 | 0·1498 | +0·0310 |
| 1928 | 753·9 | 7·8 | +0·320 | −0·187 | 0·1024 | 0·0350 | −0·0598 |
| 1934 | 754·0 | 9·5 | +0·420 | +1·513 | 0·1764 | 2·2892 | +0·6355 |
| 1933 | 754·2 | 6·6 | +0·620 | −1·387 | 0·3844 | 1·9238 | −0·8599 |
| 1924 | 754·4 | 6·9 | +0·820 | −1·087 | 0·6724 | 1·1816 | −0·8913 |
| 1932 | 754·8 | 8·4 | +1·220 | +0·413 | 1·4884 | 0·1706 | +0·5039 |
| 1929 | 755·4 | 6·6 | +1·820 | −1·387 | 3·3124 | 1·9238 | −2·5243 |
| Total | 11,303·7 | 119·8 | ... | ... | 9·9240 | 10·0578 | −4·7434 |

$$\bar{x} = \frac{11303 \cdot 7}{15} = 753 \cdot 58 \text{ mm}, \quad \bar{y} = \frac{119 \cdot 8}{15} = 7 \cdot 987°C,$$

$$\sigma_x = \sqrt{\frac{9 \cdot 924}{15}} = 0 \cdot 8134 \text{ mm}, \quad \sigma_y = \sqrt{\frac{10 \cdot 0578}{15}} = 0 \cdot 8189°C,$$

$$r_{xy} = \frac{\dfrac{1}{15} \times (-4 \cdot 7434)}{0 \cdot 8134 \times 0 \cdot 8189} = -0 \cdot 475.$$

The regression equations are obtained from formulae (XV.11) and (XV.12) (p. 445).

$$Y = \left(\frac{0 \cdot 8189}{0 \cdot 8134}\right) \times (-0 \cdot 475\,X) = -0 \cdot 478\,X.$$

$$X = \left(\frac{0 \cdot 8134}{0 \cdot 8189}\right) \times (-0 \cdot 472\,Y) = -0 \cdot 472\,Y.$$

The correlation coefficients and the regression coefficients are negative here. This means that during this period in Warsaw lower air temperature corresponded, in general, to higher barometric pressure, and vice versa.

This confirms not so much the inconclusive general impression received by looking at columns 1 and 2 in Table 15.10 as the summary of the observations in Table 15.3 (p. 427), and of the average temperatures corresponding to specific values of the barometric pressure (Table 15.4 p. 428). The many displacements in the descending order of temperatures in column 2 of Table 15.10 correspond to a relatively small correlation coefficient.

Since the two mean deviations are relatively close in this example, the two regression coefficients are almost identical. It follows from the regression equations that the average drop in the temperature by about $0 \cdot 5°C$ corresponds to an increase of 1 mm in the barometric pressure, and the average drop of about $0 \cdot 5$ mm in the pressure corresponds to an increase of 1°C in the temperature.

One important reservation should be made here. In both examples the calculation has led to the establishment of a certain relationship, and to the determination of regression equations expressing the average values of one characteristic as a function of the other. However, this is a purely formal statement, and how to give it a logical meaning is a different problem which will be discussed later.

Another problem to which we shall return is whether with as few observations as in our example the use of the correlation coefficient is permissible at all, and whether under these circumstances the results can be regarded as sufficiently conclusive.

As to the method of calculation it should be remembered that if the number of observations is small the final results of calculating the correlation coefficient and the regression coefficient should be rounded off considerably, and given with an accuracy of, say, two decimal places. When the number of observations is large the results can also be rounded off; but in the course of calculation greater accuracy is required. In calculating statistical measures the general principles of calculation by approximation should always be observed. (See a special discussion of calculation by approximation in the Appendix at the end of the book).

The method of calculation used in Tables 15.9 and 15.10 is technically easy when the number of observations is small. The calculation is usually based on the contingency table. The method of calculation is shown in the example in Table 15.11 relating to the correlation between the height and weight of 7-year-old girls.[157]

TABLE 15.11. CORRELATION BETWEEN HEIGHT AND WEIGHT OF 7-YEAR-OLD GIRLS

| Weight in kilogrammes | | Height (cm) (x) | | | | | | | tenU |
|---|---|---|---|---|---|---|---|---|---|
| | | 96 | 102 | 108 | 114 | 120 | 126 | 132 | |
| | | $X = x - \bar{x}$ | | | | | | | |
| $y$ | $Y = y - \bar{y}$ | −17·43 | −11·43 | −5·43 | +0·57 | +6·57 | +12·57 | +18·57 | |
| | | Number of girls | | | | | | | |
| 27 | +7·51 | | | | 1 | 3 | | 1 | 5 |
| 25 | +5·51 | | | 2 | 3 | 10 | 6 | 1 | 22 |
| 23 | +3·51 | | | | 23 | 35 | 8 | | 66 |
| 21 | +1·51 | | 1 | 10 | 108 | 76 | 11 | | 206 |
| 19 | −0·49 | | 5 | 77 | 158 | 31 | | | 271 |
| 17 | −2·49 | | 20 | 96 | 49 | 2 | | | 167 |
| 15 | −4·49 | 2 | 12 | 15 | | | | | 29 |
| 13 | −6·49 | 1 | 1 | | | 1 | | | 3 |
| Total $f_x$ | | 3 | 39 | 200 | 342 | 158 | 25 | 2 | 769 |

As always, we assume that all individuals in a given panel have the same weight and height, equal to the centres of the class intervals. Thus we assume that 108 girls in the height class 111–17 cm and the weight class 20–22 kg are 114 cm tall and weigh 21 kg.

These centres of the class intervals were denoted in the table by $x$ and $y$.

We calculate the arithmetic means in the usual way,

$$\bar{x} = 113\cdot43 \text{ cm}, \quad \bar{y} = 19\cdot49 \text{ kg}.$$

We now calculate $X = x - \bar{x}$ and $Y = y - \bar{y}$, subtracting the arithmetic means from the corresponding centres of the class intervals. In this way we obtain the heights, reading from left to right: − 17·43 cm, − 11·43 cm, etc., and for weight, reading from top to bottom: + 7·51 kg, + 5·51 kg, etc.

For formula (XV.8) p. 442 we have to calculate the products $XY$. i.e.

$$(-17\cdot43) \times (+7\cdot51) = -130\cdot8993,$$

$$(-11\cdot43) \times (+7\cdot51) = -85\cdot8393, \text{ etc.}$$

These products should be entered in appropriate cells in the table. The products may be positive or negative, depending upon the signs of $X$ and $Y$. To avoid errors

---

[157] The data refer to 769 girls registered in Warsaw elementary schools in 1923. The material was obtained from the Statistical Department of the Warsaw City Council.

the table is divided into four, quadrants marked off by thick lines. The upper right and the lower left quadrants have positive signs and the other two have negative signs.

Next we multiply these products by the numbers of observations in appropriate cells, i.e. by $f_{xy}$. In this way we obtain the products $f_{xy}XY$. The results can also be entered in appropriate cells in the table.

Adding up the figures—preferably separately for positive and for negative quadrants—and dividing them by the total number of observations $F = \Sigma f_{xy} = 769$, we obtain the denominator of the fraction in formula (XV.8):

$$\frac{1}{F} \Sigma f_{xy} XY = \frac{6420 \cdot 438}{769} = 8 \cdot 3491.$$

Computing in the usual way the standard deviation of height ($\sigma_x$) and of weight ($\sigma_y$) we obtain the correlation coefficient between the height and the weight of 7-year-old girls

$$r_{xy} = + \frac{8 \cdot 3491}{5 \cdot 525 \times 2 \cdot 293} = + \frac{8 \cdot 3491}{12 \cdot 6688} = + 0 \cdot 659$$

This calculation has only been described, but it should help the reader to do the calculation by himself, and in this way to learn the method of calculation according to the basic formula. In practice this method is not used, because formula (XV.8) can easily be transformed, so that a simplified method of calculation can be used, similar to the calculation used in computing the arithmetic mean and the standard deviation (see p. 222 *et seq.*). The simplification consists in (1) measuring the deviations of $x$ and $y$, not from their arithmetic means but from an arbitrary origin, and (2) counting in units equal to class intervals.

$X$ and $Y$ denote the deviation of specific values of $x$ and $y$ in each class from the corresponding arithmetic means; by $X'$ and $Y'$ we denote the deviations of $x$ and $y$ from arbitrary origins $x_0$ and $y_0$.

$$X = x - \bar{x}, \qquad X' = x - x_0,$$
$$Y = y - \bar{y}, \qquad Y' = y - y_0.$$

By $v_{1(x)}$ we denote the deviation of the arbitrary origin $x_0$ from the arithmetic mean $\bar{x}$, and by $v_{1(y)}$ the deviation of $y_0$ from $\bar{y}$.

$$v_{1(x)} = \bar{x} - x_0,$$
$$v_{1(y)} = \bar{y} - y_0.$$

Thus

$$X' = X + v_{1(x)},$$
$$Y' = Y + v_{1(y)},$$
$$X'Y' = (X + v_{1(x)}) \times (Y + v_{1(y)}) = XY + v_{1(y)} X + v_{1(x)} Y + v_{1(x)} v_{1(y)}.$$

Adding both sides and considering that each product $X'Y'$ and $XY$ is repeated $f_{xy}$ times—as many times as there are observations in a given panel, which means that each $X$ is repeated $f_x$ times and each $Y$, $f_y$ times—we obtain.

$$\Sigma f_{xy}X'Y' = \Sigma f_{xy}XY + v_{1(y)}\Sigma f_x Y + F v_{1(x)}v_{1(y)}.$$

In the right-hand side of the equation, $v_{1(x)}$ and $v_{1(y)}$ appear before the summation signs of the second and third terms, because they are constants; the product of the constants $v_{1(x)}$ and $v_{1(y)}$ is repeated as many times as there are observations in the population, i.e. by F. Since $\Sigma f_x X$ and $\Sigma f_y Y$ equal zero, being the sums of deviations from the arithmetic means, we finally obtain

$$\Sigma f_{xy}X'Y' = \Sigma f_{xy}XY + F v_{1(x)}v_{1(y)}.$$

Hence

$$\Sigma f_{xy}XY = \Sigma f_{xy}X'Y' - F v_{1(x)}v_{1(y)}.$$

Dividing both sides by $F$ we obtain

$$\frac{1}{F}\Sigma f_{xy}XY = \frac{1}{F}\Sigma f_{xy}X'Y' - v_{1(x)}v_{1(y)}.$$

Thus we can write formula (XV.8) as

$$r_{xy} = \frac{\dfrac{1}{F}f_{xy}X'Y' - v_{1(x)}v_{1(v)}}{\sigma_x \sigma_y}. \tag{XV.15}$$

This means that instead of the sum of the products $X$ by $Y$ calculated from the arithmetic means we compute the sum of the products $X'$ and $Y'$ calculated from the arbitrary origin. This simplifies the calculation considerably. The correction that we have to introduce consists in subtracting from $\dfrac{1}{F}\Sigma f_{xy}X'Y'$ the product $v_{1(x)}\ v_{1(y)}$. This is the product of the quantities that are needed in any case for the abbreviated calculation the arithmetic means and the standard deviations.

Units equal to class intervals should be used in the calculation, and while calculating the correlation coefficient $r_{xy}$ we can use these units to the end.[158] But for calculating the regression coefficients the standard deviations should be expressed in real units.

The calculation can be made in different ways. The example in Table 15.12 on the correlation between the height and weight of 7-year-old girls shows a procedure which facilitates checking the calculation.

---

[158] To shift from conventional units to real units we should multiply in the numerator both $\dfrac{1}{F}\Sigma f_{xy}X'Y'$ and $v_{1(x)}v_{1(y)}$ by the product $l_x l_y$, where $l_x$ and $l_y$ are the class intervals in both series. Similarly, the denominator should be multiplied by $l_x l_y$; thus the corrections in the numerator and the denominator cancel out.

The rectangle marked off by thick lines—with the series $f_x$ at the bottom and the series $f_y$ on the right-hand side—is the contingency table proper. In the tables below the thick line, and to the right of it the method of calculation is shown. We shall now explain the consecutive stages of the calculation.

The rows at the bottom and the columns on the right-hand side are marked alphabetically from (a) to (h), so that the letters in the vertical direction correspond to the letters in the horizontal direction: thus the explanation of the meaning of the rows applies to the corresponding columns.

In row (a) the sums of the products of the frequencies $f_{xy}$ in a given column by the corresponding values of variable $Y'$ are given; thus in the first column we have

$$2 \times (-2) + 1 \times (-3) = -7,$$

and in the second

$$1 \times (+1) + 5 \times 0 + 20 \times (-1) + 12 \times (-2) + 1 \times (-3) = -46,$$

etc.

Since the value of $X'$ is the same for all the items of a given column, by multiplying the numbers in row (a) by the corresponding values of $X'$ we obtain the sum of the products $f_{xy}X'Y'$ for a given column. In this way we obtain for the first column $(-7) \times (-3) = +21$, for the second column $(-46) \times (-2) = +92$ etc. The results are shown in row (b).

The total of row (b) is the sum of the products $X'Y'$ for all the values of $f_{xy}$, i.e. $\sum f_{xy}X'Y'$. This expression is the first term of the numerator in formula (XV.15) (p. 453). In this case it is 517 and is entered in the last column of the bottom table.

Row (c) contains the elements required for calculating $v_{(x)}$, i.e. the products of the values of $X'$ for particular classes by the frequencies of those classes. The total on the right-hand side is, of course, $\sum f X' = -73$. Similarly, row (d) contains the elements needed for calculating $v_{2(x)}$, or $\sum f(X')^2 = 659$. We can check the calculation, as usual, by multiplying the figures in row (c) by the corresponding value $X' [-9 \times (-3) = +27, -78 \times (-2) = +156,$ etc.].

Rows (e), (g) and (h) contain the calculation of the arithmetic means of the weights of the girls in particular height groups. In row (e) the averages in conventional units equal to class intervals (in this case 2 kg) measured from $y_0$ for particular height classes are given. Row (g) contains the conversion from conventional to real units, expressed in kilogrammes. The last row (h) contains the averages for particular height classes calculated as the sum

$$y(x) = y_0 + 2e.$$

The vertical columns from (a) to (h) contain analogous calculations for particular weight classes. The reader is advised to go through these columns following the explanations given above.

The total in the last row of column (b) is thus $\Sigma f_{xy}X'Y'$ and should therefore equal the total of row (b) in the bottom part of the table; indeed is is 517 in both cases. Since in calculating the sum of the products $f_{xy}X'$ and $f_{xy}Y'$ (column and row (a)) it is easy to make a mistake, such double checking is advisable.

Another cross-check is the identity of the total of row (a) with the total of column (c) which in his case is +190, and of the total of row (c) with the total of column (a) which is −73.[159]

In this way the whole calculation has been made twice, which should ensure accuracy.

We can now start final computations. Let us start with the numerical characteristic (the arithmetic mean and the standard deviation) of both series—the height and the weight.

The calculation for the height (x):

(a) in conventional units calculated from $x_0$

$$v_{1(x)} = -\frac{73}{769} = -0\cdot0949, \quad v_{1(x)}^2 = 0\cdot0090,$$

$$v_{2(x)} = +\frac{659}{769} = 0\cdot8570,$$

$$\sigma_x = \sqrt{0\cdot8570 - 0\cdot0090} = 0\cdot92209;$$

(b) in real units:

$$\bar{x} = 114 - 6 \times 0\cdot0949 = 113\cdot43 \text{ cm},$$

$$\sigma'_x = 6 \times 0\cdot9209 = 5\cdot525 \text{ cm}.$$

The calculation for the weight (y):

(a) in conventional units calculated from $y_0$

$$v_{1(y)} = +\frac{190}{769} = +0\cdot24707 \quad v_{1(y)}^2 = 0\cdot0610,$$

$$v_{2(y)} = +\frac{1058}{769} = 1\cdot3758,$$

$$\sigma'_y = \sqrt{1\cdot3758 - 0\cdot0610} = 1\cdot1466;$$

[159] Both totals are the sums of the products of all $f_{xy}$ by the corresponding $Y'$, but the calculation is made in a different order. At the bottom of the table in row (a) there are the results of multiplication and addition $2(-2) + 1(-3) = -7$, then $1(+1) + 5(0) + 20(-1) + 12(-2) +1(-3) = 46$, etc.; on the right-hand side in column (c) there are the results of multiplication $(1 + 3 + 1) \times (+4) = 5(+4) = +20$; $(2 + 3 + 10 + 6 + 1) \times (+3) = 22(+3) = +66$ etc. The total must be the same. The same applies to the sums of column (a) and row (c).

TABLE 15.12. CORRELATION BETWEEN HEIGHT AND WEIGHT OF 7-YEAR-OLD GIRLS

| Weight (kg)(y) $Y'=y-y_0$ | 96 | 102 | 108 | 114 | 120 | 126 | 132 | $f_y$ | $f_{xy}X'$ a* | $aY'$ b | $f_yY'$ c | $f_yY'^2$ d | $\dfrac{a}{f_y}$ e | $6e$ g | $x_0+g=\bar{x}(y)$ h |
|---|---|---|---|---|---|---|---|---|---|---|---|---|---|---|---|
| | $X'=x-x_0$ | | | | | | | | | | | | | | |
| | −3 | −2 | −1 | 0 | +1 | +2 | +3 | | | | | | | | |
| 27  +4 | | | | 1 | 3 | | 1 | 5 | +6 | +24 | +20 | 80 | +1·2000 | +7·20 | 121·20 |
| 25  +3 | | | 2 | 3 | 10 | 6 | 1 | 22 | +23 | +69 | +66 | 198 | +1·0455 | +6·27 | 120·27 |
| 23  +2 | | 1 | | 23 | 35 | 8 | | 66 | +51 | +102 | +132 | 264 | +0·7727 | +4·64 | 118·64 |
| 21  +1 | | | 10 | 108 | 76 | 11 | | 206 | +86 | +86 | +206 | 206 | +0·4175 | +2·50 | 116·50 |
| 19   0 | | 5 | 77 | 158 | 31 | | | 271 | −56 | 0 | 0 | 0 | −0·2066 | −1·24 | 112·76 |
| 17  −1 | | 20 | 96 | 49 | 2 | | | 167 | −134 | +134 | −167 | 167 | −0·8024 | −4·81 | 109·19 |
| 15  −2 | 2 | 12 | 15 | | 1 | | | 29 | −45 | +90 | −58 | 116 | −1·5517 | −9·31 | 104·69 |
| 13  −3 | 1 | 1 | | | | | | 3 | −4 | +12 | −9 | 27 | −1·3333 | −8·00 | 106·00 |
| $f_y$ | 3 | 39 | 200 | 342 | 158 | 25 | 2 | 769 | −73 | +517 | +190 | 1058 | | | |
| $f_{xy}Y'$  a* | −7 | −46 | −110 | +118 | +183 | +45 | +7 | +190 | | | | | | | |
| $aX'$  b | +21 | +92 | +110 | 0 | +183 | +90 | +21 | +517 | | | | | | | |
| $f_xX'$  c | −9 | −78 | −200 | 0 | +158 | +50 | +6 | −73 | | | | | | | |
| $f_x(X')^2$  d | 27 | 156 | 200 | 0 | 158 | 100 | 18 | 659 | | | | | | | |
| $\dfrac{a}{f_x}$  e | −2·3333 | −1·1795 | −0·550 | +0·3450 | +1·1582 | +1·8000 | +3·5000 | | | | | | | | |
| $2e$  g | −4·67 | −2·36 | −1·1 | +0·69 | +2·32 | +3·6 | +7·0 | | | | | | | | |
| $y_0+g=\bar{y}(x)$  h | 14·33 | 16·64 | 17·9 | 19·69 | 21·32 | 22·6 | 26·0 | | | | | | | | |

*Height in centimetres (x)* heads columns 96–132.

* The columns and the rows are marked by the consecutive letters of the alphabet except that letter $f$ has been left out because it has a special meaning here (it denotes frequency)

(b) in real units

$$\bar{y} = 19 + 2 \times 0 \cdot 247 = 19 \cdot 49 \text{ kg,}$$

$$\sigma_y = 2 \times 1 \cdot 1466 = 2 \cdot 293 \text{ kg.}$$

We can now calculate directly the correlation coefficient on the basis of formula (XV.15 p. 453). The sum $\Sigma f_{xy} X' Y'$ is 517 (the total of column and row (b) in the table); therefore

$$r_{xy} = \frac{\dfrac{517}{769} + 0 \cdot 0949 \times 0 \cdot 24707}{0 \cdot 9209 \times 1 \cdot 1466} = +0 \cdot 659$$

in conventional units.

The regression coefficients by formulae (XV.11) and (XV.12) (p. 445) are

$$a_{y(x)} = \frac{2 \cdot 293}{5 \cdot 525} \times 0 \cdot 659 = 0 \cdot 273,$$

$$a_{x(y)} = \frac{5 \cdot 525}{2 \cdot 293} \times 0 \cdot 659 = 1 \cdot 588$$

and the regression equations are

$$Y = 0 \cdot 273 \, X,$$

$$X = 1 \cdot 588 \, Y.$$

In these equations the values of $X$ and $Y$ are expressed as deviations from their arithmetic means. In order to convert them into real units we use formulae (XV.13) and (XV.14)

$$y = 0 \cdot 273 \, x + (19 \cdot 49 - 0 \cdot 273 \times 113 \cdot 43) = 0 \cdot 273 \, x + (19 \cdot 49 - 30 \cdot 97)$$

$$= 0 \cdot 273 \, x - 11 \cdot 48$$

and correspondingly

$$x = 1 \cdot 588 \, y + (113 \cdot 43 - 1 \cdot 588 \times 19 \cdot 49) = 1 \cdot 588 \, y + (113 \cdot 43 - 30 \cdot 95)$$

$$= 1 \cdot 588 \, y + 82 \cdot 48 \,.$$

To present the regression lines in a diagram we have only to calculate the values of $y$ for any two values of $x$ and the values of $x$ for any two values of $y$. Thus, for instance, for $x = 93$

$$y = 0 \cdot 273 \times 93 - 11 \cdot 48 = 13 \cdot 91 \,.$$

For $x = 134$ we obtain $y = 25 \cdot 10$; for $y = 12$, $x$ is $101 \cdot 54$; for $y = 27$, $x = 125 \cdot 36$.

The same lines are shown in Fig. 15.8 (p. 439). They satisfy the condition that the sum of the squared deviations of the averages of $x$ from the line $x(y) - \bar{x}(y)$ and of the averages of $y$ from the line $\bar{y}(x) - y(x)$ is minimum for this position of both lines.

30

The calculation of the correlation coefficient by the method of differences is even simpler.

Let us write the identity

$$\sum (X' - Y')^2 = \sum [(X')^2 + (Y')^2 - 2X'Y'] = \sum (X')^2 + \sum (Y')^2 - 2\sum X'Y'.$$

In the expression on the right-hand side $\sum (X')^2 = Fv_{2(x)}$ $(Y')^2 = Fv_{2(y)}$

$$\left( v_{2(x)} = \frac{(X')^2}{F}, \quad v_{2(y)} = \frac{(Y')^2}{F} \right).$$

From the calculation on pp. 452–3 we know that $\sum X'Y' = \sum XY + Fv_{1(x)} v_{1(y)}$.

Instead of $\sum XY$ we can write $F \sigma_x \sigma_y r_{xy}$. This follows from the formula for the correlation coefficient

$$r_{xy} = \frac{\sum XY}{F \sigma_x \sigma_y}.$$

Finally we obtain

$$\sum (X' - Y')^2 = Fv_{2(x)} + Fv_{2(y)} - 2F\sigma_x \sigma_y r_{xy} - 2Fv_{1(x)} v_{1(y)},$$

hence

$$r_{xy} = \frac{Fv_{2(x)} + Fv_{2(y)} - 2Fv_{1(x)} v_{1(y)} - \sum (X' - Y')^2}{2F\sigma_x \sigma_y}$$

$$= \frac{v_{2(x)} + v_{2(y)} - 2v_{1(x)} v_{1(y)} - \dfrac{1}{F} \sum (X' - Y')^2}{2\sigma_x \sigma_y}. \tag{XV.17}$$

In the expression on the right-hand side all $v$'s are obtained in calculating $\sigma_x \sigma_y$, so that we now have to calculate $\sum (X' - Y')^2$. This is very simple. We shall show it by the same example.

In Table 15.13 we join by slanted broken lines the panels of the table in which the values of the differences $X' - Y'$ are the same. In further calculations the sign of the difference will not matter because we operate here with the squares of the differences. To calculate $\sum (X' - Y')^2 = \sum f_{xy}(X' - Y')^2$ we design Table 15.14 (p. 460). Here $f_{xy}$ is the sum of the differences $X' - Y'$. The total $\sum f_{xy}$ should, of course, equal the total number of observations.

Introducing the sum $\sum f_{xy} (X' - Y')^2$ and the previously calculated values of $v$ and $\sigma$ to formula (XV.15) we obtain

$$r_{xy} = \frac{0 \cdot 8570 + 1 \cdot 3758 + 2 \times 0 \cdot 0949 \times 0 \cdot 24707 - \dfrac{683}{769}}{2 \times 0 \cdot 9209 \times 1 \cdot 14466}$$

$$= \frac{0 \cdot 8570 + 1 \cdot 3758 + 0 \cdot 0469 - 0 \cdot 8882}{2 \cdot 1118} = \frac{1 \cdot 3915}{2 \cdot 1118} = 0 \cdot 659$$

The result is, of course, the same as before. The calculation proceeds much more rapidly than by the previous method, since we can calculate $\sum (X' - Y')^2$ much more easily than $\sum X'Y'$. However, the method of differences does not save any time if it is necessary to calculate the arithmetic means of particular rows and columns since for computing these averages we need the series of quantities which we have denoted in Table 15.12 (p. 456) by $(a)$. It is the calculation of this series of quantities $(a)$ that is most troublesome in calculating $X'Y'$, whereas the calculation of $(b)$ according to $(a)$ is very simple. In most cases the knowledge of the averages of rows and columns, and thus of the regression lines is very useful, and often necessary, if only for evaluating approximately whether it is permissible to smooth the empirical lines by a straight line. For this reason the effective method of differences is seldom used.

TABLE 15.13. CORRELATION BETWEEN HEIGHT AND
WEIGHT OF 7-YEAR-OLD GIRLS

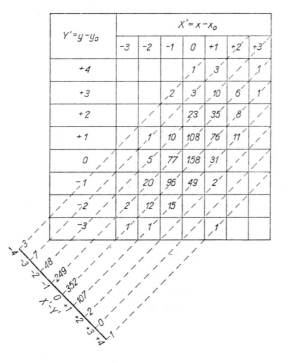

The calculation of the correlation coefficient by the method of differences has been presented here after the prominent Russian mathematician and statistician E. E. Slutsky (see E. E. Slutsky:*Teoria korelatsee ee elementy utchenya o krivych raspredyelyenia* (Kiev, 1912, pp. 108–10). In this form this method gives more correct results than the method proposed by the English statistician K. Pearson.

Other tables shown here as examples of correlation give the following numerical results:

Yields per hectare of barley and oats (Table 15.5 p. 431) $r = +0 \cdot 91$.

Yields per hectare of potatoes and wheat (Table 15.6 p. 433) $r = +0 \cdot 72$.

Average temperature in July and September (Table 15.7 p. 434) $r = +0 \cdot 001$.

TABLE 15.14. CALCULATION OF $\Sigma f_{xy} \ (X'-Y')^2$

| $(X'-Y')^2$ | $f_{xy}$ | $f_{xy} \ (X'-Y')^2$ |
|---|---|---|
| 0 | 352 | 0 |
| 1 | 356 | 356 |
| 4 | 50 | 200 |
| 9 | 7 | 63 |
| 16 | 4 | 64 |
| Total | 769 | 683 |

The above examples produce a wide range of correlation coefficients: from $+0 \cdot 98$ in the case of the yields per hectare of wheat and oats (Table 15.1 p. 425 and the calculation shown in Table 15.9 p. 448) to the complete lack of correlation in the case of average temperatures in July and September (Table 15.7 p. 434). We have also had a case of negative correlation in which decreasing average values of one characteristic correspond to increasing values of the other (Table 15.2 p. 426 and the calculation shown in Table 15.10 p. 449). If we look closely at the tables on which the calculations are based we can say that the results obtained are not surprising because we could have predicted whether or not the correlation would be strong. Naturally, only the calculation can produce a precise measure of the correlation and enable us to determine the position of the regression lines.

The cognitive value of the correlation coefficient and the regression coefficient must be carefully discussed from the point of view of the subject-matter if the complicated and time-consuming statistical calculations are not to be a useless exercise but are to help us understand reality. The interpretation of these measures is not simple and misunderstandings may easily result.

This subject will be discussed later. Before we do that, however, we should first consider the quite frequent case in which the regression curve is not a straight line.

# CHAPTER 16

# CURVILINEAR REGRESSION. INTERPRETATION OF MEASURES OF CORRELATION

## 1. CURVILINEAR REGRESSION

The formulae for calculating the correlation coefficient are based on the assumption that regression is linear. If empirical regression curves are not exactly straight lines, then we assume that the deviations from the straight line are random and due to the small number of observations. The regression line calculated by the method of least squares can be regarded, in such cases, as the best approximation to the line for a sufficiently large number of observations.

However, sometimes the averages of the columns or rows do not form a straight line, but a curve. In this case we can fit to it by the method of least squares that straight line which deviates least from the empirical points. However, this is always an artificial solution, and the correlation coefficient based on such a calculation is not a proper measure of the intensity of the correlation: as we shall see later, it is always too low.

A proper measure of correlation in cases of curvilinear regression is the *correlation ratio* denoted by the Greek letter $\eta$.

As we know, in correlation the arithmetic means of the values of characteristic $x$ change with changes in the values of $y$ (and vice versa). In calculating the correlation coefficient we assume that the curve so formed is a straight line. We begin the calculation of the correlation ratio by observing the existence of correlation means that for a given value of characteristic $x$ the dispersion of characteristic $y$ is less than its general dispersion. We pointed this out in discussing the examples of contingency tables (see p. 430 *et seq.*). Generalizing we can say that when there is a unique functional relationship between $y$ and $x$, the dispersion of $y$ corresponding to a given $x$ is zero; when there is no correlation the dispersion of $y$ corresponding to a given $x$ is the same as the general dispersion of characteristic $y$, because we can then assume, for a sufficiently large number of observations, that the values of $y$ corresponding to a given $x$ are distributed in the same way as all the values of $y$. This means that they have the same arithmetic mean, standard deviation and other numerical characteristics as $y$ in general, regardless of the value of $x$. In the case of correlation the standard deviation of the $y$'s for specific values of $x$ is greater than zero but less than the general standard deviation of $y$.

461

The starting point for determining correlation is the ratio of the variation in $y$ for definite $x$ to the general variation in $y$. If we denote the variation in $y$ for a definite $x$ by $\sigma^2_{y(x)}$ and the general variation by $\sigma^2_y$ we obtain the ratio

$$\frac{\sigma^2_{y(x)}}{\sigma^2_y}$$

By the above argument this ratio equals one when there is no correlation between the characteristics $x$ and $y$, and equals zero when the relationship is strictly functional. The definition of the correlation ratio is given by the expression

$$\eta_{yx} = \sqrt{1 - \frac{\sigma^2_{y(x)}}{\sigma^2_y}}. \qquad (XVI.1)$$

The expression under the root sign equals one when the relationship is functional $\left(\text{when } \dfrac{\sigma^2_{y(x)}}{\sigma^2_y} = 0\right)$, and equals zero when there is no correlation (because then $\sigma^2_{y(x)} = \sigma^2_y$).

The expression $\eta_{xy}$ is read: "the correlation ratio of $y$ on $x$." Accordingly

$$\eta_{xy} = \sqrt{1 - \frac{\sigma^2_{x(y)}}{\sigma^2_x}} \qquad (XVI.2)$$

expresses the correlation ratio of $x$ on $y$. It is always assumed to have the plus sign.

If we calculate from a contingency table we should compute for each column the deviations of particular values of $y$ from the arithmetic mean of $y$ for a given column, square the deviations and divide the sum of these squares for the whole table by the total number of observations. This calculation is cumbersome. We can achieve the same result more easily by calculating $\sigma^2_{y(x)}$ using a revised formula. We can prove that

$$\sigma^2_y = \sigma^2_{y(x)} + \sigma^2_{\bar{y}(x)},$$

or else

$$\sigma^2_{y(x)} = \sigma^2_y - \sigma^2_{\bar{y}(x)},$$

where $\sigma^2_{\bar{y}(x)}$ is the variation in the average values of $y$ corresponding to the specific values of $x$. This theorem is given without proof.

Substituting in the equation

$$\eta^2_{yx} = 1 - \frac{\sigma^2_{y(x)}}{\sigma^2_y}$$

we get

$$\eta^2_{yx} = 1 - \frac{\sigma^2_{y(x)} - \sigma^2_{\bar{y}(x)}}{\sigma^2_y} = 1 - 1 + \frac{\sigma^2_{\bar{y}(x)}}{\sigma^2_y} = \frac{\sigma^2_{\bar{y}(x)}}{\sigma^2_y}$$

and finally

$$\eta_{xy} = \frac{\sigma_{\bar{x}(y)}}{\sigma_x}. \qquad (XVI.3)$$

The correlation ratio of $y$ on $x$ is thus expressed by the ratio of the standard deviation of the average values of $y$ corresponding to specific values of $x$, to the general standard deviation of $y$.

The correlation ratio of $x$ on $y$ is

$$\eta_{yx} = \frac{\sigma_{\bar{y}(x)}}{\sigma_y}. \tag{XVI.4}$$

$\eta_{yx}$ is not equal to $\eta_{xy}$ except for a special case which will be discussed later.

To explain certain relations in the contingency table, let us consider an artificial example. Let $x$ assume the values 1, 2, 3, 4 or 5, and $y$ the values 1, 2 or 3; the variable in both cases is discrete. The frequency of the combinations of different values of the two characteristics is given in Table 16.1.

TABLE 16.1. EXAMPLE OF FUNCTIONAL RELATIONSHIP

| $y$ | $x$ | | | | | |
|---|---|---|---|---|---|---|
| | 1 | 2 | 3 | 4 | 5 | $f_y$ |
| 1 | 3 | | | | 3 | 6 |
| 2 | | 3 | | 3 | | 6 |
| 3 | | | 6 | | | 6 |
| $f_x$ | 3 | 3 | 6 | 3 | 3 | 18 |

When the value of $x$ is 1 or 5 the value of $y$ can only be 1, for $x = 2$ or 4, $y$ is always 2, for $x = 3$ also $y = 3$. And, vice versa, for $y = 1$ the value of $y$ can only be 1 or 5, etc. In other words only one value of $y$ corresponds to each value of $x$; only one value of $x$ corresponds to $y = 3$; and two definite values of $x$ correspond to $y = 1$ and $y = 2$. Thus we have a unique functional dependence of $y$ on $x$, and a many-one functional dependence of $x$ on $y$. But the correlation coefficient in this case is zero. We can check this easily by forming the products $XY$. The arithmetic mean of $x$ is 3, the arithmetic mean of $y$ is 2 and thus in the first row we have $(-2) \times (-1) \times 3 + (+2) \times (-1) \times 3 = 0$, and the same in the second and third rows. If $\sum XY = 0$ then, of course, the quotient $\dfrac{\sum XY}{\sigma_x \sigma_y} = 0$. We have obtained this result because the relationship is not linear.

There is no need to select artificial constructions. Yule[160] gives the following example. For each of the 632 registration districts in England and Wales the ratio of the births of boys to total births in the period 1881–90 has been calculated; the contingency table (see Table 16.2 p. 466) is designed according to the values of this ratio, and the total number of births in a given district in this period. The spread in both directions is considerable: there are 465 to 545 births of boys per thousand

---

[160] **Yule:** *Wstęp do teorii statystyki* (*Introduction to the Theory of Statistics* (Polish translation)), Warsaw, 1921, p. 193.

births. The total number of births drops below 4000 in many districts, the largest number is 150,000; this is a consequence of very unhomogeneous districts.

The distribution of the data in the table and the arithmetic means of the characteristics in relation to the values of the other characteristics reveal that the average number of births of boys per thosand births does not change in relation to the total number of births in the district. Minor fluctuations (from $508 \cdot 6$ to $51 \cdot 1$) can be regarded as accidental. But the total number of births in the district changes with the ratio of the births of boys in general; where this ratio is very low (below 495 per thousand) or very high (above 531 per thousand) the total number of births in the district is always very small. This apparent paradox can be explained very simply: the ratio of the births of both sexes, being a random phenomenon, is always close to the average when the number of observations is large (as it is in large districts) and the deviations from the average are more frequent the smaller the number of observations.

Numerically the problem can be presented as follows. The correlation coefficient between the two characteristics

$$r_{xy} = - \, 0 \cdot 0025$$

is very close to zero. The correlation ratio of the total number of births in the district and thus, in a sense, of the size of the district ($y$) in relation to the ratio of the births of boys to total births ($x$)

$$\eta_{yx} = 0 \cdot 52,$$

is fairly high. The inverse correlation ratio

$$\eta_{xy} = 0 \cdot 034$$

is very close to zero.

The first of these correlation ratios, $\eta_{yx}$, shows a formal statistical relationship of no consequence to the subject. The second, $\eta_{xy}$, can be interpreted from the point of view of the subject, but it shows what is obvious even without statistical calculation, namely that the relative frequency of the births of boys does not depend upon the size of the district (more strictly, upon the total number of births in the district) in which the births are registered.

It should be noted that the correlation coefficient has only one value expressing the relationship between the values of $x$ and $y$, whereas there are two correlation ratios: the correlation ratio of $y$ on $x$ ($\eta_{yx}$) and the correlation ratio of $x$ on $y$ ($\eta_{xy}$). These ratios differ from one another; in extreme cases one of them may equal one and the other zero.

The relationship between $r$ and $\eta$ is expressed by the formula

$$\eta \geqslant |r|, \tag{XVI.5}$$

which means that the correlation ratio may be equal to or greater than the absolute value of the correlation coefficient. They are equal only when the correlation is linear. In all other cases the value of the correlation ratio is larger than the absolute value of the correlation coefficient.

When we have regression curves which differ little from straight lines, the correlation ratios differ little from one another, and the correlation coefficient can be regarded as an approximate measure of the intensity of correlation, a measure which characterizes correlation, although it errs on the low side.

We shall show the computational procedure using the example on the effect of nitrogen fertilizer on the yield of wheat.

We calculate the correlation ratio of the yield of wheat on the amount of nitrogen used, i.e. $\eta_{yx}$. We first calculate, in the usual way, the general standard deviation of the yield of wheat (on the basis of the value of $y$ in the first column and the "total" frequencies on the right-hand side of the table).

We obtain $\sigma_y = 9 \cdot 187$. The arithmetic mean $y = 25 \cdot 005$, or roughly 25.

Now we calculate the standard deviation of $\bar{y}(x)$, allowing for the fact that the particular values of $\bar{y}(x)$ appear with different frequencies (Table 16.4).

$$\sigma^2_{\bar{y}(x)} = \frac{15,186 \cdot 88}{193} = 78 \cdot 6885,$$

$$\sigma_{\bar{y}(x)} = \sqrt{78 \cdot 6885} = 8 \cdot 871,$$

$$\eta_{yx} = \frac{8 \cdot 871}{9 \cdot 187} = 0 \cdot 97.$$

The correlation ratio reaches a very high value here, being close to one. This indicates that the dependence of the yield of wheat on the amount of nitrogen is nearly functional; in other words the amount of nitrogen almost directly determines the yield.

The inverse correlation ratio (of the amount of nitrogen on the yield of wheat) is

$$\eta_{xy} = \frac{32 \cdot 487}{36 \cdot 808} = 0 \cdot 88.$$

It is less than $\eta_{yx}$ because for very high yields of wheat amounting to 28–32 and 32–6 bushels per acre, the dispersion of the amounts of nitrogen is wide.

In this example the measure $(\eta_{xy})$ is devoid of any real meaning. However, because of the importance of the reasoning involved we shall discuss further the correlation ratios of the yield on the amount of nitrogen and of the amount of nitrogen on the yield.

It is worth noting that the empirical regression curve of the amount of nitrogen on the yield of wheat approximates a straight line, in contrast to the empirical regression curve of the yield on the amount of nitrogen.

TABLE 16.2. CORRELATION BETWEEN NUMBER OF BIRTHS OF BOYS PER 1000 BIRTHS AND TOTAL NUMBER OF BIRTHS IN THE DISTRICT[a]

| Total number of births in the district in thousands (y) | Number of births of boys per 1000 births (x) | | | | | | | | | | | | | | $f_y$ | $\bar{x}(y)$ |
|---|---|---|---|---|---|---|---|---|---|---|---|---|---|---|---|---|
| | 465–471 | 471–477 | 477–483 | 483–489 | 489–495 | 495–501 | 501–507 | 507–513 | 513–519 | 519–525 | 525–531 | 531–537 | 537–543 | 543–549 | | |
| | Number of districts | | | | | | | | | | | | | | | |
| 0–12 | 1 | 1 | 2 | 4 | 10 | 32 | 104 | 139 | 103 | 33 | 4 | 4 | 1 | 1 | 439 | 509·8 |
| 12–24 | | | | | | 1 | 17 | 44 | 23 | 4 | 1 | | | | 89 | 511·1 |
| 24–36 | | | | | | | 10 | 19 | 4 | | | | | | 34 | 508·6 |
| 36–48 | | | | | | | 2 | 18 | 5 | | | | | | 25 | 510·7 |
| 48–60 | | | | | | | 5 | 16 | | | | | | | 21 | 508·6 |
| 60–72 | | | | | | | 5 | 6 | | | | | | | 11 | 507·3 |
| 72–84 | | | | | | | 1 | 4 | | | | | | | 5 | 508·8 |
| 84–96 | | | | | | | | 4 | | | | | | | 4 | 510 |
| 96–108 | | | | | | | | 3 | | | | | | | 3 | 510 |
| 108–120 | | | | | | | | | | | | | | | — | ⋮ |
| 120–132 | | | | | | | | | | | | | | | — | ⋮ |
| 132–144 | | | | | | | | | | | | | | | — | ⋮ |
| 144–156 | | | | | | | | 1 | | | | | | | 1 | 510 |
| $f_x$ | 1 | 1 | 2 | 4 | 10 | 33 | 144 | 254 | 135 | 37 | 5 | 4 | 1 | 1 | 632 | · |
| $\bar{y}(x)$ | 6 | 6 | 6 | 6 | 6 | 6·73 | 13·84 | 21·21 | 10·09 | 7·30 | 8·40 | 6 | 6 | 6 | · | · |

[a] In the table the data are grouped in larger classes than in the original study; Yule accepts class intervals of 3 births of boys per 1000 births and of 4000 total births in registration districts.

TABLE 16.3. CORRELATION BETWEEN AMOUNT OF NITROGEN AND YIELD OF WHEAT[161]

| Yield of wheat in bushels per acre $(y)$ | Amount of Nitrogen in lb per acre $(x)$ | | | | | | | | | | |
|---|---|---|---|---|---|---|---|---|---|---|---|
| | 0–20 | 20–40 | 40–60 | 60–80 | 80–100 | 100–120 | 120–140 | 140–160 | 160–180 | Total | $\bar{x}(y)$ |
| 32–36 | | | | 5 | 16 | 12 | 4 | 5 | 2 | 44 | 107·3 |
| 28–32 | | | 1 | 20 | 21 | 8 | 4 | 1 | | 55 | 88·9 |
| 24–28 | | | 16 | 19 | | | | | | 35 | 60·9 |
| 20–24 | | | 13 | | | | | | | 13 | 50·0 |
| 16–20 | | 12 | | | | | | | | 12 | 30·0 |
| 12–16 | | 8 | | | | | | | | 8 | 30·0 |
| 8–12 | 3 | 5 | | | | | | | | 8 | 22·5 |
| 4–8 | 10 | | | | | | | | | 10 | 10·0 |
| 0–4 | 8 | | | | | | | | | 8 | 10·0 |
| Total | 21 | 25 | 30 | 44 | 37 | 20 | 8 | 6 | 2 | 193 | · |
| $\bar{y}(x)$ | 5·0 | 15·1 | 24·4 | 28·7 | 31·7 | 32·4 | 32·0 | 33·3 | 34·0 | · | · |

TABLE 16.4. CALCULATION OF $\sigma\,\bar{y}(x)$

| $\bar{y}(x)$ | $f$ | $\bar{y}(x)-\bar{y}$ | $[\bar{y}(x)-\bar{y}]^2$ | $f[\bar{y}(x)-\bar{y}]^2$ |
|---|---|---|---|---|
| 5·0 | 21 | −20·0 | 400·00 | 8,400·00 |
| 15·1 | 25 | − 9·9 | 98·01 | 2,450·25 |
| 24·4 | 30 | − 0·6 | 0·36 | 10·80 |
| 28·7 | 44 | + 3·7 | 13·69 | 602·36 |
| 31·7 | 37 | + 6·7 | 44·89 | 1,660·93 |
| 32·4 | 20 | + 7·4 | 54·76 | 1,095·20 |
| 32·0 | 8 | + 7·0 | 49·00 | 392·00 |
| 33·3 | 6 | + 8·3 | 68·89 | 413·34 |
| 34·0 | 2 | + 9·0 | 81·00 | 162·00 |
| Total | 193 | · | · | 15,186·88 |

The correlation coefficient

$$r_{xy} = +0\cdot85$$

is therefore much smaller than the correlation ratio $\eta_{yx}$ and it is also smaller, though not much, than the correlation ratio $\eta_{xy}$. But in absolute terms the value of the correlation coefficient is high, even though the regression is distinctly curvilinear.

It follows from the definition of the correlation ratio that this measure cannot be calculated directly from the individual observations. In this case only one value of $y$ corresponds to each $x$, and therefore the dispersion of $y$ for a given $x$ is always zero, and the dispersion of $x$ for a given $y$ is also zero. In this way in formula XVI.1 (p. 462).

$$\sigma^2_{y(x)} = 0,$$

and therefore $\eta_{yx} = 1$.

[161] F. C. Mills: *Statistical Methods*, New York, 1938, p. 415.

If we calculate by formula (XVI.3) (p. 462), the dispersion of the average values of $y$ for specific values of $x$ is the same as the general dispersion of $y$ (which follows from the reasoning on p. 461), the numerator of the fraction is equal to the denominator and $\eta_{yx} = 1$. The same is true with regard to formula (XVI.4).

Errors may result from calculating the correlation ratio from the table with insufficiently detailed classification when the dispersion of particular rows and columns may be apparently reduced, especially when all the observations in a given row or column happen to go into one cell. In our example (Table 16.3 p. 467) this happened in the last column (for 160–80 lb of nitrogen per acre the yields of wheat are in both cases within the limits of 32–6 bushels per acre). The same thing happened in the first, second, fourth, fifth and sixth rows from the bottom. In these rows and columns the standard deviation apparently is zero, which is almost certainly not true, and the corresponding correlation ratio is thus artificially inflated. It follows that the correlation ratio should not be calculated from $y$ contingency table with a small number of observations, particularly if in many rows and columns only one cell is filled in. In our case this reservation is particularly valid with regard to the calculation of the correlation ratio of the amount of nitrogen on the yield of wheat, and less valid only with regard to the correlation ratio of the yield of wheat on the amount of nitrogen (only in one column are all the observations in one cell).

It follows that only seldom will tables on agricultural experiments be suitable for calculating the correlation ratio, because they are usually based on a small number of observations, and cannot therefore be arranged into classes with a small class interval.

In any case, it usually happens that all observations fall in one cell only when the dispersion in a given direction, although not zero, is small. This means that in such cases even a detailed classification would produce a high correlation ratio. When it is calculated on the basis of excessively large class intervals, it tends to exaggerate the intensity of correlation but in principle it does not present a basically false picture.

The correlation ratios $\eta_{yx}$ and $\eta_{xy}$ can be interpreted to mean that a high value indicates that the value of $y$ is almost uniquely determined by the value of $x$ (and vice versa, $x$ is determined by $y$) and a low value suggests that other factors besides $x$ affect $y$ to a considerable extent (and vice versa). In a graph this will manifest ifself in the first case by the points being located very close to the regression line, and in the second case, by being widely scattered.

This information can be very important. However, a knowledge of the shape of the regression lines can be much more important in learning about reality. Both the correlation coefficient and the correlation ratio merely state the existence of correlation and the shape of the regression lines determines the nature of this correlation.

Very characteristic in this respect is the last example on the influence of nitrogen fertilizer on yield. The figures expressing the average yields for various amounts of nitrogen indicate that an increase in the amount of nitrogen at first results in a substantial increase in the yield, but when the amount of nitrogen is further increased the rate of increase in the yield declines and levels off almost completely when the amount of nitrogen becomes very large.

Even more characteristic is the example (Table 16.5) on the influence of irrigation on the yield of alfalfa[162]. It is noticeable how an increase in the amount of water at first increases the yield rapidly, then more slowly, until after a certain point the yield begins to decrease with a further increase in the amount of water. It is obvious that such results of statistical investigation enable us to draw very important practical conclusions.[163]

An important reservation should be made here. In both these experiments the impact of only one factor was considered: nitrogen or water. As we know the yields are affected not by one factor but by many. For instance, wheat will react differently to an increase in the amount of nitrogen if, at the same time, potassium and phosphorus fertilizers are used, or if the humidity of the soil is changed, and so on. In other words, on the basis of these examples it is not possible to answer the question to what extent it is worth while to increase the amount of fertilizers or irrigation. In this sense the American experiments should be regarded as incomplete. For exhaustive research it would be necessary to plan experiments and to use the method of multiple correlation analysis which we shall discuss later.

TABLE 16.5. EFFECT OF IRRIGATION ON
YIELD OF ALFALFA

| Water supply (in) | Average yield (tons per acre) |
|---|---|
| 0 | 3.88 |
| 12 | 5·63 |
| 18 | 6·80 |
| 24 | 7·92 |
| 30 | 8·98 |
| 36 | 9·27 |
| 48 | 9·02 |
| 60 | 8·42 |

Another reservation of a technical statistical nature is that in many cases experimental stations publish only the average yields obtained by varying the amount of fertilizer without the corresponding contingency tables with actual frequencies; this practice makes it difficult for a statistician to evaluate the results.

---

[162] *Ibid.*, p. 405.
[163] Compare with the example on p. 437.

Directors of experiments also sometimes limit their study to too few cases, e.g. only two or three different amounts of nitrogen.

Of course, these limitations are partly justified by the expense involved in extensive experiments. But the problem is so important that it may well be worth while to spend more money.

We shall now consider one more example of a contingency table with a very characteristic pattern of curvilinear correlation (Table 16.6 p. 471).

Some small changes have been made in the table in comparison with the source from which the data was obtained: (1) In the original publication the ages of fathers over 50 were given in 10-year groups, and we have divided them by estimates into 5-year groups. (2) In the original publication there is a group of 76 mothers over 50 years of age, and in all these cases the age of the father was given as 50–59 years: this group has been left out because the data do not seem reliable. (3) We have disregarded the few cases in which the age of the father or mother was unknown.

The table is characteristic also in that almost all the cells are filled, even those in which a very high age of the mother is combined with a very low age of the father, and vice versa. However, the greatest numbers of observations are located close to the diagonal, at a relatively low age of both mother and father. The arithmetic means calculated in both directions show, on the whole, an increase in the values of one characteristic with increasing values of the other, with one exception which comes out most clearly in the diagram (Fig. 16.1 p. 471).

As we can see, the age of the father rises with the increasing age of the mother although the line deviates from a straight line. The changes in the age of the mother with changing ages of the father are more complicated: for a very low age of the father the age of the mother rises very slowly, then more rapidly and then again more slowly until the peak for fathers of 50–54, after which a decline begins—not too rapid but quite distinct. For the most advanced ages of fathers, 70–74 years, the age of the mother is lower by 2·36 years than for fathers of 50–54. The number of observations is very large, which means that both regression lines are smooth so that there is no fear of random distortions.

The calculation of the correlation ratios and the correlation coefficient gives the following results.

The correlation ratio of the age of the mother on the age of the father is

$$\eta_{xy} = 0 \cdot 710$$

The correlation ratio of the age of the father on the age of the mother is

$$\eta_{yx} = 0 \cdot 697.$$

The correlation coefficient

$$r_{xy} = + 0 \cdot 689.$$

TABLE 16.6 CORRELATION BETWEEN AGES OF PARENTS OF LIVE LEGITIMATE INFANTS IN THE WESTERN PROVINCES IN 1932[164]

| Age of father (y) | Age of mother (x) | | | | | | | $f_y$ | $\bar{x}(y)$ |
| --- | --- | --- | --- | --- | --- | --- | --- | --- | --- |
| | 19 and less | 20–24 | 25–29 | 30–34 | 35–39 | 40–44 | 45–49 | | |
| 70–74 | | 2 | 2 | 18 | 16 | 10 | 3 | 51 | 36·32 |
| 65–69 | | 5 | 6 | 22 | 36 | 27 | 7 | 103 | 37·11 |
| 60–64 | | 7 | 14 | 48 | 143 | 100 | 12 | 324 | 37·92 |
| 55–59 | | 9 | 27 | 157 | 276 | 257 | 70 | 796 | 38·50 |
| 50–54 | 2 | 12 | 100 | 325 | 600 | 650 | 180 | 1869 | 38·68 |
| 45–49 | 5 | 58 | 286 | 890 | 1756 | 1752 | 282 | 5009 | 38·14 |
| 40–44 | 14 | 207 | 896 | 2627 | 4369 | 1951 | 114 | 10,178 | 36·07 |
| 35–39 | 36 | 753 | 3110 | 6678 | 5180 | 794 | 35 | 16,586 | 33·15 |
| 30–34 | 204 | 3913 | 12,036 | 10,042 | 2260 | 294 | 19 | 28·768 | 29·45 |
| 25–29 | 1215 | 14,946 | 16,193 | 3962 | 546 | 63 | 8 | 36,933 | 25·86 |
| 20–24 | 1249 | 5827 | 2244 | 371 | 59 | 12 | | 9762 | 23·50 |
| 19 and less | 22 | 53 | 16 | 5 | 1 | 1 | | 98 | 23·06 |
| $f_x$ | 2747 | 25,792 | 34,930 | 25,145 | 15,242 | 5891 | 730 | 110,477 | . |
| $\bar{y}(x)$ | 25.78 | 27·61 | 30·45 | 35·00 | 40·22 | 44·85 | 48·36 | . | . |

Each of the correlation ratios is only a little larger than the correlation coefficient: the shape of the regression line does not differ much from a straight line. The relatively low value of the correlation ratios is due to the fact that for each age of the mother the dispersion of the age of the father is considerable, and vice versa.

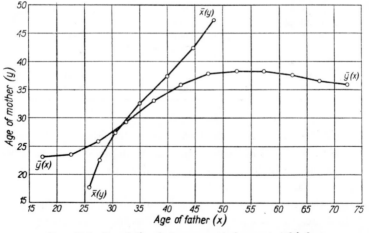

FIG. 16.1. Correlation between ages of parents of infants.

164 Małżeństwa, urodzenia, zgony (Marriages, Births, Deaths) 1931, 1932, *Statystyka Polski* Series C, No. 102, Table 13, p. 205.

The difference between the absolute value of $r$ and the value of $\eta$ can be a measure of the curvilinearity of the regression. Usually the difference of the squares $\eta^2 - r^2$ is taken as a measure. We shall return to this matter later on.

In analysing curvilinear regression it is usually more important to determine the shape of the regression line than the intensity of the correlation. We shall consider two more examples of regression empirically established.

The first is taken from *Statistics on the Insured in 1935* (Warsaw, 1938) published by the Social Insurance Agency. In this publication (Table 2, 7 p. 42) average weekly earnings in 1935 are given by age for the workers employed in December 1935 (Table 16.7).

The pattern is very characteristic. The earnings of children and young people are very low but they increase rapidly with age; the maximum for men is reached at the ages of 40–44 and for women of 35–39. Afterwards the earnings decline and for the oldest age group are lower than the maximum by 32 per cent for men and by 36 per cent for women.

TABLE 16.7. CORRELATION BETWEEN EARNINGS AND AGE OF
INSURED WORKERS

| Age (years) | Weekly earnings (zlotys) | |
| --- | --- | --- |
| | men | women |
| 10–14 | 6·25 | 6·40 |
| 15–19 | 9·17 | 7·32 |
| 20–24 | 17·77 | 9·02 |
| 25–29 | 25·13 | 10·88 |
| 30–34 | 28·23 | 11·79 |
| 35–39 | 29·19 | 13·30 |
| 40–44 | 30·64 | 12·60 |
| 45–49 | 29·63 | 12·32 |
| 50–54 | 28·69 | 12·01 |
| 55–59 | 27·31 | 10·24 |
| 60–64 | 25·59 | 10·84 |
| 65 and over | 20·96 | 8·50 |

An economic interpretation is relatively easy with respect to the first, increasing part of the series. Increases in earnings are due to improved qualifications and consequent promotions to higher positions as well as to better experience and skill, and the resultant increase in labour productivity. These factors operate in the same direction. Decreases in earnings past the maximum can probably be explained by the fact that the older workers have poorer qualifications because they had more difficulty in acquiring them, and by declining efficiency due to old age. The available statistics do not enable us to separate the influence of these two factors, which are very different from a sociological point of view.

The next example pertains to the correlation between rent per cubic metre and the size of the flat. A study of this kind of correlation was made in Warsaw in 1919.[165] The situation for one-room flats is presented in Table 16.8.

Rent calculated per unit of cubic capacity decreases with increasing size of the flat, and for small flats this decrease is very rapid: the rate of decrease slows down for larger flats. In capitalist Poland the poor, who occupied the smallest flats, paid on average the highest rent per cubic metre. A similar picture is obtained for two- and three-room flats.

TABLE 16.8 CORRELATION BETWEEN RENT
AND CAPACITY OF FLATS

| Capacity of flat (m³) | Annual rent in Polish marks per m³ |
|---|---|
| 20 and less | 8·38 |
| 21–40 | 4·70 |
| 41–60 | 3·56 |
| 61–80 | 2·80 |
| 81–100 | 2·00 |

Sometimes it is necessary to smooth empirical regression lines. In cases of linear regression the smoothing is done automatically by the method of least squares in calculating the correlation coefficient. When regression is curvilinear smoothing is not done automatically, and the calculation of the intensity of correlation (e.g. the correlation ratio) as well as the smoothing of empirical regression lines must be made separately. In cases of curvilinear regression smoothing is usually much more complicated than in cases of linear regression.

Certain simple methods of smoothing will be discussed in the Appendix at the end of the book. Here we shall confine ourselves to a few comments to explain under what circumstances smoothing is permissible and necessary.

We can replace an empirical line by a smooth line if the fluctuations in the empirical line are random and due to factors of secondary importance, not related to the essence of the problem and not controllable. Such random fluctuations are in the example in Table 15.7 (p. 434) related to temperatures in July and September. We can assume that the smoothed line gives a better picture of reality than the empirical line and is therefore better suited to drawing practical conclusions.

It should be remembered, however, that not every deviation from a smooth

[165] The results of the census of real estate property and flats in Great Warsaw in 1919, Volume II, *Accomodation Statistics*, Warsaw, 1923, p. 102 and manuscripts burned in 1944.

31

pattern is due to the insufficient number of observations. It may be due to disturbances related to the essence of the phenomenon which should be brought to light and not obscured.

For this reason we shall not smooth empirical regression lines if they are based on a large number of observations (e.g. Table 16.6, p. 471)[166]. Nor shall we smooth empirical lines with a very irregular pattern when all inferences concerning the real shape of the regression lines are uncertain.

When we decide in favour of smoothing we have the choice of two alternatives: either graphically by hand, or by one of the many mathematical methods. The graphical method is easy and fast, although it is undoubtedly fairly arbitrary. On the other hand, it enables us to adjust the line by allowing for the deviations that we consider relevant. A seemingly objective mathematical method when used without due care may distort reality by forcing it into a formal but artificial patern. This does not mean, however, that mathematical methods should not be used: they should be used with proper care and in appropriate circumstances.

## 2. INTERPRETATION OF THE MEASURES OF CORRELATION

Let us now return to the problem of the interpretation of the correlation coefficients, correlation ratios and regression lines. This problem has been touched upon earlier in this book but some generalizations should be made and essential conclusions should be drawn.

Let us first compare the correlation coefficients and the correlation ratios discussed so far and add a few more examples.

The height ($x$) and weight ($y$) of 7-year-old girls (Warsaw)
$$r_{xy} = +0 \cdot 66$$

„    „    „    „    „    „    „ 9-year-old girls (Łódź)
$$r_{xy} = +0 \cdot 71$$

„    „    „    „    „    „    „ 12-year-old girls (Łódź)
$$r_{xy} = +0 \cdot 69$$

„    „    „    „    „    „    „ 15-year-old girls (Łódź)
$$r_{xy} = +0 \cdot 51$$

„    „    „    „    „ of female university students in Warsaw in 1946, aged 18–19
$$r_{xy} = +0 \cdot 45$$

---

[166] We might think of smoothing out only the lowest and the two highest age groups of father where the number of observations is small. We might try to replace the irregular empirical line (due to the use of the age groups of several years duration) by a smooth line which is a better representation, but this is a different problem.

The height ($x$) and weight ($y$) of female university students in Warsaw in 1946, aged 20

$$r_{xy} = +0\cdot56$$

„    „    „    „    „    „ of female university student in Warsaw in 1946, aged 20–24[167]

$$r_{xy} = +0\cdot62$$

„    „    „    „    „    „ of draftees of category A (born in 1906)

$$r_{xy} = +0\cdot69$$

„    „    „    „    „    „ of draftees of poor physique (born in 1907)

$$r_{xy} = +0\cdot76$$

Yields per hectare (1948) of oats ($x$) and wheat ($y$)

$$r_{xy} = +0\cdot98$$

„    „    „    (1928–37) of oats ($x$) and barley ($y$)

$$r_{xy} = +0\cdot91$$

„    „    „        „    „    „    „ and rye ($y$)

$$r_{xy} = +0\cdot92$$

„    „    „        „ of potatoes ($x$) and wheat ($y$)

$$r_{xy} = +0\cdot72$$

„    „    „        „    „    „    ($x$) and rye ($y$)

$$r_{xy} = +0\cdot75$$

Average temperature in July ($x$) and September ($y$)

$$r_{xy} = +0\cdot001$$

Average annual pressure ($x$) and average annual temperature ($y$)

$$r_{xy} = -0\cdot47$$

Age of mother ($x$) and father ($y$) at birth of child

$$r_{xy} = +0\cdot69$$
$$\eta_{yx} = 0\cdot70$$
$$\eta_{xy} = 0\cdot71$$

Births of boys per thousand births ($x$) and total number of births in the district ($y$)

$$r_{xy} = -0\cdot0025$$
$$\eta_{yx} = 0\cdot52$$
$$\eta_{xy} = 0\cdot034$$

Amount of nitrogen fertilizer ($x$) and yield of wheat ($y$)

$$r_{xy} = +0\cdot85$$
$$\eta_{yx} = 0\cdot97$$
$$\eta_{xy} = 0\cdot88$$

---

[167] Stefan Szulc: Wzrost i waga młodzieży szkół wyższych w Warszawie w roku 1946. (The Height and Weight of University Students in Warsaw in 1946), *Przegląd Statystyczny* (*Statistical Review*), 1949, No. 1/2.

Let us now consider the correlation coefficients. It is obvious that greater height generally corresponds to greater weight, and vice versa. It is also clear that there is no functional relationship here, since other factors may cause persons of the same height to have different weights. The existence of those other disturbing factors is also reflected in the relatively low values of the correlation coefficients. The correlation coefficient between the height and the weight of 15-year-old girls is conspicuously lower than the others. This may be due to a greater influence of the disturbing factors during adolescence, but this explanation should be checked by a further investigation. Also quite striking is the exceptionally high correlation coefficient between the height and the weight of draftees of poor physique $(+0 \cdot 76)$. It is up to the physician and the antropologist to explain the causes of this phenomenon, but it is the task of the collaborating statistician to organize the statistical study of the problem so that the hypothesis suggested by them can be verified statistically.

The regression equation of weight on height may provide a hint to a physician on the state of nutrition of the patient. Certain deviations in weight are, of course, permissible and do not necessarily mean that the patient is under- or overnourished. However, the regression lines obtained on the basis of specific statistical material do not always indicate the proper weight for a given height of a healthy and properly fed man: they rather indicate the average weight for a given height in a specific population. If the state of nutrition of this population was not normal, these averages cannot be considered as indicative of what is normal.

The regression coefficient between height and weight indicates something else. According to our observations the empirical regression lines for heights of 155–80 cm for men and 145–70 cm for women are obviously similar to straight lines. This means that an increase in weight is proportional to an increase in height. The regression coefficient for men is $0 \cdot 73$ and for women is $0 \cdot 72$ which means that for each centimetre of increased height, weight increasees on the average by $0 \cdot 73$ kg for men and $0 \cdot 72$ kg for women. If all the dimensions of the human body changed proportionately to the height, then the weight would increase in proportion to the cube of the height. But in this case the regression line of weight on height could not be a straight line. The conclusion that the increase in weight is a linear function of the increase in height is of essential importance, but it should be explained by the anthropologist and the physician. The same conclusion can be reached without resorting to correlation theory, but it cannot then be expressed in numerical terms.

One more reservation should be made with reference to the example of the regression of weight on height. On the basis of Fig. 15.8 (p. 439) we have concluded that over a long range the empirical regression line can be smoothed into a straight line, except for the extremities, which create doubt. This observation leads to the conclusion that, as a rule, the calculation of a theoretical regression line can be applied only to the segment on which the regression equation is based. Extrapolation should be avoided since it is not known *a priori* what the regression is like for the values higher and lower than those on which the calculation is based.

In the example on the yields per hectare there is no proper causal relationship, because the yield of one crop does not affect the yield of the other. But there are some common factors which work in the same direction and affect the yields of different crops to a similar degree. The main factors here are the level of agricultural technique, soil, and the climatic conditions. Since the calculation is based on the average yield over a period of ten years the conditions should be understood as general conditions, stable for the whole territory, and not the specific conditions for any one year. As the requirements vary for various crops the factors mentioned above may affect different crops to a different extent, and therefore there is no functional relationship. The correlation between the yields of ear crops (between oats and wheat, oats and barley, oats and rye) is very strong (the correlation coefficient is over 0·9) and it is much weaker between the yields of potatoes and winter wheat and rye.

The lack of correlation between temperature in July and September was discussed above (p. 434): it is probable that the average temperatures of particular months are not related to each other.

The reasons for the negative correlation between the average annual pressure and the average annual temperature are complicated and should be explained by meteorology. There is probably no direct relationship between pressure and temperature. Indirectly, the existence of negative correlation can probably be explained by the fact that when the pressure is high there are fewer clouds and therefore radiation is increased, and this in turn lowers the temperature. For the time being we disregard the question whether the existence of correlation with the coefficient of $-0·48$ based only on fifteen annual observations can be considered as sufficiently conclusive.

The next example, on to the correlation between the age of the father and the mother at the time of birth is also complicated. Two factors are involved here: the correlation between the ages of spouses, and the differences in fertility at different age combinations of spouses. There is not enough material to check the influence of each of these factors separately: there are no statistics on marriages by age combinations or on fertility in relation to age combination rather than in relation to the age of one of the spouses.

The regression in the example concerning the age of parents is curvilinear. In this case the curvilinearity is not very strong so that not only the correlation ratio but also the correlation coefficient gives a fairly good picture of the relationship. However, the regression lines—at least the regression of the age of the father on the age of the mother—must not be smoothed into a straight line lest the essence of the existing relationship be lost.

In the next example, on to the correlation between the relative frequencies of the births of boys and girls and the total number of births in the district, the correlation coefficient did not describe the nature of the relationship: this was described by the correlation ratios. This example is also very characteristic for another reason. It shows numerically that the average ratio of the number of births of boys to the total number of births does not depend at all, or only to a small extent, upon the total number of births in a district, but that the number of births in the district is related to the numerical ratio of the birhts of the two sexes, or in other words, that the average number of births depends upon the relative number of births of boys. This last ratio discloses a purely formal statistical relationship with no real meaning. On the basis of the shape of the regression lines we have concluded that for the average values of the numerical ratio of the births of both sexes the districts are large, and for values higher or lower than the average the districts are smaller and the larger the deviation the smaller the district. The formal statistical relationship can be explained as indicating that in large districts with a large number of births this ratio is determined fairly accurately, and in districts with a small number of births it is subject to random fluctuations which are the greater the smaller the number of births.

Let us consider a few more paradoxes. From Russian statistics on fires in rural areas, A. A. Tschuprov[168] quotes an example indicating that the number of houses destroyed by fire increased when fire engines were used to extinguish the fires. Obviously the fact that fire engines were used did not spread the fire: the relationship is due to the fact that fire engines were available only in large villages where fires could easily spread to many buildings. Another paradox was discovered in Sweden: the existence of a distinct positive correlation between the number of storks and the relative frequency of births (urbanization reduces the birth rate, and of course also reduces the number of storks). There is very strong correlation between temperature and the position of the hands of the clock. Of course, the relationship does exist, although not between the hands of the clock and the temperature, but between temperature and the time of day, which is indicated by the position of the hands of the clock. This relationship is due to the construction of our clocks and would be quite different if the face of the clock had twenty-four hours, or if the 12-hour face were rotated through a right angle.

Examples of different types of correlation, including the last examples of statistical paradoxes, have been discussed at length in order to draw the reader's attention to the very important fact that by calculating measures of correlation we only establish formally the existence of correlation between phenomena. This is a necessary basis for drawing conclusions, but the conclusions themselves must be based on an analysis of the facts. This requirement, as we know, is a general requirement

---

[168] A. A. Tschuprov: *Grundbegriffe and Grundprobleme der Korrelationstheorie*, Berlin, 1925, p. 16.

for all studies based on statistics. However, correlation analysis helps us to see different possible formal interpretations of the same facts, or to be more exact, the danger of such interpretations if they are not based on a thorough knowledge of the problem.

Other examples of the interpretation of measures of correlation will be given during the discussion of multiple correlation and correlation between non-measurable characteristics.

# CHAPTER 17

# SOME OTHER PROBLEMS IN CORRELATION ANALYSIS

## 1. MULTIPLE CORRELATION

So far we have discussed correlation between only two characteristics although usually in real life many characteristics are involved. Simplifying the problem to two characteristics may be justified when the correlation between some particular pair is especially striking, overshadowing other relationships. But in most cases a realistic picture can only be given by considering a larger number of characteristics.

In such cases a natural scientist attempts to conduct his experiment by isolating the influence of each of the causes affecting a given phenomenon. Only this kind of analysis enables us to establish the true relationship between a phenomenon and the causes affecting it. In many cases involving statistical data it is impossible to experiment, and it is almost always impossible while studying social phenomena in the broad sense of this word. Therefore, other methods of analysis must be sought.

It should be remembered that even when the interaction of two factors can be isolated, this does not solve the whole problem, since we are usually concerned with the behaviour of a phenomenon under the influence of a whole complex set of factors.

If in statistics we deal with the three characteristics, $x$, $y$ and $z$, among which we are seeking a correlation, we can sometimes select a group of observations in which $z$ has a fixed value, and only $x$ and $y$ change. This enables us to bring out the relationship between $x$ and $y$, independently of changes in $z$. This is equivalent to experimenting. But this procedure is seldom possible: in any case, the number of observations would have to be very large to enable us to separate a sufficiently large number of events with constant $z$.

However, in many cases we can use the method of multiple correlation in which more than two variables are involved. The theory of multiple correlation is complicated, and cannot be discussed in detail in this book. We shall merely confine ourselves to giving some formulae without proof, together with a number of numerical examples to show the purpose of using this method and the circumstances under which it may be applied.

480

There are four basic objectives:

(1) To find a measure expressing the intensity of correlation between a characteristic $x$ and a whole set of characteristics $y$, $z$, $u$, ... etc.; in other words, to find the multiple correlation coefficient corresponding to the ordinary correlation coefficient or to the correlation ratio in cases when there are two variables.

(2) To find a measure of the intensity of correlation between two characteristics, say $x$ and $y$, when the influence of other characteristics $z$, $u$, ..., is excluded.

(3) To find the regression equation expressing the average values of one characteristic, say $x$, as a function of all the other characteristics.

(4) To find the regression coefficient of two characteristics when the influence of the remaining characteristics is excluded.

We shall discuss these problems with reference to a case of linear correlation.

Let us begin with the second problem, the measure of correlation between two characteristics when the influence of the remaining characteristics is removed. The formulae that we shall thus derive will serve as a basis for other calculations.

Let there be three characteristics whose correlation we want to analyse. Let us denote them by 1, 2, and 3. We are to find the correlation coefficient of two of them, eliminating the third. We shall call this coefficient the partial correlation coefficient in contrast to the total correlation coefficient expressing the correlation between a given pair of characteristics regardless of a possible correlation with other characteristics. The partial correlation coefficient with three characteristics involved we write as

$$r_{12 \cdot 3}, r_{13 \cdot 2}, r_{23 \cdot 1}.$$

The first term denotes the correlation coefficient between characteristics 1 and 2 eliminating characteristic 3; the second denotes the correlation coefficient between characteristics 1 and 3 eliminating characteristic 2; the third term denotes the correlation coefficient between characteristics 2 and 3 eliminating characteristic 1. The eliminated characteristic is always in the last place, and is separated from the other two by a dot.[169]

These coefficients of partial correlation can be expressed as a function of the coefficients of total correlation between all pairs of characteristics, i.e. 1 and 2, 1 and 3, 2 and 3, or between the coefficients $r_{12}$, $r_{13}$ and $r_{23}$. The formula is

$$r_{12 \cdot 3} = \frac{r_{12} - r_{13} r_{23}}{\sqrt{(1 - r_{13}^2) \times (1 - r_{23}^2)}} \qquad \text{(XVII.1a)}$$

For the second pair it is, by analogy

$$r_{13 \cdot 2} = \frac{r_{13} - r_{12} r_{23}}{\sqrt{(1 - r_{12}^2) \times (1 - r_{23}^2)}}, \qquad \text{(XVII.1b)}$$

---

[169] Some authors use the notation $_3r_{12}$, $_2r_{13}$, $_1r_{22}$, i.e. they place the subscript denoting the excluded characteristic on the left-hand side of the letter $r$.

and for the third

$$r_{23\cdot1} = \frac{r_{23} - r_{12}r_{13}}{\sqrt{(1 - r_{12}^2) \times (1 - r_{13}^2)}}.$$                    (XVII.1c)

In these formulae we assume that the sign of the square root in the denominator is always positive.

We can see from the formulae that the partial correlation coefficient may be greater or less than the total correlation coefficient for the corresponding pair of characteristics. A plus sign can become minus, and vice versa. The change will take place if the following conditions are satisfied simultaneously: (1) if in formula (1a) the product $r_{13}\,r_{23}$ has a different sign from $r_{12}$; (2) if the absolute value of the product $r_{13}\,r_{23}$ is greater than the absolute value of $r_{12}$. It is obvious that the partial correlation coefficient can be fairly large even when the total correlation coefficient equals zero.

Three contingency tables for the characteristic 1 and 2, 1 and 3, 2 and 3 are required, and the corresponding total correlation coefficient should be calculated on the basis of each of these tables, and then the values of $r_{12}\ r_{13}\ r_{23}$ thus found should be substituted in the respective formulae.

We shall show by examples what results are obtained by the application of these measures.

A long time ago R. H. Hooker made a study of the correlation between crops, precipitation and temperature in England.[170]

If we denote by 1 the crop of hay per unit of area, by 2 precipitation, and by 3 temperature in the spring, then we obtain the following coefficients of total correlation.

$$r_{12} = +0\cdot79$$

$$r_{13} = -0\cdot49$$

$$r_{23} = -0\cdot56.$$

It would appear that there is a very strong positive correlation between the crop of hay and precipitation, and a fairly strong negative correlation between the crop of hay and temperature. At the same time there is a strong negative correlation between temperature and precipitation (the greater the precipitation, the lower the temperature). We are less concerned with the last correlation, but it is important because of the influence it has on the relationship between the crop, temperature and

---

[170] R. H. Hooker: Correlation of the Weather and Crops, *J. R. Statist. Soc.*, Vol. LXX, 1907, p. 1, *et seq.* The observations concerning precipitation, temperature and the crop of hay pertain to the years 1886–1905. According to a note in *Vyestnik Statistiky* 1923 Book XV, No. 7–12, p. 194–5, a large scale study of correlation between crop, temperature and precipitation was also made in the Soviet Union.

precipitation. Substituting the corresponding values in formulae (XVII.1a) and (XVII.1b) we obtain the partial correlation coefficients.

$$r_{12 \cdot 3} = + 0 \cdot 714$$

$$r_{13 \cdot 2} = - 0 \cdot 094.$$

Thus it turns out that after the elimination of temperature the dependence of the crop on precipitation is still positive and very strong, but there is almost no correlation between the crop and temperature, if we eliminate the influence of precipitation. We can now talk about causal relationship: spring rains have a positive effect on crops of hay, but spring temperature hardly affects them at all. If we consider precipitation and temperature not in the spring, but in the summer the general correlation coefficients are

$$r_{12} = + 0 \cdot 33, \quad r_{13} = - 0 \cdot 49.$$

The partial correlation coefficients are

$$r_{12 \cdot 3} = - 0 \cdot 03, \quad r_{13 \cdot 2} = - 0 \cdot 39,$$

Thus precipitation in this period does not affect the crops (the coefficient $r_{12 \cdot 3}$ is close to zero), and too high a temperature has a negative effect. Of course, this conclusion applies directly only to the conditions in England: elsewhere, depending upon the level of agricultural technique, climate and soil, the relationship may be different.

In the same study, Hooker analysed the correlation between the crop of wheat (1), precipitation (2), and temperature (3), at the time of sowing. The results were as follows:

|  | Correlation coefficient | |
|---|---|---|
|  | total | partial |
| Correlation between crop and precipitation | $r_{12} = -0 \cdot 66$ | $r_{12 \cdot 3} = -0 \cdot 62$ |
| Correlation between crop and temperature | $r_{13} = +0 \cdot 36$ | $r_{13 \cdot 2} = -0 \cdot 00$ |

Hence the conclusion that in England rain at the time of sowing has a definite negative effect on the crop of wheat, and the temperature at that time has no bearing on it—contrary to what can be inferred from the value of the total correlation coefficient.

In Poland the results of studies of correlation between the physical fitness of youth and height and weight were published.[171] Fitness was checked by the 60-metre sprint, high jump, and ball throwing. The study, made in the spring of 1932, included secondary schools, teacher training colleges and trade schools in the whole country. Over 9000 boys and almost 7000 girls aged 10 or over were included.

---

[171] J. Mydlarski: *Sprawność fizyczna młodzieży w Polsce* (*The Physical Fitness of Young People in Poland*), Warsaw, 1934.

TABLE 17.1. ANNUAL INCREASES IN HEIGHT, WEIGHT AND
PROFICIENCY AT RUNNING

| Age | Annual increase in | | |
|---|---|---|---|
| | height (cm) (1) | weight (kg) (2) | running time (sec)[a] (3) |
| 10–11 | 3·65 | 1·96 | 0·28 |
| 11–12 | 3·64 | 2·28 | 0·32 |
| 12–13 | 5·04 | 3·82 | 0·20 |
| 13–14 | 6·19 | 5·32 | 0·60 |
| 14–15 | 6·08 | 5·40 | 0·23 |
| 15–16 | 3·40 | 3·69 | 0·20 |
| 16–17 | 2·02 | 2·92 | 0·16 |
| 17–18 | 1·59 | 2·48 | 0·06 |
| 18–19 | 0·84 | 1·49 | 0·00 |

[a] An increase in proficiency at running measure by the decrease in running time in seconds for 60 m.

The author does not directly consider the relationship between the characteristics studied; he analyses the relationship between annual increases in the values of these characteristics at the age 10–19. For height, weight and running time, these increases for boys are shown in Table 17.1.

A glance at the table discloses that from the age 10–19 there are periods in which increases are more rapid (in the middle years), and other periods when they are slower (at the beginning, and even more at the end). This proved true with respect to all the characteristics studied.

On the basis of such tables J. Mydlarski calculated the general correlation coefficients between annual increases in height (1) and weight (2), between increases in height and weight and increases in running proficiency (3), jump (4) and putting the shot (5); then he calculated the partial correlation coefficients between increases in height and physical fitness after eliminating the influence of increases in weight, and between increases in weight and physical fitness after eliminating the influence of increases in height. The results are given in Table 17.2.[172]

The total correlation coefficients between an increase in physical fitness and an increase in height and weight are in all cases positive and usually very high. The partial correlation coefficients are positive with respect to height (after the elimination of the influence of an increase in weight), but they are all negative with respect to weight (after excluding the influence of height). This means that an increase in

[172] The author calculated the correlation coefficients not in the sense described above but as coefficients of rank correlation, which will be discussed later. The calculation of the proper correlation coefficients would give somewhat different results but would not change the basic trend.

TABLE 17.2. CORRELATION COEFFICIENTS BETWEEN INCREASES IN HEIGHT,
WEIGHT AND PHYSICAL FITNESS

| Correlation of characteristics | Boys | | Girls | |
|---|---|---|---|---|
| | Correlation coefficients | | | |
| | total | partial | total | partial |
| Height-run | $r_{13} = +0\cdot81$ | $r_{13\cdot2} = +0\cdot88$ | $r_{13} = +0\cdot90$ | $r_{13\cdot2} = +0\cdot59$ |
| Height-jump | $r_{14} = +0\cdot94$ | $r_{14\cdot2} = +0\cdot90$ | $r_{14} = +0\cdot87$ | $r_{14\cdot2} = +0\cdot54$ |
| Height-shot-put | $r_{15} = +0\cdot65$ | $r_{15\cdot2} = +0\cdot64$ | $r_{15} = +0\cdot88$ | $r_{15\cdot2} = +0\cdot43$ |
| Weight-run | $r_{23} = +0\cdot33$ | $r_{23\cdot1} = -0\cdot65$ | $r_{23} = +0\cdot85$ | $r_{23\cdot1} = -0\cdot22$ |
| Weight-jump | $r_{24} = +0\cdot66$ | $r_{24\cdot1} = -0\cdot24$ | $r_{24} = +0\cdot82$ | $r_{24\cdot1} = -0\cdot20$ |
| Weight-shot-put | $r_{25} = +0\cdot32$ | $r_{25\cdot1} = -0\cdot30$ | $r_{25} = +0\cdot85$ | $r_{25\cdot1} = -0\cdot03$ |

weight has a negative effect on proficiency at running, jumping and putting the shot if an increase in weight is not accompanied by an increase in height: the positive total correlation coefficients can be explained by the existence of a strongly marked positive correlation between height and weight (for boys $r_{12} = +0\cdot73$, for girls $r_{12} = +0\cdot92$).

In each of these cases the elimination of the third factor leads to conclusions contrary to those that could be derived from the total correlation coefficients.

In the next example we deal with four characteristics. We want to find out what factors affected the local prices of crops—more specifically of rye—in the various counties of capitalist Poland. The factors considered were the prices of rye paid to farmers (1), the yields of rye per hectare (2), the population density per square kilometre (3), the percentage of population deriving their livelihood from agriculture (4). We give only the final results (Table 17.3).

The partial correlation coefficient between the price of rye and the yield is close to zero. But the partial correlation coefficient between the price of rye and the population density is clearly positive, and between the prices and the percentage of the population living from agriculture it is clearly negative. This means that the farmers obtained higher prices in counties where a relatively larger proportion of the population derived their income from sources outside agriculture and in which the population density was greater: the differences in the yield per hectare in particular counties did not affect the prices.

TABLE 17.3. CORRELATION BETWEEN PRICE
OF RYE AND SELECTED FACTORS

| Correlation coefficient | |
|---|---|
| total | partial |
| $r_{12} = +0\cdot326$ | $r_{12\cdot34} = -0\cdot026$ |
| $r_{13} = +0\cdot576$ | $r_{13\cdot24} = +0\cdot43$ |
| $r_{14} = -0\cdot603$ | $r_{14\cdot23} = -0\cdot24$ |

We shall now deal with the problem of calculating the multiple correlation coefficient, i.e. the coefficient expressing the relationship between the value of one characteristic and a set of other characteristics. We denote this coefficient by $R$ and write

$$R_{1 \cdot 234 \cdots n}$$

thus expressing the relationship between the value of characteristic 1 and the total value of characteristics 2, 3, etc., up to $n$.

The general formula for calculating the multiple correlation coefficient can be written thus:

$$R_{1 \cdot 23 \cdots n} = \sqrt{1 - (1 - r_{12}^2) \times (1 - r_{13 \cdot 2}^2) \times (1 - r_{14 \cdot 23}^2) \times \ldots \times (1 - r_{1n \cdot 234 \cdots n-1}^2)}.$$

$$(XVII.2)$$

When there are three characteristics we have

$$R_{1 \cdot 23} = \sqrt{1 - (1 - r_{12}^2) \times (1 - r_{13 \cdot 2}^2)} \qquad (XVII.3)$$

for four characteristics we have

$$R_{1 \cdot 234} = \sqrt{1 - (1 - r_{12}^2) \times (1 - r_{13 \cdot 2}^2) \times (1 - r_{14 \cdot 23}^2)} \qquad (XVII.4)$$

etc.

Identical results are obtained by transposing the subscripts: for instance, for three characteristics

$$R_{1 \cdot 23} = \sqrt{1 - (1 - r_{13}^2) \times (1 - r_{12 \cdot 3}^2)}. \qquad (XVII.3a)$$

We can take advantage of this possibility of transposition to check the calculation. In the case of three characteristics we can calculate by the equivalent formula:

$$R_{1 \cdot 23} = \sqrt{\frac{r_{12}^2 + r_{13}^2 - 2 r_{12} r_{13} r_{23}}{1 - r_{23}^2}}. \qquad (XVII.3b)$$

This formula does not require the calculation of partial correlation coefficients.

Let us go through a calculation on the example of the correlation between the crop of hay (1), precipitation (2) and temperature (3). In this case we are interested in

$$R_{1 \cdot 23},$$

but not in the dependence of temperature on crop and precipitation on crop and temperature. According to the data on p. 481 we have $r_{12} = +0 \cdot 79$, $r_{13} = -0 \cdot 49$, $r_{23} = -0 \cdot 56$, $r_{13 \cdot 2} = -0 \cdot 94$.

Substituting in formula (XVII.3) we have

$$R_{1 \cdot 23} = \sqrt{1 - (1 - 0 \cdot 79^2) \times (1 - 0 \cdot 094^2)} = 0 \cdot 79.$$

The same result is, of course, obtained by formula (XVII.3a) or (XVII.3b).

In connexion with the correlation between an increase in physical fitness and increases in height and weight (p. 485), we obtain the correlation for boys between running time (3) and height (1) and weight (2)

$$R_{3 \cdot 12} = 0 \cdot 89.$$

The multiple correlation coefficient between the price of rye and the yield per hectare, the population density nad the percentage of population living from agriculture is

$$R_{1 \cdot 234} = 0 \cdot 69.$$

The multiple correlation coefficient is always taken to be positive. It expresses the intensity of the correlation between the characteristic in which we are interested and all other characteristics considered. If it is close to unity, as in the case of the correlation between an increase in the proficiency at running and increases in height and weight, this means that increases in height and weight almost fully determine an increase in physical fitness, and that other factors are of little importance. If it is fairly far from one, this means that other factors that we have not considered come into play.

The general form of the equation of linear regression when there are many characteristics is

$$x = a + by + cz + du + \ldots$$

If we count thes values of characteristics $x$, $y$, $z$, etc. from the arithmetic means, i.e. instead of $x$, $y$ $z$, etc., we write $X$, $Y$, $Z$, etc., the term $a$ will disappear and we shall finally have

$$X = bY + cZ + dU + \ldots$$

where $b$, $c$, $d$, etc. are the partial regression coefficients expressing changes in the values of $X$ in relation to $Y$, eliminating the influence of $Z$, $U$, ...; changes in $X$ in relation to changes in $Z$ eliminating the influence of $Y$, $U$, ..., and so on. Denoting $X$ by 1, $Y$ by 2, $Z$ by 3, etc., we write

$$X = b_{12 \cdot 34 \ldots n} Y + c_{13 \cdot 24 \ldots n} Z + d_{14 \cdot 23 \ldots n} U \ldots \qquad \text{(XVII.5)}$$

In the case of three characteristics we have

$$X = b_{12 \cdot 3} Y + c_{13 \cdot 2} Z. \qquad \text{(XVII.6)}$$

The partial regression coefficients are calculated by formulae

$$b_{12 \cdot 3} = \frac{r_{12} - r_{13} r_{23}}{1 - r_{23}^2} \times \frac{\sigma_1}{\sigma_2}, \qquad \text{(XVII.7)}$$

$$c_{13 \cdot 2} = \frac{r_{13} - r_{12} r_{23}}{1 - r_{23}^2} \times \frac{\sigma_1}{\sigma_3}. \qquad \text{(XVII.8)}$$

In this way we have solved the problem of calculating the partial regression coefficients and the regression equation when there are three characteristics involved.

Were it is necessary to calculate coefficients for correlation of a number of characteristics, the formulae for transforming from a correlation of a lower order to a correlation of a higher order could be used. In the case of correlation between several characteristics a correlation of zero order is the total correlation between particular pairs of characteristics, i.e. coefficients of the type $r_{12}$, $r_{13}$, $r_{14}$, $r_{25}$, etc.; a correlation of order one is the partial correlation of pairs of characteristics eliminating the third characteristic, i.e. $r_{12 \cdot 3}$, $r_{13 \cdot 2}$, $r_{13 \cdot 4}$, $r_{23 \cdot 1}$ etc.; a correlation of order two is the partial correlation of particular pairs of characteristics eliminating the third and fourth, and so on.

Formulae of the type (XVII.1)

$$r_{12 \cdot 3} = \frac{r_{12} - r_{13} \times r_{23}}{\sqrt{(1 - r_{13}^2)(1 - r_{23}^2)}}$$

enable us to switch from correlation coefficients of a lower order to those of a higher order. The above formula makes possible the conversion of a correlation coefficient of order zero to a correlation coefficient of order one. An analogous formula is used for converting correlation coefficients of order one to correlation coefficients of order two.

The formula is

$$r_{12 \cdot 34} = \frac{r_{12 \cdot 3} - r_{14 \cdot 3} \times r_{24 \cdot 3}}{\sqrt{(1 - r_{14 \cdot 3}^2)(1 - r_{24 \cdot 3}^2)}} \tag{XVII.9}$$

and analogously

$$r_{13 \cdot 24} = \frac{r_{13 \cdot 2} - r_{14 \cdot 2} \times r_{34 \cdot 2}}{\sqrt{(1 - r_{14 \cdot 2}^2)(1 - r_{34 \cdot 2}^2)}} \tag{XVII.10}$$

and

$$r_{14 \cdot 23} = \frac{r_{13 \cdot 2} - r_{13 \cdot 2} \times r_{34 \cdot 2}}{\sqrt{(1 - r_{13 \cdot 2}^2)(1 - r_{34 \cdot 2}^2)}} \tag{XVII.11}$$

The same results can be obtained by using the formulae

$$r_{12 \cdot 34} = \frac{r_{12 \cdot 4} - r_{13 \cdot 4} \times r_{23 \cdot 4}}{\sqrt{(1 - r_{13 \cdot 4}^2)(1 - r_{23 \cdot 4}^2)}}, \tag{XVII.9a}$$

$$r_{13 \cdot 24} = \frac{r_{13 \cdot 4} - r_{12 \cdot 4} \times r_{23 \cdot 4}}{\sqrt{(1 - r_{2 \cdot 4}^2)(1 - r_{23 \cdot 4}^2)}}, \tag{XVII.10a}$$

$$r_{14 \cdot 23} = \frac{r_{14 \cdot 3} - r_{12 \cdot 3} \times r_{24 \cdot 3}}{\sqrt{(1 - r_{12 \cdot 3}^2)(1 - r_{24 \cdot 3}^2)}} \tag{XVII.11a}$$

In the above formulae, coefficients of a higher order are expressed as functions of the correlation coefficients of a lower order. Therefore, the calculation in the case of $n$ variables proceeds as follows:

(1) We make out contingency tables for each pair of variables, and calculate for them the coefficients of total correlation, i.e. of the correlation of order zero.

(2) On this basis we calculate the correlation coefficients of order one, two, etc., up to the highest order: $n—2$.[173] Coefficients of the highest order are the coefficients of partial correlation between pairs of variables.

(3) On the basis of the correlation coefficients of an appropriate order we calculate the multiple correlation coefficient $R$ and the regression coefficient; for calculating the regression coefficients the knowledge of the corresponding standard deviations is needed.

The above calculation is very arduous. Most time-consuming of all is the calculation of the total correlation coefficients for particular pairs of variables. The number of these coefficients increases rapidly as the number of characteristics increases. For three characteristics we have three such coefficients, for four characteristics there are six, for five, ten coefficients, etc. Further calculations is relatively simple, especially since not all coefficients of the highest order are of interest to us, and some of them may be omitted, just at the calculation of the multiple correlation coefficients is usually limited to one, or at the most two.

This great amount of calculation involved is the reason why in statistical practice the calculation of correlation between many characteristics is considerably limited. There are also other reasons why the statistician, and especially the beginner, should exercise great care in dealing with multiple correlation. They are the following:

(1) Reasons of a computational nature. In the above brief exposition of the methods of correlation calculus only the most important difficulties involved in this calculation could be pointed out. First of all, the formulae for multiple correlation in the form presented above may be applied only to cases of linear regression; if the regression is non-linear, they can at best serve as an approximation, but they can also lead to incorrect results. In mathematical statistics methods of analysing curvilinear regresion are also known, but they cannot be presented here. Similarly, more complicated problems involved in linear correlation cannot be discussed in this book.

(2) The possibility of drawing conclusions from the numerical results obtained depends upon a proper selection of the quantities for which correlation is to be calculated. This is not a mere technical statistical problem, but a basic one; we emphasize again that statistical methods should be used only by those who possess

---

[173] In the case of two variables $n - 2 = 0$ and therefore we calculate only the coefficients of total correlation; in the case of, say, 4 variables $n - 2 = 2$ which means that we must also calculate the coefficients of order one, two, etc.

a good knowledge of the subject studied. An additional difficulty is how to find a proper numerical expression for the factor that we want to analyse; there are factors which cannot be expressed numerically. On the other hand it is possible to solve correctly a problem in correlation only if it is posed properly from the mathematical point of view. For these reasons good results in more complicated cases can be obtained only when the work is the result of the combined efforts of an expert statistician and an expert in the field of study.

(3) The interpretation of the results and their application in practice and in scientific studies is always a serious problem. Some examples of the difficulties involved in interpretation were given above. These difficulties may stem from the subject of the study, and therefore the nature of the formulae used should be well understood if wrong conclusions are to be avoided.

On the other hand, the importance of correlation analysis and especially of multiple correlation cannot be over-emphasized. Without it many problems could not be solved at all.[174]

## 2. THE COEFFICIENT OF RANK CORRELATION

The correlation coefficients and the correlation ratios are not by any means the only measures of correlation. There is one more measure that we shall discuss here. It is the coefficient of rank correlation which is easy to calculate and which can be used when the number of observations is small, as in Tables 15.1 and 15.2 (p. 425 and p. 426).

We begin the calculation by arranging the observation in descending or ascending order of the values of one characteristic, by numbering the observations and writing beside them the ordinal numbers in the ascending or descending order of the values of the other characteristic, just as we did in Tables 15.1 and 15.2 to find out whether or not there is correlation. Then we find the differences between consecutive numbers according to the two characteristics, and calculate the sum of the squares of these differences. For our example concerning average barometric pressure and average annual temperatur in Warsaw in Table 15.2 (p. 426) the calculation will proceed as shown in Table 17.4 (p. 491).

The coefficient of rank correlation is calculated by the formula

$$Q = 1 - \frac{6 \sum (v_x - v_y)^2}{N^3 - N} = 1 - \frac{6 \times 795}{15^3 - 15} = 1 - \frac{4770}{3360}$$

$$= 1 - 1 \cdot 42 = -0 \cdot 42. \qquad \text{(XVII.12)}$$

The correlation coefficient $r$ in this case is $-0 \cdot 47$ (see p. 449).

---

[174] The problems mentioned here are extensively discussed in *Voprosy statisticheskavo ismeryeniya sviazey miezidhu yavlienyami* edited by S. G. Strumilin, Moscow, 1950.

In the case of correlation between increases in height, weight and physical fitness, Mydlarski calculated the coefficients by the same formula. For boys he obtained (see p. 483) the coefficient of total correlation between an increase in height and an increase in the proficiency at running of $+0 \cdot 81$, the coefficient of correlation between an increase in height and an increase in the proficiency at jumping of $+0 \cdot 94$; the correlation coefficient $r$ is $+0 \cdot 77$ and $+0 \cdot 91$.

The two types of coefficients cannot produce the same result because of the differences in their mathematical content.

Technically the coefficient of rank correlation can be calculated without difficulty only when the number of observations is small, i.e. when we can really do without expressing the intensity of correlation numerically. When the number of observations is small every correlation coefficient, and especially the coefficient of rank correlation, is an unreliable measure, unless the value obtained is large. Therefore the usefulness of this measure is rather limited.

TABLE 17.4. CALCULATION OF RANK CORRELATION FOR BAROMETRIC PRESSURE AND TEMPERATURE

| Number of the years according to | | $v_x - v_y$ | $(v_x - v_y)^2$ |
|---|---|---|---|
| pressure $v_x$ | temperature $v_y$ | | |
| 1 | 11 | $-10$ | 100 |
| 2 | 6·5 | $-4 \cdot 5$ | 20·25 |
| 3 | 8 | $-5$ | 25 |
| 4 | 12·5 | $-8 \cdot 5$ | 72·25 |
| 5 | 12·5 | $-7 \cdot 5$ | 56·25 |
| 7 | 9·5 | $-2 \cdot 5$ | 6·25 |
| 7 | 4 | $+3$ | 9 |
| 7 | 14 | $-7$ | 49 |
| 9 | 5 | $+4$ | 16 |
| 10 | 6·5 | $+3 \cdot 5$ | 12·25 |
| 11 | 15 | $-4$ | 16 |
| 12 | 1·5 | $+10 \cdot 5$ | 110·25 |
| 13 | 3 | $+10$ | 100 |
| 14 | 9·5 | $+4 \cdot 5$ | 20·25 |
| 15 | 1·5 | $+13 \cdot 5$ | 182·25 |
| | | | 795 |

However, this measure can be used in special cases where the characteristics studied cannot be measured, but where the observations can be arranged with a reasonable approximation in some definite order. For instance it might be difficult to assign to each student a number expressing both his musical and mathematical ability, but is is possible to make out a list of students from the least to the most able by assigning them ordinal numbers. If we number the same students in the order of their abilities in different subjects, we can determine by calculating the rank correlation whether these abilities are related or opposed to each other. This method of research is used in psychology.

## 3. CORRELATION BETWEEN NON-MEASURABLE CHARACTERISTICS

We discussed above the correlation between measurable characteristics. In some cases it may be necessary to measure the relationship between non-measurable characteristics.

In such cases it is often enough to calculate simple percentage ratios. For instance, there undoubtedly exists, especially in capitalistic countries, a relationship between sex and occupation. From the 1931 census we take the data pertaining to the city of Warsaw (Table 17.5).

Considerable differences in the employment of the two sexes can be seen in the table; in some occupations men are employed almost exclusively (as locksmiths, in painting and upholstery, communication and horse-drawn transport, etc.) and in others—women (in kindergartens, as domestic servants, etc); in some occupations a balance is maintained between the two sexes. These relations can be described with sufficient clarity by calculating the percentages of men and women in relation to all employees in particular occupations, as shown in the last two columns of the table. Since in this case there are only two alternatives—men and women—the percentage add up to 100 and it is enough to give only one figure—the percentage of men or the percentage of women: the picture will thus gain in clarity. Out of the two figures let us select the one that we consider as more important and characteristic of a given case. Apart from this consideration related to the substance, we should also take account of a formal aspect: as a rule a clearer picture is obtained if the lower of the two figures is selected.

If the two figures are approximately equal (as for sex in the total population) it is convenient to denote one of them by 100, and take the ratio of the two figures to one another rather than the ratio of each of them to the total (e.g. "there are $x$ women per 100 men").

However, the calculation of such percentages does not always suffice to explain the problem. Let us take illiteracy as an example. It is a known fact that when the level of culture is low the percentage of the illiterates is almost always greater for women than for men. Table 17.6 shows the data for Warsaw and the then province of Bialystok, based on the 1931 population census. Besides the total population from the age of 10 upwards, two separate age groups are shown: children from 10 to 14 who should have received education according to the regulations in bourgeois Poland and in which, therefore, there should have been no

TABLE 17.5. EMPLOYMENT IN SELECTED OCCUPATIONS BY SEX IN WARSAW
IN 1931 — HIRED WORKERS

| Occupation | Employed | | | | |
|---|---|---|---|---|---|
| | total | men | women | men | women |
| | (absolute numbers) | | | (percentage) | |
| Locksmiths | 2935 | 2866 | 69 | 97·6 | 2·4 |
| Fat processing | 733 | 528 | 205 | 72·0 | 28·0 |
| Manufacturing of cosmetics and pharma-ceuticals | 1721 | 778 | 943 | 45·2 | 54·8 |
| Tailoring | 13,459 | 7007 | 6452 | 52·1 | 47·9 |
| Linen manufacturing | 3371 | 497 | 2874 | 14·7 | 85·3 |
| Painting and upholstery | 1578 | 1555 | 23 | 98·5 | 1·5 |
| Communication and horsedrawn transport | 1611 | 1607 | 4 | 99·75 | 0·25 |
| General education | 3424 | 1176 | 2248 | 34·3 | 65·7 |
| University education | 1289 | 1060 | 229 | 82·2 | 17·8 |
| Creches and nursery schools | 2481 | 30 | 2451 | 1·2 | 98·8 |
| Hairdressing and beauty parlours | 3298 | 2605 | 693 | 79·0 | 21·0 |
| Domestic servants | 57,862 | 824 | 57,038 | 1·4 | 98·6 |

illiteracy, and persons aged 30–39 who were at school age when Poland was occupied and when there was no compulsory education.

The table shows: (1) that illiteracy in the province of Bialystok was much higher than in Warsaw, (2) that in both districts the level of illiteracy was much higher at the age of 30–39 than at the age of 10–14, but in the province of Bialystok (Poland "B") even in the latter group the number of the illiterates was fairly high. Moreover, it is quite noticeable that the percentage of illiteracy is higher among women than among men with the excepion of the age group of 10–14 years in Warsaw for which the ratio is reversed.

To emphasize the relationship between sex and illiteracy the percentage could also be calculated in the same way as in the last two columns of Table 17.6: the number of men and women per hundred illiterates and per hundred literates. In accordance with the previous finding the percentage of women is higher among the illiterates than among the literates. with the exception of the age group of 10–14 in Warsaw. The percentage of women among the illiterates should be set against the percentage of women among the literates; it is not enough to say that this percentage is over fifty. This last figure by itself would be conclusive only if in the total population of a given age group the number of women was the same as the number of men. For instance, in Warsaw there were also more women than men among the literates at the age of 30–39, because the majority of women among the total population in this age groups was considerable, but the percentage of women among the illiterates was 72·3 whereas among the literates it was only 53·8.

The two methods of comparison give a more or less equally good general idea of the problem. The picture is somewhat less clear when the relations in one population group are compared with the relations prevailing in the whole population; it is better to compare the two groups with one another, i.e. the percentage of illiterates among women with the percentage of illiterates among men, instead of comparing it with the percentage of the illiterates in the whole population, or to compare the percentage of women among the illiterate with the percentage of women among the literate instead of comparing it with the percentage of women in the total population.

It would be desirable, however, to have a measure which expresses the correlation between characteristics in one number. A number of coefficients have been suggested for this purpose, but we shall describe only some of them.

One of them, probably the oldest, is the coefficient of convergence, suggested by Yule.

Let us introduce the following notations. In the four-cell table with frequencies arranged from the point of view of two characteristics $A$ and $B$ which each unit may have $(+)$ or may not have $(-)$, we denote the frequencies in particular cells by $a$, $b$, $c$, and $d$, as shown below.

|  |  | Characteristic $A$ | |
| --- | --- | --- | --- |
|  |  | $+$ | $-$ |
| Charac-<br>teristic<br>$B$ | $+$ | $a$ | $b$ |
|  | $-$ | $c$ | $d$ |

Here $a$ denotes the number of cases in which both $A$ and $B$ appear, $b$ denotes the number of cases in which $B$ appears but $A$ does not appear, etc. The sum $(a+c)$ denotes all cases in which characteristic $A$ appears regardless of whether or not characteristic $B$ also appears, and the sum $(b+d)$ denotes the cases in which $A$ does not appear. The sums $(a+b)$ and $(c+d)$ have analagous meanings for characteristic $B$. The total $(a+c)+(b+d)=(a+b)+(c+d)=(a+b+c+d)=F$ is the total population. These notations with reference to the example on illiteracy are interpreted so that the appearance of characteristic $A$ means that a given person is illiterate and the lack of characteristic $A$ means that the person can read and write; we also assume that characteristic $B$ appears when a person is a man, and it does not appear when it is a women. Of course the choice of notation is arbitrary, but the order in which the characteristics are placed in the table should be remembered, since the interpretation of the results depends upon it.

TABLE 17.6. ILLITERACY AMONG THE POPULATION AT THE AGE OF 10
AND OVER IN 1931[175]

| Age and sex | Total population | Illiterates | Literates | Total population | Illiterates | Literates | Men and women per 100 | |
|---|---|---|---|---|---|---|---|---|
| | | (absolute numbers) | | | (percentage) | | illiterates | literates |
| *City of Warsaw* | | | | | | | | |
| 10 years and over | | | | | | | | |
| total | 966,987 | 121,922 | 845,065 | 100·0 | 12·6 | 87·4 | 100·0 | 100·0 |
| men | 431,510 | 35,163 | 396,347 | 100·0 | 8·1 | 91·9 | 28·8 | 46·9 |
| women | 535,477 | 86,759 | 448,718 | 100·0 | 16·2 | 83·8 | 71·2 | 53·1 |
| 10–14 years | | | | | | | | |
| total | 77,724 | 1705 | 76,019 | 100·0 | 2·2 | 97·8 | 100·0 | 100·0 |
| men | 38,999 | 932 | 38,067 | 100·0 | 2·4 | 97·6 | 54·7 | 50·1 |
| women | 38,725 | 773 | 37,952 | 100·0 | 2·0 | 98·0 | 45·3 | 49·9 |
| 30–39 years | | | | | | | | |
| total | 193,791 | 21,423 | 172,368 | 100·0 | 11·1 | 88·9 | 100·0 | 100·0 |
| men | 85,646 | 5940 | 79,706 | 100·0 | 6·9 | 93·1 | 27·7 | 46·2 |
| women | 108,145 | 15,483 | 92,662 | 100·0 | 14·3 | 85·7 | 72·3 | 53·8 |
| *Province of Bialystok — rural areas* | | | | | | | | |
| 10 years and over | | | | | | | | |
| total | 901,347 | 341,061 | 560,286 | 100·0 | 37·8 | 62·2 | 100·0 | 100·0 |
| men | 435,732 | 101,956 | 333,776 | 100·0 | 23·4 | 76·6 | 29·9 | 59·6 |
| women | 465,615 | 239,105 | 226,510 | 100·0 | 51·4 | 48·6 | 70·1 | 40·4 |
| 10–14 years | | | | | | | | |
| total | 102,028 | 6600 | 95,428 | 100·0 | 6·5 | 93·5 | 100·0 | 100·0 |
| men | 51,671 | 3014 | 48,657 | 100·0 | 5·8 | 94·2 | 45·7 | 51·0 |
| women | 50,357 | 3586 | 46,771 | 100·0 | 7·1 | 92·9 | 54·3 | 49·0 |
| 30–39 years | | | | | | | | |
| total | 160,156 | 61,312 | 98,844 | 100·0 | 38·3 | 61·7 | 100·0 | 100·0 |
| men | 80,115 | 15,223 | 64,892 | 100·0 | 19·0 | 81·0 | 24·8 | 65·7 |
| women | 80,041 | 46,089 | 33,952 | 100·0 | 57·6 | 42·4 | 75·2 | 34·3 |

The coefficient of convergence, denoted by $Q$, is expressed by the simple formula

$$Q = \frac{ad - bc}{ad + bc} \qquad \text{(XVII.13)}$$

Thus we cross multiply the numbers in the table, and write the difference of these products in the numerator and their sum in the denominator.

Pearson's coefficient, $V$, is considered more mathematically correct.

$$V = \frac{(ad - bc)}{\sqrt{(a + b) \times (a + c) \times (b + d) \times (c + d)}} \qquad \text{(XVII.14)}$$

---

[175] *Statystyka Polski*, Series C, No. 49 and 83, Warsaw 1937, Table 16. An illiterate was considered a person who could not read or write and also one who could only read: the literate, a person who could read and write. Those whose ability to read or write and whose age was unknown were omitted.

Here in the numerator we have the same difference of the products as in formula (XVII.13). In the denominator under the square root sign there is the product of the sums $(a+b)$, $(a+c)$, etc; $(a+b)$ are all units that possess characteristic $B$, $(a+c)$ are all units that possess characteristic $A$, $(b+d)$ are all units without characteristic $A$, and $(c+d)$ are all units without characteristic $B$.

It is easy to show that when there is no correlation both $Q$ and $V$ are zero. The lack of correlation means that

$$\frac{a}{b} = \frac{c}{d} \quad \text{and} \quad \frac{a}{c} = \frac{b}{d},$$

i.e. the relative number of persons possessing or not possessing characteristic $A$ does not depend upon whether they possess, or do not possess characteristic $B$, and the relative number of persons possessing or not possessing characteristic $B$ does not depend upon their possessing or not possesing characteristic $A$. With reference to illiteracy this means that the percentage of illiterates and of literates is the same for men and for women and that the percentage of men and women is the same among illiterates and literates.

In this case $ad=bc$, the difference $ad-bc=0$, and hence $Q=0$ and $V=0$.

The correlation is complete when $Q=1$ and $V=1$. But in calculating $Q$, unity is obtained if zero appears in any cell in the table, because then either $ad$ or $bc$ will then equal zero, the numerator will be equal to the denominator and the quotient will equal $+1$ or $-1$ (the significance of the plus or minus sign will be discussed later). But $V$ will equal one only if zero appears in two cells in the table located on the diagonal ($a$ and $d$ or $b$ and $c$). Only in this case, assuming, for instance, that $b=0$ and $c=0$, do we obtain

$$V = \frac{ad - 0}{\sqrt{a \times a \times d \times d}} = \frac{ad}{ad} = 1.$$

Thus the interpretation of full correlation is different in the two cases. Let us take an example from medicine. Let us suppose that a disease, if not treated, results in four deaths and six recoveries. The same disease, when treated, always results in recovery.

|  | Deaths | Recoveries |
|---|---|---|
| Not treated | 4 | 6 |
| Treated | 0 | 10 |

In this case

$$Q = 1,$$

$$V = \frac{40}{\sqrt{10 \times 10 \times 4 \times 16}} = +0.5.$$

According to $Q$, we would say on the basis of the above table that the correlation between the outcome of the disease and the treatment is complete, because all persons treated recover, and according to $V$ we would make a reservation that the correlation is only partial because some of those not treated also recover.

$V$ would equal one only if all the ten persons not treated died, because then

$$V = \frac{100}{\sqrt{10 \times 10 \times 10 \times 10}} = \frac{100}{100} = 1.$$

If $Q$ or $V$ assumes values between 0 and 1 this means that there is a partial correlation. The meaning of the plus or minus sign is conventional. If, as in Table 17.6 (p. 495) we put illiterates in the first place in the horizontal direction and men in the vertical direction, the plus sign indicates a higher percentage of illiterates among men than among women; if we put literates in the first place, the plus sign indicates a higher percentage of illiterates among women.

If in calculating $Q$ we increase or decrease the figures in one row (e.g. $a$ and $b$), or in one column (e.g. $b$ and $d$) in the same proportion the value of $Q$ will not change. Indeed

$$Q = \frac{an \times d - bn \times c}{an \times d + bn \times c} = \frac{ad - bc}{ad + bc}.$$

But the value of the coefficient $V$ will change in this case.

In the example concerning medical treatment $V$ decreases as the number of the untreated cases increases and vice versa (with the preservation of the same ratio of deaths to recoveries). With respect to illiteracy the value of $Q$ does not change regardless of whether we calculate: (1) on the basis of absolute figures (the absolute numbers of illiterates and of literates among men and women), (2) on the basis of percentages calculated in the horizontal direction (the percentage of illiterates and literates among men and women), (3) on the basis of percentages calculated in the vertical direction (the percentages of men and women among the illiterate and the literate). But the value of $V$ will be different in different cases. For instance for the age of 30–39 in Warsaw we obtain $Q = -0 \cdot 38$ regardless of the method of calculation (the sign is negative because there are more illiterates among women than among men) while the results for $V$ are: (1) $-0 \cdot 20$, (2) $-0 \cdot 120$, (3) $-0 \cdot 118$.

In a paper published in Poland, L. Bykowski[176] suggested the coefficient

$$W = \frac{(a+d) - (b+c)}{(a+d+b+c)} = \frac{(a+d) - (b+c)}{F}. \qquad \text{(XVII.15)}$$

This coefficient, like Pearson's coefficient, equals one only if $a$ and $d$ or $b$ and $c$ are zero. Its advantage is that it is easy to compute, but cometimes it produces completely misleading results.

---

[176] L. Bykowski: *Zasady pedagogiki doświadczalnej ze szczególnym uwzględnieniem szkoły polskiej* (*The Principles of Experimental Pedagogy with Particular Consideration of the Polish School*), Lwow–Warsaw 1920, p. 72.

In the case of medical treatment (p. 496)

$$W = \frac{14 - 6}{20} = \frac{8}{20} = 0 \cdot 4.$$

However, if we assume that the number of untreated cases was ten times as great as shown in the table, then for the same percentage of deaths the number of persons treated remains unchanged, i.e.

|              | Deaths | Recoveries |
|--------------|--------|------------|
| Not treated  | 40     | 60         |
| Treated      | 0      | 10         |

$$W = \frac{50 - 60}{110} = -0 \cdot 09.$$

Which means that treatment produces negative results although we know that all those treated recovered, and of those not treated 40 per cent died.

Other coefficients suggested have similar faults, or at least similar differences in interpretation. This is more true of Yule's coefficient than of Pearson's coefficient. To prove the point we shall modify somewhat the example on p. 496 on to the results of medical treatment. We write

|              | Deaths | Recoveries |
|--------------|--------|------------|
| Not treated  | 6      | 4          |
| Treated      | 1      | 9          |

This means that out of 10 ill persons not treated 6 die, and out of 10 ill persons treated only 1 dies. The correlation is obvious. The results of the calculation are

$$Q = \frac{54 - 4}{54 + 4} = +0 \cdot 86,$$

$$V = \frac{54 - 4}{\sqrt{10 \times 10 \times 7 \times 13}} = \frac{50}{\sqrt{9100}} = +0 \cdot 52.$$

Multiplying by 100 the number of those who were treated and died and the number of those who were not treated and died we obtain

|              | Deaths | Recoveries |
|--------------|--------|------------|
| Not treated  | 600    | 4          |
| Treated      | 100    | 9          |

A certain beneficial effect of treatment is now also noticeable but it appears to be very weak: out of 604 ill persons not treated 99·3 per cent died and out of

109 ill persons treated 91·7 per cent died. But the coefficient $Q$ is, as before, +0·86 (all products in the numerator and denominator increase a hundred-fold) and it will remain at the same level even if we keep multiplying the number ill who died by larger numbers, so that the percentage of deaths among those who were treated approaches closer and closer to the percentage of deaths among those who were not treated. The coefficient $V$, though, will be +0·52 in the first case and only +0·20 in the second and will decrease as the number of deaths is increased.

However, Yule's or Pearson's coefficients can be used when the figures are not extreme. For instance, in the case of illiteracy the coefficients $Q$ and $V$ are

| Age | City of Warsaw | | Province of Bialystok | |
|---|---|---|---|---|
| | $Q$ | $V$ | $Q$ | $V$ |
| 10–14 years | +0·09 | +0·013 | −0·11 | −0·026 |
| 30–39 years | −0·38 | −0·12 | −0·71 | −0·40 |

It is noticeable that at age 10–14 the correlation between sex and illiteracy is low (the plus sign for the City of Warsaw means that the number of the illiterates is greater among boys than among girls) and at age 30–39 it is clearly marked, more strongly for the province of Bialystok than for Warsaw. The values of $V$ are smaller than the values of $Q$

However, the statistician would be well advised to use coefficients of this type with caution, and first to think of the logic of the relationship, which can be done without calculating the coefficients.

In the study by L. Bykowski cited above, the following example is given concerning the correlation between smoking among students and their marks.

| | Marks | |
|---|---|---|
| | Bad | Good |
| Smokers | 4 | 8 |
| Non-smokers | 0 | 16 |

The distribution of the figures in the table resembles the table concerning the effects of medical treatment (p. 496).

If we assume that the number of observations is sufficiently large to eliminate random factors, we can see that there is definitely a correlation between smoking and marks. Among the non-smokers there is not even one student with bad marks and among the smokers about one-third have bad marks. The coefficients determining correlation between non-measurable characteristics give the following results

$$Q = +1$$
$$V = +0·47$$
$$W = +0·43$$

The plus sign means that bad marks are related to smoking (the students with bad marks who smoked are placed in the top left corner of the table, and the students with good marks who did not, in the bottom right).

From the point of view of the teacher or the physician it is unimportant which of these coefficients better describes the intensity of correlation. The existence of such a correlation is obvious without calculating the coefficients. But the important question is whether smoking is the cause of the bad marks, or whether less conscientious students who get bad marks are more inclined to become addicted to smoking. The teacher and the physician will be interested in what will happen when some of the non-smoking students with good marks start smoking, say, under the influence of a current fad. This will undoubtedly change the ratio of the students with bad marks to the students with good marks among those students who smoke, but the point is whether all students with good marks will continue getting good marks or not. The answer to this question cannot be given on the basis of the table shown above; an additional statistical investigation will have to be made to check the results obtained by each student before and after he started smoking.

Similarly as we analyse the relationship between non-measurable characteristics we can analyse the relationship between a measurable and a non-measurable characteristic.

The second general population census of 9 December 1931 describes the housing situation of some socio-occupational groups in Warsaw as shown in Table 17.7 (p. 501).[177]

The description of the housing situation is not complete because there is no information concerning the number of persons per room, but even in this form the information provided by the table is valuable. We can gather from it, for instance, that the housing conditions of the owners of large and medium enterprises (from the first to the seventh category of industrial licences) were good (more medium-sized and large flats) and the housing conditions of the workers were bad (the majority of flats were small).

We obtain a more readable picture if we apply to the frequency distributions the methods discussed above: the calculation of the percentage for each class, the averages, and, if necessary, the measures of dispersion and other measures.

The percentages are shown in Table 17.8. The results are clearer than before: very good housing conditions for the owners of medium and large enterprises, good for the lawyers, physicians, educational and cultural workers (most of whom were professional people like lawyers, medical practitioners who were relatively well-to-do), very poor for workers and not much better for independent craftsmen who did not employ hired labour. The median gives the following values: 4·2 rooms for the independent owners of medium and large enterprises, 3·8 rooms for lawyers,

---

[177] *Statystyka Polski*, Series C, No. 49, pp. 14 and 15.

TABLE 17.7. POPULATION OF SOME SOCIO-OCCUPATIONAL GROUPS BY NUMBER
OF ROOMS IN FLATS IN WARSAW
(absolute numbers)

| Socio-occupational groups | Population | | | | | | |
|---|---|---|---|---|---|---|---|
| | Total | 1-room | 2-room | 3-room | 4-room | 5- or 6-room | 7-room and more |
| Owners employing labour: | | | | | | | |
| 1. In mining and industry | | | | | | | |
| in enterprises of 1st to 5th category | 9247 | 255 | 713 | 2191 | 2010 | 2999 | 1078 |
| in enterprises of 8th category | 21,511 | 3219 | 5553 | 6948 | 3229 | 2155 | 387 |
| 2. In commerce and insurance | 18,958 | 869 | 2077 | 4972 | 4487 | 5383 | 1070 |
| Owners not employing labour | | | | | | | |
| 1. In mining and industry | 111,498 | 46,325 | 33,629 | 21,698 | 6064 | 3209 | 573 |
| 2. In commerce and insurance | 100,214 | 21,188 | 26,963 | 27,495 | 12,553 | 9645 | 2370 |
| Lawyers, physicians, educational and cultural workers | 16,746 | 1715 | 2299 | 3559 | 2866 | 4559 | 1748 |
| White-collar workers | 183,268 | 21,545 | 33,303 | 48,311 | 35,917 | 34,218 | 9974 |
| Physical workers | 536,002 | 297,252 | 155,314 | 61,738 | 14,234 | 6154 | 1310 |

TABLE 17.8. POPULATION OF SOME SOCIO-OCCUPATIONAL GROUPS BY NUMBER
OF ROOMS IN FLATS IN WARSAW
(percentage)

| Socio-occupational groups | Population | | | | | | |
|---|---|---|---|---|---|---|---|
| | Total | 1-room | 2-room | 3-room | 4-room | 5- or 6-room | 7-room and more |
| Owners employing labour: | | | | | | | |
| 1. In mining and industry | | | | | | | |
| in enterprises of 1st to 7th category | 100·0 | 2·8 | 7·7 | 23·7 | 21·7 | 32·4 | 11·7 |
| in enterprises of 8th category | 100·0 | 15·0 | 25·9 | 32·3 | 15·0 | 10·0 | 1·8 |
| 2. In commerce and insurance | 100·0 | 4·6 | 11·0 | 26·2 | 23·6 | 28·4 | 6·2 |
| Owners not employing labour | | | | | | | |
| 1. In mining and industry | 100·0 | 41·5 | 30·2 | 19·5 | 5·4 | 2·9 | 0·5 |
| 2. In commerce and insurance | 100·0 | 21·1 | 26·9 | 27·5 | 12·5 | 9·6 | 2·4 |
| Lawyers, physicians, educational and cultural workers | 100·0 | 10·3 | 13·7 | 21·3 | 17·1 | 27·2 | 10·4 |
| White-collar workers | 100·0 | 11·7 | 18·2 | 26·4 | 19·6 | 18·7 | 5·4 |
| Physical workers | 100·0 | 55·5 | 29·0 | 11·5 | 2·5 | 1·1 | 0·2 |

educational workers etc., 1·4 rooms for workers, 1·8 rooms for craftsmen who did not employ hired labour, etc.[178]

After a closer analysis we can see that the group "Lawyers, Physicians, Educational and Cultural Workers", which generally enjoyed good housing cond- itions, had relatively many small flats with one or two rooms. This group is not uniform from the sociological point of view and, in addition to professional people, it includes educational and cultural workers who, like other white-collar workers, were not too well off financially.

---

[178] The calculation of the arithmetic mean in this case is difficult or impossible because the upper class of flats with seven or more rooms is open. But the median—the limit below which lies one-half of the population in a given class and above which lies the other half—describes the situation well. In calculating the median the centres of the classes should be taken as: 1·5, 2·5, 3·5 rooms, etc.

# PART V
## *Introduction to Sampling*

CHAPTER 18

# CERTAIN DEFINITIONS AND THEOREMS FROM PROBABILITY THEORY

## 1. THE MATHEMATICAL CONCEPT OF PROBABILITY

It is not the purpose of this book to give an exposition of the theory of sampling. Such an exposition would have to be much more extensive and would have to be based on mathematics to a much greater extent is justified by the nature of this book. Our task is more modest. We want to give the reader a general idea of methods of sampling, to enable him to understand the purpose of sampling and when it may be used. A study of these remarks should enable the reader to use sampling in very simple cases and to realize when such an independent analysis might be dangerous, and when a mathematical statistician should be consulted. When this is necessary, the reader should be sufficiently well prepared to be able to convey the essence of the problem to the mathematical statistician and to understand the conclusions reached by the latter on the basis of mathematical analysis.

In any case we have to begin with an explanation of certain basic concepts of the mathematical theory of probability on which sampling is based.

*The probability of an event is the ratio of the number of cases favouring the event to the number of all possible cases (those favouring the event and those not), assuming that all these cases are equally possible.*

This is the classical definition. This definition is not correct from the formal point of view. However, the elementary nature of this book does not permit the use of a precise definition based on higher mathematics. There are other definitions and we shall discuss them later.

Let us explain this definition by an example. Let us suppose that there are 1000 balls in a box, of which 300 are white. The balls are exactly the same with respect to size, shape, weight, smoothness, etc., and they only differ in colour. If we take one ball out of the box without looking, each has the same chance of being drawn (because all the balls are identical, except for colour). The probability of taking out a white ball is the ratio of the number of white balls to the total number of balls in the box; in this case it is $300/1000 = 3/10 = 0 \cdot 3$.

We deal with this kind of probability in games of chance such as roulette, dice, lottery, etc.: the assumption is that there is "an equal chance" but this is not always true.

505

J. Neyman[179] gives a different definition of probability: the probability that in the collection of objects $A$ a certain object possesses characteristic $B$ is the relative frequency of the objects possessing characteristic $B$ among all objects $A$. In this sense we can talk about "the probability of being married" as the ratio of the number of married men to the total number of men, or "the probability that a widow will marry again" as the ratio of the number of widows who married again to the total number of widows, etc.

This definition of probability has certain merits from the statistical point of view. Conceptually it is not identical with the classical definition, but this is not the place to discuss differences in definitions. Let us note, though, that in this definition there is no assumption of "equal chance" as in the classical definition. Let us illustrate this by an example. On one of the six sides of a dice there are six dots and according to the definition the probability of obtaining a six is ⅙, providing, of course, that the dice is true, i.e. it is not biased so as to have a tendency to fall in a certain way.

These are not the only definitions of probability.[180] The different definitions do not contradict each other. The mathematician will choose the one that enables him to develop the full theory of probability in the simplest and most consistent way.

We shall not discuss here the complicated problem of the definition of probability for an infinite population.

It follows from the definition of probability that it is always a proper fraction. The extreme cases are the values of 0 and 1. 0 means the impossibility that an event will occur; 1 means the certainty that it will occur. It also follows from the definition that if we denote by $p$ the probability that a given event will occur and by $q$ the probability that it will not occur, then

$$q = 1 - p,$$
$$p = 1 - q,$$
$$p + q = 1 \text{ (certainly either } p \text{ or } q, \text{ i.e. the event either will occur or}$$

will not occur).

Let us now consider more complicated cases. Let us suppose that in a box there are balls of different colours: blue, red, yellow and grey. The ratio of the blue balls to all the balls is 0·1, of the red balls it is 0·2, of the yellow balls 0·4 and of the grey balls 0·3. What is the probability that a ball is not grey? Obviously, it is $0·1 + 0·2 + 0·4 = 0·7$. Similarly, the probability that a ball is blue or yellow and not red or grey is $0·1 + 0·4 = 0·5$. We have thus arrived at the rule for adding probabilities. It states that if there are several mutually exclusive[181] events,

---

[179] J. Neyman: *First Course in Probability and Statistics,* New York, 1950, p. 16.

[180] For an extensive exposition of different definitions of probability see B. W. Gnyedenko: *Kours teorii vyeroyatnostiey,* Moscow–Leningrad, 1950, p. 16 *et seq.*

[181] If the ball is yellow it cannot be blue or red or grey.

and if each of them has a definite probability of occurrence, then the probability that at least one of them will occur is the sum of the probabilities of these events.

Let us imagine now that there are two dice on the table. What is the probability of obtaining 6 on both of them? When one of them turns up 1, the other may have 1, 2, etc. up to 6, i.e. 6 different possibilities; and if one turns up 2, the other has 6 possibilities. In all there are 36 possible combinations with two dice and of them only one is a 6 on both dice. Therefore, the probability of obtaining two 6's is 1/36, i.e. $1/6 \times 1/6$. This is the rule for multiplying probabilities. It means that if there are several independent events,[182] each with a definite probability, then the probability that all these events will occur together is the product of their probabilities.

If we have three boxes, each containing balls of various colours and each with the same ratio of blue, red, yellow, and grey balls (in relation to the total, as before: 0·1, 0·2, 0·4, and 0·3) then the probability that three balls, one drawn from each box, will be non-grey is $0·7 \times 0·7 \times 0·7 = 0·343$. If the first box contains 1 blue and 9 grey balls, the second contains 2 yellow and 8 grey balls and the third contains 4 red and 6 grey balls (the probabilities 0·1, 0·2, 0·4) then if we draw one ball from each box the probability of drawing only non-grey balls is $0·1 \times 0·2 \times 0·4 = 0·008$, the probability of drawing only grey balls is $0·9 \times 0·8 \times 0·6 = 0·432$. The difference $1 - (0·008 + 0·432) = 0·560$ is the probability of obtaining grey and coloured balls in various combinations.

Let us suppose that a lottery player has one ticket for one lottery and one for another; in the first lottery one out of every 5 tickets wins (the probability of winning is 1/5) and in the second one out of every 10 tickets wins (the probability of winning is 1/10). The probability of winning in both lotteries is $1/5 \times 1/10 = 1/50$. In order to obtain the combined probability we have to multiply the separate probabilities because the events are independent. In this case we cannot add up the separate probabilities in order to obtain the probability of winning in one of the lotteries because the events are not mutually exclusive: we can win or lose in one lottery and also in the other. It is easy to see what nonsensical results would be obtained were we to add up the two probabilities. Let us assume that in both lotteries every second ticket wins (the probability of winning is $\frac{1}{2}$). By adding up we would get

$$\frac{1}{2} + \frac{1}{2} = 1.$$

This would mean that a player having one ticket for each of the two lotteries must win, which is contrary to intuition. If there were three lotteries, each with the probability $\frac{1}{2}$ of winning, the result of adding up would be $1\frac{1}{2}$ which is more

---

[182] The number of dots obtained on the second die does not depend on the number of dots obtained on the first.

than 1, and therefore is obviously nonsense, being contrary to the definition of probability.

Similarly we cannot add probabilities if we have balls of different colours not in one box but in several, because in this case the events are not mutually exclusive; they are mutually exclusive if there is only one box.[183]

According to Table 16.6 (p. 471) on the age of the father and mother at the time the child is born, for 110,477 of all births there were 16,193 births in which both father and mother were aged between 25 and 29. Dividing 16,193 by 110,477 we obtain the number 0·14657 expressing the probability that both parents are aged 25–29. On the other hand, according to the table there were 36,933 births in which the age of the father was 25–29 years and 34,930 births in which the age of the mother was 25–29 years. Hence the probability that the age of the father was 25–29 years is 36,933/110,477 = 0·33430 and the probability that the age of the mother was 25–29 years is 34,930/110,477 = 0·31617. To calculate the probability that both father and mother are 25–29 years old we cannot apply the rule for multiplying probabilities because the probabilities that the age of the father is 25–29 years and that the age of the mother is 25–29 years are not independent of one another. If the age of the father is 25–29 then the probability that the mother is in the same age group is not 34,930/110,477 = 0·1617, as for all mothers, but it is much greater: 16,193/36,933 = 0·43844 (compare the table on p. 471). This is called a conditional probability, i.e. the probability that an event will occur given the occurrence of another event. Multiplying the simple probability that the age of the father is 25–29 by the conditional probability of the mother being 25–29 years old if the father is 25–29, we obtain the correct probability of both father and mother being 25–29 years old. It is 0·33430 × 0·43844 = 0·14657, which is the same as obtained by calculating this probability directly. We obtain the same result by multiplying the simple probability that the age of the mother is 25–29 years (0·31617) by the conditional probability that the age of the father is 25–29 if that is also the age of the mother (16,193/39,430 = 0·46358). In this case we also obtain 0·31617 × 0·46358 = 0·14658.

In this case the product of simple probabilities gives too low a value for the compound probability (0·33430 × 0·31617 = 0·10570 instead of the correct number 0·14658). This is due to the fact that the event of one parent being 25–29 years

---

[183] One false notion among players should be corrected here. A roulette player, seeing that a certain number has not occurred for a length of time, is inclined to bet on this number in the mistaken belief that in this way he increases his chances of winning. The fact that a certain number has not been called for a long time does not change the probability of its occurring in the future. Betting on such a number that does not increase the chance of winning, just as it does not diminish the chance of winning to bet on a number which has been called five times in a row, providing, of course, the wheel is not biased to make a certain number appear more frequently; if it is biased, betting on the number that has occurred five times in a row increases the chance of winning.

old increases the chance of the other being the same age. But if we take the combination: age of mother 25–29 and age of father 45–49, then the probability that the father is 45–49 when the mother is 25–29 (the conditional probability) is much less than the simple probability expressing the ratio of all births with fathers 45–49 years old to the total number of births. Therefore, in this case the product of simple probabilities would give too high a value.[184]

## 2. BINOMIAL DISTRIBUTION—NORMAL DISTRIBUTION

Let us suppose that we toss coins and are interested in whether they fall heads or tails. The probability that we get heads is equal to the probability that we get tails, i.e. is 0·5. If there is only one coin then the only alternatives are heads or tails. Let us denote this by the numbers 1 −1. If we have two coins both may give heads, or the first may give heads and the second tails, or the first may give tails and the second heads, or both may give tails. If we consider it indifferent which coin gives heads and which tails, then the combination heads tails may occur in two different ways, but the combinations heads–heads and tails–tails may occur in only one way. Denoting heads by $h$ and tails by $t$ we can write this schematically

| | | |
|---|---|---|
| Heads twice | $h\ h$ | frequency 1 |
| Heads once, tails once | $\begin{Bmatrix} h\ t \\ t\ h \end{Bmatrix}$ | ,,   2 |
| Tails twice | $t\ t$ | ,,   1 |

With three coins we have

| | |
|---|---|
| $h\ h\ h$ | frequency 1 |
| $\begin{matrix} h\ h\ t \\ h\ t\ h \\ t\ h\ h \end{matrix}$ | ,,   3 |
| $\begin{matrix} h\ t\ t \\ t\ h\ t \\ t\ t\ h \end{matrix}$ | ,,   3 |
| $t\ t\ t$ | ,,   1 |

It is easy to check that the frequencies of occurrence of particular combinations of heads and tails are arranged in a Pascal triangle.

---

[184] It is evident why conditional probabilities are sometimes greater and sometimes less than simple probabilities: cases in which both parents are approximately the same age are more frequent than cases in which their ages differ considerably.

| Number of coins (n) | | | | | | | | | | | | Sum of possibilities ($2^n$) |
|---|---|---|---|---|---|---|---|---|---|---|---|---|
| | | | | | 1 | | | | | | | |
| 1 | | | | | 1 | | 1 | | | | | 2 |
| 2 | | | | 1 | | 2 | | 1 | | | | 4 |
| 3 | | | 1 | | 3 | | 3 | | 1 | | | 8 |
| 4 | | 1 | | 4 | | 6 | | 4 | | 1 | | 16 |
| 5 | 1 | | 5 | | 10 | | 10 | | 5 | | 1 | 32 |
| 6 | 1 | 6 | 15 | | 20 | | 15 | | 6 | 1 | | 64 |
| 7 | 1 | 7 | 21 | 35 | | 35 | | 21 | 7 | 1 | | 128 |
| 8 | 1 | 8 | 28 | 56 | 70 | | 56 | 28 | 8 | 1 | | 256 |
| 9 | 1 | 9 | 36 | 84 | 126 | 126 | 84 | 36 | 9 | 1 | | 512 |
| 10 | 1 | 10 | 45 | 120 | 210 | 252 | 210 | 120 | 45 | 10 | 1 | 1024 |

etc.

Each number in a row of this table, with the exception of unity at the beginning and at the end, is obtained by adding the two numbers above it. In each row the numbers denote the frequency of the occurrence of different combinations. Thus, in our example the first number (always unity) denotes the occurrence of heads only, the second $n-1$ heads and the rest tails, the third number $n-2$ heads and the rest tails, etc. The second number corresponds to the number of coins. It is equal to $n$ written in the first column headed: "Number of coins". The total for each row denotes the total number of all possible combinations with a given number of coins. It is easy to check that the total number of possible combinations with $n$ coins is always $2^n$; thus with three coins we get $2^3 = 8$, with ten coins (the last row of the table) $2^{10} = 1024$, etc.

The relative frequency of occurrence, i.e. the probability of a given combination of heads and tails is obtained by dividing the appropriate number in the $n$-th row by the total for this row, i.e. by $2^n$. For instance, according to the last row for 10 coins, the probability that all coins will fall heads up or tails up is $1/1024 = 0 \cdot 00098$; the probability that one coin will fall tails up and nine heads up, or nine tails up and one heads up is $10/1024 = 0 \cdot 00977$; the probability that half of the coins will be heads up and half tails up is $252/1024$, etc.

The frequency of the occurrence of different combinations can be derived directly by proceeding as in the example on p. 509. Of course, for a large $n$ it would be very troublesome. If $n$ is not too large, Pascal's triangle may be used. Mathematically the frequency of combinations is given by the consecutive terms of the developed form of Newton's binomial expansion of

$$(p + q)^n.$$

In this case $p$ denotes the probability that the event will occur and $q = 1 - p$ denotes the probability that it will not occur. When $p = q$, as in the above example, $p = 0 \cdot 5$, the frequencies of different combinations are expressed directly by the coefficients of the terms of the binomial, of which the $(r + 1)$th term is[185]

$$\binom{n}{r} = \frac{n!}{r! \, (n - r)!} = \frac{1 \times 2 \times 3 \times \ldots \times n}{(1 \times 2 \times 3 \times \ldots \times r) \times (1 \times 2 \times 3 \times \ldots \times (n - r))}$$

$$= \frac{n \times [n - 1] \times [n - 2] \times \ldots \times [n - (r - 1)]}{1 \times 2 \times 3 \times \ldots \times r} \qquad \text{(XVIII.1)}$$

If $p \neq q$ the relative frequencies of the combinations should be calculated allowing for the values of $p$ and $q$ according to the formula

$$1 = p^n + np^{n-1} q + \binom{n}{2} p^{n-2} q^2 + \binom{n}{3} p^{n-3} q^3$$

$$+ \ldots + npq^{n-1} + q^n. \qquad \text{(XVIII.2)}$$

In this way an asymmetric frequency polygon is obtained. However, as $n$ increases the asymmetry decreases. When $n$ tends to infinity the series tends to complete symmetry.[186] However, this applies only when $p$ is not too small and $q$ is very close to unity, or vice versa.

We have elaborated this reasoning in great detail to make it easier for the reader to understand that in Pascal's triangle, Newton's binomial expansion and the normal curve (which we shall discuss later) we are not dealing with mathematical abstraction, but with facts from real life.

The binomial distribution, i.e. the distribution obtained by the binomial expansion, has certain characteristic features which are very important from the statistical point of view. It is a distribution that we know from the analysis of frequency distributions: a distribution with a maximum decreasing gradually in both directions.[187] Let us consider the simple example in which $p = q$ and the binomial distribution is symmetric. Here, in the middle of the distribution we have the

---

[185] The symbol $\binom{n}{r}$ is read "$n$ over $r$". The value of this expression is equal to $\dfrac{n!}{r! \, (n - r)!}$

The expression $n!$ is called factorial $n$. It is the product of the consecutive integers from 1 to $n$: $(1 \times 2 \times 3 \times \ldots \times n)$. The next expression in the formula (XVIII.1) is the expansion of the factorial. After appropriate abbreviations the last expression in the formula is obtained. It is convenient for calculations in which $n$ not too large and, of course, gives results identical with the corresponding rows of Pascal's triangle. When $n$ is large it is more convenient to calculate directly by formula $\dfrac{n!}{r! \, (n - r)!}$ if we have tables of factorials, or better still tables of the logarithms of factorials; these tables are at the end of this book.

[186] We give this theorem without proof.

[187] In the extreme case the binomial distribution can be increasing or decreasing (without a maximum in the middle).

value which appears most frequently. Indeed, we can see from Pascal's triangle that when $n$ is even, the most frequent cases are those in which heads occur as often as tails: $n/2$ times (twice with 4 coins, 5 times with 10 coins, etc.). When $n$ is odd, the most frequent are the numbers closest to $n/2$, i.e. $(n + 1)/2$ and $(n - 1)/2$. Thus for $n = 5$ the combination of 2 heads and 3 tails is as frequent as the combination of 3 heads and 2 tails. The greater the deviations from this most frequent value, the less frequent they are. With 10 coins the probability of 5 heads and 5 tails is 252/1024 the probability of 4 heads and 6 tails (or vice versa) is 210/1024, the probability of 2 heads and 8 tails is 45/1024, and finally the probability of all heads or all tails is 1/1024. Let us consider the last case. The probability that all are heads (or all tails) with 2 coins is 1/4 (1 case out of 4 possible cases), with 5 coins it is 1/32, with 10 coins 1/1024. If we extend the triangle, we see that for $n = 20$ the probability of all heads or all tails is about one-millionth, for $n = 30$ it is about one-thousand millionth, etc. We can see that the extreme probabilities (of all heads or all tails) decrease rapidly as the number of coins increases.

In the binomial distribution the average value of the frequencies of the occurrence of different combinations is expressed by the formula

$$\bar{\xi} = np, \tag{XVIII.3}$$

where $n$ is the number of units in the group (in our example $n$ is the number of coins), $p$ is the probability of the occurrence of a given event. If, as in our example, $p = 1/2$, then

$$\bar{\xi} = \frac{1}{2}n, \tag{XVIII.3'}$$

Thus, if we have 6 coins the average frequency with which heads will occur is 3, if we have 9 coins the average frequency is 4·5, etc. This is obvious because the distribution is symmetric.

The standard deviation is expressed by the formula

$$\sigma = \sqrt{np(1 - p)} = \sqrt{npq}, \tag{XVIII.4}$$

and for $p = 1/2$

$$\sigma = \sqrt{0 \cdot 25n} = 0 \cdot 5\sqrt{n}. \tag{XVIII.4'}$$

$n$, as before, denotes the number of units in the group.

According to this formula, the standard deviation of the occurrence of heads for 4 coins (or tails) is

$$\sigma = 0 \cdot 5 \times \sqrt{4} = 1,$$

and with 10 coins it is

$$\sigma = 0 \cdot 5 \times \sqrt{10} \approx 1 \cdot 5811.$$

We obtain the same result by calculating the standard deviation directly from the corresponding row of Pascal's triangle, using the general formula

$$\sigma_x = \sqrt{\sum \frac{(x - \bar{x})^2}{N}},$$ which is easy to check.

The diagrams shown here give the relative (percentage) frequency of the appearance of heads when $p = 0 \cdot 5$ and we have 6, 12, and 24 coins. We obtain symmetric histograms. If we further increase the number of coins the bars in the histograms will become narrower and at the limit when $n \to \infty$ we obtain a continuous symmetric curve. It is called the normal curve (or the probability curve or the Gauss curve).

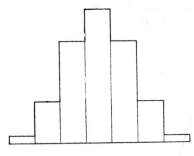

FIG. 18.1. Binomial distribution, $n = 6$.

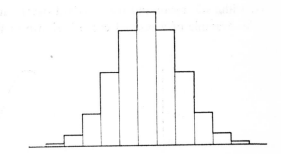

FIG. 18.2. Binomial distribution, $n = 12$.

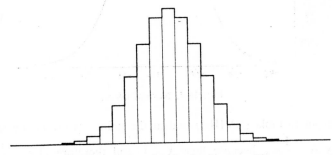

FIG. 18.3. Binomial distribution, $n = 24$.

It follows from what has been said above that the normal curve is symmetric about the maximum ordinate, which corresponds to the value of the mean (and also the median and the mode which in a symmetric frequency distribution equal the mean).

From the theorem given without proof on p. 511 it follows that the symmetric normal curve is obtained within limits (i.e. when $n \to \infty$) also when $p = q$, or if $p$ (or $q$) is not close to zero or unity.

However, not every symmetric curve is a normal curve. If the area under the normal curve is taken to be unity then the equation of the curve is

$$y = \frac{1}{\sigma\sqrt{2\pi}}\, e^{-\frac{1}{2}\left(\frac{X}{\sigma}\right)^2}. \tag{XVIII.5}$$

In this formula $\pi$, as usual, denotes the ratio of the circumference of a circle to its diameter (approximately $3 \cdot 14159$), $e$ is the base of natural logarithms (approximately $2 \cdot 71828$), $X$, as usual, denotes the deviation of the value of $x$ from the arithmetic mean of $x$, $(X = x - \bar{x})$; $\dfrac{X}{\sigma}$ is the deviation of variable $x$ from its arithmetic mean expressed in units of mean deviation.

It follows from the equation that the shape of the curve is fully determined by the arithmetic mean and the standard deviation of variable $x$.

An example of a normal curve is shown in Fig. (18.4).

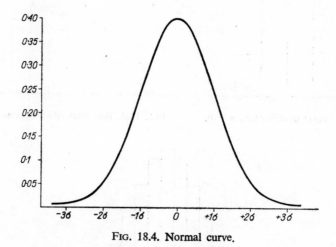

FIG. 18.4. Normal curve.

It follows from formula (XVIII.5) that at the point corresponding to the arithmetic mean $y = \dfrac{1}{\sigma\sqrt{2\pi}}$, because then $X = 0$ and therefore also $-\dfrac{1}{2}\left(\dfrac{X}{\sigma}\right)^2 = 0$ and thus $e^{-\frac{1}{2}\left(\frac{X}{\sigma}\right)^2} = 1$. If $\sigma = 1$ then the middle ordinate is $\dfrac{1}{\sqrt{2\pi}} \approx 0 \cdot 399$. If, for instance, $X = \pm 0,5\ \sigma$ then $y = 0 \cdot 352$, for $X = \pm \sigma$, $y = 0 \cdot 242$, for $X = 3\ \sigma$, $y = 0 \cdot 0044$. The points corresponding to $\pm \sigma$ are the points of inflexion of the curve; at these points it is steepest to the axis of abscissae.

Starting from the maximum ordinate the curve falls symmetrically on both sides, which means that the more variable $x$ moves away from its average value, the less frequent are the deviations this is in line with the observations resulting from the analysis of the binomial distribution. The curve approaches the horizontal axis asymptotically, which means that deviations from the average may be considerable but they are very infrequent.

It follows from what has been said above that not every symmetric curve is a normal curve. The normal curve is not only symmetric but it has a definite shape determined by the arithmetic mean and the standard deviation. For instance, the pattern for the height of the draftees born in 1906–9 (see Chapter 4, Table 4.9 and Fig. 4.9 p. 153 and 154) was almost completely symmetric, if we disregard considerable but very infrequent deviations towards the lowest height. But the curve is not a normal curve. In the upper part the curve is steeper and in the middle and lower parts it decreases more gradually than the normal curve. We shall return to this subject in connexion with other problems.

From the point of view of the application to sampling the important thing is not so much the values of the ordinates, but the area under the curve corresponding to definite segments on the horizontal axis.

The calculation of these areas requires the use of integral calculus, but it has been done with considerable accuracy so that we can use calculated tables. A table of the probability integral is at the end of the book.

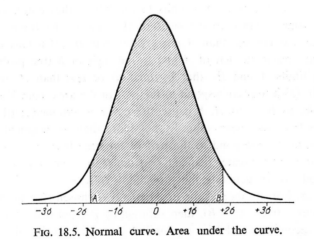

FIG. 18.5. Normal curve. Area under the curve.

Let us explain the problem by an example. In Fig. 18.5, showing the normal curve, identical with that in Fig. 18.4, a part of the area on both sides of the mean, between $A$ and $B$ is shaded; the distance from the centre ($X = 0$) to $A$ is the same as the distance from the centre to $B$, and is equal to $1 \cdot 8$ σ. We read off from the table in the Appendix that the value of the integral corresponding to $x = 1 \cdot 8$ is approximately $0 \cdot 928$. This means that $92 \cdot 8$ per cent of all observations are within the limits from $A$ to $B$, i.e. in $92 \cdot 8$ cases out of 100 the value of $x$ is not less than $A$

and not more than $B$. We can also say that in $100 - 92 \cdot 8 = 7 \cdot 2$ cases out of 100 the value of $x$ is equal to or less than $A$, or equal to or greater than $B$. Since the curve is symmetric the part of the area to the left of $A$ is equal to the part to the right of $B$ and each of them constitutes $0 \cdot 072/2 = 0 \cdot 036$ of the total area under the curve. Therefore we can also say that in $3 \cdot 6$ cases out of 100 the value of $x$ is equal to or less than $A$, and in $3 \cdot 6$ cases out of 100 it is equal to or greater than $B$.

Or we can say that in $92 \cdot 8/3 \cdot 6 = 96 \cdot 4$ cases out of 100 (the area under the curve from the left end, i.e from $X = - \infty$ to $B$) $x$ is equal to or less than $B$.

The values of the probability integral (the part of the area under the curve within defined limits) are given in the tables as the function $X/\sigma$, i.e. $x$ measured from the arithmetic mean in multiples of the standard deviation.[188]

For instance, if $x = 181$, the arithmetic mean $x = 172$, the standard deviation $\sigma = 6$, then $X = 181 - 172 = + 9$, $X/\sigma \frac{9}{6} = + 1 \cdot 5$ ($X$ is $1 \cdot 5$ times the standard deviation). Next to this figure in the table of probability integrals a fraction is given expressing the part of the area under the curve corresponding to a given value of $X/\sigma$, on the assumption that the whole area under the curve equals one. This fraction may have different meanings. For instance: (1) it may correspond to the part of the area under the curve within the limits $A$ and $B$, where $A$, as in Fig. 18.5, denotes the point $X/\sigma$ units to the left of the centre, and $B$ denotes the point the same distance to the right of the centre; the fraction is then the probability that $x$ is not less than $A$ nor greater than $B$; (2) it may correspond to the parts of the area to the left of $A$ and to the right of $B$ (the probability that $x$ is outside the limits $A$ and $B$—that is equal to or less than $A$ or equal to or greater than $B$); (3) it may correspond to the part of the area from $X = 0$, i.e. from the mean value, to $B$ or to $A$, because the curve is symmetric (the probability that $x$ deviates from the mean value by not more than the segment from 0 to $B$ or to $A$); (4) it may correspond to the part of the area from $x = - \infty$ to $A$ (the probability that $x$ is not greater than $A$), or from $B$ to $+ \infty$ ($x$ is not less than $B$).

All these methods of denoting the probability integral can easily be converted into one another. For instance, if the first method is chosen (the probability that $x$ is within the limits from $A$ to $B$), then subtracting $P$ from one we obtain the notation by the second method (the probability that $x$ is outside the limits of the segment from $A$ to $B$). Multiplying by 2 the values of $P$ denoted by the third method (the probability that $x$ is located between the mean value and $B$, or between the mean value and $A$) we obtain $P$ denoted by the first method. The numbers

---

[188] In older statistical studies usually not the standard deviation but the probable deviation was used, i.e. the deviation within whose limits lie one-half of all observations. Accordingly, in the tables for the probability integral not the units of standard deviation were used, but the units of probable deviation. If we denote the probable deviation by $w$ then in the case of the normal curve we obtain approximately $w = 0 \cdot 67449 \, \sigma$.

for $P$ in the fourth method (the probability that $x$ is not greater than $B$) are greater by 0·5 than the values of $P$ in the third method, because the probability that $x$ is less than the arithmetic mean is 0·5. It follows that to switch over from the fourth to the first method the corresponding values of $P$ must be multiplied by 2 and should be subtracted from the result; we shift from the fourth to the second method by subtracting 0·5 from the corresponding $P$. The reader is advised to practice these calculations, taking as a starting point, say, the example on p. 449 ($X/\sigma = 1 \cdot 08$; $P$ by the first method $= 0 \cdot 928$).

Although these calculations are not complicated it is more convenient to have the tables so designed that the results can be read off directly, without additional calculation. Which method is most convenient depends upon the object of the study.

It is also possible to use a completely different method of notation in which the starting point is not $X/\sigma$, but the probability of P. Then the values of $X/\sigma$ are given for specific values of $P$ (for instance, for $P$ to be equal to 0·9 or 0·95, or 0·99). In some cases this method is most convenient.

In the table in the Appendix the first method (p. 516) is used.

We show below certain values of $P$ denoting the probability that $x$ is within the limits from $A$ to $B$ (the first method).

TABLE 18.1. SELECTED VALUES OF THE PROBABILITY INTEGRAL

For $\dfrac{x}{\sigma} = 1$          $P = 0 \cdot 683$

For $\dfrac{x}{\sigma} = 1 \cdot 5$          $P = 0 \cdot 866$

For $\dfrac{x}{\sigma} = 1 \cdot 96$          $P = 0 \cdot 95$

For $\dfrac{x}{\sigma} = 2$          $P = 0 \cdot 954$

For $\dfrac{x}{\sigma} = 2 \cdot 5$          $P = 0 \cdot 988$

For $\dfrac{x}{\sigma} = 2 \cdot 58$          $P = 0 \cdot 99$

For $\dfrac{x}{\sigma} = 3$          $P = 0 \cdot 997$

For $\dfrac{x}{\sigma} = 4$          $P = 0 \cdot 99994$

For $\dfrac{x}{\sigma} = 5$          $P = 0 \cdot 99999994.$

As we have already mentioned, we do not always deal in statistics with a normal distribution. For instance, if in a binomial distribution $p$ (or $q$) is very small we obtain the Poisson distribution. There are many other distributions corresponding to different conditions encountered in statistics.

Probabilities corresponding to most distributions having practical applications are shown in appropriate tables and their use does not present any difficulty. However, difficulties may arise when it comes to choosing the table most appropriate for the case at hand. Since our task is not to give a systematic exposition of the theory of probability and of mathematical statistics, but—as stated in the title—to give "an introduction to sampling", we shall not consider these special distributions, but shall confine ourselves to the normal distribution. This should suffice to enable the reader to grasp the essence of reasoning in sampling. Besides this the normal curve plays a distinctly leading role in statistics.

## 3. THE THEORY OF PROBABILITY AND STATISTICAL REALITY

Certain observations in statistical practice are distributed in a manner approximating the normal curve. If we measure the same quantity many times, e.g. the distance between two points, we do not obtain identical results. Either because of a lack of precision in the measuring instruments, or because of the lack of accuracy in reading the results, the figures differ. If the instrument is not faulty and if the investigator is not biased to read more, or less, than the measurement indicates, we find that, when the number of measurements is sufficiently large, the most frequently obtained result is located in the middle, between deviations up and down; this result we accept as the true distance between the two points. Readings too high or too low appear with approximately the same frequency. The greater the errors, the less frequent they are. Their frequencies are arranged approximately in the pattern of the normal curve (hence another name for this curve: the curve of errors).

If we calculate the ratios of the births of boys or girls to all births in certain districts, this ratio will fluctuate around a certain average value, and the frequencies of the deviations from this average will form an approximately normal curve.

A more or less normal curve is formed by the weight of infants at birth. The weights of older children as well as the weights of adults usually form an asymmetric pattern.

We shall assume now that the average height (e.g. of adult women) is 160 cm and the standard deviation of height is 5·5 cm. These figures are close to those actually observed among the female students who began their university studies in Warsaw in 1946.

If we assume that the distribution of height is that of the normal curve we obtain the curve as in Fig. 18.6.

There are two scales for height here: in centimetres and in standard deviations; as we know, the standard deviation is 5·5 cm so that, for instance, $-2\sigma$ (149

$= 160 - 2 \times 2 \cdot 5)$ corresponds to the height of 149 cm $+ 2\sigma$, $(171 = 160 - 2 \times 5 \cdot 5)$ corresponds to the height of 171 cm, etc. On the basis of the above, using the table from p. 517, we can say that out of all women making up a given population, 95·4 per cent are not shorter than 149 cm, and not taller than 171 cm; in other words, the probability that a woman is between 149 and 171 cm tall is

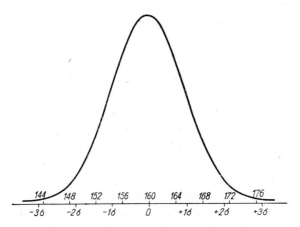

FIG. 18.6. Normal curve. Example of height distribution.

0·954, the probability that she is 171 centimetres or taller is $(1-0\cdot954)/2 = 0\cdot023$, the probability that a woman is not taller than 171 cm is $0\cdot954/0\cdot023 = 1 - 0\cdot023 = 0\cdot977$, etc.

We can take any other height, say 165 cm, and calculate the probability that a woman is taller or shorter than that height. The calculation proceeds as follows.

The height of 165 cm exceeds the average height of women by $165 - 160 = 5$ cm. Dividing 5 by the standard deviation $\sigma = 5 \cdot 5$ cm we get 0·91. In the appropriate probability integral table we find for the argument $X/\sigma = 0 \cdot 91$ that the part of the area between the left-hand side of the curve $(X = -\infty)$ and $X = + 5$, corresponding to $X/\sigma = 0 \cdot 91$, constitutes 0·819 of the whole area under the curve. This means that of all women in the population 81·9 per cent are not taller than 165 cm and the remaining 18·1 per cent are not shorter than 165 cm.

## 4. DRAWING. THE LAW OF LARGE NUMBERS

There are black and white balls in the box. Their number is 700 and 300 respectively; thus the ratio is 7/3. Using the terminology of probability calculus we say that the probability that a ball is white is $3/(3 + 7) = 0\cdot3$. The balls differ only with respect to colour and otherwise are identical. They are perfectly mixed. Suppose now that, without looking, we take one ball out of the box, record its colour and put it back into the box, mix the balls perfectly, draw another one, etc.[189] This procedure, in which all the units have an equal change of being drawn, is called random drawing.

If we draw 10 balls in this way, and if the frequencies of black and white balls correspond to their respective probabilities, we have 7 black balls and 3 white balls. Experience and intuition tell us that this ratio will only occur sometimes; we may have all black or all white balls or different combinations of black and white balls.

Experience and intuition also tell us that if this kind of drawing is repeated many times, then in the final result the relative frequency of black and white balls drawn will be very close to the ratio in which they are in the box: the relative frequency of black balls drawn will be close to $0 \cdot 7$, and that of white balls close to $0 \cdot 3$. Moreover, the relative frequency of different combinations (all black, 9 black and 1 white, 8 black and 2 white, etc.) will approach the relative frequencies obtained from Newton's binomial expansion, for $p = 0 \cdot 7$, $q = 1 - p = 0 \cdot 3$, $n = 10$ (see p. 511).

The principle that many repeated drawings reproduce the situation prevailing in the population from which we draw, its accuracy increasing with the number of drawings, is called the Law of Large Numbers. This law is the basis of sampling.

The intuitive definition of the law of large numbers is not quite precise. A more precise exposition can be found in: *Kours Vyeorye vyeroyathostyey*, by B. Gnyedenko, (Moscow–Leningrad, 1950, p. 158 *et seq.*) or in *Elementy rachunku prawdopodobieństwa (The Elements of Probability Calculus,* Polish translation), by B. Gnyedenko and A. Khintchyn, (Warsaw, 1952 p. 117 *et seq.*).

At the time of the printing of this book an extensive study appeared in Polish: *Rachunek prawdopodobieństwa i statystyka matematyczna (Probability Calculus and Mathematical Statistics)* by Marek Fisz (Warsaw, 1954). All the problems involved as well as the latest achievements in this field are extensively discussed in this book, but a knowledge of higher mathematics is required.

---

[189] In this experiment we have to put the ball back in the box to maintain the same probability. If we drew a white ball first and did not put it back, the ratio of white balls to all the balls in the box at the second drawing would be 299/999 and the probability that the ball was white would be less than before (299/999 < 300/1000). If the first ball was black, the probability that the ball would be white at the second drawing becomes greater than before (300/999 > 300/1000).

# CHAPTER 19

# SAMPLING

## 1. BASIC CONCEPTS AND FORMULAE

Sampling is a form of partial research, of research in which inferences concerning the whole population are based on the part studied. The feature distinguishing sampling from other forms of partial research is that in sampling the portion to be studied is selected at random. As we shall see, in partial research this is the only method that ensures objectivity in the results, and permits an evaluation of their accuracy.

Suppose that we have a large population, say, the adult male population of the City of Warsaw. To learn about this population we draw[190] a certain number of individuals from the whole male population of Warsaw. This group is called a sample in contrast to the total population. Our task may consist in: (1) estimating on the basis of the sample: (a) the relative or absolute frequencies of persons with a specific characteristic in the whole population, (b) the arithmetic mean, the median, the mode, the standard deviation or some other numerical characteristic of a given measurable characteristic, (c) the correlation among different characteristics of the units in the population; or in (2) estimating whether a given statistical hypothesis, i.e. the hypothesis concerning a certain fact and based on the sample, may be consider true (or false).

Let us suppose that on the basis of a sample composed of, say, 100 individuals, we want to estimate the arithmetic mean of the heights of the male population of Warsaw. Suppose further that on the basis of the measurements of the sample the arithmetic mean is 170 cm. However, if from this population of the adult males in Warsaw we draw a second sample, a third sample etc., each containing 100 individuals, the arithmetic means may not be 170 cm as before, but may deviate from this number in either direction.

Only if we could continue drawing batches of 100 individuals an infinite number of times could we say that the average of all samples equals the actual average for the whole population, in this case the male population of Warsaw. But we are not in a position to determine exactly, on the basis of a single sample, the actual average height in Warsaw.

---

[190] We shall discuss the technical aspects of such drawing later.

However, if we could determine the frequencies of the different results of calculating the arithmetic mean of a sample, we would be able to determine the limits within which the actual average is located and the probability that these limits will not be exceeded.

It turns out that the averages of samples, provided the samples are sufficiently large, are normally distributed regardless of whether in the whole population from which we draw these samples the values of a given characteristic are normally distributed or not. We can then write (we give this without proof)

$$\sigma_{\bar{x}} = \frac{\sigma_x}{\sqrt{n}} \,. \tag{XIX.1}$$

On the right-hand side of this expression we have in the numerator $\sigma_x$, the standard deviation of the individual values of the variable in the whole population; $n$ (under the square root sign) denotes the number of units in the sample; $\sigma_{\bar{x}}$ on the left-hand side denotes the standard deviation of the arithmetic mean corresponding to the distribution of the values of the average $\bar{x}$ in consecutive drawings, each containing $n$ units. This standard deviation in sampling is called the standard error.

It follows from the equation that the standard error of the arithmetic mean is larger, the larger the standard deviation of the characteristic in the whole population; and smaller, the larger the number of units in the sample. This is in agreement with intuition which tells us that an estimate based on a sample is the less exact, the greater the heterogeneity of a population (the greater $\sigma_x$), and it is the more exact, the more units are studied (the law of large numbers). Of course, intuition by itself does not suffice to state these relationships precisely, namely that (1) the standard error of the arithmetic mean is directly proportional to the standard deviation of the characteristic studied in the general population, and not to some function of the standard deviation, (2) the standard error of the arithmetic mean is inversely proportional to the square root of the number of units in the sample, i.e. to $\sqrt{n}$.

Since we know that the values obtained in calculating $\bar{x}$ for consecutive drawings, each of them containing $n$ units, form a normal distribution, we can apply to the standard error of the arithmetic mean the same reasoning as outlined on pp. 515–18.

Analogous formulae, as in the case of the standard error of the arithmetic mean, can be derived for other numerical characteristics. For instance, the formula for the standard error of the standard deviation is

$$\sigma_{\sigma_x} = \frac{\sigma_x}{\sqrt{2n}} \,, \tag{XIX.2}$$

where $\sigma_x$ denotes, as before, the standard deviation for characteristic $x$ in the whole population, and $n$ the number of units in the sample. However, this formula is accurate only when the distribution of the whole population with respect to characteristic $x$ is normal. If the distribution is not normal the estimate of the standard error may be too high or too low. The error is small if $n$ is large.

The standard error of the correlation coefficient is expressed by the formula

$$\sigma_r = \frac{1 - r^2}{\sqrt{n}}, \qquad (XIX.3)$$

where $r$ is the correlation coefficient, $n$ the number of units in the sample. This formula, like the formula for the standard error of the standard deviation, is accurate only under certain limiting conditions which we shall not discuss here. However, the result may be considered as sufficiently accurate for practical purposes if the number of units in the sample is not small and $r$ is not close to $+1$ or $-1$.

We shall not give here the formulae for the standard errors of other statistical measures.

*Example* 1. Suppose that, as in the example on p. 518, we are concerned with a population of women of which we know that the standard deviation of height is $5\cdot5$ cm. We have drawn 100 individuals from this population and we have obtained $\bar{x} = 148\cdot8$ cm. Of course, it does not follow that the arithmetic mean of the height of all the women is actually $148\cdot8$ cm, but we can say something about the size and the probability of the error that we commit in accepting $\bar{x} = 148\cdot8$ cm.

There is a true value of the arithmetic mean of height unknown to us; we denote it[191] by $\bar{\xi}$.

Since the values of the arithmetic mean obtained from the sample form a normal curve they are distributed symmetrically around the true value $\bar{\xi}$, and the standard error of the arithmetic mean indicates the shape of the curve.

Substituting in formula (XIX.1) $\sigma_x = 5\cdot5$ cm and $n = 100$ we obtain

$$\sigma_{\bar{x}} = \frac{5\cdot5}{\sqrt{100}} \text{ cm} = 0\cdot55 \text{ cm}.$$

By marking off from the value we obtained, $\bar{x} = 148\cdot8$ cm, say, $2\cdot5\ \sigma_x$ in both directions we get the segment from $148\cdot8$ cm $- 2\cdot5 \times 0\cdot55 = 147\cdot425$ cm, to $148\cdot8 + 2\cdot5 \times 0\cdot55$ cm $= 150\cdot775$ cm, of which we can say that if under the given conditions ($\sigma_x = 5\cdot5$ cm, $n = 100$) we have obtained from the sample the mean $\bar{x} = 148\cdot8$, we can expect with the probability of $0\cdot988$ (see Table 18.1 on p. 517) that the actual mean $\bar{\xi}$ is not less than $\bar{x} - 1\cdot375$ (i.e. $147\cdot425$) and not greater than $\bar{x} + 1\cdot375$ (i.e. $150\cdot175$). These limits are called confidence limits; the probability that the confidence limits will not be exceeded is called the confidence coefficient. In our case the confidence interval is $150\cdot175 - 147\cdot425 = 2\cdot75$ cm, and the confidence coefficient is $0\cdot988$.

---

[191] In mathematical statistics it is customary to denote magnitudes pertaining to the general population by Greek letters, and those obtained from the sample by Latin letters. For technical reasons in this book. This system of notation is not always rigidly observed.

The above definitions of the confidence interval and the confidence coefficient are not precise. If from the same general population we draw consecutive samples each containing 100 units, we obtain from the samples different values of the arithmetic mean, and, therefore, also different limits of the confidence interval.

Only the length of the confidence interval will not change since it depends only upon $\sigma_{\bar{x}} = \dfrac{\sigma_x}{\sqrt{100}}$ and on the chosen confidence coefficient, i.e. on the coefficient by which we multiply $\sigma_{\bar{x}}$. Strictly speaking we should write only $\bar{x} - 2 \cdot 5\,\sigma_{\bar{x}} \leqslant \xi < x + 2 \cdot 5\,\sigma_{\bar{x}}$ without defining the limits of the confidence interval, which will vary with $\bar{x}$ in a given sample. The distance between the upper and lower limits of the confidence interval will remain unchanged, always being $2 \times 2 \cdot 5 \times \dfrac{5 \cdot 5}{\sqrt{100}} = 2 \cdot 75$, if we assume that $\sigma_x = 5 \cdot 5$ and $n = 100$. If in this and in the several following examples we write that $\bar{\xi}$, the true mean from the sample with a definite confidence coefficient, is between specific values of the limits of the confidence interval, we use a mathematically inaccurate simplification since, in fact, the limits of the confidence interval are random variables depending upon the value of $\bar{x}$ in the sample.

Nevertheless, we can say of each such pair or limits of the confidence interval with the same confidence coefficient that it includes $\bar{\xi}$, the true value of the mean in the general population.

If we draw not 100 units, but, say 400, 1600, 10,000, etc., the standard error of the arithmetic mean will diminish;

$$\text{for } n = \quad 400, \quad \sigma_{\bar{x}} = \frac{5 \cdot 5}{\sqrt{400}} \text{ cm} = 0 \cdot 275 \text{ cm}$$

$$\text{for } n = \quad 1600, \quad \sigma_{\bar{x}} = \frac{5 \cdot 5}{\sqrt{1600}} \text{ cm} = 0 \cdot 1375 \text{ cm}$$

$$\text{for } n = 10,000. \quad \sigma_{\bar{x}} = \frac{5 \cdot 5}{\sqrt{10,000}} \text{ cm} = 0 \cdot 055 \text{ cm}$$

If $n = 400$ and therefore the standard error is $0 \cdot 275$ cm, then marking off $2 \cdot 5\,\sigma_{\bar{x}}$, as above, we obtain the same confidence coefficient, but the confidence interval is within the limits from $148 \cdot 8 - 2 \cdot 5 \times 0 \cdot 275 = 148 \cdot 1125$ cm and $148 \cdot 8 + 2 \cdot 5 \times 0 \cdot 275 = 149 \cdot 4875$ cm. Thus it is $1 \cdot 375$ cm, which is one half of what we obtained before. If we keep the same confidence interval as before then its limits, as before, will be $1 \cdot 375$ cm on both sides of $148 \cdot 8$ cm but $1 \cdot 375$ cm now exceeds the standard—which is reduced by half—not by a factor of $2 \cdot 5$, but of 5. The confidence coefficient is then expressed by the decimal with seven nines after the decimal point only the eighth decimal will be less than nine.

This means that less frequently than once in ten million times may it happen that we exceed the limits of the accepted confidence interval.

Thus the situation is as follows:

(1) When we use sampling we never get the exact answer for the value of the arithmetic mean (or of some other statistical magnitude); we only find out that there is a definite probability expressed by the confidence coefficient that it is located

within certain limits (confidence interval). By subtracting the confidence coefficient from one we obtain the probability that a given magnitude is located outside the accepted confidence interval.

(2) For a given number of units in the sample there is a definite value of the standard error $\sigma_{\bar{x}}$, but we can arbitrarily either (a) extend or narrow the limits of the error that we consider permissible, or (b) accept a greater or smaller probability that the limits will not be exceeded; both these values (the limits of the error and the probability that these limits will not be exceeded) are functionally related to one another so that the extension of the permissible limits of the error corresponds to an increase in the probability that these limits will not be exceeded, and vice versa.

By extending the limits of the permissible error, which is tantamount to diminishing the accuracy of the estimate, we can achieve any desired degree of approximation to unity for the probability that the limits of the error will not be exceeded. Thus we have two opposing alternatives: to diminish accuracy and increase confidence, or to increase accuracy and decrease confidence. We must choose between these two alternatives.

(3) By changing the number of units in the sample we can influence the size of the standard error $\sigma_{\bar{x}}$, and thus also the accuracy of, and the confidence in, the results obtained. For instance, by increasing the number of units drawn we increase the accuracy, or the confidence, or both.

(4) We cannot influence the accuracy of, or the confidence in the results by changing $\sigma_x$ in the numerator of the fraction on the right-hand side of formula (XIX.1), because for a given population $\sigma_x$ is a constant quantity, independent of us. However, with constant $\sigma_x$ and $n$ we can sometimes influence the size of the standard error in some other way that we shall discuss later.

*Example* 2. Consider the following experiment. Ten identical coins, after thorough shaking, were tossed onto a table and the number of heads counted. This was repeated 1024 times. If we assume that a coin does not display a tendency to fall heads up more often than tails up, or vice versa, we can apply here formulae (XVIII.3) and (XVIII.4) (p. 512) assuming that $p = q = \frac{1}{2}$, $n$ (the number of coins tossed) $= 10$; the average number of heads in one toss is 5, the standard error of this number is $1 \cdot 5811$.

Actually, in 1024 tosses 4989 heads were obtained. Thus, the average number of heads in one toss was not 5 but $4989/1024 = 4 \cdot 872$, i.e. too little by $0 \cdot 128$. The question is: what is the probability that this deviation from the expected number of heads is random?

The problem consists in testing a statistical hypothesis. The hypothesis in this case is the assumption that the difference $5 - 4 \cdot 872 = 0 \cdot 128$ is caused by random factors.

The reasoning is as follows.

Since the experiment was repeated 1024 times, the standard error of the arithmetic mean is

$$\sigma_{\bar{x}} = \frac{1 \cdot 5811}{1024} = 0 \cdot 0494.$$

The observed deviation from the expected number of 5 heads exceeds the standard error by a factor of

$$0 \cdot 128 / 0 \cdot 0494 = 2 \cdot 59.$$

In the table of the probability integral at the end of the book we find that the probability of obtaining a random difference equal to or less than $2 \cdot 59$ times the standard error is $0 \cdot 9905$ or roughly $0 \cdot 99$; in other words, only in one case out of 100 does it happen that in 1024 tosses the average number of heads in a toss is 4872 or less, or 5128 or more. If we want to determine the probability that under these conditions the average number of heads in a toss is less by $0 \cdot 128$ than in the hypothesis (the probability of obtaining a head $= \frac{1}{2}$), or the probability that the result obtained will be within the limits from $-\infty$ to $-2 \cdot 59 \dfrac{X}{\sigma_{\bar{x}}}$, then we should reason as follows. The probability that the average number of heads in a toss is equal to or less than $4 \cdot 872$, or equal to or less than $5 \cdot 128$, is $0 \cdot 01$. Since the curve is symmetric the probability that the average number of heads in a toss is equal to or less than $4 \cdot 872$, is $0 \cdot 005$, i.e. five in a thousand—a very small probability.

The conclusion is: It is very probable that either (1) the coins used in this experiment had a greater tendency to fall tails up than heads up (e.g. because of the uneven shape of the coin), or (2) the experiment was carried out without ensuring equal chances for both sides of the coin. If we assume that under the circumstances the second alternative should be excluded, we have to accept the first alternative from which it would appear that with the coins used in this experiment playing "heads or tails" probably is not a "fair" game because it gives a better chance to the player who bets on tails.

Experiments carried out by patient mathematical statisticians have shown that the game of dice is usually also not fair, because large numbers occur more often then small numbers. This might be explained by the fact that the dots on the dice are gouged out, and therefore the side on which there are fewer dots is heavier and tends to fall to the bottom more frequently.

The procedure is as follows. We calculate the standard error of a given numerical characteristic of the population and, using appropriate tables, determine the probability that a given value of this characteristic is random. If the probability is small we reject the hypothesis.

If, on the contrary, the probability is high we accept the hypothesis.

The question remains what probability should be considered sufficiently small to reject a hypothesis, and what probability should be considered sufficiently large to accept a hypothesis. This question cannot be solved once and for all in a dogmatic manner. We shall return to this problem later.

*Example* 3. In this example we want to estimate the frequency with which units with a given characteristic appear.

If we denote by the probability that a unit has the characteristic (i.e. the ratio of the number of units with this characteristic to the total number of units), by $q$ the probability that it does not have this characteristic ($q = 1 - p$), and by $n$ as above, the number of units drawn, then the standard error of the probability of the relative frequency is expressed by the formula

$$\sigma_p = \sqrt{\frac{pq}{n}}. \qquad (XIX.4)$$

In this formula, as in the formula for the standard error of the arithmetic mean, $n$ is in the denominator under the square root sign.

This means that in this case also the standard error is inversely proportional to the square root of the number of units in the sample. In the numerator, under the square root sign, we have the product $pq$ in which $p$ and $q$ can have any values from 0 to 1 such that $p + q = 1$. It is easy to show that this product is a maximum when $p$, and therefore $q$, equals $0 \cdot 5$. Then the product $pq = 0 \cdot 25$ and $\sqrt{pq} = 0 \cdot 5$.

The further $p$ and $q$ move from $0 \cdot 5$, the smaller the product $pq$. For instance, for $p = 0 \cdot 1$, $pq = 0 \cdot 09$, $\sqrt{pq} = 0 \cdot 3$. But the relative error of the estimated value of $p$ increases as $p$ decreases. This follows from the following calculation.

If, as above, the standard error $\sigma_p = \sqrt{\dfrac{pq}{n}}$, then this error in relation to $p$ is

$$\frac{\sigma_p}{p} = \frac{\sqrt{\dfrac{pq}{n}}}{p} = \sqrt{\frac{\left(\dfrac{pq}{n}\right)}{p^2}} = \sqrt{\frac{q}{np}} = \sqrt{\frac{1-p}{np}} = \sqrt{\frac{1}{np} - \frac{1}{n}} \qquad (XIX.5)$$

$$= \sqrt{\frac{1}{n}\left(\frac{1}{p} - 1\right)}.$$

Here $p$ appears in the denominator and, therefore with $n$ given, the standard error $\sigma_p$ in relation to $p$ increases as $p$ decreases.

The series of values of $\sigma_p$ is symmetric; $\sigma_p$ reaches a maximum for $p = q = 0 \cdot 5$. But the relative error of $p$ is monotonically increasing: the smaller $p$, the greater the standard error of $p$ in percentage relation to $p$. When $p$ is small the percentage error is large and the estimate obtained in this way—for $n = 100$—would be of no practical value.

If $n$ were not 100 but $n_1$ we should have to divide the figures in the table $\sqrt{\dfrac{n_1}{n}}$.

Thus for $n_1 = 1000$ we divide by $\sqrt{\dfrac{1000}{100}} = \sqrt{10} \approx 3 \cdot 16$; for $n_1 = 10{,}000$ we divide by $\sqrt{\dfrac{10{,}000}{100}} = 10$, and so on.

For $n = 1000$ and $p = 0 \cdot 1$ $\sigma_p$ is $0 \cdot 03/3 \cdot 16 \approx 0 \cdot 0095$, $\dfrac{100\,\sigma_p}{p}$ is $30/3 \cdot 16 = 9 \cdot 5$; for $n = 10{,}000$ we obtain $0 \cdot 003$ and 3 per cent respectively.

TABLE 19.1. ABSOLUTE AND RELATIVE
STANDARD ERROR OF THE RATIO OF A PART
TO THE TOTAL FOR $n = 100$

| $p$ | $\sigma_p$ | $\dfrac{100\sigma_p}{p}$ |
|---|---|---|
| 0·9 | 0·03 | 3·5 |
| 0·8 | 0·04 | 5·0 |
| 0·7 | 0·045 | 6·6 |
| 0·6 | 0·049 | 8·0 |
| 0·5 | 0·05 | 10·0 |
| 0·4 | 0·049 | 12·0 |
| 0·3 | 0·045 | 15·0 |
| 0·3 | 0·04 | 20·0 |
| 0·1 | 0·03 | 30·0 |

Since in estimating $p$ the absolute error is not of essential importance, but the error in relation to the value of $p$ sought, it follows that when $p$ is small a relatively large sample is required.

It also follows from the asymmetric pattern of the last column in the table that the percentage standard error in estimating $p$ (the relative frequency of the units possessing the characteristic studied) is different from the error in estimating $q$ (the relative frequency of the units not possessing the characteristic studied). For instance, if the relative number of married women aged 40–9 is large (in Poiand in 1931 it was 92·5 per cent) then even when the sample is small there is small risk of a large error in estimating this ratio: but the relative error in estimating the percentage of unmarried women may be very large, and may render useless the information obtained. This is obvious. According to formula (XIX.4) the absolute standard error in estimating the percentage of married persons is the same as the error in estimating the percentage of unmarried persons. But if this error is, say, 2 per cent it will be only $\dfrac{2 \cdot 100}{92 \cdot 5} = 2 \cdot 16$ per cent for married women and $\dfrac{2 \cdot 100}{7 \cdot 5}$ $= 26 \cdot 7$ per cent for unmarried women.

Formulae (XIX.4) and (XIX.5) determine the standard error of a probability (relative frequency). However, sometimes we want to know the standard error not of the relative frequency but of the absolute frequency: we want to know by how many units we can be mistaken. The standard error of the absolute frequency is obtained by multiplying the standard error of the relative frequency by the number of observations in the population, i.e. with respect to the general population, by $N$:

$$\sigma'_p = N \sqrt{\frac{pq}{n}}.$$

(XIX.6)

With regard to the standard error of the absolute frequency in a sample we multiply by $n$ and obtain

$$\sigma''_p = n \sqrt{\frac{pq}{n}} = \sqrt{\frac{n^2 pq}{n}} = \sqrt{npq}.$$

(XIX.7)

This is the form in which the formula is often given in textbooks.

To convert formula (XIX.7) into formula (XIX.6) we have to multiply $\sigma''_p$ by the ratio of the number of observations in the general population to the number of observations in the sample:

$$\sigma'_p = \sigma''_p \times \frac{N}{n} = \frac{N}{n} \sqrt{npq} = N \sqrt{\frac{npq}{n^2}} = N \sqrt{\frac{pq}{n}}.$$

These formulae can also be applied to the problem dealt with in the example on p. 525, pertaining to tossing coins. Altogether 102,240 coins were tossed (1024 $\times$ $\times$ 10), since $p = 0 \cdot 5$, there should have been 5120 heads; in fact, there were 4989, that is 131 too few. The standard error of $p$ (in the absolute figures) is

$$\sigma_p = \sqrt{0 \cdot 5 \times 0 \cdot 5 \times 10{,}240} = 0 \cdot 5 \sqrt{10{,}240} = 50 \cdot 596$$

(see formula (XIX.7)).

The difference actually observed exceeds this error by a factor of $131/50 \cdot 596$ $= 2 \cdot 59$, as on p. 526.

The identical result is obtained, of course, when we calculate by formula (XIX.4) which gives the standard error of the relative frequency:

$$\sigma_p = \frac{0 \cdot 5}{\sqrt{10{,}240}} = 0 \cdot 004941.$$

The theoretical frequency of the occurrence of heads is $0 \cdot 5$ and the figure actually obtained is $4989/10{,}240 = 0 \cdot 4872$, i.e. too little by $0 \cdot 0128$. This difference exceeds the standard error by a factor of $0 \cdot 128 - 0 \cdot 004941 = 2 \cdot 59$, as before. Looking at the formulae and calculations on p. 526 and here, we see that we are dealing with identities.

Let us consider another example. According to the 1931 population census among the total population of Warsaw of 1,171,898 inhabitants there were 22,461 (in relation to the total population $p = 0 \cdot 019$ or $1 \cdot 9$ per cent) children born in 1925 who, according to the rules then in force, should have entered the first grade of the elementary school in 1932, when they were 7 years old. Let us imagine that there was no population census, but that we must know the number of children so that they will have enough room in school, there are enough teachers, books, etc. To estimate the number of these children we conducted a population census in Warsaw using the sampling method and drawing 10,000 persons.

By substitution in formula (XIX.4) we obtain

$$\sigma_p = \sqrt{\frac{0 \cdot 019 \times 0 \cdot 981}{10,000}} = \frac{\sqrt{0 \cdot 0186}}{100} = \frac{0 \cdot 136}{100} = 0 \cdot 00136.$$

Subtracting from, and adding to $0 \cdot 019$ the standard error multiplied by $1 \cdot 96$, we obtain the interval from $0 \cdot 01633$ to $0 \cdot 02167$, and the probability that we have not committed an error is approximately $0 \cdot 95$ (see table on p. 517 or the table of the Probability Integral at the end of the book).

But from the point of view of good school organization we have to know not $p$, the ratio of 7-year old children to the total population, but the absolute number of these children. If we know that the total population of Warsaw is 1,171,898, then for the given values of $p$ the absolute numbers of children would be between 19,137 and 25,395. The difference between the upper and lower limits is thus 6258, which is about 30 per cent of the average between the two limits.

If a statistician passed on this result to the school authorities, his information would probably be regarded as useless.

The organization of schools cannot be properly planned if it is not known whether the number of pupils will be 19,000 or almost 25,500. Therefore, the statistician in his sampling inquiry would probably have to take a much larger sample, say, 100,000 persons, which would still constitute a small percentage of the total population (about $8 \cdot 5$ per cent). Then the standard error would be $\dfrac{0 \cdot 136}{\sqrt{100,000}} = \dfrac{0 \cdot 136}{316}$ or approximately $0 \cdot 00043$.

Multiplying the standard error by $1 \cdot 96$, as above, and switching over to absolute figures, we estimate that the number of children for whom room must be prepared in the schools is within the limits from 21,278 to 23,254. If we extend the limits, say, from 20,966 to 23,566 ($2 \cdot 58$ times the standard error) we shall be able to say that these limits will not be exceeded in 99 cases out of 100. The difference between the upper and lower limits is now $8 \cdot 9$ per cent for the first alternative and for the second alternative $11 \cdot 7$ per cent of the value of the average between the two limits.

These results are much more satisfactory. The number of pupils for whom room in the schools must be prepared is not exactly fixed, but the amount by which it will be greater or less than estimated should not disorganize the school system.

It is up to the authorities responsible for planning to decide which alternative to choose: whether it is more convenient to take the upper limit and thus to be more certain that the limit will not be exceeded (this corresponds to the second alternative: a larger interval and a larger confidence coefficient) or to accept the lower limit and run the risk that there may be an error in a larger number of cases (the first alternative). Under certain conditions the choice of the second alternative would be more economical: to organize the school system so that there would be room for 21,278 to 23,254 pupils and to make an alteration only if it turns out that the estimate was wrong.

The meaning of choosing a confidence coefficient will appear in the following example in which, as in Example 2, the problem is the testing of a statistical hypothesis.

*Example* 4. Let us suppose that a factory wants to determine, by checking a part of its product whether a given batch is "good" (corresponds to the established technical requirements), or "bad" (does not correspond to the requirements).[192] In this case the error may consist in declaring a batch bad when it is good, a rejection of the hypothesis that the batch is good or in the acceptance of the hypothesis that the batch is good when it is bad. By setting the requirements too high, i.e. by choosing too great a confidence coefficient we run the risk in a certain number of cases of committing the error of rejecting a batch as bad when it is good. By accepting too low a confidence coefficient we run the risk that in a certain number of cases a batch will be declared good when it is actually bad. The choice of the confidence coefficient in this case is a compromise and must be based on intuition.

Previously, very high confidence coefficients were usually selected in statistical practice; they were of the order of 5 or 6 times the probable error, i.e. approximately 3·4 to 4 times the standard error. The acceptance of four times the standard error as the criterion means that we run the risk of committing an error not more than 6 times in 100,000 (see Table 18.1 p. 517). Today, the requirements are usually not so high. Quite frequently a confidence coefficient of the order of 0·99 or 0·95 is chosen, which means that there is a risk of error in 1 case or 5 cases out of 100. This corresponds to 2·58 or 1·96 times the standard error. This lowering of the confidence coefficient is connected with the scope of application of the sampling method: very often it could not be applied if the standard required was very high.

Since the choice of the confidence coefficient is a matter of convention we can *a priori* assume certain definite values of the coefficient; in this way we can design the probability integral tables in a more convenient and economical way.

It should be remembered, however, that in particular cases a much higher confidence coefficient may be required, especially when the consequences of error may be serious. This is the case, for instance, in analysing a new medicine to be introduced on to the market. The side effects of this medicine may be toxic; by

---

[192] This is a problem in statistical quality control which we shall discuss more extensively later.

means of a number of tests on animals we try to find out whether there are such toxic effects. In this case it is important to protect the patient from the danger of poisoning, and a very high confidence coefficient must be used before we can accept the hypothesis that "the medicine does not have toxic effects".

J. Neyman introduced into statistics the distinction between "type 1 error" and "type 2 error". If we want to prove a hypothesis by sampling, the error may consist in: (1) accepting the hypothesis as true when it is false and when the contrary hypothesis is true (type 1 error), (2) rejecting a hypothesis which is true (type 2 error). In the above example of analysing a medicine the error may consist in: (1) accepting the hypothesis that the medicine produces no toxic effects when in fact it is toxic, (2) rejecting the hypothesis that the medicine is not toxic when this hypothesis is true. We may agree that we shall call type 1 error the more dangerous error, and type 2 error the less harmful error. In our example, because of the need to consider the patient's safety, it is much more dangerous to accept the hypothesis that the medicine is not toxic when in fact it is. This will be type 1 error; in this case we shall use particularly stringent criteria.

It should be remembered that sampling will never give complete certainty that a hypothesis *is* true; it can only determine the probability of its being true. When experiments are involved the situation is all the more difficult because the number of observations can almost never be large enough to ensure a very high confidence coefficient. (Application of sampling to experimentation will be discussed later).

In some cases the danger involved in committing type 1 or type 2 error is more or less the same, and then of course it is a matter of indifference how they are numbered.[193]

In many cases an evaluation must be made whether the differences which appear between samples from two different populations prove that the populations actually differ, or whether these differences are due to random factors. For the arithmetic mean, the standard error of the difference is calculated using the formula

$$\sigma_{(\bar{x}-\bar{y})} = \sqrt{\sigma_{\bar{x}}^2 + \sigma_{\bar{y}}^2}. \qquad \text{(XIX.8)}$$

The standard error of the differences in the frequencies of appearance of units with a specific characteristic is determined by the formula

$$\sigma_{(p_1-p_2)} = \sqrt{\sigma_{p_1}^2 + \sigma_{p_2}^2}. \qquad \text{(XIX.9)}$$

Substituting for $\sigma_{\bar{x}}$ and $\sigma_{\bar{y}}$ and for $\sigma_{p1}$, and $\sigma_{p2}$ the corresponding expressions from formulae (XIX.1) and (XIX.4) we obtain

$$\sigma_{(\bar{x}-\bar{y})} = \sqrt{\frac{\sigma_x^2}{n_x} + \frac{\sigma_y^2}{n_y}}, \qquad \text{(XIX.10)}$$

$$\sigma_{(p_1-p_2)} = \sqrt{\frac{p_1 q_1}{n_1} + \frac{p_2 q_2}{n_2}}. \qquad \text{(XIX.11)}$$

It follows from the formulae that the standard error of the difference is always greater than the standard error of each of the quantities whose difference is being

---

[193] On type 1 and type 2 errors consult: *First Course in Probability and Statistics* by J. Neyman, New York, 1950, p. 261 *et seq.*

measured. If both standard errors are the same and are, say $\sigma_{\bar{x}} = \sigma_{\bar{y}}$ then formula (XIX.8) assumes the form

$$\sigma_{(\bar{x}-\bar{y})} = \sqrt{2\sigma_{\bar{x}}^2} = \sigma_{\bar{y}}\sqrt{2} \approx 1\cdot414\sigma_{\bar{x}}.$$

Let us consider several examples.

Observations of 1000 male infants and 1000 female infants gave an average weight for boys ($\bar{x}$) of $3\cdot23$ kg, with a standard deviation ($\sigma_x$) of $0\cdot433$, and an average weight for girls ($\bar{y}$) of $3\cdot10$ kg, with a standard deviation ($\sigma_y$) of $0\cdot405$ kg. The difference in the average weights of the infants of the two sexes was $0\cdot13$ kg and is relatively small. The question arises whether this difference is not random, as a result of a small number of observations.

By substitution in the formulae we obtain as the standard errors of the arithmetic means for the boys

$$\sigma_{\bar{x}} = \frac{0\cdot433}{\sqrt{1000}} = 0\cdot0137,$$

and for the girls

$$\sigma_{\bar{y}} = \frac{0\cdot405}{\sqrt{1000}} = 0\cdot0128.$$

Hence

$$\sigma_{(\bar{x}-\bar{y})} = \sqrt{0\cdot0137^2 + 0\cdot0128^2} \approx 0\cdot0183.$$

The actual difference ($0\cdot13$ kg) is almost seven times this number. Thus we can say with almost complete certainty[194] that a difference of this order cannot be random, and that, the average weight of male infants is indeed, larger than the average weight of female infants.

The application of the above formulae for standard errors calculated from a sample, e.g. the standard error of the arithmetic mean (formula XIX.1, p. 522), of the standard deviation (formula XIX.2 p. 522), of the correlation coefficient (formula XIX.3 p. 523) and of the relative frequency (formula XIX.4 p. 527) encounters serious difficulties in practice. The quantities $\sigma_x$, $r$, $p$, appearing in these formulae are parameters of general populations. These parameters are usually not known when the sampling method is used.

For instance, in calculating the standard error of the arithmetic mean by formula

$$\sigma_{\bar{x}} = \frac{\sigma_x}{\sqrt{n}}$$

we do not know $\sigma_x$, the standard deviation of the individual observations in the general population. To calculate it we should also have to calculate the arithmetic mean of the general population and then estimate the arithmetic mean by sampling,

---

[194] According to Table 18.1 (p. 517) for $\frac{X}{\sigma_x} = 5$ the probability of error is already only 6 in 100,000,000.

and the calculation of the standard error of this mean would be superfluous because we should have the true result.

When we use sampling we almost never know the standard deviation in the general population in advance, and therefore we must use the values obtained from the sample instead of the values obtained from the general population. In other words, in the above formula we should write $s_x$ instead of $\sigma_x$, if we accept the custom of denoting values obtained from the sample by Latin letters, and values obtained from the general population by Greek letters.

It can be proved that in estimating the standard deviation from the sample we obtain a better result if we substitute $n-1$ for $n$. From this it follows that

$$\sigma_x = \frac{s_x}{\sqrt{n-1}},$$

$$\sigma_p = \sqrt{\frac{pq}{n-1}}, \quad \text{etc.}$$

However, the difference between using this more correct form and the previously given formulae, in which $n$ appears instead of $n-1$, will be negligible if $n$ is not small. Even if the sample comprises several dozen units the results of the calculation by the more precise formula in which we use $n-1$ will be almost identical with the results by the formulae in which $n$ is used. In other words we should use the more precise formulae only when the sample is small.

## 2. SMALL SAMPLE

The essential difference between a small sample and a large sample does not consist in substituting $n-1$ for $n$. As a rule $n-1$ should always be used, though with large $n$ the difference between using $n$ and $n-1$ is negligible. But when the sample is small we cannot assume that the standard deviation of the sample equals the standard deviation of the general population and therefore we must not use the values of the probability integral given in Table 1 at the end of the book. The points is that by substituting $s_x$ for $\sigma_x$ we introduce a random error into the estimate of $\sigma_x$, which increases as the number of observations decreases. These random errors should be allowed for when the number of observations is small (not more than about 20 or 30). When the number of observations is larger, the difference between the correctly calculated probability for a small sample and the probability calculated on the basis of the probability integral is negligible.

In Table 2 at the end of the book the probabilities are given that is not less than $x-t$ and not greater than $x+t$ depending upon the number of degrees of freedom ($k$) (i.e. in this case, the number of observations less one). Here $t$ is the quotient of the difference $X = x - \bar{x}$, by the deviation calculated from the sample by the formula

$$s_x = \sqrt{\frac{\sum X^2}{n-1}}.$$

The number of degrees of freedom shown in the table is 20; in other words the table goes up to $n = 21$. In the last column the probabilities for $n = \infty$ are given, when this probability equals one minus the probability read off from Table 1.

As we can see, the probabilities in Table 2 differ considerably from the probabilities in Table 1 based on the normal curve when $k$ is small, but the difference diminishes as $k$ approaches 20, so that in practice large sample methods can be used when $n$ exceeds 20.

It should be noted that the table of probabilities $t$ is based on the assumption that the distribution of the general population from which we draw is normal, which, as we know, is often approximately true. If the distribution of the general population does not differ much from the normal distribution we can use the corresponding table with due caution. It should never be used if the general population is, for example, extremely asymmetric, e.g. monotonically increasing or decreasing.

With this reservation we can say that inference based on probabilities $t$ is as certain as inference based on the probability integral (Table 1) for the normal curve. It is quite another matter that a small sample often leads to so large a confidence interval that conclusions based on calculations are of no practical value.

Suppose that in analysing the height of a group of adult men six persons are drawn and their heights are: 164, 170, 170, 175, 178 and 181 cm. The arithmetic mean of the height is $\bar{x} = \dfrac{1038}{6} = 173$ cm, the standard deviations

$s_x = \sqrt{\dfrac{\sum X^2}{6-1}} = \sqrt{\dfrac{192}{5}} \approx 6 \cdot 20$. Let us assume that we want to determine the

arithmetic mean of the height of men with a probability of error not larger than $0 \cdot 05$, i.e. with a confidence coefficient of $0 \cdot 95$.

This confidence coefficient for $k = 5$ is obtained for $t$ between $2 \cdot 5$ and $2 \cdot 6$, or more strictly for $t = 2 \cdot 57$. Then we write

$$\frac{s_x}{\sqrt{n}} \times 2 \cdot 57 = \frac{6 \cdot 20}{\sqrt{6}} \times 2 \cdot 57 \approx 6 \cdot 5.$$

This means that we can say with probability equal to $0 \cdot 95$, that the actual average height is not less than $173 - 6 \cdot 5 = 166 \cdot 5$ cm, and not greater than

173 + 6·5 = 179·5 cm. The confidence interval is 13 cm. This information on the average height of a given group of men is useless.

When the height of students entering universities in 1946 at age 20–24 was analysed, the average height obtained was also 173 cm, and the standard deviation was very close to that in the above example, being 6·23 cm. The number of observations was 1692, which permits the use of the probability integral from Table 1 without any reservations. Corresponding to the confidence coefficient 0·95 is $X/\sigma = 1·96$ and we obtain

$$\frac{6·23}{\sqrt{1692}} \times 1·96 \approx 0·3.$$

Thus, by taking the confidence coefficient equal to 0·95 we assume that the arithmetic mean of height is located within the narrow limits from $173 - 0·3 = 172·7$ cm to $173 + 0·3 = 173·3$ cm. The confidence interval is narrower here, both because we multiply by 1·96 times of the standard deviation instead of 2·57 times, as before, and because we divide the standard deviation by $\sqrt{1692} = 41·134$ instead of by $\sqrt{6} = 2·449$.

However, if the formula for a small sample does not produce satisfactory results in the above example, this does not mean that it is useless in practice. On the contrary, it is a very valuable tool of analysis in those very numerous cases in which, for one reason or another, we cannot have a large sample. This applies primarily to experiments of all kinds in which the small sample method, when properly used, is often the only means of obtaining trustworthy results. Similarly, in statistical quality control studies we often have to resort to a small sample when for technical reasons it is impossible to study a large number of units.

In this book we cannot enter into the details of the application of small samples.

## 3. CONSISTENCY OF THE STRUCTURE OF TWO POPULATIONS

Sometimes the object is not to find out if a particular measure of the sample population (e.g. the arithmetic mean or the standard deviation) can be regarded as consistent with the corresponding measure of the general population, but to find out whether the whole structure (e.g. the age distribution) of the population of the sample can be considered as corresponding to the structure of the general population.

Let us consider the example from p. 525, in which the theoretical distribution of the tosses of 10 coins was compared with the distribution actually obtained with 1024 tosses. The question is: can we assume that the empirical distribution was drawn from the general population whose theoretical distribution is known, or do we have to assume that the empirical distribution corresponds to some other theoretical distribution? This could mean, for example, that the probability of obtaining heads is not $\frac{1}{2}$ but some other number. Previously we used the arithmetic mean for estimating the consistency of the empirical with the theoretical distribution and the result obtained was negative. This indicates that with the results of the experiment it could happen only in 1 case out of 100 that the actual average number of heads would be 5, as should be expected theoretically. We could also have asked whether the empirical frequency of a combination (say, 3 heads and 7 tails, or vice versa) is consistent with the theoretical expectation of that combination.

Let us now consider whether the whole empirical distribution can correspond to the theoretical distribution. We have to take into account all deviations. For this purpose we use the $\chi^2$ test which was first proposed in 1876 by F. R. Helmert, and then, probably independently of Helmert, by K. Pearson in 1900. This test permits us to determine the level of confidence with which we can assume the consistency of the structure of two populations.

The meaning of this measure and the way it should be used will be illustrated by the example from page 525. We are concerned here with the distribution of heads in tosses of 10 coins. The "theoretical" distribution in this case is the binomial distribution based on the assumption that the probability of obtaining heads is $\frac{1}{2}$, and the actual distribution is the distribution obtained by tossing 10 coins 1024 times.

We shall modify the series somewhat by combining both extreme groups with the neighbouring ones (0 heads with 1 and 10 heads with 9) to avoid very small frequencies.

(As a practical hint we assume that in no group should there be fewer than 10 observations). If the total number of observations in the two series was not the same they would have to be adjusted to the same number. The calculation is shown in Table 19.2.

TABLE 19.2. CALCULATION OF $\chi^2$
Example 1.

| Number of heads in the toss | Number of tosses according to | | $f'-f$ | $(f'-f)^2$ | $\dfrac{(f'-f)^2}{f}$ |
|---|---|---|---|---|---|
| | theoretical distribution $f$ | empirical distribution $f'$ | | | |
| 0 or  1 | 11 | 16 | $+5$ | 25 | 2·27 |
| 2 | 45 | 48 | $+3$ | 9 | 0·20 |
| 3 | 120 | 128 | $+8$ | 64 | 0·53 |
| 4 | 210 | 217 | $+7$ | 49 | 0·23 |
| 5 | 252 | 266 | $+14$ | 196 | 0·78 |
| 6 | 210 | 197 | $-13$ | 169 | 0·80 |
| 7 | 120 | 108 | $-12$ | 144 | 1·20 |
| 8 | 45 | 36 | $-3$ | 81 | 1·80 |
| 9 or 10 | 11 | 8 | $-9$ | 9 | 0·83 |
| *Total* | *1024* | *1024* | *0* | . | 8·63 |

The procedure is as follows. For each class we form the difference $f'—f$, where $f$ is the frequency of the theoretical distribution and $f'$ the frequency of the empirical distribution.

We square these differences and divide the squares by the corresponding $f$, thus obtaining the relative values of the squared differences. The sum of the latter is $\chi^2$, and it is expressed by the formula

$$\chi^2 = \sum \frac{(f'-f)^2}{f}. \tag{XIX.12}$$

In this case $\chi^2 = 8 \cdot 63$. Now we have to determine the probability $P$ that $\chi^2$, as a result of random fluctuations, will assume a value equal to or smaller than the value found.

It is obvious that this probability decreases as $\chi^2$ increases. On the other hand, it is also obvious that for a given probability $\chi^2$ increases as the number of classes in the distribution increases, or, to be exact, the degrees of freedom (which is always at least one less than the number of classes).

We shall explain the notion of degrees of freedom by an example. In this case the number of classes is 9. But if in 8 classes the difference $f'—f$ may assume certain fixed values this difference in the ninth class is automatically determined, because of course the sum of all differences must equal zero if the total number of observations in both the empirical and the theoretical distribution is to be the same. The ninth difference is, therefore not "free"; we thus have 8 degrees of freedom. Later on we shall give an example in which the number of the degrees of freedom is three less than the number of classes.

The probabilities $P$ corresponding to a given $\chi^2$ for different degrees of freedom have been calculated, and they are available in tables of various designs. One such table is reproduced at the end of the book. We read off from this table that with 8 degrees of freedom the probability that $\chi^2 = 8 \cdot 63$ is $0 \cdot 38$.

We calculate as follows. We read in the table that with 8 degrees of freedom and $\chi^2 = 8$ the probability $P = 0.4335$ and for $\chi^2 = 9$ the probability $P = 0.3423$. Using linear interpolation we obtain for $\chi^2 = 8 \cdot 63$ the probability $P = 0.4335 - (0.4335 - 0.3423)0 \cdot 63 = 0 \cdot 376$.

This probability $P = 0 \cdot 38$ means that with 8 degrees of freedom, in 38 cases out of 100 we can obtain $\chi^2$ equal to or less than $8 \cdot 63$ as a result of random fluctuations.

This probability is not small, and it does not entitle us to reject the hypothesis that the differences between the theoretical distribution and the empirical distribution are due to random fluctuations. This result is contrary to the result previously obtained (p. 525), that the arithmetic mean calculated from the empirical series is significantly smaller than the theoretical mean (which equals 5). This apparent contradiction can be explained if we look at the signs of the differences $f'—f$ in Table 19.2 (p. 537). These signs are arranged in a very systematic way: they are positive when the number of heads in the toss is 5 or less, and negative when the number of heads is 6 or more, without exception. The distribution of signs confirms our previous supposition that the coins used in this experiment tend to fall tails up rather than heads up, and that therefore, the actual probability of obtaining heads is less than $\frac{1}{2}$.

At the same time this example reminds us that the $\chi^2$ test, like all other tests, cannot be used schematically. In particular attention should always be paid to the distribution of the signs of the differences $f'-f$. But if $\chi^2$ is large for a given number of degrees of freedom and consequently we obtain a very small $P$—the probability that a given difference between the two distribution is due to a random error—we can consider this as a proof that the difference is significant. This would be our conclusion if $P$ were, say, $0 \cdot 01$, which for 8 degrees of freedom happens only when $\chi^2$ is more than 20 (see Table 3 at the end of the book).

From the formula for $\chi^2$ it follows that the value of this test depends only on the absolute values of the differences (because in the formula we have the squares of the differences) and it does not depend upon the distribution of the signs of these differences. A careful statistician will take the distribution of these signs into consideration. If their distribution is not random, i.e. if the plus and minus signs are not mixed, but form a systematic pattern of plus or minus signs over a long range, we should not consider this as a direct proof that the distributions are not consistent, but should check the consistency by other means.

The next example will show: (1) the method of calculating frequencies in particular classes in the normal distribution and (2) the method of calculating the degrees of freedom if they differ from the number of classes by more than one.

The example refers to the weight of female infants. The frequency distribution is not quite symmetric because the right arm of the curve is a little longer than the left (the deviations toward larger weights are a little more frequent than those toward smaller weight). However, the asymmetry is slight. The question is: Can we assume that the distribution of the weight of the infants is normal and the minor deviations are random? We have to plot the normal curve corresponding to the empirical data.

It follows from the calculation that for the empirical curve the arithmetic mean $\bar{x} = 3102$ grammes and the standard deviation $\sigma_x = 402 \cdot 78$. We assume that for the normal curve $\bar{x}$ and $\sigma_x$ are the same. These two quantities fully define the shape of the curve.

In Table 19.3. on p. 541 in column 1 the arithmetic mean is shown in bold-face type as are the limits of the classes into which the series has been divided. Column 2 gives the differences between the class limits and the arithmetic mean $x - \bar{x} = X$; column 3 gives the above differences expressed in units of standard deviation. From the table of the probability integral we find $0 \cdot 9924$ for $X/\sigma = 2 \cdot 67$ and $0 \cdot 9926$ for $X = 2 \cdot 68$. By interpolation we obtain the value $0 \cdot 9925$ for $X/\sigma = 2 \cdot 674$.

This number expresses the area under the normal curve from $X/\sigma = -2 \cdot 674$ to $X/\sigma = 2 \cdot 674$. Because of the symmetry of the normal curve the area under the curve from $X/\sigma = -2 \cdot 674$ to $X/\sigma = 0$ is the same as the area from $X/\sigma = 0$ to $X/\sigma = 2 \cdot 674$. These two areas together give the area from $X/\sigma = -2 \cdot 674$ to $X/\sigma = 2 \cdot 674$ or $0 \cdot 9925$. If follows that the area under the normal curve from $X/\sigma = 0$ to $X/\sigma = 2 \cdot 674$, when rounded off to the third decimal place is $0 \cdot 496$. Since the whole area under the curve up to $X/\sigma = 0$ equals $0 \cdot 5$, then beyond the limit $X/\sigma = 2 \cdot 674$ there remains $0 \cdot 500 - 0 \cdot 496 = 0 \cdot 004$. Multiplying by 1000 we get 4. This means that if we denote the total frequency by 1000, in the normal curve 4 observations will have a value less than 2025 g. In a similar way we read off that in 15 cases out of 1000 the weight will be less than 2225 g, etc. Since the argument $X/\sigma$ in the table of the probability integral is given to two decimal places we may have to interpolate in some cases. In this way we obtain two cumulative distributions, with frequencies from 4 for $X = 2025$ g to 500 for $X$ equal to the arithmetic mean. By subtracting the consecutive values of the cumulative distributions, we obtain in the last column $f$ the frequencies corresponding to the classes from 2025 (and less) to 4425 (and over). In the middle class, 3025–3225 g, there are $500 - 424 = 76$ observations below the arithmetic mean, and $500 - 380 = 120$ observations above the arithmetic mean, 196 observations altogether. The figures in column $f$ denote the normal distribution based on the assumption that: (1) the total frequency is 1000, (2) the arithmetic mean is 3102 g, (3) the standard deviation is $402 \cdot 78$ g. The figures in column $f$ are asymetrically distributed, although we are dealing with a normal distribution, because the class limits are asymmetric in relation to the arithmetic mean. The distribution of $f$ would be symmetric if we selected the classes 2802–3002, 3002–3222, 3222–3422 etc., but then we could not compare the theoretical distribution with the empirical distribution.

The calculation of $\chi^2$ is done according to the formula in Table 19.2 (p. 537). In order to avoid class frequencies that are too law, we combine the first two and the last three classes.

$\chi^2$ is $13 \cdot 02$. There are 11 classes, which would correspond to 10 degrees, of freedom, except that the calculation of the normal distribution assumed two calculations $M$ those of the arithmetic mean and the standard deviation. We therefore have only 8 degrees of freedom.

For 8 degrees of freedom $\chi^2 = 13 \cdot 02$ corresponds to the probability $0 \cdot 11$, which is again not sufficiently low to reject the hypothesis that the differences between the theoretical distribution and the empirical distribution are caused by random deviations. However, if we look at the signs of the deviations, we see that their distribution is systematic: the minus signs (with one exception) are in classes below 2825 g, the plus signs $x$ in the two middle classes, the minus sign in the next three classes and the plus signs in the last two classes. The last signifies the asymmetry of the empirical distribution. The distribution of signs in the remaining classes indicates that the empirical distribution is much "steeper" than the normal distribution.

TABLE 19.3. CALCULATION OF CLASS FREQUENCIES OF THE NORMAL CURVE
FOR $\bar{x} = 3102$ AND $\sigma = 402.78$
Total number of observations $= 1000$

| Class limits | $x - \bar{x} = X$ | $\dfrac{X}{\sigma_x}$ | Probability of deviation from the arithmetic mean $\times$ 1000 | Classes | $f$ |
|---|---|---|---|---|---|
| 2025 | −1077 | −2·674 | 4 | $\leqslant$ 2025 | 4 |
| 2225 | −877 | −2·177 | 15 | 2025–2225 | 11 |
| 2425 | −677 | −1·681 | 46 | 2225–2425 | 31 |
| 2625 | −477 | −1·184 | 118 | 2425–2625 | 72 |
| 2825 | −277 | −0·688 | 246 | 2625–2825 | 128 |
| 3025 | −77 | −0·191 | 424 | 2825–2025 | 178 |
| 3102 | 0 | 0 | $\begin{cases}500\\500\end{cases}$ | 3025–3225 | $\begin{smallmatrix}76\\120\end{smallmatrix}\}$ 196 |
| 3225 | +123 | +0·305 | 380 | 3225–3425 | 169 |
| 3425 | +323 | +0·802 | 211 | 3425–3625 | 114 |
| 3625 | +523 | +1·298 | 97 | 3625–3825 | 61 |
| 3825 | +723 | +1·795 | 36 | 3825–4025 | 25 |
| 4025 | +923 | +2·292 | 11 | 4025–4225 | 8 |
| 4225 | +1123 | +2·788 | 3 | 4225–4425 | 2 |
| 4425 | +1323 | +3·285 | 1 | $\geqslant$ 4425 | 1 |
| | | | | Total | 1000 |

TABLE 19.4. CALCULATION OF $\chi^2$
Example 2.

| Classes | Number of observations according to: | | $f'-f$ | $(f'-f)^2$ | $\dfrac{(f'-f)^2}{f}$ |
|---|---|---|---|---|---|
| | theoretical distribution $f$ | empirical distribution $f$ | | | |
| $\leqslant$ 2225 | 15 | 13 | −2 | 4 | 0·27 |
| 2225–2425 | 31 | 24 | −7 | 49 | 1·58 |
| 2425–2625 | 72 | 79 | +7 | 49 | 0·68 |
| 2625–2825 | 128 | 125 | −3 | 9 | 0·07 |
| 2825–3025 | 178 | 200 | +22 | 484 | 2·72 |
| 3025–3225 | 196 | 198 | +2 | 4 | 0·02 |
| 3225–3425 | 169 | 256 | −13 | 169 | 1·00 |
| 3425–3625 | 114 | 98 | −16 | 156 | 2·25 |
| 3625–3825 | 61 | 59 | −2 | 4 | 0·07 |
| 3825–4025 | 25 | 35 | +10 | 100 | 4·00 |
| $\geqslant$ 4025 | 11 | 13 | +2 | 4 | 0·36 |
| Total | 1000 | 1000 | 0 | . | 13·02 |

As noted above, this distribution was analysed primarily in order to show the calculation procedure. In the next example the $\chi^2$ test leads to completely unambiguous results.

The table referred to anti-typhus injections, and a comparison was made between the number of persons who did contract the disease and those who did not, among those injected, and the number of persons who did and did not contract the disease among these who were not injected, and who were equally exposed to the danger of disease.

TABLE 19.5. CONCENTRATION OF TYPHUS IN RELATION TO ANTI-TYPHUS INJECTION

| Particulars | Contracted | Not contracted | Total |
|---|---|---|---|
| Injected | (a)  56 | (b)  6759 | 6815 |
| Not injected | (c) 272 | (d) 11,396 | 11,668 |
| *Total* | *328* | *18,155* | *18,483* |

We can analyse this table in an elementary way by calculating the percentage of typhus cases among those injected and those not injected.

TABLE 19.6. PERCENTAGE OF TYPHUS CASES AMONG THOSE INJECTED AND NOT INJECTED

| Particulars | Contracted | Not contracted | Total |
|---|---|---|---|
| Injected | (a) 0·8 | (b) 99·2 | 100·0 |
| Not injected | (c) 2·3 | (d) 97·7 | 100·0 |

The differences are strongly in favour of those injected, and they indicate that injection offers considerable protection against typhus. We could also calculate one of the coefficients characterizing the intensity of correlation among non-measurable characteristics (which were discussed in Chapter 17), say $Q$ or $V$ (see the formulae on p. 495). However, neither the table in the above form, nor the coefficients $Q$ and $V$ answer the question whether the correlation disclosed in this case is due to random fluctuations. The answer can be obtained by the $\chi^2$ test. To be able to use it we must calculate the theoretical distribution which would appear if injection had no influence on contracting the disease.

We reason in the following way. If injection had no influence on contracting the disease, then the numbers for items denoted by (a), (b), (c) and (d) would be arranged in the same ratio as for the whole population studied, i.e. as shown in the "Total" at the bottom and on the right-hand side of the table.

Then, for instance, item (a)—those injected who contracted the disease—would be $6815 - \dfrac{328}{18,483} = 121$.

The remaining items do not have to be calculated in this way: they can be arrived at by subtracting the result from the totals at the bottom and on the right-hand side.

It follows that we have only one degree of freedom—the calculation of any of the values (a), (b), (c) or (d) uniquely determines all the rest.

TABLE 19.7. THEORETICAL DISTRIBUTION CALCULATED ON THE ASSUMPTION THAT INJECTION HAS NO EFFECT

| Particulars | Contracted the disease | Dit not contract the disease | Total |
|---|---|---|---|
| Incjected | (a) 121 | (b) 6694 | 6815 |
| Not injected | (c) 207 | (d) 11,461 | 11,668 |
| *Total* | *328* | *18,155* | *18,483* |

TABLE 19.8. CALCULATION OF $\chi^2$
Example 3.

| Item | Frequency in: | | $f'-f$ | $(f'-f)^2$ | $\dfrac{(f'-f)^2}{f}$ |
|---|---|---|---|---|---|
| | theoretical distribution | empirical distribution | | | |
| (a) | 121 | 56 | −65 | 4225 | 34·91 |
| (b) | 6694 | 6759 | +65 | 4225 | 0·63 |
| (c) | 207 | 272 | −65 | 4225 | 20·41 |
| (d) | 11,461 | 11,396 | +65 | 4225 | 0·37 |
| *Total* | *18,483* | *18,483* | *0* | . | *56·32* |

$\chi^2$ is very large. In the tables in the Appendix such large values of $\chi^2$ are not shown. However, we can see from them that with one degree of freedom even for $\chi^2 = 13$ the probability is less than 0·001. Therefore it is almost certain that the differences between the theoretical distribution and the empirical distribution are not due to random causes (absolute certainty can never be achieved by using the sampling method); the conclusion is therefore, that anti-typhus injections significantly affect the chances of contracting the disease.

## 4. DETERMINATION OF REQUIRED SIZE OF SAMPLE

Let us now reverse the problem. So far we have been asking the question in this way: we know the standard deviation in the general population (or the standard deviation in the sample, which we substitute for the standard deviation in the general population), we know $n$—the number of units in the sample drawn from the general population—and we should like to find the accuracy of the results obtained, or the limits within which the true value is located, given the confidence coefficient. This is the way in which a problem is posed when we want to find out the accuracy of the results by sampling.

Now we shall try to determine how to organize a sampling inquiry to achieve the required accuracy in the results. We shall show the reasoning by the example of the arithmetic mean; it will be analogous in other cases, too.

Let us take formula (XIX.1) for the standard deviation of the arithmetic mean.

$$\sigma_{\bar{x}} = \frac{\sigma_x}{\sqrt{n}}.$$

In the denominator on the right-hand side of the formula $\sigma_x$ is given and is independent. This, *in principle*, is always the property of the general population. We can only affect the quantity $n$—the number of units drawn for the sample.

On the basis of $\sigma_{\bar{x}}$—the standard error of the arithmetic mean—we can calculate the accuracy of the results—the confidence coefficient, and the confidence interval which is functionally related to it. As we know, if we use $\sigma_{\bar{x}}$, alone, the confidence coefficient is approximately $0 \cdot 68$ (i.e. an error may occur in 32 cases out of 100); if we take $1 \cdot 96 \, \sigma_{\bar{x}}$, the confidence coefficient is $0 \cdot 95$ (an error may occur in 5 cases out of 100); if we take $2 \cdot 58 \, \sigma_{\bar{x}}$, the confidence coefficient is $0 \cdot 99$ (an error may occur in 1 case out of 100), etc.[195]

Thus, in order to obtain the required confidence coefficient we have to multiply the standard error by a certain coefficient which we denote by $m$. The product $m \, \sigma_{\bar{x}}$, being one-half of the confidence interval, determines the confidence interval.

Denoting the confidence half-interval by $\delta$ we have

$$\delta = m\sigma_{\bar{x}} = \frac{m\sigma_x}{\sqrt{n}}.$$

From the equation

$$\delta = \frac{m\sigma_x}{\sqrt{n}}$$

we can easily calculate $m$. After squaring, we obtain

$$\delta^2 = \frac{m^2 \sigma_x^2}{n},$$

hence                                                    (XIX.13)

$$n = \frac{m^2 \sigma_x^2}{\delta^2}.$$

In this expression $\sigma_x$, and therefore also $\sigma_x^2$ is given, being a permanent characteristic of the general population which we estimate on the basis of the sample. But the quantities $m$ and $\delta$ must be arbitrarily determined. If follows from formula (XIX.13) that the number of units in a sample is proportional to the squared coefficient $m$, proportional to the square of the standard deviation of the characteristic studied in the general population (i.e. to the variance), and inversely proportional to the square of the error that we can risk (or to the square of the confidence half-interval).

If we want the confidence coefficient to be, say, $0 \cdot 99$ then $m$ should be $2 \cdot 58$. However, we should not automatically use the same confidence coefficient; it should be determined by the circumstances of each case and upon the seriousness of the

---

[195] See Table 18.1 on p. 517 and the table of the probability integral at the end of the book.

consequences of committing an error. Sometimes we may have to exceed $0 \cdot 99$, and in other cases $0 \cdot 95$ or even $0 \cdot 9$ may suffice. Let us remember that the confidence coefficient increases very rapidly with increasing $m$.

Similarly, $\delta$ should also be determined by the circumstances of the case. If, for anthropological purposes, we determine the average height of an adult with the confidence interval of 1 cm (the deviation one way or the other is $\delta = 0 \cdot 5$ cm) we shall probably consider this as a sufficiently accurate result. If, as in the example on p. 519, the standard deviation of the height is $5 \cdot 5$ cm, and if we choose $0 \cdot 99$ as the confidence coefficient the calculation will be as follows:

$$n = \frac{2 \cdot 58^2 \times 5 \cdot 5^2}{0 \cdot 5^2} \approx 805 .$$

This means that if we want to make a study with the degree of accuracy determined above we should draw approximately 800 units.

However, whereas the quantities $m$ and $\delta$ can be determined arbitrarily, the standard deviation of the characteristic studied in the general population ($\sigma_x$) remains unknown. Usually we learn about $\sigma_x$ by substituting for it $s_x$, the standard deviation of characteristic $x$ in the sample. However, we should have to know $\sigma_x$ before we start sampling if we want to calculate by formula (XIX.13). We therefore have to estimate $\sigma_x$ in some other way.

We can do it, for instance, by substituting the value of the standard deviation of a given characteristic obtained before in some analogous study, or even $\sigma_x$ for some other characteristic which may be supposed to have a similar dispersion. Of course, this can only be done with great caution, and the statistician doing it should have considerable experience and intuition with regard to what is permissible, but this procedure is often quite acceptable.

However, there is another, better way: before we start calculating the required number of units in the sample we estimate $\sigma_x$ on the basis of a very small number of units drawn from the population that we want to study.

In the latter case, but much more so in the former case, the estimate is subject to a considerable error. This is not of great importance because formula (XIX.13) is not designed to determine $n$ very precisely.

The true accuracy of the results will be determined later, after completing the study. If possible, to be on the safe side, we should make the sample a little bigger than indicated by the calculation using formula (XIX.13).

In the example on p. 548 a fairly high value could have been accepted for the confidence half-interval $\delta$. But it is not always possible to accept such a high degree of uncertainty. If for instance, we produce, cylinders as machine parts it is impossible to make them with the exactly the same diameter. A certain degree of tolerance which does not affect the functioning of the machine is permissible. But while in studying height we could have ignored even a difference of 1 cm, in producing machine parts the tolerance is usually not greater than a few hundredths of a millimetre. This means that with a given stndard deviation the sample must be very large, even if we reduce the requirements concerning the confidence coefficient. If we reduce it from 0·99 to 0·95 this is tantamount to reducing $m$ from 2·58 to 1·96. Even with a very low confidence coefficient, say 0·9 $m$ will still have to be as high as 1·65.

On p. 544 we stated that $\sigma_x$ is a constant property of the general population, and added the, qualifying expression *in principle*. Indeed, under certain conditions we can influence the standard deviation of characteristic $x$. In production processes the lack of precision in the diameter of the cylinder may be due to insufficient precision of the machine tools or differences in the quality of raw materials used. We can diminish the dispersion by increasing the precision of the machine tools or by using more standardized raw materials. In both cases the product will become more homogeneous. From the point of view of production we will have a better product and fewer rejects, and from the point of view of statistics we will be able to achieve the required degree of accuracy using smaller sample. Of course, sometimes the cost of achieving such an improvement in the standard of quality may be so high that it would be cheaper to have more rejects.

In analysing height we can reduce the standard deviation by selecting more uniform population groups, e.g. by dividing the population of the whole country in accordance to certain characteristics that affect height. From the statistical point of view this enables us to diminish the size of the sample.

When we want to determine the size of the sample for calculation the relative frequency $p$ we have to use formula (XIX.4)

$$\sigma_p = \sqrt{\frac{pq}{n}}.$$

Introducing the notations as on p. 544 we have

$$\delta = m\sqrt{\frac{pq}{n}},$$

whence, by squaring both sides we easily calculate $n$

$$n = \frac{m^2 pq}{\delta^2}. \tag{XIX.14}$$

This formula is analogous to formula (XIX.13) with this difference that instead of $\delta_x$ we have $pq$—the product of the ratio of the units posessing a given characteristic to the total population ($p$), by the ratio of the units not possessing this characteristic ($q = 1 - p$). As we already know, the product $pq$ is a maximum when $p = q = 0·5$ (then it is 0·25) and it decreases the further $p$ moves in either direction from 0·5, and thus the further $q$ moves from 0·5. In other words, the closer $p$ is to zero or one, the smaller $n$ can be.

Further reasoning is analogous to that outlined on p. 544 *et seq.* We select $\delta$ and $m$ arbitrarily according to the circumstances of the study; $p$ should be estimated in a similar way as we estimated $\sigma_x$ there. This can often be done approximately on the basis of previous studies; if this is not possible a trial analysis based on a few units should be made.

In formula (XIX.14) $\delta$ denotes the permissible limits of error (the confidence interval) expressed as a ratio to the total number of units, as does $p$. If we have to determine the acceptable error in absolute terms we have to use formula (XIX.6) from p. 529.

$$\sigma'_p = N \sqrt{\frac{pq}{n}}.$$

Introducing the notations as before except that we write $d$ instead of $\delta$ to stress that the permissible error is expressed in absolute terms and not as a ratio, we have

$$n = \frac{N^2 m^2 pq}{d^2} \qquad \text{(XIX.15)}$$

If we determine the permissible limits of error in relation to the value measured we have to use formula (XIX.5) from p. 527.

$$\frac{\sigma_p}{p} = \sqrt{\frac{1}{n}\left(\frac{1}{p} - 1\right)},$$

Denoting the confidence half-interval by $\delta'$ and substituting for other symbols as before, we obtain

$$\delta' = m \sqrt{\frac{1}{n}\left(\frac{1}{p} - 1\right)},$$

whence

$$n = \frac{m^2\left(\dfrac{1}{p} - 1\right)}{\delta^2} \qquad \text{(XIX.16)}$$

Let us consider several examples.

Let us first take an example for formula (XIX.15), in which we shall calculate the required number of observations in the sample on the basis of certain assumptions obout the permissible deviations in the absolute terms. The example chosen for this purpose is the one from p. 529 and p. 530 on the number of 7-year-old children in Warsaw. The population in Warsaw was 1,171,898, $p$—the number of 7-year-old children in relation to the total population of the city—was $0 \cdot 019$. Let us assume that the error should not be greater than 1000 either way ($\delta = 1000$), and that we shall be satisfied with the confidence coefficient $0 \cdot 95$ ($m = 1 \cdot 96$).

Then

$$n = \frac{1,171,898^2 \times 1 \cdot 96^2 \times 0 \cdot 019 \times 0 \cdot 981}{1000^2} = 98,336.$$

This agrees with the result of another calculation on p. 530, where it turned out that by drawing 100,000 units under the same conditions we obtain the confidence interval of 23,254 − 21,278 (a confidence half-interval of 988).

Let us use the same example for calculating by formula (XIX.16). Let us suppose that we agree to have a deviation within the limits of 5 per cent either way, i.e. that the confidence half-interval is to be $\delta' = 0 \cdot 05$. Other quantities are as before.

$$n = \frac{1 \cdot 96^2 \left( \dfrac{1}{0 \cdot 019} - 1 \right)}{0 \cdot 05^2} \approx 79 \cdot 340.$$

This result also agrees with the previous one. In the previous example $\delta = 1000$ was about $0 \cdot 045$ in relation to the measured value and now we have assumed $\delta = 0 \cdot 05$. Since $\delta$ and $\delta'$ are in the denominator and are squared $n$ should be smaller than before in the same ratio as $45^2(= 2025)$ is to $50^2(= 2500)$, i.e. in the ratio of 8100 to 10,000. This ratio has been maintained fairly accurately: $98,125 \times$ $\times \dfrac{81}{100} = 79,481.$

The small difference in the last three digits is due to the insufficiently accurate calculation of the ratio $0 \cdot 045$ to the quantity measured.

We shall obtain completely different results in trying to establish the size of the sample when $p$ is large. As we know, the relative standard error increases rapidly as $p$ decreases (see discussion and table on p. 528).

Let us suppose that we want to estimate not the number of children born in one year but the total number of persons able to work, aged 18–64. Let the number of such persons be 70 per cent of the total population of city. Leaving the other assumptions unchanged ($m = 1 \cdot 96$, $\delta' = 0 \cdot 05$) we obtain

$$n = \frac{1 \cdot 96^2 \times \left( \dfrac{1}{0 \cdot 7} - 1 \right)}{0 \cdot 05^2} = 658.$$

To achieve the same accuracy as before (the confidence interval not greater than 10 per cent of the quantity measured, the confidence coefficient $0 \cdot 95$) a sample composed of 658 units will suffice.

In the application of formulae (XIX.13)–(XIX.16) p. 544–7, a serious difficulty is encountered in practice. If we embark upon a sampling study, particularly in socio-economic statistics, we almost never confine ourselves to studying only one characteristic. On the contrary, we almost always intend from the beginning to take full advantage of the study, and to analyse the whole population from all possible angles. But the formulae given above enable us to determine the size of the sample on the basis of certain specific assumptions about a single characteristic studied from a definite point of view (e.g. in calculating the arithmetic mean or the standard deviation). Thus we would have to determine $n$ as many times as there are problems that we want to study, and each time the result would be different. Of course, the least favourable result, i.e. the one requiring the largest sample, should be chosen because then the other requirements would certainly also be met.

However, such an automatic choice can be used only in exceptional cases. In general, if some of the objectives of the study require particularly large samples, we should consider the possibility of diminishing the accuracy of the results, or even of abandoning the idea altogether.

To determine the required size of the sample, while considering all aspects of the problem studied, is very troublesome, and it cannot be recommended for general use. On the other hand, a preliminary determination of the required size of the sample is very important.

An experienced statistician may try the following procedure. He may arrange the problems to be studied by the increasing "difficulty" of analysing them by sampling, i.e. according to increasing size of the sample required to achieve a sufficiently high degree of accuracy. In many cases this can be done by intuition with a few easy calculations. For problems requiring the largest sample he calculates $n$ as accurately as possible. If it is practicable to take a sample of this size he accepts the size as the basis of the study. Thus problems for which a sample of this size is not necessary can be solved with a greater degree of accuracy than required, but the cost is also higher. To avoid this a smaller sample can be taken from the large one, and used in problems for which $n$ can be smaller.

If it turns out that the required size of the sample is too large, we have a choice of several alternatives. If the problem for which the largest sample is required is not very important to the whole study, we can simply leave it out of the analysis, or we can make the study a little less detailed, e.g. instead of dividing the population into 1-year or 5-year age groups, we can divide it into a few large groups. If these solutions are not acceptable, we can either abandon the study altogether or try to obtain more money for it. But it should be remembered that increasing the size of the sample beyond a certain limit ceases to make sense because an exhaustive study may then be relatively cheaper since the cost per unit studied is greater in sampling than in an exhaustive study.

This sort of preliminary determination of the size of the sample should, as a rule, always constitute the first step in organizing a sampling enquiry, because it will protect one from unpleasant surprises, and will usually help reduce the cost. Yet this sound principle is not always observed. This may sometimes be justified if the available resources cannot be exceeded and thus the size of the sample is automatically limited. Moreover, in certain methods of drawing it is easiest to determine the size of the sample as a percentage of the whole population. This is not the most correct method but under certain circumstances it may be tolerated.

## 5. CONCLUSIONS. GENERAL COMMENTS ON SAMPLING

The above discussion should suffice to give a general idea of sampling. Let us recapitulate. Sampling consists in random drawing from the population that we want to analyse a certain number of units which are called a sample. The characteristics determined in the sample can, under certain conditions, be ascribed to the whole population. The essential feature of sampling is that we do not obtain uniquely determined results, but only determine the limits within which the true value should lie. By using theorems from probability theory we can determine the confidence coefficient, i.e. the probability that the limits determined will not be exceeded. The accuracy, i.e. the interval within which the true answer may be located, and the confidence coefficient for a given number of units drawn for the sample are strictly related to one another. By changing the number of units drawn, we can change both the accuracy and the confidence coefficient. We shall see later that the accuracy (and the confidence coefficient) can be increased not only by increasing the size of the sample, but also in other ways.

We have given a number of formulae that can be applied to the evaluation of certain results obtained by sampling (the arithmetic mean, the standard deviation, the relative frequency of the units possessing a given characteristic, the correlation coefficient, etc.). These formulae were illustrated by simple examples. This exposition appeals to intuition more than to strict mathematical reasoning, but it should give the reader an understanding of the problem and should enable him to use the above formulae in simple cases of course, he must be careful.

Certain reservations have been given above. The most important hint for the person not too well versed in mathematical statistics is to apply a simple, mechanical rule: Use the formulae only when the number of units in the sample is relatively large, say, of the order of at least several dozen, or, preferably, 100 or more, i.e. when there is no need to use small sample methods.

Here is where the mathematical statistician and practizing statistician have, perhaps, the greatest scope for co-operation. Of course the mathematical statistician must not be an "ivory tower" type and must understand the essence of the problem, and the practizing statistician must know at least the rudiments of sampling so that they can find a common language. The presentation of these rudimentary principles of sampling is the task of this chapter.

Those who use the results of statistical research, and particularly those who are not statisticians themselves, often have a wrong attitude to the results of a sampling enquiry. Either they are suspicions and distrust the results, or treat them as if they were obtained by an exhaustive, comprehensive study, without considering the fact that these results are subject to random error. This error may be small and of no practical consequence but it may also be large enough to make an uncritical and unreserved interpretation of the results most dangerous. When this happens the blame is usually put, not on the culprit and the improper use of the results of the study, but on the sampling method itself. In both cases—distrust or wrong interpretation of the results—the consequence may be to reject the method, which would be especially unfortunate in a socialist economy where certain facts often have to be learned quickly, are not included in the regular reporting system, and therefore cannot be analysed by exhaustive research (even disregarding the high cost of such research).

To avoid such undesirable consequences we should stick to the principle of not making the results of a sampling enquiry public without appropriate comments on the accuracy of the results and the extent to which they can safely be applied.

We shall give below many examples of the application of sampling to a study of reality. These examples will explain better the purpose of this method and the advantage of using it; they will also indicate when it can be used without reservations, when certain reservations should be made and when it must not be used at all.

However, before we come to this, we have to discuss certain problems involved in drawing a sample.

# CHAPTER 20

# SAMPLE DESIGN AND TECHNIQUE

## 1. SAMPLE DESIGN

### a. The Concept of Sample Design. Independent and Dependent Sampling

We shall explain the meaning of sample design by a simple example.

The reasoning and the formulae presented before are based on the assumption that the sample is drawn in the way outlined on p. 519 in the example of drawing balls from a box: each ball is returned to the box after drawing and is there for subsequent drawings. In this way the probability of drawing a ball of a specific kind always remains the same. This is the basic, and theoretically the simplest, sample design. It is called *independent sampling* (since the probability in each drawing is independent of the result of the preceding drawing) or *sampling with replacement*. For example, if in a demographic study we arrange the drawing in such a way that a person once drawn can be drawn again, which means that the same person can find his way into the sample several times, then this is independent sampling.

Another type of design consists in arranging the drawing so that the ball drawn is not returned to the box: thus the unit once drawn is not included in the drawing again (*dependent sampling* or *sampling without replacement*). Intuitively this design seems to be more natural, and it is usually more convenient in practice.

We shall see that there are many types of sampling design. Before we begin discussing them, however, let us compare the designs of sampling with and without replacement.

It turns out that with the same sample size, sampling without replacement gives more accurate results (a smaller standard error) than sampling with replacement.

The correctness of this theorem can be shown intuitively in the following way.

If there are 30 white balls and 70 black balls in the box, then, after drawing 100 balls with replacement—that is, as many balls as there are in the box—we shall not know for certain how many black balls and how many white balls there were in the box. If we denote by $p$ the ratio of white balls to all balls (the probability that the ball is white) then we obtain the standard error of $p$ by the formula

$$\sigma_p = \sqrt{\frac{pq}{n}}.$$

If 100 balls are drawn, this will be fairly large. But if we use the method of drawing without replacement, then after drawing 100 balls we shall empty the box, and we shall know with certainty how many balls were white and how many black.

From the mathematical point of view the situation is as follows. In sampling with replacement the standard error and thus the accuracy of the results obtained by using the formulae depend upon the number of units in the sample but not upon how large a part of the total population the sample is. Thus, if we draw 10,000 units the standard error is always the same, no matter whether the whole population numbers 20,000, 100,000 or 100 units.

The standard error in sampling without replacement in estimating, for instance, the arithmetic mean, is obtained by multiplying the standard error in sampling with replacement by

$$\sqrt{\frac{N-n}{N-1}},$$

where $N$ is the number of units in the whole population and $n$ is the number of units in the sample. If $N$ is large there is no need to subtract one in the denominator. Then this expression will assume a form easier to understand intuitively.

$$\sqrt{\frac{N-n}{N}} = \sqrt{1 - \frac{n}{N}}.$$

Thus, the standard error in sampling without replacement is

$$\sigma_{\bar{x}}' = \sigma_{\bar{x}} \sqrt{1 - \frac{n}{N}} = \frac{\sigma_x}{\sqrt{n}} \sqrt{1 - \frac{n}{N}}.$$

The expression $\sqrt{1 - \frac{n}{N}}$ is always less than one (if $n$ is not zero, which in this case would not make sense because it would mean that we have not drawn a single unit).

Assuming that $n$ constitutes 10 per cent of $N$ we have

$$\sqrt{1 - \frac{10}{100}} = \sqrt{\frac{90}{100}} \approx 0 \cdot 95.$$

If $n$ is 30 per cent of $N$ the result is

$$\sqrt{1 - \frac{30}{100}} = \sqrt{\frac{70}{100}} \approx 0 \cdot 84.$$

When $n = N$, then, of course

$$\sqrt{1 - \frac{100}{100}} = 0.$$

i.e. the standard error in sampling without replacement equals zero and the result obtained is completely accurate (with no standard error).

In other words, we can say that in sampling without replacement the standard error (and the accuracy of the results) depends both on $n$ (the number of units in the sample), and on the ratio $\frac{n}{N}$ (the percentage that the number of units in the sample constitutes of the whole population).

When $\frac{n}{N}$ is close to zero i.e. the size of the sample is relatively small in comparison with the whole population), an increase in accuracy due to the substitution of sampling without replacement for sampling with replacement will be relatively small (the expression $\sqrt{1 - \frac{n}{N}}$ is close to one). This happens quite frequently.

When the value of the fraction $\frac{n}{N}$ is large, sampling ceases to be worth-while and an exhaustive study is usually more advisable. It appears from these considerations that sampling without replacement should always be used unless the technical difficulties are too great.

On the other hand, if $n$ is small in relation to $N$, a decrease in the standard error will be negligible, and the accuracy of the results can be obtained by the simpler formulae for sampling with replacement. In this way the standard error is somewhat overstimated, but this is of little importance, and, in any case, it is less dangerous than underestimating the standard error. Only for large values of $\frac{n}{N}$ does it become important whether we estimate the standard error from the formula for sampling with or without replacement.

It should be noted that in sampling we often use the term: 5 per cent sample, 10 per cent sample, 20 per cent sample, etc. We can see from the above argument that always, even in sampling with replacement, the accuracy of the result is affected primarily by the absolute size of the sample and only to some extent, and only in sampling without replacement— and even here not very much—by the size of the sample in relation with the whole population. A 5 per cent sample of a population numbering 100,000 units will always give a more accurate result than even a 20 per cent sample of a population consisting of 1000 units. For instance, if $p = 0 \cdot 1$, $q = 0 \cdot 9$ then with $N = 100,000$ and a 5 per cent sample

$$\sigma_p = \sqrt{\frac{0 \cdot 1 \times 0 \cdot 9}{5000}} \times \sqrt{1 - \frac{5}{100}} \approx 0 \cdot 004135,$$

for $N = 1000$ and a 20 per cent sample

$$\sigma_p = \sqrt{\frac{0 \cdot 1 \times 0 \cdot 9}{200}} \times \sqrt{1 - \frac{20}{100}} \approx 0 \cdot 01897.$$

In the second case the standard error is $4 \cdot 6$ as great as in the first.

If we used sampling with replacement, the standard error with 200 units drawn would be 5 times as great as with 5000 units drawn, because this error is inversely proportional to the square root of the number of units in the sample and the square root of 200 five times smaller than the square root of 5000. When we apply sampling without replacement we reduce the standard error, but the reduction is relatively small: the coefficient by which the error in sampling for a 5 per cent sample with replacement must be multiplied is $\sqrt{0.95} \approx 0.975$, and for a 20 per cent sample it is $\sqrt{0.80} \approx 0.894$.

The coefficient $\sqrt{\dfrac{N-n}{N-1}}$, $\left(\text{or if } N \text{ is large, } \sqrt{1 - \dfrac{n}{N}}\right)$, which enables us to calculate an increase in the accuracy of the estimate in sampling without replacement, is used for estimating the standard error of the arithmetic mean, of the ratio of a part to the total, and, under certain conditions, of the difference between two independent means (see formula (XIX.8) p. 532). It cannot be applied to other numerical characteristics (e.g. the standard deviation, the correlation coefficient).

Sampling with and without replacement are examples of two different sampling designs. As we have seen, the accuracy of the result is greater in sampling without replacement. Since in most cases sampling without replacement is also simpler than sampling with replacement, we should always try to choose the former.

On the other hand, it follows from the formulae above that the increase in accuracy is significant only when the sample constitutes a large percentage of the total population. Since a sample usually constitutes only a small part of the whole population, the difference in accuracy between using one design or the other is usually negligible. Therefore, if only a small percentage of the whole population is included in the sample, we can use sampling with replacement without hesitation, since it will not give significantly worse results. Similarly, for estimating the results (the calculation of the confidence interval and coefficient) we can use simpler formulae for sampling with replacement; at worst, it will lead to a more pessimistic appraisal of the results, which undoubtedly is a lesser evil than too optimistic an appraisal.

We shall now review other more important sample designs. There are meny of them, and they serve different purposes. Some, like sampling without replacement, are designed to increase the accuracy of statistical estimates which are sometimes of great importance. Others do not increase accuracy, and they may even actually reduce it, but they are sometimes used when a better design cannot be applied because of technical difficulties or high cost. In such cases, it may pay to increase the size of the sample rather than to resort to a more perfect, but also more technically difficult, design.

It is the task of the mathematical statistician to find for each case appropriate formulae to determine the degree of change in the accuracy of the calculation. However, it is not always possible to find such formulae. In this exposition, in compliance to the objects of this book we shall, as a rule, not give these formulae but shall try to emphasize the advantages and disadvantages or dangers of using the designs discussed.

## b. Stratified Sampling

Instead of drawing directly from the whole population ("unlimited" drawing) we may first divide the population into parts ("strata") and draw separately from each stratum, estimate the magnitudes sought for each stratum separately, and then calculate for the whole population the sum or the weighted arithmetic mean of the data for the strata under certain circumstances. Such stratified sampling may considerably increase the accuracy of the estimate.

The intuitive proof, which state is due to J. Neyman, is as follows. Let us imagine that we have managed to divide the population into strata so that all units in each stratum are identical from the point of view of the characteristic studied. Then the drawing (or arbitrary selection) of one unit from each stratum determines without error the value of this characteristic for the stratum, and the general value for the whole population can also be determined without error as the weighted arithmetic mean. If the units within the stratum are not identical but similar, the drawing from each stratum will enable us to characterize the stratum more accurately than is possible when the units differ considerably.

An additional advantage of stratification is that each important part of the whole population is properly represented in sampling, whereas in unlimited sampling it may happen that some parts are represented better than others.

The above remarks indicate the course to be chosen in stratifying the population so as to obtain the most accurate results. Strata should be selected in such a way as to make each of them as internally homogeneous as possible from the point of view of the characteristics studied. This means that the strata should differ from each other as much as possible.

The application of this simple rule encounters serious difficulties in practice. It should be remembered, however, that even an imperfect stratification leads to better results than unlimited sampling, and therefore a compromise may sometimes be advisable.

In some cases a division into strata suggests itself automatically because of the type of material available. For instance, in studying farms or industrial enterprises a division by size seems obvious and advisable. Also the division in territorial stratification (provinces, counties or groups of counties) is self-evident. The differences between territories are usually known, at least in general terms. In such cases stratification can be based on two criteria, territory and size: this should lead to quite satisfactory results.

If a given problem has already been the subject of a study in the same or a similar context, or if the laws governing the phenomena are known, we can usually take advantage of such experience. In this way we shall probably not achieve the best stratification possible, because the data on which it is based may be obsolete or too general, but we should be able to come fairly close to the target. If we do not have appropriate data of this kind it is sometimes possible to obtain it in two stages and first to draw a relatively small number of units. This does not give accurate results but should enable us to establish more or less correct criteria of stratification. Since the units thus drawn in the first stage are also used in later stages, there is not much additional work involved. This method has already been mentioned on p. 545.

The most difficult situation arises when, as is quite usual, several characteristics are to be analysed by sampling. It may happen that the dispersion of one characteristic within one stratum is very small, whereas the dispersion of other characteristics in the same stratum is considerable, and it can be diminished only by some other kind of stratification. Thus we might have to use a different stratification for studying different characteristics.

This is usually impossible for technical reasons, and, more important, it would in most cases be beside the point, because generally the object is not only to study each characteristic separately, but also to discover the correlation among them. In most cases only one stratification is possible for the whole study.

The remedy against this limitation is to select one characteristic which is considered most important and most strongly correlated with others, and to divide into strata so that the variations of this characteristic within the strata are as small as possible. Of course, the accuracy of the estimates of other characteristics will then be smaller, but even for them the accuracy of the estimates will be much greater than can be achieved in unlimited sampling.

The number of units drawn from each stratum may be proportional to the frequency of the stratum. This is called *proportional sampling*. The procedure is simple, but this is not the best method. Much more accurate results can be obtained by drawing from each stratum a number of units proportional to the product of the frequency of the stratum by the standard deviation of the characteristic studied, within this stratum. This is called the *optimum allocation method*. Increased accuracy in this case should be understood either as a smaller standard error obtained with the same number of observations, or as the same standard error obtained with a smaller number of observations. The difference between the result obtained by the optimum allocation method and the proportional sampling method is small as far as $p$ (the relative frequency of the units possessing a given characteristic) is concerned.

However, one important reservation should be made. In some strata there may be so few units that neither the optimum allocation method nor proportional sampling will provide a sufficient basis for describing the characteristics studied. For such small strata the number of units drawn should be increased and sometimes an exhaustive study must be made.

The estimation of the accuracy of the results obtained by stratified sampling is not very complicated but it cannot be discussed here.

In comparison with unlimited sampling the increase in accuracy achieved by the method of stratified sampling is considerable, and therefore it should be used when circumstances warrant it. Stratified sampling is probably the most effective method of increasing the accuracy of the results.

### c. The Element of Sampling: A Unit or a Cluster?

The sampling unit should be a unit constituting an element of the population that we want to study. It may be simple or complex: if the object of a population study is the family structure or a group of people living in a given flat we may well draw single persons and group them to form a family, but it would be more convenient to draw a whole family or a group of people living in a given flat. Such a unit of a higher order must, of course, be strictly defined to eliminate doubt in separating it from other units, but in principle we deal here with drawing units.

However, it may happen that drawing simple or complex units is impossible for technical reason, or too difficult. For instance, in studying the population of a city it may be too difficult to draw single inhabitants, but it may be relatively easy to draw houses; then we study all the persons living in these houses and draw conclusions with regard to the whole city. In studying the population of a country instead of houses we draw whole communities.

The drawing of clusters usually produces less precise results than the drawing of units. The results are most precise when the dispersion among the clusters is least and the dispersion within the cluster is greatest. In an extreme case, if the structure of each cluster were the same as the structure of the population, then if would be enough to draw (or select) any cluster to learn about the whole population. The trouble is that usually we do not know the structure of the clusters before we start the study. What is worse, we may come across homogeneous clusters which differ considerably from each other. For instance, in a population census the census districts which are composed of neighbouring houses may comprise a fairly uniform type of population, which may differ considerably from the populations of other districts.

To remedy the situation, suggestions have been made to combine pairs of clusters which differ from one another and then to study only a part of such a combined cluster. This may present serious difficulties, and may be impossible in practice.

Another way of increasing accuracy is to choose relatively small clusters. The basic difficulties are the same, but when the clusters are small we may draw more of them, and thus achieve greater accuracy.

We can also increase accuracy considerably by a careful preparation of the division into strata before we start drawing. In spite of such serious reservations cluster sampling is in common use because of its convenience. It is also used in the first stages of multi-stage sampling.

## d. Two-stage and Multi-stage Sampling

This method consists of dividing the general population into a certain number of parts, drawing some of them, and then drawing units from the parts previously drawn. This is a two-stage sample. Analogously, sampling may be done in three or more stages.

The results of multi-stage sampling are less accurate than the results of direct sampling with the same number of units drawn, but under certain circumstances it has important practical advantages. The point is that the organization of drawing in the field is a difficult task and the difficulty increases with the size and wider geographical spread of the population from which we draw. This subject will be discussed in greater detail later on in this chapter (sampling technique) and also in examples in Chapter 21.

The difficulties may be so great that we may, of necessity, content ourselves with less accuracy. Sometimes it may be cheaper to increase the sample in multi-stage sampling than to draw directly within more narrow limits.

## e. Two- and Multi-phase Sampling

Multi-stage sampling should be distinguished from multi-phase sampling.

Multi-phase sampling consists in studying certain characteristics in the whole sample and others only in a sub-sample drawn from the original sample. Multi-phase sampling is used when greater accuracy is required with respect to some characteristics the required degree of accuracy can be achieved with a smaller number of observations (for instance, because of a smaller dispersion for those characteristics). This possibility has already been mentioned on p. 548. The difference between two-stage sampling and two-phase sampling is that in the former units are drawn from the previously drawn parts of the general population and in the latter units are drawn in both phases. In contrast to two-stage sampling two- or multi-phase sampling does not result in less accurate results.

If the results of drawing in the first phase are known before the beginning of the next phases they can be used in organizing the following phases, e.g. in the division into strata.

## f. Interpenetrating Samples

There are many advantages in taking from a population two or more samples drawn in the same way. First of all, we can obtain preliminary, though less accurate, results faster by analysing one of the samples first. Then, if each sample is analysed independently of the others, the accuracy of the results may be compared. This is particularly convenient when those who are not too familiar with statistics are to evaluate the results, for then such a comparison is much more convincing than mathematical formulae. Finally, this method of sampling enables a comparison of results when sampling in the field was conducted by different investigators or by different methods, on the condition that all such independent samples be drawn in exactly the same manner; or, at least, that each of them gives reliable results. This method is more expensive than simple sampling but it makes possible the control of the results and can be recommended if cost is not of decisive importance.

### g. Systematic Selection—Drawing Every *n*-th unit

The essence of this design consists in drawing units located at even intervals from each other in time or space, e.g. every tenth unit, or events occurring every 5 min, or units separated by the same distance. This method is most frequently used when the units are numbered and we select for the sample each unit whose number ends with a certain figure, say, 7/10 per cent selection (or several figures, say, 3 and 8/20 per cent selection); or if in the production of a certain commodity a number of units of the product are selected for the sample at fixed intervals, etc. We shall discuss the details of this method in the part dealing with the sampling technique.

This is not random sampling in the strict sense of the word, since not every unit has an equal chance of being selected for the sample. Nevertheless, this is a correct sampling design. Sometimes the results may even be more accurate than those obtained by a proper random drawing procedure. The point is that if the material from which we draw is heterogeneous, e.g. in certain parts there are more units with a given characteristic than in others, different parts of the material are uniformly selected for the sample. Thus, something in the nature of imperfect stratification takes place.

Of course, one fundamental condition must be statisfied: the selection of a unit must in no way be related to the possession of a given characteristic by the unit selected. This might happen if the cycle of changes occurring in the units was identical with the cycle the selection of units for the sample. This might easily occur if we selected for the sample the events occurring on specific days of the week or month. A particularly striking example of an error of this kind would be the selection of the sample of persons in a specific place on the familly questionnaire for the population census, since almost invariably the first place is occupied by the father, the second by the mother and the third by a child.

This brief survey of sampling designs is not, by any means exhaustive. Naturally, these designs are not mutually exclusive, and they can be combined in different ways. To some of them we shall return in Chapter 21, in discussing the examples of actual statistical enquiries.

Before we come to this subject, however, we must consider certain essential problems related to sampling technique.

## 2. SAMPLING TECHNIQUE

The first condition for a proper drawing is to have a list of the units of which the general population is composed. They may already exist as records prepared for administrative purposes or they may have to be especially prepared for the sampling survey.

It is important that such records satisfy certain requirements. They must be accurate, complete and without repetition and they must be up-to-date since obsolete records are useless.

With the exception of some cases that will be discussed later, these records should be numbered, or at least arranged in a certain order. The latter may suffice, for instance, when we use the systematic selection design, not according to numbers but according to the order of cards, or we draw clusters, not units. But even then the total number of units in the general population should be known.

Let us assume now that we have a complete, correct and numbered record of units in the general population. The numbers corresponding to the particular units should be written on identical balls of the kind used for drawing from a box. If we use the stratified sampling design, we take as many boxes as there are strata, and place in each box the balls belonging to a given stratum, and then draw from each box the required number of balls.

In practice this method is not used since writing numbers on the balls is awkward and some other, more convenient method can be used.

### a. Tables of Random Numbers

The most generally used method of selecting units for random samples is selection based on the tables of random numbers. In these tables, the numbers are placed in random order, as if each of them had been obtained by independent drawing.

There are several sets of such tables in English and Soviet literature, but not all of them satisfy the requirement of "randomness". There are also Polish tables which seem to be as good as any published abroad.[196]

To give the reader a general idea of how such tables are designed, and how to check whether they satisfy the requirements, we shall describe here the design used by E. Vielrose.

We start with a series of numbers obtained by using adding machines which print results. These machines record all the totals on a narrow strip of paper. In many cases, it can be assumed that these totals are independent of each other

---

[196] They are *Tablice liczb losowych* (*Tables of Random Numbers*) prepared by E. Vielrose and published by the Central Statistical Office (Warsaw, 1951). These tables are reprinted in part at the end of this book.

(e.g. when we add up the population of particular counties to obtain the total population of the country, or the number of quintals of a grain harvested in the particular counties, etc.). In these numbers the last digit has been crossed out because, with inaccurate material, it may often be rounded off to zero, and also the first two digits have been crossed out because there small numbers (0, 1, 2, 3, 4) may appear more frequently than large ones.[197]

In follows that numbers with fewer than three digits had to be omitted. All the totals and those components which were added up several times were also omitted, because of an observed error. The remaining numbers were written down one beside the other and combined into four-digit groups. These groups provided the first outline of random numbers.

It might be thought that the tables so designed should satisfy the condition of "randomness". However, the "randomness" was checked by the following three tests:

(1) *The frequency test* consists in counting how many times each figure (0, 1, 2, etc.) appears in the tables. When the number of figures is large, each should appear with more or less the same frequency.

(2) *The independence test* consists in checking whether the frequency of particular figures is independent of the preceding figure, which, of course, it should be.

(3) *The sum test.* The sums of five consecutive figures are formed. When there are many such sums they should be arranged around an average according to the binomial distribution. The average sum of five figures from 0 to 9 should tend to 22·5.

The $\chi^2$ test was applied to all tests with a confidence coefficient of 0·95.[198]

The tests were applied to each thousand figures (250 groups of four digits). Some of the tables with 1000 figures turned out to be faulty and they were either eliminated or revised. In the final result the tables contain 40,000 figures (10,000 groups of four digits). This is the first part of the set of tables.

In the second part the additional 4000 figures are shown in 2000 groups of two digits each.

These tables were subjected to more severe tests: the tests were applied to each group of a hundred figures separately.

---

[197] If particular items do not exceed ten to fifteen thousand it is obvious that in five digit numbers there will be many one's not only in the first digit but also in the second (e.g. 10, 11 or 12 will occur more frequently than 17, 18 or 19). The disregard of the possibility of a greater frequency of small numbers in the first two digits makes some of the tables of random numbers designed abroad virtually useless.

[198] In this kind of checking we should avoid the tendency toward too rigid elimination of all disturbances in the arrangement of the numbers, or in other words the tendency toward forming too correct tables. In random drawing it may happen that the same figure is repeated many times. Too frequent and too striking cases should be removed but exaggeration in this direction should be avoided because the tables would then lose their random nature.

It follows that the first part can be used for large samples if the size of the samples is not less than several hundred.

For small samples in which the numbers of units drawn do not exceed several hundred, the numbers from the second part should be used.

The reason is that when the tests are applied to thousands (as was the case with respect to the first part of these tables) we check whether random deviations cancel out within each thousand but we cannot be sure that they cancel out within smaller groups.

We shall illustrate by an example how the tables of random numbers should be used.

Let us suppose that there are not more than 10,000 elements of sampling in the general population. In this case we need for our drawing the groups of four digits which are in the first part of Vielrose's Tables. The first operation is to number the elements of the general population. Then we open the tables at any place. Let us suppose that we find there the following group of 4 digit numbers (the table on page 644 at the top).

| 1498 | 3222 | 5087 | 8199 | 3133 | 5466 | 8986 | 3423 | 9013 | 6476 |
| 3284 | 8491 | 2283 | 6283 | 4067 | 8115 | 1066 | 3240 | 0434 | 3676 etc. |

The simplest procedure is to read off the fours as they come: 1498, 3222, 5087, etc., and to consider as drawn the corresponding numbers on the list. The fours can be read off in any other order, say, every second, every third, or starting from the end of each row. 6476, 9013, 3423, etc.

There are many possibilities, but of course combinations that are too difficult should be avoided. If the number drawn is larger than the total number of units in the general population, it can simply be disregarded.

If the number of units in the general population is larger than 10,000 we must form the groups of numbers with five, six or more digits, for instance: 149,832, 225,087, 819,931, etc., or 149,832, 498,322, 983,222, etc. When the general population is very large, the method of forming groups of five, six or more digits may have to be changed because from the given collection of 40,000 digits only 8000 five-digit groups can be formed, or 6666 six-digit groups. Thus, if the number of units in the general population is, say, 100,000 and therefore we need five-digit numbers, after the 8000-th item we would have to use the same groups of five-digit numbers all over again and therefore we would be drawing the same units and in the same order as at the start of the first 8000. This would be "drawing with replacement" and certain items would be included in the sample not at all in a random manner, whereas others could not be selected for the sample at all.

If we use sampling without replacement we simply omit the numbers that have already been drawn.

## b. **Substitute Methods of Drawing**

Although drawing with the help of the tables of random numbers is a relatively simple operation, it is time-consuming. That is why substitute methods are sometimes used, particularly when the sampling elements in the general population are not numbered. Some of these methods are correct but others are subject to reservations, or are even totally faulty.

One frequently used substitute method—especially when the elements are numbered—is the method of systematic selection: every $n$th unit (see p. 560). The favourite is the 10 per cent selection, being the simplest (e.g. we take the items: 1, 11, 21 etc. or 7, 17, 27 etc.). The method of systematic selection is generally used when the interval between the selected numbers is ten or a simple multiple of ten: $10n$ where $n$ is a small integer, or $10/n$ where $n$ is 2 or 5. When the method of systematic selection is used the first figure should be chosen by drawing.

Providing that conditions discussed in the first part of this chapter (p. 561) are satisfied, the method of systematic selection may produce correct results, not worse than a proper drawing.

A disadvantage of this method is its rigidity. As we have already mentioned, for technical reasons every 10th, 20th, 50th of 5th unit is selected so that we have 10, 5, 2 or 20 per cent samples, but not, say, 7 or 23 per cent samples. But the 10 per cent sample may be too large to obtain the required degree of accuracy, and therefore would cost more than is justified, or it may be too small, and thus the accuracy of the results would be diminished. But this is not an essential reservation, since the results of sampling are subject to random error anyway, so it is not essential whether the confidence interval is within rather narrow limits or whether the confidence coefficient is a little larger or smaller than originally intended, provided that these deviations are not too large. Besides, because of the simplicity of this method and its consequent cheapness, we can afford to increase the number of units drawn, and achieve an accuracy slightly greater than really needed.

Under certain circumstances the method of systematic selection can also be used when the units are not numbered. For instance, if the data are recorded on cards of the same thickness, we can use a measure with intervals marked, and corresponding to a definite number of cards.

Tantamount to systematic selection is the procedure sometimes used in studies on mass production. At fixed intervals a special device removes from the machine samples of the product to be analysed. The method is correct, providing that the production runs smoothly and evenly, without changes in the quality of the product. The results will be incorrect if the rhythm of changes in the quality of the product coincides with the rhythm of taking samples.

Automatic selection can also be made with the help of statistical machines. If the material is properly sorted, a stratification with the help of machines is better than one accomplished in the usual way.

If the material is not numbered we can sometimes draw the units for the sample on the basis of some easily distinguishable characteristics, providing that we know that they are not correlated with the characteristics studied. For instance it may be the date of birth: we can choose the persons born in a certain month disregarding the year, or in a certain week of the year, or on a certain day of the month. In the first case the sample constitutes approximately 1/12 of the total, in the second case about 1/52, and in the third about 1/30. The date of death can also be used in the same way.

This method is basically correct. It should be remembered, though, that certain demographic phenomena are of a seasonal nature. Sometimes the dates are given incorrectly. However, with due, care deformations of the result can be avoided.

The method of "letter drawing" is subject to more reservations. If a list of names in alphabetical order is available sometimes the sample is drawn by selecting names beginning with certain letters. We shall show by examples how serious errors can be committed in this way.

In Mannheim (Germany) an enquiry was undertaken to determine the number of children per family in this city at the beginning of the nineteenth century. Family sheets arranged in the alphabetical order of surnames were available. It was decided to select for the sample the names beginning with A, B and M. Thus the characteristic selected for this purpose did not seem at all related to the number of children.

It turned out later that the results obtained were incorrect. A closer investigation revealed that many Jewish names begin with these letters, and at the beginning of the nineteenth century there were more children in Jewish families than in non-Jewish families.[199]

This example, as well as other similar experiences, showed that the first letter of the surname may be related to the characteristics studied.

Nevertheless, the "letter drawing" method is sometimes used, mainly because it is very simple, and it can easily be checked with regard to the requirement of completeness.

The method of "letter drawing" was used by the Central Statistical Office in Poland to determine the population structure by sex and age on 1 January 1949. Instructions were issued to extract from the population registration records in towns and villages the data concerning the residents whose surnames started with N and O. Moreover, the total numbers of registered residents were to be given. In this way a 4·4 per cent sample was obtained.

Two letters were chosen instead of one in order to enable the checking of ran-

---

[199] This example is taken from *Statistik* by S. Schott, Leipzig–Berlin, 1913, pp. 41–42.

domness by comparing the results calculated for each letter separately. Allowing for a possible relationship between the area and the frequency of the occurrence of particular letters on the one hand, and certain characteristics of the persons studied on the other hand, estimates were made separately for each province, and within each province separately for towns and villages. It appears that the results obtained are correct. The differences between the two letters, with few exceptions, were negligible.

In general, it can be said that the method of "letter drawing" should be avoided. If it had to be used, great care is advisable (not one but several letters should be chosen, estimates should be made for small groups, etc.). The results should be carefully checked, either against other similar studies or by an analysis of the arrangement of the figures in the final tables.

### c. Sampling from Records and Direct Sampling

It is obvious that in sampling from records we should make sure that the records available are suitable for the purpose, particularly with regard to their being complete, correct and up-to-date. It is also important that the records actually refer to the population we want to study. Let us suppose that we are interested in the structure (by sex, age and other characteristics) of children at school age, regardless of whether they go to school or not. We cannot use records of school children as a basis for a study of this kind, if all children in the area are not subject to compulsory education. But even if they are, and the rule is generally observed, it may happen that some children do not go to school, perhaps because of a prolonged illness. In this case inference based on the data pertaining to school children is dangerous because it is quite likely that the nature of the children who do not go to school is different from that of those who do.

The situation is easier when the reverse happens, and the records include more units than we want to analyse. Suppose that we have the full record of the whole population (based on the census) and we want to analyse a part, say, those at the working age 18–64. We can extract these people from the records, but this will usually be impossible before drawing. But there is no difficulty in crossing out of the sample drawn from the whole population those aged less than 18 and more than 64, if we have the data on age. However, in determining the size of the sample we must remember that a large number of persons will have to be crossed out from the sample drawn. Let us suppose that for achieving the desired accuracy we should have $n$ persons aged 18–64 in the sample. For this purpose we should draw from the whole population a larger sample of $n'$ persons such that the ratio of $n'$ to $n$ is the same as the ratio of the total population to those aged 18–64. This ratio can almost always be determined with sufficient accuracy for this purpose.

In cases when the information available is not complete, additional data may have to be collected. This can be done simply by going to the source of information and collecting the additional data, or by deciding beforehand which units are to participate in the sample, and by instructing the census enumerators to obtain the required additional information on those who have been selected for the sample. Care should be taken, however, that the census enumerator does not make his task easier by changing the order, and by taking the required information where it is easiest.

In spite of these difficulties when the records do not contain all the required information, it is usually better to draw from the records than to resort to direct sampling. A "hit and miss" method of sampling cannot be regarded as random in the statistical sense and it is usually not worth while to analyse such "samples" with the help of proper statistical formulae or to attempt an evaluation of the results.

If we have no records of the geographical distribution of certain objects or events, we can draw a district and study the distribution there. For this purpose we can use administrative districts or we can form special districts for the enquiry. But in this way we are changing the sample design and are actually using the cluster sampling design, which, as we know, can sometimes produce very good results but usually reduces the accuracy. In Chapter 21 we shall give several examples of such sampling.

When proper sampling is not possible various substitute methods can be used. Some of them are quite correct but some are bound to give incorrect results. For instance, if the telephone book is used for sampling public opinion, it should be remembered that, as a group, those who are telephone subscribers differ from those who are not. There are many examples of incorrect and correct methods of substitute sampling. Some of them will be discussed in the next chapter.

# CHAPTER 21

# APPLICATION OF SAMPLING

## 1. FROM THE HISTORY OF SAMPLING

If we understand by sampling not what it means in the strictly statistical sense but the drawing of conclusions concerning the whole population on the basis of an analysis of a part—regardless of whether the choice of this part was random or not—it is a very old method. We shall start our review of the application of sampling with Graunt and the political arithmeticians.[200]

Graunt estimated the population of London in the following way. For some parishes he calculated the number of families and of deaths. There were 3 deaths for every 11 families (in the years free from the plague). Since the total number of deaths in London at that time was 13,000, he obtained $13,000 \times 11/3 = 47,667$ families. Assuming that there were 8 persons per family, Graunt arrived at the approximate population of London as 384,000 inhabitants. This is a typical example of inference on the basis of a sample, although the sample was not random. It should be remembered that Graunt was well aware of the "stability" of sufficiently representative statistics, which is a foundation of inference based on sampling.

An excellent study *Recherches et considérations sur la population de la France* was written by Moheau in 1778. His method of reasoning in this study would be called sampling today. He selected certain districts in France either *au hasard,* or planned to obtain a representation of different characteristic areas. Then he applied the conclusions concerning the observed relations in the selected districts to the population of the whole country. He rightly observed that such generalizations are permissible if the relations observed in particular districts do not differ much. In this way, for instance, to arrive at the total population of France he conducted a population census in selected districts and determined the frequencies of certain quantities for which the data were available for the whole country, e.g. the number of parishes, village communities, houses, births, marriages and deaths. The analysis showed that the first three quantities—the number of parishes, village communities

---

[200] We shall disregard here the application of sampling to the natural sciences in which the use of the method of partial research dates back to the beginning of the sciences. But the understanding of the essence of sampling and of the significance of the accuracy of the results, are the achievements of modern times.

and houses—cannot be estimated because their ratio to the population varies considerably from district to district.

The most stable was the ratio of births and deaths to the population. The total population of France was estimated on the basis of 23,687,000 births, and on the basis of 23,818,000 deaths.

The difference is obviously insignificant. In a similar way, Moheau estimated the population structure by sex, age, and family status; the number of domestic servants, fertility, the number of children per family, deaths by age, and so on. In this way in obtained a relatively correct picture of the demographic structure of France. From the point of view of modern requirements, his errors consist in taking too few and too large districts. On the basis of the available material it is impossible to estimate the accuracy of the results. This problem, of course, was not posed by Moheau.

However, only shortly afterwards, in the first years of the 19th century, the mathematician Laplace estimated the population of France on the basis of a census conducted in 30 departments (about one-third of the whole) and on the basis of the data on births, deaths and marriages in 1799–1802. He determined the precision of the estimate, stating that with the probability of 1 to 1161 it can be maintained that the error does not exceed 500,000 persons, which is less than 2 per cent of the total population. Laplace's estimate of the accuracy was criticized as incorrect, but the problem was posed—and forgotten for almost 100 years.

An interesting example of an early application of sampling—this time based on drawing—has recently been brought back from obscurity by W. Murzewski.[201] In 1801 in France a decision was made to embark upon a general revision of tax records. The Commission appointed by Bonaparte decided that a *cadastre* should be made. "However, because of the great cost of making a survey of the whole country, a survey and assessment was made of only 1800 communities selected by drawing. It was hoped that by comparing the old and the new assessment of these communities a key could be found to a new land tax assessment". However, before the survey was finished "the government, seeing that the venture was purposeless, ordered a new survey and a new assessment of all communities".

Sampling was used very early in pre-revolutionary Russia. Ostroumov[202] says that already in the 17th century special books were kept on large estates in which the results of trial threshings were recorded (trial threshings used for estimating total crops can be considered as sampling). Numerous studies were also made by progressive statisticians. Enquiries were conducted in different provinces and counties as early as 1875, and they were based on selected typical villages; often the method of drawing, say, every tenth farm, was also used. Although the method of selection is subject to reservations, valuable results were obtained.

[201] Cadastral Surveys: *Czasopismo Techniczne (Technical periodical)*, 1946, No. 10–11.
[202] S. S. Ostroumov: *Soudyebnaya Statistika Tchast Obschaya*, Moscow, 1949, p. 216.

The method of sampling was discussed at the Berne meeting of the International Statistical Institute in 1895 on the instigation of its great propagator, the Norwegian statistician A. N. Kiaer. In his paper delivered in 1895, he could quote successful studies carried out by this method in Norway. Kiaer's initiative was not well received.

In a heated discussion, different statisticians, and particularly the Germans who were accustomed to expensive, exhaustive labour- and time-consuming studies, showed a lack of understanding and a reluctance to accept this new idea. The matter was discussed at several consecutive meetings, and only in 1903 in Berlin was a vague resolution passed recommending the use of the sampling method on the condition that a detailed report be enclosed, including an evaluation of the results. The problem was to be raised again at the next meeting, but it was not. Only in 1925 in Rome did the Institute begin dealing with this subject in a completely changed atmosphere. From the beginning of the 20th century, the application of sampling spread to many countries and to various types of research with results that could not be disregarded. In a textbook by A. L. Bowley, which was first published in 1901 and became very popular, there was an extensive exposition of the sampling method. The main speaker at the meeting in Rome, the Danish statistician A. Jensen, in addition to the main paper, delivered a dissertation on the practical applications of sampling in which he outlined its history and Bowley discussed extensively the problem of the accuracy of the results obtained by sampling.

In the following years both the theory and the practical application of sampling developed by leaps and bounds. A great contribution to the development of the theory was made by a Polish statistician Jerzy Neyman (living abroad since 1934) whose work, incidentally, is based on a thorough knowledge of the achievements of Russian and Soviet statisticians in probability theory and mathematical statistics.

In line with the objectives of this book we shall not go into the details of the further development of the sampling method, but we shall give a few examples of its application. The examples will be both good and bad, to illustrate some of the theorems presented above and to warn the reader against the danger of a mechanical approach in applying the sampling method.

Almost all these examples are authentic. We shall describe the object of the study, its circumstances and we shall make a critical appraisal of the method used and of the results obtained.

## 2. SAMPLE SURVEYS RELATED TO THE CENSUS

We shall deal mainly with cases related to general population censuses. We shall distinguish between two possibilities: (1) we have in our possession raw data collected by an exhaustive census; we shall apply sampling to this material in order: (a) to obtain more rapidly some basic information, (b) to analyse certain problems in greater detail than envisaged for the whole stury and (c) to obtain additional information. (2) There is no census material available and we select the units for the sample directly from the field. The first case is simple, and we can use whatever sampling design we regard as appropriate in a given case, at least in theory; in practice some technical difficulties may arise. The difficulties involved in the second case may be quite serious in practice.

### a. Analysis of Census Data

In 1920 a meteorologist and astronomer, R. Merecki, analysed the age structure of the population of the villages in the former Polesie Province. The problem was to find an objective criterion for the losses caused by the war. R. Merecki thought that losses caused by war are bound to affect the age structure of the population and should cause some deviations of the actual structure from the structure of the stationary population based on life tables. The facts have confirmed his thesis: it turned out that in destroyed villages frequencies were very small for the age group from 0 to 4 and partly also from 5 to 9. He used the lists of inhabitants made in connexion with the 1919 census. He drew for the sample 1000 persons from each village, usually 500 from the middle and 500 from the beginning or the end of the list. From some villages he took 2000 persons for an extra check: the samples pertaining to the Jewish population in towns were also larger. This is not the best method of selection but the objective seems to be obvious: an attempt to obtain a random sample. The enquiry was not finished because of the death of the author.[203]

In Japan a great earthquake in 1923 stopped the work on the population census made on 1 October 1920. Although the raw data were saved there was no hope of resuming the work for financial reasons. In order to obtain quickly some of the most important results for the whole country (sex, age in 5-year groups, size of household) the following method was used. All census reports (pertaining to households) were numbered and every thousandth report, beginning with the number 500, was drawn for the sample (0·1 per cent). A total of 11,216 reports was obtained (55,849 persons).

It turned out that sampling gave good results, they were consistent with the results obtained by a full study made later, with the exception of the oldest age groups of over 80.[204] This is understandable because the relative frequencies in these age groups are small (see p. 527).

---

[203] *Przegląd Wschodni* (*Eastern Review*), 1920, No. 10–11, and *Dziennik Urzędowy Województwa Poleskiego* (*The Gazette of the Polesie Province*), 1921.

[204] T. Kameda: Application of the Method of Sampling to the First Japanese Population Census, *Bulletin d'Institut International de Statistique*, Tome XXV, 2e Livre, 1930.

In Italy, on 1 December 1921, the objective was different. The census was made in the usual way, and then the raw data were to be destroyed to make room for other files. However, a part of the material was to be kept in case new studies, not included in the basis analysis, would have to be made. For this purpose out of 214 districts (*circondari*) into which the country had been divided, 29 were selected so that the averages for the main characteristics in the selected districts would be as close as possible to the averages for the whole country. The characteristics taken into account were: the birth rate, the death rate, the population of urban areas, the male population over 10 years of age, total income, the elevation above the sea level, and so on. This was then a conscious selection made with extreme caution. The whole sample was large and comprised 15 per cent of the total population of Italy. However, Neyman was right in commenting that consistency of the averages for certain characteristics does not ensure consistency for others, and that a random sample composed of small units would have been more representative.[205]

In the post-war period three population censuses[206] were made in Poland. The first of them made on 16 February 1946 was of a "summary" type and, not having been based on the data on each individual person, could not serve as the subject of a sampling enquiry for each home; the census enumerators recorded only the number of men and women, the number of persons in three basic age groups and in the main nationalities.

The totals for particular administrative districts and for the whole country were obtained by summing up.

The census of 1 January 1949 was in principle supposed to be a sample census. It was based, not on information especially collected for census purposes, but on the records of the population registration bureaux which were instructed to submit the data concerning the sex and age of the registered persons whose surnames began with N and O. This was, then "letter sampling", the dangers of which were discussed above. These dangers, of course, were fully appreciated. But this was undoubtedly the easiest way of obtaining material on which sampling could be based.

These data can also be very easily checked from the point of view of their completeness. To reduce possible errors two letters were chosen instead of one. The drawing was conducted by stratified sampling, i.e. separately for each province, and within each province separately for villages and towns. The lack of accuracy in the records kept by registration bureaux could have been a source of additional errors, but of course these errors have nothing to do with sampling.

The results were published in *Wiadomości Statystyczne* (*Statistical News*), No. 20,

[205] C. Gini and L. Galvani: Di una applicazione del metodo rapresentativo al ultimo cesimento italiano della popolazione, *Annali di Statistica*, Serie IV, Rome, 1929.
[206] The fourth post-war census took place in 1960.

1949 (by 5-year age groups, with the division into towns and villages, old territories and regained territories) and No. 5, 1950 (by age and sex).

The published results appear plausible. In any case they made possible the calculation of the death rate by age, of the fertility coefficient by the age of the mother and of the first post-war life tables.[207]

Apart from the reservations concerning the "letter drawing" method the following comments can be made about this census.

The sample design ensured a high degree of accuracy in the results, because each village community was sampled and thus no minor district could have been left out. Certain doubts could arise with reference to the schematic division into strata (provinces, and within them the division into urban and rural areas). However, in this case a proper stratification would require the setting up of districts in which there would be no correlation between the characteristics studied (age and sex) and the selected letters N and O; no data were available for making such a division.

The sample was large (about 4·4 per cent of the total population or not much less than one million people) and was undoubtedly sufficient to estimate 1-year age groups for very young ages and 5-year groups right up to a very old age. But the sample was insufficient for estimating the division by age and sex in certain small provinces, particularly with regard to the urban aged.

An estimate by territories was impossible also for another reason: the nature of the material from which the sample was drawn. Only the registered population in the whole country can be considered as equivalent to the total population of Poland; the same cannot be said about the population in particular provinces.

At the time of the census some people were absent from the province in which they were registered, and some people registered in a given province as temporary residents were in fact permanent residents. It was thus impossible to establish on the basis of the registration records either the "present" population, or the "actual" population, or the "resident" population in the sense in which these words are used in population censuses.

In the General National Census of 3 December 1950, sampling was to be used in order to obtain, as quickly as possible, the information needed for planning. Before the Census many discussions were held at the Central Statistical Office and in some of them Professor J. Neyman participated as one of the best theoreticians and practitioners in this field. He was also invited to take part in the works of the Committee on Mathematical Statistics.[208]

It was finally decided to use sampling stratified by census districts. The strata were the provinces and within them the towns and the villages. The sample was

[207] E. Vielrose: Polskie tablice wymieralności 1938 roku (Polish Life Tables for 1948), *Studia i Prace Statystyczne*, (*Statistical Studies and Papers*), 1951, No. 2–3.

[208] See *Studia i Prace Statystyczne* (*Statistical Studies and Papers*), 1950, No. 1, pp. 50–67 (*papers by M. Fisz and S. Szulc*) and No. 3–4, pp. 20–32 (paper by M. Fisz).

large: 10 per cent of the urban census districts and 5 per cent of the rural census districts.

The results would undoubtedly have been better if the census sheets for particular households were used for selection. (The selection of single persons would not have permitted the inclusion of such characteristics as living conditions, family structure and other problems related to a group of persons living together. It would also have prevented a proper analysis of farm problems, which were one of the main abjectives of the sampling). However, decisions about the choice of sample design must also be influenced by technical considerations.

We shall now describe in some detail the sampling method used in the Polish population census of 1931. This was probably the first study of this kind in the world. It was based on a very careful analysis of theoretical aspects with a simultaneous adaptation to practical considerations, organization and technique. An analysis of the methods used will give us an opportunity to elaborate on certain problems of a more general nature.

The theoretical aspects were dealt with by J. Neyman.[209] The object of the study was to provide the Ministry of Welfare with the necessary data for actuarial purposes. The workers were divided into three groups: (1) agricultural, (2) mining and metallurgy and (3) other branches of industry and commerce. For each of these groups the following information had to be obtained:

(a) The number of persons eligible for insurance.

(b) The age and sex distribution of those to be insured with division into active and non-active groups.

(c) The probability that a married woman was independent (by age).

(d) The probability that a man in the "active" category was married (by age).

(e) The average age of the wife corresponding to the age of a man in the "active" category.

(f) The average number of children up to the age of 17 per man in the "active" category in each age group.

(g) The average age of the children in each age group in the "active" category.

(h) The probability that a child up to the age of 17 was in the "active" category (by the age of the child).

As we can see, the scope of the investigation was considerable. But when we

---

[209] The theoretical foundations of new ideas which have since become standard tools of statistical analysis were published in Professor Neyman's Study, *Zarys teorii i praktyki badania struktury ludności metodą reprezentacyjną* (*Theory and Practice of Analysing the Population Structure by the Sampling Method*), Institute of Social Affairs, Warsaw, 1933, p. 123. The technical details of the study and the numerical results were discussed by Jan Piekałkiewicz in the publication of the Institute on *Sprawozdanie z badań składu ludności robotniczej w Polsce metodą reprezentacyjną na podstawie materiałów spisu powszechnego ludności w dn. 9.XII.1931 r. (A report on the Sampling Analysis of the Composition of the Working Population in Poland on the Basis of the General Population Census of 9 December 1931)*, Warsaw, 1934.

want to use the results of the census for actuarial purposes two serious difficulties arise:

(1) the majority of the combinations of the characteristics that we are concerned with are outside the scope of a normal population census: therefore, if the census were to serve actuarrial purposes its scope would have to be expanded considerably;

(2) the processing of the census data always takes a long time.

Under these circumstances, the Institute of Social Affairs decided to use the sampling method.

The investigation was conducted under specific conditions to which it had to be adapted. The first of them was the fact that the funds earmarked for the purpose were limited, which automatically limited the scope of the study. Thus the question was not how many units should be drawn from the general population to obtain the required accuracy of the results, but (1) whether, with the given number of units in the sample, the results would be sufficiently accurate, and (2) how to conduct the study in order to obtain the best possible results with the given sample size.

Secondly, the object of the study was to determine with a definite accuracy not just one characteristic, but a set of characteristics, and the important question was not only to obtain the required figures but also to establish the total effect of all errors on the finances of the insurance agency. Therefore the appraisal of the accuracy of the results had to be based not on particular results, but on the final financial effect.

Thirdly, even with the optimum number of drawings from each stratum (of course, stratified sampling was used) a difficulty arose in estimating the internal variance for each stratum (as we know, the optimum number of drawings from each stratum is a number proportional to the product of the frequency of the stratum and its internal variance). The difficulty arose because the variances of the characteristics studied may be different. It turned out, however, that the variances of the characteristics in question were fairly strongly correlated, and therefore, by a choice of the optimum number of drawings for one of the characteristics, the optimum number of drawings for other characteristics was approached. As a basic characteristic for determining the internal variance in each stratum the total working population in the stratum was chosen.

Another difficulty was the choice of the unit of selection. The smallest unit for sampling in this case could not be a person, because this would necessitate the recording of all the characteristics related to the family status of each person. It would be simple to draw not sheets on individuals but those on households, but this too was impractical, because of the need to keep the census material in order. It turned out that the most practical solution was to draw whole batches of sheets on households, completed in each census district by one census enumerator and comprising about 250 persons. From the point of view of the theory of sampling such a drawing by "clusters" is worse than individual drawing. Apart from considerations of the technical nature the choice of sample design was influenced by the fact that in individual sampling (which is more expensive), the sample size would have to be limited.

The whole country was divided into 26 relatively homogeneous partial populations which in turn were divided into a total of 113 sub-populations. The variance for each partial population was calculated on the basis of a preliminary sampling which comprised 5 sampling elements (census districts) selected from each of the 2 sub-populations from each partial population. This preliminary sampling served as a basis for determining the "proper" number of drawings from each partial population.

However, the number of drawings arrived at in this way had to be revised. It was necessary to determine the size and the structure of certain groups of workers very unevenly distributed in the country—primarily the miners and cottage industry workers. To estimate the distribution of such groups the number of drawings was increased in the districts involved and correspondingly reduced in other districts so that the total number of drawings remained unchanged.

Altogether 1621 census districts were selected from the total of 123,382. The population of the districts drawn was 403,967 or 1·27 per cent of the total population of Poland. The number of workers (both active and non-active, including those receiving retirement pensions) in the sampled districts was 121,857.

The selection was based on Tippett's tables of random numbers. On the basis of the sample an estimate was made for each partial population (stratum): the results for the whole country were obtained by adding up the data for separate strata. This method of estimating the absolute data for each stratum, and then estimating the total by adding up the data for particular strata, is the essence of stratified sampling.

The analysis of all results enabled an *ex post facto* estimate of the confidence interval. The interval was calculated not for particular results, but for the total disability pensions resulting from insuring all workers in the "active" category. With the confidence coefficient of 0·95, the confidence interval was 3·4 per cent. Thus the accuracy of the estimate was high, in spite of the fact that the sample comprised a relatively small number of units and the drawing was based on fairly large census districts.

Another way of checking the accuracy is a comparison of the estimate obtained by sampling with the final results of the complete analysis of the census. Such comparisons are possible only for a few characteristics, and are troublesome because of the difficulty of reconciling the criteria of classification for the census with those for the sample, and vice versa. Comparisons of this kind were made to a very limited extent, and they showed considerable discrepancies, greater than could be explained by random factors only. However, these discrepancies do not prove that the sample design was wrong, or that the number of sample elements drawn was insufficient. The reason for the discrepancies may lie in a different interpretation of the data recorded in the census. In this study such differences were conceivable because the instructions concerning the analysis of the census were not ready at the time the sampling study was undertaken, and the personnel employed was not skilled.

Hence get the important conclusion that in order to avoid discrepancies between a sampling survey and a complete analysis the instructions for the two studies should be consistent and prepared in advance. This applies both to the interpretation of the available material and the general definitions and principles of classification.

One more comment should be made. Drawing from each stratum a number of units proportional to the product of the frequency of the stratum and the internal variance of a given characteristic, results in the minimum error in estimating the characteristic for the whole population, but does not give the best approximation as far as the particular sub-populations are concerned. If we were more concerned with the latter we should determine the number of elements to be drawn from particular sub-populations after allowing for the frequencies in these populations (from smaller populations relatively more elements should be drawn).

A similar situation arises when certain units included in the sample are unevenly distributed over the whole territory to which the census relates. If we know in which districts the individuals of interest to us appear we can proceed in the same way as in the sampling investigation of the 1931 census: we can increase the number of drawings in appropriate districts. If these individuals are very unevenly distributed, and we do not know where they appear, we may be forced to abandon the idea of using a sampling survey because the sample would have to be so large that it would not be economical.

The study of the 1931 census is an example of the application of sampling to obtain results more rapidly, and to obtain data excluded from a complete analysis.

## b. Geographical Sampling

We shall use the 1934 census in Bulgaria as an example of sampling by territorial units.

This sampling survey pertained to agrarian relations. The village was chosen as the sample unit. The stratification was very carefully designed. Villages in which a specific type of crop predominated (tobacco, rice, etc.) were singled out first. The remainder, which were fairly homogeneous, were divided according to physiographical conditions (climate, elevation etc.) Altogether there were 28 strata. From each of them about 1/50th of all villages were selected in such a way as to obtain the same distribution by the size of farm as prevailed in the whole stratum according to the 1927 census. A check then revealed that the averages for most of the characteristics determined in the 1927 census in selected villages agreed with the averages for the whole strata. Since, as the study showed, there was in Bulgaria a linear regression between most farm characteristics and size of farm, it was assumed that the sample would give correct averages for the characteristics to be studied in 1934.

The use of purposeful selection instead of random drawing at this stage was due to practical considerations of speed and limited resources (it was established that with random drawing 1000 villages would have to be studied instead of 100 with purposeful selection).[210]

As a further example we shall discuss monthly labour force studies conducted in the United States, not because the sample design used was perfect but because they show various theoretical and practical problems involved in studies of this kind.

These statistics were obtained before World War II to study unemployment, which at that time assumed particularly dangerous proportions in the United States and in other capitalistic countries. Later the objectives of the study were expanded. The sample design now in use was introduced in 1944.[211]

The sample was to provide national statistics on labour force, unemployment, employment in and outside agriculture, non-workers, together with data on age, sex and some other characteristics of these groups. The sample was also to be used for other general purposes.

Of course there was no difficulty in dividing the whole country into a sufficiently large number of small territorial units and drawing an appropriate number of such units. However, two things should be kept in mind: (1) the study was to be repeated every month, which makes the problem of cost important; and (2) the study in the field was to be as precise as possible, and therefore a very careful system of checking was essential.

The following design was chosen. To each district a skilled instructor with a few census enumerators was assigned. The number of districts was 68.

The multi-stage method of sampling was used. The unit at the first stage was the county. For greater accuracy some counties were joined into groups of 2 or 3 in order to obtain a more diversified population structure. In consequence there were about 2000 units from which the first stage sample of 68 counties could be drawn. The results would be completely unreliable had the sample not been very carefully stratified.

From each stratum one county (or a group of 2–3 counties) was drawn so that the probability of drawing each county was proportional to its population, which

---

[210] Compare J. Neyman: On the Two Different Aspects of the Representative Method, *J. R. Statist. Soc.*, 47, 1934, pp. 558–622.

[211] A brief description of the method can be found in the publication of the U.S. Census Bureau by M. H. Hansen and W. N. Hurwitz: *A New Sample of the Population*, 1944.

is more correct than drawing with the same probability for each county. Each county selected was to represent the whole stratum.

The 68 "first stage units" drawn in this way were divided into very small territorial units from which a stratified sample was drawn. In the units drawn in this way a list of all households was made from which an appropriate number was drawn again. The drawing was designed in such a way as to obtain a sample constituting a predetermined percentage of all households. The number of persons drawn from each "first stage unit" was between 1000 and 1500. The total number of households in the sample was about 25,000—much less than 0·1 per cent of all households.

This sample design reduced the amount of work in the field, and ensured a relatively high degree of accuracy under the circumstances.

According to the U.S. Census Bureau, in estimating the total number of the employed with a confidence coefficient of 0·95, the random error should be less than 2 per cent for men, and 5 per cent for women, and in estimating the number of the unemployed the error could reach 18–20 per cent of the estimated quantity, which is very high.[212]

In another table on labour force the size of possible error, with the same confidence coefficient of 0·95, was given in absolute figures.

When the total population is estimated at 10 million the error may reach 540,000, i.e 5·4 per cent of the estimated quantity; when it is 1 million the error may be 142,000 or 14·2 per cent; when it is 10,000 the random error may be 10,000, or 100 per cent of the estimated quantity.[213]

In spite of the possibility of such large random errors, the material thus obtained gives an idea about changes in labour force and its structure, and in unemployment.

Another method of geographical sampling was used in labour force studies in Canada and in France.

For Canadian rural districts, in the first stage large strata were formed in such a way as to obtain a fairly high degree of internal heterogeneity, and from each stratum one district was drawn. Each district was divided into stratified segments (corresponding to census districts) which, in turn, were divided into small territorial units of 3–7 families each; from each such unit one family was drawn. All towns over 30,000 were taken into consideration.

In the final analysis the sample constituted about 1 per cent of the population. A survey was made every quarter and served the purpose of determining the labour force, unemployment and migration, as well as special studies such as housing conditions and fires.

Labour force studies in France are made twice a year. Eight large districts have been formed, each divided into ten strata. In rural areas stratification is based on

---

[212] See the *U.S. Statistical Abstract.*
[213] *Current Population Reports, Labour Force Series.*

the percentage of population living from agriculture, and in urban areas on the size of the town. In two-stage sampling, villages are used in the first stage, and households within the villages drawn in the second. The size of the sample is small, less than 0·1 per cent of the population.

The application of sampling to population studies in England is facilitated by the fact that very exact records are kept. The most important is the general population register, which comprises the population living permanently or temporarily in a given district, with a breakdown into children below 16 and adults from 16 up. The register is always kept up-to-date. Another source are taxation records which include all households. They can be used for selecting households. For some purposes lists of persons eligible to vote can be used.

The existence of such records facilitates sampling considerably. Of course, the special features of each record must be taken into account in designing the sample. Usually the records do not contain the data needed for the sampling survey required and therefore they can often be used only for selecting the people that are to be included in the sample: the investigation must then be conducted by special investigators.

In England the biggest organization undertaking such studies is the Social Survey established in 1941 to aid the war economy. It conducts numerous surveys for national and local governmental authorities. In the years 1946–49 this organization conducted 140 different studies in which 374,000 social workers were employed. Studies are also undertaken by some government departments and by social and scientific institutions.

Single or continuous studies are made for specific purposes. We shall mention some of them.

(1) Studies of the incidence of diseases and accidents were conducted for population registration purposes and included the population from the age of 16 onwards. Stratified, two-stage sampling was used. From each stratum two administrative districts were selected. In each district units were drawn systematically from the general population register. The sample at first comprised 70 administrative districts and 3000 persons: later, 110 districts and 4000 persons: and each month a new sample was drawn.

(2) A study of pneumoconiosis was made in 1946 in order to find out what occupations were chosen by the miners who contracted the disease, and whether their choice was appropriate. Every seventh name was selected from the official register of the persons suffering from the disease. The sample comprised 900 persons.

(3) A study was made of different groups of consumer's expenditures such as clothing, textiles, pharmaceuticals and various services (laundry, shoe repair, etc.). Two-stage sampling was used: in the first stage, stratified drawing of administrative districts; in the second, systematic drawing of households according to taxation

records. The samples comprised from 500 to 4800 households. Particular groups of expenditures were not analysed simultaneously, and the questions relating to them were usually repeated. In this case housewives in the sampled households were queried.

These few examples do not exhaust the wide scope of the subjects and the variety of the methods used by the Social Survey for government administration purposes in a war-time and a postwar economy.

Apart from the studies undertaken by the Social Survey, various government departments and agencies conducted sample surveys to meet the current needs of the administration.

One of the biggest surveys of this kind was a census of families conducted in 1946 by the Royal Commission on Population established to study demographic problems. About one-tenth of all married, widowed and divorced women were included in the survey (1,600,000 altogether). The selection was based on food ration cards. About 12,000 investigators collected the information on the family status, the date of birth, the date of first marriage, the date of terminating the marriage—if applicable—the dates of the births of all live-born children, the number of the surviving children below 16, the occupation of the husband. The study was conducted with great care, all women selected for the sample were queried and no substitutions were allowed.[214]

We should also mention here demographic studies undertaken by countries holding African colonies, particularly by the British administration. The unit was a village (*kraal*) and drawing was systematic. In the villages chosen for the sample all inhabitants were queried by census enumerators. Surveys included Southern and Northern Rhodesia (1948 and 1950 respectively). The population was divided by sex, and by the three basic age groups: below one year, from one year to maturity and adults. Moreover, all deaths during the preceding year were recorded. All adult women were asked about the total number of live births, the number of live births during the year preceding the census the number of children aged less than one year who died within that period and the number of surviving children. The sample was designed so that the error in the total population would not exceed 10 per cent, with a confidence coefficient of 0·95.

Substantial errors could have occurred because of incorrect answers given by the women queried. Nevertheless, valuable information concerning demographic problems was obtained under difficult conditions.

A different design was used in studying population problems in British East Africa (Kenya, Tanganyika, Uganda) in 1948.

Errors in surveys of this kind may be due to two reasons:

---

214 See C. A. Moser: "The Use of Sampling in Great Britain", *J. Amer. Statist. Assoc.*, 1949, Vol. 44, No. 246 and P. G. Gray and T. Corlett: "Sampling for the Social Survey", *J. R. Statist. Soc.* 1950, vol. CXIII, Part. II.

(1) The method of drawing which may produce insufficiently accurate results: the random error for all territories was not supposed to exceed 10 per cent with a confidence coefficient of 0·95, but it was much larger in some districts;

(2) Incorrect answers may be given by the persons queried. Although the number of questions was limited and they were formulated so as to be easily understood, there must have been many errors due to the low level of education of the population studied. However, such sampling surveys were useful for analysing demographic relations in Africa.

## 3. STUDIES OF YIELDS

Yields per unit of area can be analysed in a variety of ways.

The simplest and, it might seem, the only theoretically correct method would be to take stock of the crop on a given farm. By dividing the crop by the area from which it was harvested we would obtain the yield per unit of area. By simple arithmetic corresponding data could be obtained for the whole province.

This precise system, however, has many drawbacks. First of all, it can only be used on large farms. It is difficult to imagine obtaining information in this way from millions of peasants with small farms. Secondly, the information obtained in this way would be considerably delayed since the necessary data would be available only after the harvests. And this kind of information is usually required well ahead of time.

In agricultural statistics various methods are used to provide the information on yields and crops much earlier.

A widely used system is an estimate of crops, based on their appearance and made by agricultural experts (see below). An estimate can be made either by giving standard marks or by estimating deviations from the average yield.

If an estimate is made not long before the harvest the marks can be converted into yields per hectare by relating the observations to the results from previous years. A regression line of the yield per hectare on the standard grade can be calculated and the expected yield can thus be estimated.

This system has a very great advantage in that it enables an early estimate of yields, but it is not very accurate.

A much more accurate estimate is that based on trial threshings. In a sense this is a sampling method, but the choice of the sample is usually not random.

A much more precise method of estimating yields at harvest time is widely used in the Soviet Union.[215] The same method was also introduced in the United

---

[215] See M. P. Altunin: *Praktyczny kurs statystyki ogólnej i rolnej* (*A Practical Course in General and Agricultural Statistics*) (translated from Russian into Polish), 1950 pp. 171–2, and *Radziecka statystyka społeczno-gospodarcza* (*Soviet Socio-Economic Statistics*), Vol. IV, *Statystyka Rolnicza*, (*Agricultural Statistics*), 1950, pp. 51–3. The most detailed description was given by S. W. Sholtz, *Course syelskokhaziaystvijennoy statistiki*, Moscow, 1945.

States. England and West Germany without, it seems, acknowledging that it originated in the Soviet Union.[216] In 1951 and 1952 the method was also introduced in Poland. It consists in placing at regular intervals special frames of 1 m² in a field under a crop whose yield we want to measure. The grain within the frame is then cut, threshed, dried to the same degree as it would be in the granary, and then weighed. This should be done separately for each sample, but in practice it is often done together for all those taken from one field.

The number of such samples that should be taken depends on the accuracy of the results desired, and on the uniformity of yields in a given area. The dispersion of yields is not known in advance and can only be estimated afterwards.

Since the area sampled is usually only a small part of the total area, the accuracy of the results can be estimated using the formulae for sampling with replacement. In this case the accuracy depends only on the number of units in the sample and not on the ratio of that number to the total number of units. However, large fields may be more heterogeneous than small ones and, therefore, more units should be taken for a sample from large than from small fields.

When the investigation is complete the average yield is expressed in grammes per square metre. Dividing the result by ten we obtain the yield in quintals per hectare (one quintal = 100 kg = 100,000 g; one hectare = 10,000 m²).

Let us now state precisely what information this sort of investigation gives us. If it is conducted correctly it will give us the amount of grain (or other crops) in the field just before the harvest. This is not identical with the amount that will be in the granary after the harvest, since certain losses are inevitable. In other words sampling will tell us how much grain we would have if there were no losses.

Thus a very important consequence of using this method is that it tells us what losses are actually incurred.

However, the main advantage of the method is that it gives a quick and accurate estimate of expected yields, and thus of expected crops. We must allow for the above mentioned losses, which can be determined by experience.

Studies conducted by the Ministry of State Farms with the co-operation of the Central Statistical Office in 1951 and 1952 consisted of two parts: the first part dealt with state farms and the second with seed-grain stations.

Studies conducted in the first part were to comprise 5 per cent of all state farms in each district, drawn at random: they dealt with the yields of winter rye and spring wheat.

For the second part 6 seed-grain stations were selected in 1952 for studying the

---

[216] See Hans Kellerer: Stichprobenverfahren in der amtlichen deutschen Statistik seit 1946, *Bull. Inst. Int. Statist.*, Bern, 1950, Vol. XXXII, No. 2, pp. 250–3. The author describes the application of this method in the United States and England without mentioning the Soviet Union. Although the method is the same it could have been arrived at in other countries independently of the Soviet experience.

yields of winter rye and winter wheat. The object of the study was to establish the number of samples of 1 m² that should be taken to obtain proper estimates of yields.

The results had to be checked for each square metre separately. The number of samples of 1 m² was four times as great as on state farms. In addition another study was made in which the number of samples of 1 m² was only one-quarter of the main study, in order to find out whether sufficiently accurate results could be obtained with a smaller sample.

Let us suppose now that the results obtained on Farm A were as shown in Table 21.1:

TABLE 21.1. YIELDS IN GRAMMES PER SQUARE METRE

| Yield (g) | Number of observations | Yields (g) | Number of observations |
|---|---|---|---|
| 151–160 | 1 | 251–260 | 6 |
| 161–170 | 1 | 261–270 | 8 |
| 171–180 | 1 | 271–280 | 1 |
| 181–190 | 4 | 281–190 | 6 |
| 191–200 | 8 | 291–300 | 2 |
| 201–210 | 10 | 301–310 | 2 |
| 211–220 | 13 | 311–320 | — |
| 221–230 | 17 | 321–330 | 1 |
| 321–240 | 9 | Total | 93 |
| 241–250 | 3 | | |

The pattern is fairly irregular. The range is considerable and the highest yields per square metre are more than twice as high as the lowest. The most frequently encountered yields are within the limits 211–30 g, but two other maxima are also fairly distinct: within the limits of 251–70 g, and 281–90 g per m². Single observations deviate considerably up and down outside the limits where we would expect the series to end. Under these circumstances we cannot expect that the accuracy of estimating the average will be high.

The calculation reveals that:

The arithmetic mean $\bar{x} = 231 \cdot 4$ g.

The standard deviation $\sigma_x = 33 \cdot 26$ g.

The standard error of the arithmetic mean calculated by formula (XIX.1) (p. 522) is

$$\sigma_{\bar{x}} = \frac{33 \cdot 26}{\sqrt{93}} = 3 \cdot 34 \text{ g}.$$

Taking twice the standard error (6·7) we can say with a probability slightly greater than 0·95 that with the arithmetic mean of 231·4 g calculated from the sample the actual average yield per m² might be between 224·7 and 238·1 g per m², or between 22·5 and 23·8 quintals per hectare. For most practical purposes this accuracy is insufficient.

Even less sufficient, then, is the sample based on one-quarter of the number of square metre observations. Actually 26 m² samples were measured and their arithmetic mean was 229·0 g per m². Taking the standard deviation, as above, as 33·26 g[217] we obtain the standard error of the arithmetic mean:

$$\sigma'_{\bar{x}} = \frac{33\cdot26}{\sqrt{26}} = 6\cdot52 \text{ g}.$$

This is too great. The smaller sample is in this case definitely insufficient.

It follows that when yields vary considerably, as in the example in Table 21.1, the number of observations on 1 m² should not only be less than 93, but much larger.

Let us suppose now that from two fields on one farm the average yields obtained were $\bar{x}' = 218\cdot3$ g and $\bar{x}'' = 229\cdot8$ g.

The standard error of the arithmetic mean is:

$$\sigma'_{\bar{x}} = 1\cdot22 \text{ g} \quad \text{and} \quad \sigma''_{\bar{x}} = 1\cdot61 \text{ g}.$$

The question is: is the difference between $\bar{x}'$ and $\bar{x}''$ significant, or could it be due to random factors?

Assuming that in both cases the size of the sample was the same we can calculate the standard error of the difference by the formula

$$\sigma_{\bar{x}'-\bar{x}''} = \sqrt{\sigma^2_{\bar{x}'} + \sigma^2_{\bar{x}''}} = \sqrt{1\cdot39 + 2\cdot59} = \sqrt{4\cdot08} = 2\cdot02 \text{ g}.$$

The actual difference was 11·5 g which is 5·7 times as great as the standard error. It is most unlikely that such a big difference could be due to random factors. It is another matter that the statement of this fact does not entitle us to any conclusions concerning the cause of this large difference. The soil in one field may have been more fertile, the method of cultivation better or there may have been some other difference. To the question which variety of seed was more fertile no valid answer is obtained from this experiment. Yet the sample was sufficient to establish the existence of a significant difference in the yields from the two fields.

Let us now imagine the distribution on page 586.

This distribution, like the one in Table 21.1, has three maxima.[218] But its range of variation is even larger: from about 70 to 370 g per m². The standard deviation is 53·6 g, and therefore, even though the sample is relatively large, an estimate of the arithmetic mean would be fairly inaccurate. However, we shall now consider a different problem.

---

[217] It is better to take the standard deviation obtained from the larger sample since it is more accurately estimated than in the small sample, and it refers to the same general population.

[218] These maxima would be more distinct of smaller class intervals were used.

TABLE 21.2. YIELDS IN GRAMMES PER SQUARE METRE (B)

| Yield (g) (x) | Number of observations (f) | Yield (g) (x) | Number of observations (f) |
|---|---|---|---|
| 60–79 | 1 | 220–239 | 36 |
| 80–99 | — | 240–259 | 29 |
| 100–119 | 5 | 260–279 | 36 |
| 120–139 | 5 | 280–299 | 41 |
| 140–159 | 17 | 300–319 | 13 |
| 160–179 | 14 | 320–339 | 2 |
| 180–199 | 13 | 340–359 | 2 |
| 200–219 | 31 | 360–379 | 2 |
| | | Total | 247 |

In discussing Farm A (Table 21.1 p. 584) we pointed out the large differences in yields from different observations of 1 m². The range is even greater in Table 21.2 (the highest yields per square metre are more than five times as great as the lowest). So large a range of yields per unit of area—in both cases three maxima when the two fields are not very big (A is 14 hectares and B less than 50 hectares)—indicates the existence of some special conditions. Normally yields from one field properly cultivated and sown with one variety of grain should be fairly uniform, not less so than in the example in Table 21.1. The causes of large dispersion may be manifold and can be discovered after further investigation.

## 4. EXAMPLES OF OTHER APPLICATIONS OF SAMPLING

### a. Social Surveys

Social surveys are studies of social relations based on partial research by sociologists.

To this category belong some studies of relations in rural areas undertaken in Russia in the last quarter of the nineteenth century. Social surveys were made in England in several medium-sized towns in 1911–13. They dealt the living conditions of the workers and were conducted on the initiative of the statistician A. L. Bowley. Every twentieth household was chosen by systematic sampling and investigators were sent to them. They were allowed to substitute a neighbouring house only if the one selected for the sample was unoccupied. Substitution for other reasons was not allowed. Sampling by households could give good results in this case because the houses were usually one-family homes. (The average number of persons per household fluctuated from town to town between 4·6 and 6). In cities where large apartment houses predominate this method of sampling could be dangerous.

In 1928 the London School of Economics and Political Sciences started a detailed study *The New Survey of London Life and Labour*. Its results were published in nine volumes in 1931–35. The study was a sequence to the study on *Life and Labour of the People of London*, undertaken by Carl Booth in 1866, and published in eighteen volumes in 1889. Booth's study was not based on sampling. In later studies sampling by households was used (one house out of fifty in large districts, and one out of twenty in small districts). The first house in each district was selected by drawing and the others by systematic selection. Substitutions (except when the house was uninhabited) were not allowed. In both the eastern and western parts of London most houses were small.

In Poland social surveys based on sampling were made in 1935 by the Institute of Social Affairs. The study covered four districts of Warsaw.[219] Of course, sampling by houses could not be conducted in Warsaw, and therefore census district records of 1931 were used. By systematic sampling several precincts were drawn from each district, and the first tweenty households were chosen in each precinct. Flats with more than two rooms and kitchen were excluded on the premise that they were occupied by wealthier families than were the subject of the study. Finally 387 flats were chosen but from 57 of them (about 15 per cent) no information could be obtained. The emphasis was laid on the impact of unemployment on housing conditions.

This study is subject to some reservations from the point of view of sample design. Nevertheless, these examples show that sampling can be used in social surveys. Proper sampling methods may prevent the bias involved in other methods of selecting objects of study.

### b. Studies of the Order of Birth

In 1950 the Central Statistical Office in Poland made a sampling study of the order of birth (whether one particular child is the first, second, third, etc.). The relevant question was introduced in statistical birth registration forms in 1950. Since the order of birth is very important from the point of view of fertility studies, a full analysis was made of the results for the first quarter of 1950. The second quarter was analysed by the sampling method. The results for both the first and the second quarter were published by the Central Statistical Office in *Studia i Prace Statystyczne* (*Statistical Papers and Essays*), together with an evaluation by mathematical methods.[220]

---

[219] The results were published in *Bezrobocie i stopa życiowa ludności dzielnic robotniczych Warszawy* (*Unemployment and the Standard of Living in the Workers' Districts in Warsaw*) by Ludwik Landau, Warsaw, 1936, pp. 135–71.

[220] R. Zasępa: Reprezentacyjne opracowanie urodzeń zarejestrowanych w II kwartale 1950 r. według kolejności urodzenia dziecka i matki (A Sample Survey of Births Registered in the Second Quarter of 1950 in the Order of Birth), *Studia i Prace Statystyczne* (*Statistical Papers and Essays*), 1951, No. 2–3, pp. 68–75.

From the point of view of sample design the study does not contribute anything new to the methods discussed above: every tenth birth was selected systematically, and the first was drawn at random. But some of the results are worth noting. The accuracy of the results for the whole country can be regarded as quite satisfactory: the standard error of the quantity measured[221] is not large, the largest being 2·36 per cent.

In particular provinces some standard errors are very high, sometimes exceeding 20 per cent of the measured quantity. Therefore no valid comparison can be made of the differences between individual provinces.

### c. Rhythm in Numbers

We shall now consider an example from a different field. Kazimierz Wóycicki, a specialist in rhythm structure in prose and poetry, published a study entitled *Rytm w liczbach (Rhythm in Numbers)*.[222] The study is based on statistical methods. Wóycicki selected a certain number of syllables or verses from different works, and analysed the features that lead themselves to numerical analysis (e.g. the frequency of one-syllable words, two syllable words, the accents in prose, and so on).

From the point of view of statistical methods the study is subject to many reservations. The choice of excerpts is not random. Wóycicki states that several thousand syllables constitute a sufficient basis for drawing conclusions with a high degree of probability. The statement may be true but it has not been proved statistically. No attempt has been made to check whether the differences between various works are random. Some averages are calculated in completely unacceptable way (e.g. in Table XI in some columns five out of six panels are empty).

However, even if we disregard statistical errors, the basic questions is whether the use of time-consuming and elaborate statistical methods in this case contributes to a greater knowledge of the subject. It may. Numerical answers substantiate subjective impressions. But the answer to this question can only be given by combined efforts of a skilled statistician and a specialist in the subject.

### d. The Height and Weight of University Student

This example will show that conclusions from sample surveys should be drawn with great caution, since sometimes a bias may occur in the selection where we would least expect it.

---

[221] The quantity measured in this case is the percentage of the first born, second born, etc., in relation to the total number of children. In calculating the standard error the fifth and later born were combined into one group. Were this group divided into smaller classes the standard errors would have been much greater since the frequency of the fifth born, sixth born etc., declines rapidly.

[222] K. Wójcicki: *Rytm w liczbach (Rhythm in Numbers)*, Wilno, 1938, pp. 59 and Table XXVIII.

In 1946 a study was made of the height and weight of university students in Warsaw.[223] In some respects the results were somewhat puzzling.

With regard to those who enrolled at Warsaw institutions of higher learning in 1946 the study can be considered as exhaustive. Although some students were not measured, their number was small. In this case a probability analysis would be superfluous. However, if the conclusions from this study were to be applied to all young people, they would have to be regarded as obtained from a sample of 6635 persons of both sexes. We shall show that this sample is not representative enough.

The most striking are the following two conclusions of the study: (1) the average height of the individuals measured was unexpectedly great, greater than that obtained in any pre-war study of this type; (2) the height of the individuals commencing their studies, at age 18–19, was greater than in other age groups; this applies to both men and women. The numerical results were as follows:

TABLE 21.4. HEIGHT OF YOUNG PEOPLE ACCORDING TO THE STUDY IN 1946

| Sex | Age (years) | | | |
| --- | --- | --- | --- | --- |
| | 18–19 | 20–24 | 25–29 | 30–39 |
| Men | 173·4 | 173·0 | 172·0 | 170·9 |
| Women | 161·0 | 160·5 | 160·1 | 158·6 |

Only the difference between those commencing studies at the age of 18–19, and those aged 20–24 are so small that they can be attributed to random factors. Persons commencing their studies when over 25, and even more when over 30, are distinctly shorter than those aged 18–19.

The average height of Polish men before the war was 166·3 cm. This average can be regarded as correct since it is based on the height of the draftees (over one million persons). The study made in 1946 was less precise (those measured had shoes on), but this cannot possibly explain the 7 cm increase in height. Similar conclusions can be drawn from comparisons of the heights of women.

The pre-war data indicate the prevalence of one phenomenon very strong social selection. For instance, in Warsaw the height of boys aged 17–18 was 159·6 cm in primary schools,[224] and 169·9 cm in secondary schools, i.e. 10·3 cm more. The difference among the girls was a little smaller, but also quite substantial: 151·9 cm in primary schools and 158 cm in secondary schools, i.e. 6 cm more. Obviously social selection in schools in Poland before the war was quite strong: the majority of students in higher grades in secondary schools were from well-to-do families.

---

[223] Stefan Szulc: Wzrost i waga młodzieży szkół wyższych w Warszawie w 1946 (The Height and Weight of University Students in Warsaw in 1946), *Przegląd Statystyczny (Statistical Survey)*, 1949.

[224] The age 17–18 years in primary school indicates that the boy was considerably delayed in his studies.

There is no doubt that such a social selection could also be felt in 1946 with respect to university enrolment. University entrants at the normal enrolment age of 18–19 years were those who attended secondary school partly before the war or during the German occupation, and who same from relatively wealthy families. Those who could begin their university education at a later age usually lived in less favourable circumstances while attending secondary school because they came from under-privileged classes in the old system.

If we assume that height depends in part on the conditions under which children grow up, then social selection would explain both the relatively high percentage of those beginning their studies early and a decrease in height with an increase in age.

However the significance of this example, is much wider. The anthropologist studying the relationship between the height of weight and the age of the child has two alternatives open to him: either to select a group of children and measure and weigh them at certain intervals (e.g. once or twice a year), or to measure and weigh simultaneously a large number of children at different ages and calculate the annual increases on the basis of the differences obtained. The first method is more correct but rarely used because of the technical difficulties involved. When the second method is used there is a danger that in capitalist countries different populations will be compared: in higher grades some students drop out, usually those who are poor. This sort of bias may effect the results.

### e. Anthropological Studies for the Clothing Industry

At the request of the Polish Standards Committee mathematical statisticians from Warsaw and Wrocław worked out a method of analysing the size and shape of the human body for the use of the clothing industry. The knowledge of typical measurements is obviously a great help in streamlining production and avoiding the production of unsaleable stocks or shortages in odd sizes.

The study, must be extensive of its very nature. At the first stage 30,000 persons were to be measured to arrive at standard norms. At the second stage the study was to include 300,000 persons to establish differences between different parts of the country.

## 5. STATISTICAL QUALITY CONTROL IN MASS PRODUCTION

Statistical quality control of production is very important from an economic point of view. The object is to prevent the sale of substandard products not suitable for use or having only a limited use.

A certainty that a given batch of products meets all the requirements can be achieved only by a full and exhaustive control in which each object is checked. "Statistical" control means that only some of the products from a given batch are checked, or in other words, that the sampling method is used in which mistakes may occur with respect to a certain number of products.

In some cases full control is possible and necessary. Every locomotive must be checked to make sure that it meets the technical requirements. This also applies to all basic parts on which the functioning of the engine depends.

However, such full control is not always possible: it is sometimes also uneconomical. We cannot have full control if checking the object destroys it. Electric bulbs can be easily checked to find out if they give light. But if we were to check whether the bulb lasts the number of hours specified by standard technical norms, this would destroy the bulb and it would obviously be nonsense to impose this sort of control.

An example of a feasible but uneconomical full control was given by J. Oderfeld with reference to a newspaper printing.[225] Obviously, it is possible to check all copies in order to reject the faulty ones, but the total cost of such a control would be very high. If we know that the printing machine functions properly it is better to sell the whole edition and exchange the faulty copies.

The same example will show how technical considerations may prevent full control. With respect to a daily newspaper it is imperative to make a check with the minimum of delay. Full control would require a large staff and would result in a considerable delay. Moreover, the constant repetition of the task would result in blunting the awareness of those who make the check. Thus they would also pass faulty copies and the check would no longer be complete.

The obvious practical solution is to institute "statistical" control comprising only a certain number of copies. To make sure that the machine functions properly we have to check it at regular intervals. Experience will show whether it should be done once or twice daily, or at some other interval. But it is obviously necessary to check the first few copies when the printing starts in order to eliminate the risk of wasting the whole edition.

In statistical quality control we have to determine what percentage of "rejects" is permissible and on this basis we can determine the control design. In accordance with the calculus of probability we can say that the predetermined percentage will be exceeded only in a limited number of cases (e.g. in one case out of twenty if we choose the confidence coefficient of $0 \cdot 95$) and that only in exceptional cases will this percentage be substantially exceeded.

Generally we can say that if full control is at all possible then we should use statistical control when the loss caused by the sale of a small number of sub-standard products is small in comparison with the cost of full control. The cost of full control is high if either the cost of checking each product is high or if the number of products is high. Full control, if it does not destroy the product, is

---

[225] J. Oderfeld: *Statystyczna kontrola jakości (Statistical Control of Quality)*, 1949, p. 4.

always advisable if there are few units produced, and the defects can easily be discovered (e.g. furniture). Full control is necessary if the sale of faulty products endangers the life or the health of the consumer.

Statistical control can take place at different stages of production, or when the product is finished. It may be carried out by the producer or the purchaser and the latter may want to make a control of his own even when he knows that the product has already been checked by the producer. Very often control is carried out at certain stages of production (control of the raw material, of the parts to be used) regardless of whether the material used was produced in the same factory or obtained from outside suppliers.

The economic importance of statistical control cannot be over-emphasized and it is an indispensable tool in obtaining better quality. Besides, it is usually inexpensive and easy to apply.

We shall describe statistical quality control, using a simple example in which the product can easily be divided into pieces, and the object of control is to determine whether a given piece is good or not. Let us note that a "piece" is not necessarily a separate object, e.g. a match, but it may be a collection of objects in a single package, e.g. a box of matches. Complicated methods will be described where the product cannot be divided into pieces (e.g. clay, coal), or where the purpose of control is not simply to establish whether the product is good or not, but to determine to what extent it deviates from the norm.

The problem of determining whether the product is "good" or "bad" belongs in the field of technology. Sometimes it is obvious: a box of matches is bad if it has no surface against which to strike a match; it is also bad if the box has fewer matches than it should. A steel wire is bad if its strength is below standard: it is also bad if its strength is much greater than required, because then there is obvious waste. We can check one or several characteristics, but they must be clearly defined, and the method of checking must be determined.

From the statistical point of view the object is to select from a given batch a sample of an appropriate size, and by checking the units in the sample to decide whether the batch should be accepted or rejected. This should be accomplished by the statistical methods used in sampling. But the functions involved in control will be performed by workers who have no statistical training, and therefore the whole procedure must be clearly and simply described.

The procedure is usually expressed in norms set by committees of standards. In Poland the norms are set by the Polish Standard Committee. The rules deal primarily with the method of taking a sample. The choice, of course, must be random. Sometimes multi-stage sampling is required.

If a batch of goods has been produced under varying conditions (e.g. from different raw materials, with different machines) it should be divided into subgroups and each of them should be checked separately.

Control should begin with determining how many substandard products may be tolerated in the batch. This should be decided by the management. The rest of the procedure follows from the tables of norms. Thus we read off from the table that with a given percentage of acceptable faulty products the sample size should be, say, 400 pieces. From the same table we can read off that under the given conditions the batch can be considered acceptable when the number of faulty pieces in the sample does not exceed four. The task of the sorter will then be: (1) to draw 400 pieces properly; (2) to check each piece; and (3) to reject the batch if the number of faulty pieces is more than four. This decision may sometimes be reached before all 400 pieces have been checked.

We shall not here go into the details of the table design or their mathematical derivation. It should be noted, however, that in Polish norms the number of faulty pieces that results in rejecting the batch is set with the confidence coefficient of 0·95. This means that in one case out of twenty the decision may be wrong: we accept a batch which does not meet the requirements or reject a batch which does meet the requirements. This kind of uncertainty is inevitable in all decissions based on sampling.

To determine whether the confidence coefficient is sufficiently large requires other calculations.

It follows that in every large organization there should be a group of people familiar with the technological process, technical rules, and sampling methods: their task is to conduct quality control.

If a batch of products has been rejected different courses of action are open. Sometimes all pieces may be sorted and the faulty ones removed; or the purchaser may accept the batch at a lower price; or the substandard product may be used for other purposes.

More important is another consequence of statistical quality control: it should result not only in intercepting faulty products but also in removing the causes of faults in production. That is why it is important to have quality control, not only after the completion of the production process but also during the process. This helps in locating the sources of error and saves money by giving a chance to correct the process before the product is finished.

A very important problem is the sample design. Difficulties arise particularly when the product is not in packages or in easily distinguishable units, but in bulk. The task is easier when the product can be regarded as relatively homogeneous (e.g. fluids). If it is not, special care must be taken to design the sample so that different parts of the product can be checked. Sometimes automatic control devices help in overcoming this difficulty.

Particular care should be taken in conducting quality control according to norms established long ago. They may be correct from the point of view of production technique but may be wrong from the point of view of statistics. Here again the co-operation between the production expert and the statistician is essential.

The application of statistics to quality control is not the only instance when statistics helps in production. There is no doubt that there are many possibilities of using statistical methods for improving production and eliminating waste in the national economy.

# CHAPTER 22

# PARTIAL STUDIES BASED PARTIALLY OR NOT AT ALL ON SAMPLING METHODS

## 1. EXAMPLES OF RESEARCH

We shall now discuss cases in which partial research is either an incorrect form of a pseudo-sampling survey, or should not be called sampling at all.

### a. Postal Statistics

Pseudo-sampling studies are frequently resorted to by post offices.

Not all mail deliveries are counted directly. Some forms of deliveries are estimated by a method somewhat resembling sampling. In Poland before the last war the deliveries of ordinary (non-registered) mail were estimated on the basis of exact statistics for one week a year. The letters were counted from noon on the second to noon on the third Monday of September. To obtain the annual figure the total for this week was multiplied by 52. All the periodicals were counted in April and the total was multiplied by 12. Telephone calls were counted on the third Wednesday of each month and the result multiplied by the number of days in the month was regarded as the monthly total. The remaining data in postal statistics were based on actual figures. Before 1937 some other data were also obtained by similar estimates.[226] This method of keeping the statistics on ordinary mail was in accordance with the rules of the International Postal Convention. According to this convention ordinary mail was to be counted at least for a week during a period in which the turnover is close to the average during the year.

In addition to these annual data, certain cities published in *Wiadomości Staty-styczne (Statistical News)* monthly data for ordinary mail on the basis of a sample. At first these data were considered as independent of the calculation of the annual data, so that the total for the months did not agree with the total for the year. Later the annual figure was taken as the sum of the monthly estimates.

This method of selection is subject to serious reservations. The choice of a specific week in September for letters, the month of April for periodicals, or the third

---

[226] See: Statystyka pocztowa, telefoniczna i telegraficzna 1937. (Mail, Telephone and Telegraph Statistics for 1937). *Statystyka Polski (Statistics of Poland)*, Series C, No. 90, Warsaw 1938, Foreword, pp. V–VI.

Wednesday of each month for telephone calls, is actually based on the assumption that these are the periods when the mail turnover or the frequency of telephone calls are closest to the average. However, such assumptions are unreliable. It should also be considered that mail turnover or telephone calls are subject to random fluctuations, and these may cause the intensity of the phenomena we wish to estimate to be exceptionally high or exceptionally low in the period selected. Therefore this method is not only unreliable for estimating the annual data, but is also useless for recording changes from year to year. Only very considerable changes will be reflected by this very imperfect method.

Since the war postal statistics have been considerably improved. The counting of unregistered mail is done much more frequently. In small post-offices the mail is counted for two weeks in every month; in medium-sized ones it is counted for one week every month (on different dates) and in large offices it is counted for four days in every month (each day in a different week). In the biggest post offices the weighing of the mail (letters and post-cards separately) is allowed and the average weight for a post card is assumed to be $2 \cdot 73$ g and for a letter $7 \cdot 54$ g. It follows that the number of days in which the mail is to be counted depends upon the turnover in the post-office. For the smallest offices it is 168 days in a year, in medium-sized ones 84, and in large ones 48 days. This reduction in the relative size of the sample as the turnover increases is statistically justified.

Some rules of the new system are also subject to reservations. For one thing the mail is not counted at all in the first days of the month, and we cannot be certain that at that time the intensity of turnover does not differ much from the average. Apart from this detail, however, the new system of estimating the mail turnover should give very good results. It may even constitute an excessive burden, and a different sample design may produce sufficiently accurate results with a smaller sample.

## b. Family Budget Studies

It seems almost impossible to find a method of applying sampling to family budget studies. The purpose of a family budget study is to determine the level and structure of family income and expenditures. The results are used to determine the standard of living of workers and working intellectuals; they also constitute a basis for calculating the cost-of-living index.

Attempts to use sampling for this purpose have been made in capitalist countries, but they have not produced satisfactory results. The problem is that good results can be obtained only if detailed records of daily expenditure are kept over a long period of time, such as a year. This is necessary both because of the seasonal nature of certain types of expenditures and because some expenditures are made at quite long intervals (e.g. clothes, furniture, etc.).

Extensive studies were conducted in England in 1937–38. By systematic drawing, about 31,000 families of manual and white-collar workers in the lowest income groups were selected from the records of those insured against unemployment, and from other records; of these about 9000 families were rejected after personal interviews as not suitable for the study. From the remaining 22,000, less than 13,000 (i.e. less than 60 per cent of those who qualified) submitted completed book-keeping records. Considering the nature of the study, this is undoubtedly a very large number, but the lack of answers from more than 40 per cent of the families undermines the representativeness of the sample, because there is little doubt that the families that did not reply differed from those that did. Nevertheless the results could be very valuable if the whole investigation were not rendered useless by further procedure. A great deal of attention was paid to detail as far as different types of expenditure were concerned, but there was no breakdown of families according to expenditure per person. This was a basic error and it led to fictitious and meaningless averages. The results were further distorted because the level of expenditure in the families that did not answer was probably different from the level in those that did. The lumping together of the families of manual and white-collar workers should also be considered an error; the only distinction made was between those working in industry, commerce, etc, and those working in agriculture.

From this point of view a much better study was that made in Poland in 1927, even though quantitatively its scope was much more limited (only several dozen families were included from particular centres). We shall give as an example some data for the City of Warsaw. Only fourty families were included in the survey and yet the results were significant and conclusive.[227]

In Table 22.1 a very close relationship can be seen between the level and the structure of expenditure. This is not surprising as it has been known for a long time that such a relationship exists (Engel's Law). As income increases the percentage of expenditure for food decreases, and the share of other expenditure increases. What is surprising, though, is the consistency of this law despite the small number of families studied (in most groups only 7–9 and in one group 16 families). The drops in the items "bread" and "potatoes" (smaller amounts consumed in Group IV in comparison with Groups I–III, in which the consumption increases with expenditures) only seem to deny this consistency: lower income groups are evidently underfed and as the level of expenditure increases the deficiencies are made up by increasing the consumption of the cheapest food-stuffs, such as bread and potatoes. The relatively better-off families in Group IV can afford to substitute more expensive food for bread and potatoes. Whether the change in the item "rent" (an increase in the percentage of expenditures for rent in Group IV) is random caused by the small number of observations, it is hard to judge on the

---

[227] The results were published in the *Concise Statistical Yearbook*, 1939, pp. 281 and 283.

basis of the material available; it may be because wealthier families could afford to have better and more expensive homes.

Apart from the data for the above four groups, the Central Statistical office also published the structure of the "typical" budget which was determined by estimating from other sources the average expenditures of a family of four in Warsaw, taking into account the level of earning of all workers in Warsaw. According to these calculations the average was 2104 zlotys a year, which is well

TABLE 22.1. WORKERS' FAMILY BUDGETS IN WARSAW IN 1927

| Particulars | Groups according to annual expenditures per consuming unit | | | |
|---|---|---|---|---|
| | I<br>up to 599<br>zlotys | II<br>600–899<br>zlotys | III<br>900–1199<br>zlotys | IV<br>1200 zlotys<br>and over |
| Number of families studied | 9 | 16 | 7 | 8 |
| *Expenditures in zlotys* | | | | |
| Annual total per family of four[a] | 1566 | 2366 | 3081 | 4854 |
| *Selected expenditures in percentages* | | | | |
| Total | 100·0 | 100·0 | 100·0 | 100·0 |
| Food | 68·6 | 64·6 | 60·3 | 50·1 |
| Liquor and tobacco | 1·7 | 2·8 | 2·5 | 3·7 |
| Rent | 7·8 | 5·6 | 4·6 | 5·6 |
| Household equipment | 1·1 | 2·0 | 2·5 | 4·4 |
| Medical | 1·2 | 1·3 | 1·8 | 2·4 |
| Clothing | 9·3 | 11·2 | 12·6 | 13·4 |
| Cultural and educational | 1·7 | 3·5 | 5·8 | 7·2 |
| *Average annual consumption of selected products per consuming unit* | | | | |
| Bread kilogrammes | 147·5 | 160·2 | 168·8 | 130·0 |
| Potatoes kilogrammes | 181·5 | 201·5 | 219·0 | 176·0 |
| Other vegetables kilogrammes | 42·6 | 49·2 | 71·4 | 106·3 |
| Milk litres | 38·6 | 85·1 | 121·5 | 141·7 |
| Eggs pieces | 14·9 | 50·9 | 74·4 | 182·0 |
| Butter kilogrammes | 1·4 | 2·2 | 3·2 | 5·1 |
| Meat, fish kilogrammes | 22·8 | 36·9 | 44·0 | 65·1 |
| *Calories* | | | | |
| Total | 2099 | 2607 | 2992 | 3146 |
| of vegetable products | 1760 | 2051 | 2201 | 2127 |
| of meat products | 339 | 556 | 791 | 1019 |

[a] Conventional family: head of the family—1 consuming unit, wife—0·85 consuming units, child aged 14–17–0·80 consuming units, child aged 3–7–0·50 consuming units; total—3·15 consuming units. Families studied were converted into conventional families according to the above figures.

below the level of Group II. With this average an estimate of the percentages of expenditure for different needs was made by interpolation; the average consumption of selected commodities and the caloric value consumed by a typical family were also calculated.

The general average does not tell much. More important information is provided by each of the four income groups. But at least the general average is not misleading, and if reflects correctly the average level and the structure of the worker's family budget in Warsaw in 1927. This average may be useful if in addition to it we also have data on budgets by groups of expenditure. It can also be used to find the budget structure for calculating the cost-of-living index or for making international comparisions.

Another important reservation should also be made. The family budget studies relate to the families of employed workers, and leave out the unemployed. Since the latter should not be left out of the picture altogether the Central Statistical Office made a special study in 1932 of the budgets of unemployed workers.

The average annual expenditure of a typical family deviates considerably from the average for all the families studied, which is 2809 zlotys, i.e. 33·5 per cent above the typical budget and not much less than for Group III.

The lack of a division into expenditure groups in English family budget statistics deprives them almost entirely of any practical value. Even though the random error in calculating the average level and the structure of the family budget in the English survey is undoubtedly smaller than in the much more limited Polish study, the average in the former is distorted by the lack of answers from over 40 per cent of those queried. Moreover, the average relate to a rather vaguely defined family, since it includes both manual and white-collar workers. No attempt was made to study the social conditions of the family as related to the level of expenditure.

From the statistical point of view it should be emphasized that partial research which is basically not a sampling survey, as we could see in the example of the Polish survey described above, may, under certain conditions, enable us to calculate correct averages for the whole population. It is possible to calculate the average correctly if: (1) the material is divided into groups and an analysis of each group is made separately; (2) one or more characteristics are correlated with all the others; and (3) the data concerning the frequencies of these characteristics are available not only for the selected part of the population, but for the whole population. In our example such a characteristic was the general level of expenditures per consuming unit, and it thus was possible to calculate the typical budget as the average for all workers in Warsaw. It should be remembered, however, that more important than the calculation of the average is a correct picture of properly formed, homogeneous classes and the frequencies of their appearance.

Against the background of family budget studies in capitalist countries similar studies in the Soviet Union appear to be definitely superior. They are conducted on a large scale and are considered an essential part of national statistics.

Separate studies are made of the budgets of the members of collective farms (*kolhoz*), of workers and of clerical personnel. In all of them, in addition to general information about the family, all incomes (in money and in kind) and expenditure are taken into account. They also give the amounts and the prices of particular goods and services, as well as the sources from which they are purchased (socialized trade, *kolhoz* markets, etc.).

To obtain a correct representation of the population, both the groups of employing establishments and the groups of families are taken into account in proportion to their frequencies.

Cooperative farms are divided according to their specialization and the size of income to be distributed among the members. Industrial establishments are classified by industries, size and average wage; the families of manual and white-collar workers are divided according to qualifications and income.

After this classification the representativeness of the sample is checked against general statistics (e.g. the data on the average earnings of manual and white-collar workers, which should agree with the average earnings of the individuals selected for the sample).[228]

In spite of certain reservations about the sample design from the point of view of theory, the results obtained probably give the most that can be expected, both with regard to the representativeness of the selected families, and to the scope of the study.[229]

### c. Studies of Peasant Farms

Somewhat similar to the problems encountered in family budget studies are those that arise in analysing peasant farms in Poland. These studies are now conducted by the Institute of Agricultural Economics, and before the war by the Section on the Economy of Small Farms of the State Institute for Studies of Rural Economy.

Before the war attempts were made to study "dwarf" farms by sampling. Three special belts from west to east were formed in the south of Poland and "dwarf" farms located along those belts at 5 km intervals were investigated. Altogether 100 farms were studied, 33 or 34 on each belt.[230]

One may question whether the method of sampling was the best, whether the number of farms chosen was sufficient but it was certainly representative in the exact meaning of this term. In any case, expanding the scope of the study to

---

[228] Based on: *Course ekonomitchyeskoy statistiki*, Moscow, 1952, pp. 478–482. See also S. Postnikov: O metodach otbora syemycy robotchyh, slouzyashtchyh i kolkhoznikow dlya obslyedovanya ikh budgyeta. *Viestnik Statistiki*, 1953, No. 3, pp. 14–25.

[229] Since 1957 similar methods were used for studies of family budgets of industrial workers in Poland.

[230] W. Krzysztofik: *Gospodarstwa karłowate w świetle ankiety losowej. (A Questionnaire Survey of Dwarf Farms)*, Warsaw, 1939.

include the whole country would involve stratified sampling and would be very expensive, especially if all categories of peasant farms were to be included.

In studies of peasant farms based on book-keeping records, the method of random sampling cannot be used. They would require very detailed records for each farm studied over the period of one year. The records would have to show all income and expenditures both in cash and in kind, including the consumption of the farm's own produce. A very detailed description of the farm would also be required. It is obvious that such studies can be conducted only on a few farms and their selection cannot be made by random sampling. For this reason the number of farms selected for study must be small; before the war several hundred farms were included in a survey and after the war the Institute of Agricultural Economics published the data based on 1200 farms.[231] Their number is steadily increasing, and now considerably exceeds this figure.

Before the war farms with an area of more than 50 hectares were excluded from surveys. Attention was focused on farms with an area of from 3 to 30 hectares, divided into 4 groups (3–5, 5–10, 10–15, and 15–30 hectares). At present, particular groups of farms are represented according to their actual number in a given district. This does not make the sample fully representative for the reasons mentioned on p. 557 and also because "the farms which keep accounting records are, as a rule, wealthier than the average in a given group".

In 1932 the Institute of Social Economics embarked upon the study of agrarian relations in Poland, with emphasis on the surplus of manpower in rural areas. After long studies and preparations a detailed questionnaire survey was made in the winter of 1934–35. The selection of villages for the survey was based on the following procedure: (1) 46 counties were selected which could be considered as typical of different agricultural districts; (2) from each county one or several villages were chosen as typical for the county: the total number of villages was 53.[232]

This is a typical example of conscious selection coloured by a certain amount of arbitrariness in choosing "typical" counties and villages which could be done only by persons familiar with the area. The value of the study was increased by stratification (districts), and by the fact that no farm was omitted in the selected villages so that a curb was put on the natural tendency of the research worker to select better farms.

The general impression is that the study was fairly representative. Its importance consists in bringing to light certain facts characteristic of the relations in villages before the war.

---

[231] *Wieś w liczbach* (*Rural Statistics*), 1952, 2nd ed. p. 35.

[232] Quoted from *Struktura społeczna wsi polskiej* (*The Social Structure of Polish Rural Areas*) Instytut Gospodarstwa Społecznego (Institute of Social Economy), Warsaw 1937, pp. 6–7.

## d. **Fertility Studies**

The fertility studies in Poland conducted by the Polish Institute of Population Studies since 1931 make no attempt to design a sample representative of the whole country. Studies were based on information on to particular social groups. Such information usually characterized the socio-economic relations of the family and provided the date of birth of the husband, wife and children, the date of marriage and the dates of death of the deceased children. The choice of a social group to be studied was often random, and usually depended upon the chance that a man or an institution was willing to use its connexions and undertake the investigation in the field. Efforts were made, of course, to select clearly defined socio-economic groups: certain types of workers, clerical staff, rural areas.

Thus the study was based more or less on the principle of squeezing out of it as much as possible. In spite of this the results were quite good. The conclusions can be summarized as follows: (1) There were considerable differences in fertility among different socio-economic groups. (2) Substantial differences in fertility also existed among identical socio-economic groups in different geographical locations; this indicates that fertility also depends on general conditions in a given area. (3) Almost without exception fertility declined in each socio-economic group with the passage of time.[233] (4) As the age of married women increased their fertility decreased, which was obvious; but a new discovery was that the decline in fertility was not so much due to the aging of women (of course it was to some extent) as to the "aging" of marriages; in new marriages fertility is high even when the woman is not young—say up to the age of 30–35 years, and in older marriages fertility is almost always low even when the woman has not passed the age of 30–35.

Thus, on the basis of this study important conclusions were reached, although it was impossible to arrive at the averages for the whole country.[234]

## 2. CONCLUSIONS

There are different types of statistical research:

(a) *Full studies comprising the whole population.* This is not the place to discuss them.

(b) *Sample surveys in the strict sense.* A general outline together with examples of the application of type b studies, has been given above. This should suffice to give the reader some idea of their potential scope and advantages. In comparison

---

[233] The chosen method of analysis permitted the tracing of the changes in fertility in the families studied back to the time of marriage.

[234] The study had not been finished before the outbreak of war and no summary of the results could be published. The method of analysis was described in the publication: *Badania nad rozrodczością w Polsce (Studies on Fertility in Poland)*, reprinted from *Kwartalnik Statystyczny (Statist. Quart.)* No. 1, 1933.

with a full study these advantages consist in (1) lower cost, (2) quicker results, and (3) information on details which often would not be feasible in a full study.

The results obtained by sampling are, of course, less accurate since they are always subject to random errors. In spite of the existence of random errors, sampling can sometimes produce better results than an exhaustive study. In a full study conducted on a large scale certain errors in describing the unit are unavoidable, and their magnitude cannot usually be determined. In a sample survey the number of units is smaller and therefore it is easier to obtain an accurate description of the units investigated and the size of the random error can always be determined numerically.

Let us now summarize the requirements that have to be satisfied for the sample survey to produce good results. First of all, the research worker has to know the subject of the study. He also must have considerable experience and good statistical intuition. We have pointed out many pitfalls into which an inexperienced statistician may fall. Third, the research worker should know at least the rudiments of mathematical statistics. Sometimes the knowledge of mathematical statistics must be considerable, and it may often be necessary to obtain the help of a skilled mathematical statistician.

(c) *Incomplete studies*. To this category belong studies which were originally designed as full studies, but which for some reason or other have not included all the units of a given population.

If the number of units left out is small, we can often simply ignore them and use the units studied for determining the structure of the population and the averages. If the number of units left out is considerable then two alternatives are possible:

(1) The units left out do not differ much from the units studied: then the total population is defined as the sum of the frequencies of the units studied and left out, and the structure, the averages and the other characteristics of the whole population are determined on the basis of the units studied.

(2) The units left out differ from the units studied: then we cannot draw conclusions about the whole population on the basis of the units studied.

The second alternative should be considered the general rule, and the first alternative an exception: almost always the units left out differ from the units studied.

If the number of units left out is not large it may be possible to determine the margin of error which will be committed when the omissions are ignored. Assuming that the units omitted differ greatly in one direction from the units studied, and knowing the percentage of the units left out we can find out how these omissions would affect the whole population. Sometimes it may be possible to determine in this way not only the margin of error, but also its direction.

What has been said above about incomplete studies originally designed as full studies can be applied to sampling surveys in which it was not possible to study all the units selected at random.

(d) *Incomplete studies based on conscious choice.* Such studies are always risky if the object is to characterize the whole population, because the choice is bound to be subjective and may be based more on impressions than on facts. There are cases, however, when random sampling is impossible, and we have to resort to conscious selection. In such cases the accuracy of the results may be considerably increased if we first divide the population into relatively homogeneous strata.

Only in a very few cases can conscious choice produce more accurate results than random sampling. Let us take the following paradox as an example. Suppose that the object is to calculate the average length of the right arm of those attending a meeting. Sampling would not give good results here because of the small number of people. But if we happen to know the length of the left arm of every person present at the meeting we can obtain a very accurate result if we measure the right arm of those whose left arm has a length close to the average.

(e) *Pseudo-random choice.* Choice is pseudo-random when units are selected either by a faulty method of drawing or by a correct method but with two few units, or by a "hit and miss" rather than by a random method. There are many varieties of pseudo-random choice and it would be impossible to list them all or even to arrange them in a systematic order. Sometimes the results may be fairly good if the author had a good knowledge of the problem studied and was lucky. But in most cases the value of such studies is small and they often are misleading if the wrong conclusions are presented as having been proved when, in fact, they are not.

(f) *Questionnaire surveys.* This term is used when we approach a selected group of people with questions pertaining to the problem under study. Since we cannot force the person queried to reply, the investigation will include only those who are willing and able to answer the questions. A questionnaire survey may be based on written answers on questionnaires, or on oral answers recorded by special investigators during personal interviews. The second method is better, since in this way more answers are usually obtained, and they are more complete. But it is more costly, since it requires a number of specially trained and capable investigators.

A characteristic feature of a questionnaire survey is that invariably a certain number of the persons queried fail to answer. Thus, in a sense, it is an incomplete study, and all the comments on such studies are also applicable here. It should be stressed that in a questionnaire survey the persons who do not answer almost always differ from those who do: answers come from those who either are interested in the subject of the survey or expect some personal advantage from answering, and this advantage may depend upon their replies. Answers are difficult to obtain from those who are not interested in the survey or who could be inconvenienced or embarrassed by their own answers.

It follows that a questionnaire survey almost never provides a direct basis for characterizing the population. But this does not mean that it is worthless. If it is well designed it may increase our knowledge of the subject and often it is necessary since it may reach problems inaccessible by other studies and may bring to light many valuable details. But the reservations concerning this kind of survey should always be kept in mind.

(g) To complete the picture another type of study should also be mentioned. These are *studies designed to provide information only about certain sections of a problem* and are not meant to deal with the whole. If they are properly designed such studies may also be quite valuable.

In general we must conclude that a correct and exhaustive picture concerning the whole population can be obtained only by a full study or by a proper sample survey. Other types of studies only rarely give a correct picture of the whole. This does not diminish their importance as a means of studying certain aspects of a problem and of revealing new features.

The most important condition that must be satisfied if such partial studies are to produce satisfactory results is the exact determination of the population that is to be studied, and of its groups and subgroups. This, in a sense, is a requirement identical with that of designing stratification before embarking upon a study.

In drawing conclusions from such partial studies it should be remembered that they always apply to the part studied and are not automatically applicable to the whole population. Moreover, these conclusions may often be distorted in consequence of a one-sided approach. Limitations of such studies should always be kept in mind and they should be clearly stated.

# Appendix

**1. An Analysis of Three Special Problems by Egon Vielrose: (a) The Smoothing out of Statistical Series, (b) Interpolation, (c) Operations with Approximate Numbers.**
**2. The more Important Tables Required for Statistical Analysis.**

## A. THE SMOOTHING OF STATISTICAL SERIES

The smoothing of statistical series consists in replacing the terms of a series having an irregular pattern by other terms having a smooth pattern so that we can assume that the latter represent the essential phenomenon better than the original series. The terms of the original series may display random irregularities, particularly when they are based on a small number of observations. The rounding off of some figures may also result in some irregularities. In a graph such a series is represented by a zigzag line with many kinks. It can be assumed that a smooth line would better reflect the phenomenon than this kind of empirical line.

For instance, the probabilities of death calculated on the basis of the number of deceased and the number of survivors at particular ages almost never display a smooth pattern. Intuition tells us that discrete changes up and down do not reflect the real pattern of the death rate, and that such changes are due to random factors. Therefore a smoothed series should better represent the actual pattern.

Another example can be taken from population statistics by age. Almost always a certain number of people round off their ages and give, say 60, instead od 59 or 61, or even instead of 58 or 62. The series thus obtained does not represented the actual age distribution of the population. Therefore, we have to "scatter" the excess clustered about round numbers: this can be done by smoothing out.

However, the actual pattern of the population by age series is not completely smooth and even if we had most accurate statistics it would turn out that the frequencies in some years are greater than in others. This, of course, is due to the fact that in some years more children are born than in others and that the frequency of deaths is not the same in all years. The smoothing out usually eliminated these minor fluctuations, and thus the smoothed series will not reflect every detail of reality.

While we may accept the fact that minor fluctuations are lost in the process of smoothing out, it is not permissible to obscure the irregularities related to the essence of the phenomenon studied. For instance, the age structure of the population of Poland in 1949 shows "dents" caused by a decline in the number of births during World Wars I and II as well as by population losses caused directly

609

by war. The methods of smoothing out should be selected so as to reflect these dents in the smoothed-out series in appropriate years and in correct proportions.

The condition that has to be satisfied by smoothed series is that they should be sufficiently smooth but should not obscure the essence of the phenomenon studied. The deviations of the actual from the smoothed-out data should not indicate the existence of a systematic bias, and therefore they should often change sign; there should not be cases when a long series of deviations with a plus sign is followed by a long series with a minus sign.

The smoothing does not produce the desired results if there is a bias in the statistical material, i.e. if there is a tendency to give values that are too low or too high.

The methods of smoothing out are graphical and arithmetical, and the latter are divided into analytical and mechanical. Analytical methods are those in which it is assumed *a priori* that the smoothed series can be represented by a function, e.g. a straight line, a parabola, etc. The parameters of such functions are chosen so that the smooth line corresponding to them be as close to the empirical points as possible. This kind of smoothing is used for calculating trends and regression lines.

In mechanical methods it is not assumed that a series is expressed by a specific function. The simplest example of mechanical smoothing out is the moving average. To this group also belong the methods based on tangential interpolation and osculatory interpolation.

### a. Graphical Methods

Graphical methods are very simple. In the rectangular system of coordinates we plot the points corresponding to the actual values of the series and then we draw a smooth curve by hand, as close as possible to these points. We then read off on the vertical scale the values of the ordinates corresponding to points on the curve, and thus obtain the smoothed values. The results can be read off more easily when the paper used is divided into small squares.

This method appears to be very arbitrary. There are many possible ways in which a curve may be fitted into a set of empirical points. In practice the problem is not so formidable if random or systematically biased deviations are not too large. It should be realized that every method of smoothing contains an element of arbitrariness. In graphical smoothing we can check more easily than in other methods whether we are proceeding arbitrarily because we constantly have in front of our eyes all empirical points and the smoothed part of the curve. Thus we can easily evaluate the effect of smoothing and the consistency of the curve with the empirical points. However, the person doing this should be a statistician, and should know the subject to which the study pertains.

Sometimes it is possible to check the accuracy of smoothing, especially when the individual values of the series are subject to error but it can be assumed that the total of a certain number of consecutive values (say 5, or 10) is correct. This happens in population censuses. The rounding off to a number ending in zero is considerable (e.g. 40, 50, 60 years), and it is less frequent to a number ending in 5. Thus the data for particular years are not exact, but it can be assumed that the total number of persons, at say age 33–42, as well as at age 43–52, etc. fairly accurately corresponds to the data recorded in the census. Then we can check whether the sums of smoothed values correspond to the sums of actual values. It should be remembered, however, that this method enables us to establish the existence of an error only when the two sums do not agree, but the equality of the sums does not prove that the snoothing is correct.

A similar check of the consistency between the smoothed and original series can also be made by other methods (analytical and mechanical) which will be discussed later on. Some of these methods are based on the assumption that certain sums of the smoothed values equal the corresponding sums of the original values. However, in general a lack of equality between these sums does not prove that there are errors in the calculation or that the result of smoothing out is wrong.

### b. **Analytical Methods**

Analytical smoothing out is based on the assumption that: (1) the phenomenon studied can be represented by a definite function (e.g. a straight line, a parabola), and that (2) deviations of the actual data from this function are random. The function itself depends upon a certain number of parameters which are determined on the basis of empirical data. If the function is linear we have two parameters, if it is a second degree parabola, we have three parameters, etc.

The crux of the problem is to find an appropriate function. The smoothing out would be analytical in the strict sense of the word if we could determine in advance for a given phenomenon the type of function to which its pattern corresponds. This is possible only in the field of inanimate nature, and, to some extent, in biology: but not where human society is involved.

In studies concerned with human society a number of functions have been proposed which were supposed to represent "laws" covering certain phenomena. One of them is the function

$$y = \frac{a}{x^b}, \tag{1}$$

representing Pareto's Law on the distribution of income in society. In this formula $x$ stands for income expressed in monetary units, $y$ denotes the number of persons with an income equal to, or greater than, and $a$ and $b$ are constant parameters. This function does not express a general law for the distribution of income but under certain historical conditions it can represent the actual state of affairs fairly well. But Pareto and his bourgeois followers presented this empirical relation as a universal law of nature and thus the "Pareto's Law" has become a glaring example of the reactionary apology for capitalism.

In the field of demography a function was suggested to represent the formula for population growth. This function is connected with the name of the Belgian mathematician Verhulst (1848) and of the late American biologist and statistician R. Pearl. The function has the following form

$$N_t = \frac{N_\infty}{1 + e^{-aN\infty(t-t_0)}} \tag{2}$$

where $N_t$ denotes the population at the time $t$, $N_\infty$ is the upper limit of the population for $t = \infty$, $t_0$ is the starting period, $e$ is the base of natural logarithm, $a$ is a constant parameter. The formula is based on the assumption that the rate of natural increase at the moment $t$ is proportional to the difference $N_\infty - N_t$, and therefore the rate steadily decreases to zero at the end period. The growth of the absolute population figure then is represented in the graph by a logistic curve. This curve increases, at first slowly, then more rapidly, then slowly again and finally approaches a limiting value asymptotically.

Attempts were made to prove empirically that the Verhulst–Pearl formula is correct. Flies were bred in a closed vessel and counted at certain intervals. The results were consistent with the formula. The growth of human societies can also be represented by certain segments of the logistic curve. However, it can be shown that the same population figures in different periods can be represented by different functions. What is more, the posing of the problem is wrong: where we deal with a human society there are not, and cannot be, any "eternal" laws; all laws are valid under specific historical conditions. Even if we assumed that under certain conditions the society did develop according to a logistic curve, then undoubtedly before the end of the growth cycle a change in conditions would take place, the cycle would be broken, and the Verhulst–Pearl formula would turn out to be without any consequence for the forecast of the future population growth.

However, there are many instances in which we can empirically arrive at certain functions which correspond quite well to reality. From the examples discussed earlier in this book it can be seen that some statistical facts can be well expressed by a straight line. For instance the relationship between the height and the weight of a man is distinctly linear over a long segment, i.e. equal increments in height always correspond to equal increments in weight. But it should be remembered that this "law" can be considered as proved only for the region in which its existence has been established. Any extrapolation beyond the limits of this region is not permissible, or at least, risky.

More complicated is the question of smoothing growth lines (see p. 323 *et seq.*). In the example described earlier (the consumption of electric power) a straight line or a parabola could be used only with reservations and over a short range. However, such smoothing may be useful for special purposes, such as the determination of seasonal fluctuations and business cycles, and the systematic error would be smaller than would be possible without taking the dynamics of growth into account.

Of course, instead of a straight line, we can also use some other function for smoothing. However, since we do not know in advance the pattern of the phenomenon, we can only evaluate *ex post* fact which curve fits the empirical values best. An empirical series can be smoothed by any type of curve, but not every type is appropriate in a specific case. An important condition of proper smoothing out is fitting the curve as constistently as possible to the pattern of the actual values. This consistency can be evaluated, for instance, by checking the sum of the squared deviations of the actual values from the smoothed line: the smaller the sum the greater the consistency. Of course, there is always a function that corresponds to a curve passing through all the empirical points if we consider functions of a sufficiently high degree. In practice, however, the problem consists in finding a function such that the deviations of this curve from the empirical points are not too great and yet the curve is sufficiently smooth. Most frequently used are straight lines, parabolas of the second degree and functions that can be reduced to a linear relationship.

In analytical smoothing out the problem can be approached in two ways: the method of least squares and the method of moments.

The method of least squares consists in finding a curve (from among all possible curves of a given type) such that the sum of the squared deviations of the actual values from this curve is the least. This condition enables us to determine the values of the parameters of the function, since the expression for the sum of the squares of these deviations is a minimum when its partial derivatives with respect to each parameter equal zero. Hence we obtain as many equations as there are parameters.

The method of least squares is related to the Gauss–Laplace Law of Errors. It turns out that if the deviations of the terms of the empirical series from the corresponding theoretical values obtained by substituting specific values in the function are consistent with the Law of Errors, then the function arrived at by the method of least squares is the most probable of all the functions of a given type.

If the smoothed curve is to be a straight line then its equation is

$$y = ax + b \tag{3}$$

and it has two parameters, $a$ and $b$. The sum of the squared deviations from this line is to be as small as possible, hence the derivatives of this sum with respect to $a$ and $b$ equal zero. Thus we obtain two equations for determining the parameters $a$ and $b$

$$\sum y = a\sum x + bN,$$
$$\sum xy = a\sum x^2 + b\sum x, \tag{4}$$

where $N$ is the number of observations.

If the smoothed curve is to be a second degree parabola its equation is of the type

$$y = ax^2 + bx + c \tag{5}$$

and it has three parameters, $a$, $b$, and $c$. Thus we obtain three equations

$$\sum y = a\sum x^2 + b\sum x + cN,$$
$$\sum xy = a\sum x^3 + b\sum x^2 + c\sum x, \tag{6}$$
$$\sum x^2 y = a\sum x^4 + b\sum x^3 + c\sum x^2.$$

All these equations assume a simpler form if the intervals between the empirical points are the same. The origin of the system of coordinates is then moved to the middle point if the number of observations is odd, or the mid-point between two middle observations if the number of observations is even. In this way we get rid of the sums of the odd powers of variable $x$ since they equal zero, and thus we can easily derive directly the formulae for constant parameters appearing in the equation.

For the straight line we obtain the equations

$$a = \frac{\sum xy}{\sum x^2},$$
$$b = \frac{\sum y}{N}, \tag{7}$$

and for a second degree parabola

$$a = \frac{\sum x^2 \times \sum y - N \times \sum x^2 y}{\sum^2 x^2 - N \times \sum x^4}.$$

$$b = \frac{\sum xy}{\sum x^2}, \tag{8}$$

$$c = \frac{\sum x^2 \times \sum x^2 y - \sum x^4 \times \sum y}{\sum^2 x^2 - N \times \sum x^4}.$$

We shall now give several examples of using the method of least squares for smoothing out.

The calculation is very easy if we deal with a straight line and it becomes more cumbersome as we move to curves of a higher degree. Therefore we shall seek methods of reducing the calculation to a straight line.

As we have already mentioned the Italian economist Pareto expressed the relationship between the number of persons with a specific income and the level of income in the form

$$y = \frac{a}{x^b}.$$

As we already know this "law" is subject to serious reservations (see p. 611). From the point of view of the method of least squares the object is to find parameters $a$ and $b$ on the basis of empirical values $x$ and $y$. Calculations based on the above formula are very cumbersome. It is much more convenient to take the logarithm of both sides. Then we have the formula

$$\log y = \log a - b \log x,$$

expressing a linear relationship between $\log y$ and $\log x$ and the parameters $\log a$ and $b$. To determine there parameters we obtain two equations

$$\sum \log y = N \times \log a - b \sum \log x,$$
$$\sum \log x \times \log y = \log a \sum \log x - b \sum{}^2 \log x. \tag{9}$$

In the next example we have the relationship between the turnover of a cooperative society and the ratio of selling costs to turnover, in percentages. This example is taken from the book by B. Riausov and N. Titelbaum: *Course torgovoy statistiki,* (Moscow, 1947, p. 188).

| Turnover in 100 roubles $x$ | Number of observations $f$ | Selling costs as percentages of turnover $y$ |
|---|---|---|
| 10·0 | 5462 | 12·3 |
| 17·5 | 3024 | 10·2 |
| 25·0 | 5478 | 9·6 |
| 35·0 | 4191 | 8·7 |
| 45·0 | 3193 | 8·2 |
| 62·5 | 4720 | 7·7 |
| 87·5 | 2133 | 7·2 |
| 150·0 | 2458 | 6·7 |
| 250·0 | 668 | 6·0 |
| 400·0 | 512 | 5·7 |
| *Total* | *31,839* | . |

The regression of the selling costs $y$ on turnover $x$ is not linear but the regression of $y$ on the new variable $t = \dfrac{1}{\sqrt{x}}$ is approximately linear. In calculations we also take into account the frequencies of observations in particular classes.

The equation of the straight line sought is

$$y = at + b,$$

where the parameters $a$ and $b$ are determined by the equations

$$\sum yf = a\sum tf + b\sum f,$$
$$\sum tyf = a\sum t^2f + b\sum tf.$$

Substituting the values calculated from the table we obtain the equations

$$5823{\cdot}72\,a + 31{,}839\,b = 288{,}357{\cdot}1,$$
$$1249{\cdot}06\,a + 5823{\cdot}72\,b = 57{,}185{\cdot}5,$$

and therefore

$$a = 24{\cdot}174,$$
$$b = 46{\cdot}35.$$

Thus the equation of the smoothed straight line (the regression line) is

$$y = \frac{24{\cdot}174}{\sqrt{x}} + 4{\cdot}635. \tag{10}$$

Substituting in this equation the values of variable we obtain the corresponding values of variably $y$. We show below the original values of $y$ and the smoothed out values $y_w$:

| $x$ | $y$ | $y_w$ | $y - y_w$ |
|------|------|------|------|
| 10 | 12·3 | 12·28 | 0·02 |
| 17·5 | 10·2 | 10·41 | −0·21 |
| 25 | 9·6 | 9·47 | 0·13 |
| 35 | 8·7 | 8·72 | −0·02 |
| 45 | 8·2 | 8·24 | −0·04 |
| 62·5 | 7·7 | 7·69 | 0·01 |
| 87·5 | 7·2 | 7·22 | −0·02 |
| 150 | 6·7 | 6·61 | 0·09 |
| 250 | 6·0 | 6·16 | −0·16 |
| 400 | 5·7 | 5·84 | −0·14 |

The differences between the actual values and the smoothed-out values are small and show a random pattern because positive and negative differences alternate and are not systematic. Therefore, we can conclude that function (10) smoothes out the series quite well.

The method of moments is based on completely different assumptions. If to the values $x_1$, $x_2$, .... of one variable correspond certain values $y_1$, $y_2$, .... of another then the $i$th moment of variable $x$ is the expression

$$\mu_i = \sum yx^i.$$

We usually calculate moments from the arithmetic mean but they can also be calculated from zero. Particular moments have definite meanings if the quantities $y$ are frequencies. The zero moment is then the sum of the frequencies. The ratio of the first moment to the zero moment is the arithmetic mean and the ratio of the second moment calculated from the arithmetic mean to the zero moment is the variance. The third moment is connected with the asymmetry of the frequency curve, and the fourth with the flattening of the curve at the top.

If we want to smooth out the empirical data by the function

$$y = f(x),$$

depending on $k$ parameters then we have the condition that the first $k$ moments of variable $x$ should equal the first $k$ moments of the function $f(x)$. In this way we obtain as many equations as there are parameters and we can—at least theoretically—determine these parameters. The equations are:

$$\sum y = \sum f(x),$$
$$\sum xy = \sum xf(x),$$
$$\cdot \quad \cdot \quad \cdot \quad \cdot \quad \cdot \quad \cdot \quad \cdot$$
$$\sum x^{k-1}y = \sum x^{k-1}f(x),$$

and all moments are calculated from the same value of variable $x$, i.e. all from zero or all from the arithmetic mean.

If the smoothing function is a polynomial, and its degree is integral, then it is easy to show that the method of moments leads to the same equations as the method of least squares.

The method of moments was used by K. Pearson in working out a system of functions which were to correspond to the most important types of statistical series. However, Pearson's functions do not correspond to specific reality. Moreover, these functions are not suitable for representing series with several minima or maxima. Besides this, these functions depend on at most, five parameters, and therefore their constistency with the actual data is not always sufficient, and the computations involved in determining these parameters are fairly cumbersome.

We shall show by an example the difference in calculations by the method of least squares and the method of moments. Let us take the relationship between selling costs and turnover discussed above. The equation had the form

$$y = \frac{a}{\sqrt{x}} + b,$$

and parameters $a$ and $b$ were determined by equations (4) which we can also write in the form

$$\sum yn = a \sum \frac{n}{\sqrt{x}} + b \sum n,$$

$$\sum \frac{yn}{\sqrt{x}} = a \sum \frac{n}{x} + b \sum \frac{n}{\sqrt{x}}. \tag{11}$$

If we used the method of moments we would have the equations

$$\sum yn = a \sum \frac{x}{\sqrt{x}} + b \sum n,$$

$$\sum xyn = a \sum \sqrt{xn} + b \sum xn. \tag{12}$$

Thus the first equation would remain unchanged and the second would be replaced by another equation. Therefore, the values of the parameters determined by the method of moments are in this case somewhat different, being 24·404 and 4·593 instead of the previously obtained values 24·174 and 4·635.

Below are the values smoothed out by the method of $y_m$ moments and the differences between the original and smoothed out values.

| $x$ | $y_m$ | $y - y_m$ |
|---|---|---|
| 10 | 12·31 | −0·01 |
| 17·5 | 10·43 | 0·23 |
| 25 | 9·47 | 0·13 |
| 35 | 8·72 | −0·02 |
| 45 | 8·23 | 0·03 |
| 62·5 | 7·68 | 0·02 |
| 87·5 | 7·20 | — |
| 150 | 6·59 | 0·11 |
| 250 | 6·14 | −0·14 |
| 400 | 5·81 | −0·11 |

## c. Mechanical Methods

In mechanical methods the individual terms of the smoothed series are expressed as linear functions of a certain number of consecutive terms of an empirical series, usually of the term corresponding to a smoothed term, a certain number of the preceding terms, and the same number of the following terms.

The simplest example of mechanical smoothing out is the moving average. If we have the moving average with an odd number of terms, we can consider each value of this average as the smoothed value of the middle term. The greater the number of terms included in the average, the more intense is the smoothing process. If we want to eliminate periodic fluctuations, we have to take as many terms as needed to coincide with the whole period or with a multiple of it.

However, the moving average dampens the curvatures of the series and thus obscures its pattern, and therefore its use should be limited to cases in which the pattern of the series is approximately linear. Another drawback of the moving average is that the results are equally affected by the terms close to the middle term and those far from it; and logically it would seem that the influence of end terms should be less than the influence of the middle terms. In this way we arrive at the concept of calculating the moving average of the moving averages.

For instance, if from the terms $a_1$, $a_2$, $a_3$, $a_4$, $a_5$ we calculate three averages each with three terms

$$\frac{a_1 + a_2 + a_3}{3}, \quad \frac{a_2 + a_3 + a_4}{3}, \quad \frac{a_3 + a_4 + a_5}{3},$$

then we can assume that the middle term $a_3$ can be smoothed by the average of these three averages. If we denote this smoothed term by $a_3$ then we have

$$a_3' = \frac{1}{3} \left( \frac{a_1 + a_2 + a_3}{3} + \frac{a_2 + a_3 + a_4}{3} + \frac{a_3 + a_4 + a_5}{3} \right)$$

$$= \frac{1}{9} (a_1 + 2a_2 + 3a_3 + 2a_4 + a_5).$$

In this expression the weight of the smoothed term is greater than the weights of the others.

In this way we can have the average of 5 averages with 5 terms each (Wittstein's Formula), or the average of 5 averages of 5 averages with 5 terms each (Finlaison's Formula). Wittstein's Formula has 9 terms and the following form:

$$a_5' = \frac{1}{25} (a_1 + 2a_2 + 3a_3 + 4a_4 + 5a_5 + 4a_6 + 3a_7 + 2a_8 + a_9).$$

All formulae of this kind smooth the curvatures of a series to a lesser degree than the ordinary moving average, but all of them are subject to the same systematic error: the values of the smoothed curve within segments convex to the horizontal axis are too high and within concave segments are too low. This always happens when the coefficients of all terms have a positive sign.

There are formulae which are not subject to this kind of systematic error. They usually have a very large number of terms. For instance, Woolhouse's Formula has fifteen terms and the following form:

$$a_8' = \frac{1}{125} [25a_8 + 24(a_9 + a_7) + 21(a_{10} + a_6) + 7(a_{11} + a_5)$$

$$+ 3(a_{12} + a_4) - 2(a_{13} + a_3) - 3(a_{15} + a_1)].$$

Formulae of this kind, with a large number of terms, "smooth" empirical series very strongly and are fairly well adapted to the actual pattern if the "real" pattern of the series (after eliminating random fluctuations and distortions) is fairly regular. They do not properly reflect minor dents and bulges and usually do not properly reflect periodic fluctuations. Also they do not allow us to smooth a certain number of terms at the beginning and at the end.

As we have already mentioned, tangential interpolation is also a mechanical method. The principle used consists in dividing the series into segments which are smoothed by separate curves, and every pair of consecutive curves must be tangent to one another at their common point.

Of all the methods in this category the best results are obtained by Glover's method. It begins not with the data of the series but with the sums of a certain number of terms of the series. The sums of 5 or 10 terms are generally used. To obtain smoothed values in a given group (of 5 or 10 terms) the sums for 5 such groups are taken into account: for the group to be smoothed out, for the two preceding groups and for the two following groups. The smoothing out is done by fourth degree parabolas.[235] The extreme values of the series are smoothed out on the basis of the first and the last of these parabolas.

In smoothing out by Glover's method the sums of the smoothed-out values are equal—within particular groups—to the sums of the original values. This property is particularly important for smoothing out demographic series.

Another advantage of Glover's method is that it enables us—by an appropriate choice of the size of the groups and by the placing of the groups—to retain in the smoothed series the essential peculiarities which appear in a certain number of the neighbouring values. In this way, for instance, breaches in the number of births caused by wars can be reproduced in the form of distinct "valleys" in the smoothed series.

Interpolation by tangential methods, as well as the other mechanical methods, do not properly reflect minor fluctuations. They require much computation and are largely formalistic, i.e. detached from the reality studied. For this reason they are not extensively used in statistics.

## B. INTERPOLATION

Let us suppose that we have a series arranged according to the value of some characteristic, for instance a time series or a frequency distribution. Interpolation consists in determining hypothetical values of this series intermediate to the values of the characteristic which appear in the series. We can only interpolate in series which are sufficiently smooth. Very irregular series with frequent breaks cannot be interpolated. In fact no statistical series is quite smooth, and therefore interpolation is only a certain approximation to intermediate values and the actual value may differ somewhat from this approximation. No method of interpolation, even a most precise one, can guarantee that the true value will be obtained. There-

---

[235] Examples of the applications of various methods of smoothing out are given in a study by S. Fogelson: O wyrównywaniu szeregów statystycznych ze szczególnym uwzględnieniem rozkładu ludności według wieku (On the Smoothing Out of Statistical Series with Particular Attention to the Age Distribution of the Population), *Kwartalnik Statystyczny* (*Statist. Quart.*), 1931.

fore, the application of interpolation in practice, in addition to posing a technical problem of computation, also requires a great deal of experience and the knowledge of the subject studied.

Interpolation is simplest when the pattern of the series is approximately linear, at least near the value which we want to interpolate. In such cases we use the simple rule of three. We now give an example of this most simple type of interpolation.

The population of Warsaw on January 1, 1948 was 576,000 and on January 1, 1949 it was 604,900. We want to determine the population of Warsaw on August 1, 1948.

We assume that within the year 1948 the population can be presented as a linear function of time. This means that in each month the absolute increase in the population of Warsaw was the same. Since from the beginning of the period under consideration, i.e. from January 1, 1948 to the moment for which we want to determine the population (i.e. to August 1, 1948) 7 months elapsed, and the whole period under consideration is 12 months, then in the period of 7 months we have $7/12$ of the yearly increase. Therefore the population on August 1, 1948 is

$$576 \cdot 0 + \frac{7}{12}(604 \cdot 9 - 576 \cdot 0) = 592{,}900.$$

The actual population figure on this day was 590,600 and the result obtained by interpolation is fairly close to the actual figure.

However, very often the assumption of linearity does not correspond to reality and then we must use less simple but more accurate methods. We distinguish two cases: (1) the values of the series are given for the values of the characteristic at equal intervals; and (2) the values of the series are given for the values of the characteristic at unequal intervals. We shall discuss both these cases.

Let us suppose that we have the values of the series

$$y_0, y_1, \ldots, y_n$$

corresponding to the values of the characteristic

$$x_0, x_1, \ldots, x_n$$

and let us assume that this is case i.e.

$$x_1 - x_0 = x_2 - x_1 = \ldots = x_n - x_{n-1} = h.$$

The first differences are the quantities

$$\triangle_0^{(1)} = y_1 - y_0, \quad \triangle_1^{(1)} = y_2 - y_1, \quad \ldots$$

The second differences are the quantities

$$\triangle_0^{(2)} = \triangle_1^{(1)} - \triangle_0^{(1)}, \quad \triangle_1^{(2)} = \triangle_2^{(1)} - \triangle_1^{(1)}, \quad \ldots$$

and, in general, the $k$th differences are the quantities

$$\triangle_0^{(k)} = \triangle_1^{(k-1)} - \triangle_0^{(k-1)}, \quad \triangle_1^{(k)} = \triangle_2^{(k-1)} - \triangle_1^{(k-1)}, \quad \dots$$

In practice we calculate these differences in turn as shown in the table below:

$$
\begin{array}{llllll}
x_0 y_0 \\
& \triangle_0^{(1)} \\
x_1 y_1 & & \triangle_0^{(2)} \\
& \triangle_1^{(1)} & & \triangle_0^{(3)} \\
x_2 y_2 & & \triangle_1^{(2)} & & \triangle_0^{(4)} \\
& \triangle_2^{(1)} & & \triangle_1^{(3)} & & \triangle_0^{(5)} \\
x_3 y_3 & & \triangle_2^{(2)} & & \triangle_1^{(4)} \\
\end{array}
$$

. . . . . . . . . . . . . . .

The general interpolation formula is

$$y = y_0 + \frac{(x-x_0)}{1 \times h} \triangle_0^{(1)} + \frac{(x-x_0)(x-x_1)}{1 \times 2 \times h^2} \triangle_0^{(2)} + \frac{(x-x_0)(x-x_1)(x-x_2)}{1 \times 2 \times 3 \times h^3} \triangle_0^{(3)} +$$

$$\dots + \frac{(x-x_0)(x-x_1)(x-x_2)\dots(x-x_{k-1})}{1 \times 2 \times 3 \dots k \times h^k} \triangle_0^k. \tag{1}$$

This is Newton's Interpolation Formula.

Depending upon what we need we can stop after the first differences, or we can proceed further. If we consider only the first differences then the formula is based on two values of the series: $y_0$ and $y_1$. If we also consider the second differences then the formula is based on three values of the series, and generally, if we consider the $k$th differences then the formula is based on $(k + 1)$ values of the series. Depending upon the number of the differences considered we obtain polynomials (1) of various orders: when we consider the first differences we get a polynomial of the first degree with respect to variable $x$, when we consider the second differences we get a polynomial of the second degree and when we consider the $k$th differences we get a polynomial of the $k$th degree. An exception to this rule occurs when the differences beginning with a certain order all equal zero. Then if the $k$th difference equals zero or at least is small as far as its absolute value is concerned then in the corresponding range a parabola of the $(k - 1)$th degree represents the pattern of the series quite well.

It is impossible to give detailed instructions for practical applications of interpolation. But certain general rules can be given. The number of differences considered should be such that the degree of the polynomial (1) obtained should correspond to the pattern of the series. Polynomials of too high a degree should be avoided because they make computation difficult and may even produce worse results. The value of the characteristic that we want to interpolate should be, if possible, midway between the values between which we interpolate. If a series displays considerable fluctuations and some of its terms are close to zero it may be advisable to interpolate not on the basis of the values themselves but on the basis of their logarithms.

In this way we always obtain positive values. In the interpolation of the values themselves it may happen that we obtain negative values, which is absurd.

The average annual number of births in Europe was as follows: in the decade 1821–30—8,893,000, in 1841–50—9,833,000, in 1861–70—11,267,000, in 1881–90—13,223,000, and in 1901–10—14,792,000. We want to find the average number of births in the period 1871–80.

The calculation of the differences is made in the form of the table

| $x$ | $y$ | $\triangle^{(1)}$ | $\triangle^{(2)}$ | $\triangle^{(3)}$ | $\triangle^{(4)}$ |
|---|---|---|---|---|---|
| 1821–30 | 8893 | | | | |
| | | 940 | | | |
| 1841–50 | 9833 | | 494 | | |
| | | 1434 | | 28 | |
| 1861–70 | 11,267 | | 522 | | −937 |
| | | 1956 | | −909 | |
| 1881–90 | 13,223 | | −387 | | |
| | | 1569 | | | |
| 1901–10 | 14,792 | | | | |

If we consider the number of births in the periods from 1821–30 to 1881–90 and their consecutive differences then it turns out that the third difference, 28, is quite small in comparison with the values of the first and the second differences. Thus, during this whole period the pattern of the number of births corresponds approximately to a parabola of the second order. If we want to determine the number of births in the period 1871–80 it is enough to consider the number of births in the decade 1841–50 and the corresponding first and second differences. Hence we have the interpolation formula

$$y = 9833 + \frac{(x - 1841)}{1 \times 20} \times 1434 + \frac{(x - 1841) \times (x - 1861)}{1 \times 2 \times 20^2} \times 522. \qquad (2)$$

Substituting the value $x = 1871$ we obtain

$$y = 12,180,000.$$

The actual figure is 12,332,000.

In this case to determine the parabola of the 2nd order we used the data for the decades 1841–50, 1861–70, 1881–90. We could also determine a parabola of the 2nd order on the basis of the data for the decades 1821–30, 1841–50, and 1861–70, but then we would be seeking values for a period outside these three decades and the result would be less accurate.

If we considered not only the decades from 1821–30 to 1881–90 but also the decade 1901–10, then we would obtain a very large fourth difference. This proves that the series over the whole period of time under consideration cannot be represented even by a parabola of the third order. This is due to the fact that in the decade 1901–10 there was a markedly declining trend in the number of births and this caused disturbances in the regularity of the pattern. Therefore the number of births in 1871–80 estimated by interpolation of the basis of the data for the whole period, being 12,081,000, differs more from the actual number of births than the analogous figure obtained before on the basis of the data for three decades only.

The numbers of wireless sets in Poland were: at the beginning of 1925—200, of 1927—48,000, of 1929—184,300, of 1931—245,900. We want to determine by interpolation the number of wireless sets at the beginning of 1928.

Since the range of values is considerable and the lowest is close to zero we interpolate not on the basis of the figures themselves but on the basis of their logarithms.

First we calculate the logarithms and their differences

| $x$ | $y$ | $\log y$ | $\triangle^{(1)}$ | $\triangle^{(2)}$ | $\triangle^{(3)}$ |
|---|---|---|---|---|---|
| 1925 | 0·2 | −0·69897 | | | |
| | | | 2·38021 | | |
| 1927 | 48·0 | 1·68124 | | −1·79592 | |
| | | | 0·58429 | | 1·33586 |
| 1929 | 184·3 | 2·26553 | | −0·45906 | |
| | | | 0·12523 | | |
| 1931 | 245·9 | 2·39076 | | | |

In this case $h = 2$. No difference is small in relation to the preceding one and therefore we consider the data for all four years and use the first four terms of formula (1). Hence we have

$$\log y = -0·69897 + \frac{(x-1925)}{1\times 2}\times 2·38021 - \frac{(x-1925)\times(x-1927)}{1\times 2\times 2^2}\times 1·79592$$

$$+ \frac{(x-1925)\times(x-1927)\times(x-1929)}{1\times 2\times 3\times 2^3}\times 1·33686, \tag{3}$$

substituting $x = 1928$ we obtain $\log y = 2·12341$ and therefore $y_{1928} = 132·900$.

The actual number of wireless sets at the beginning of 1928 was 118,900. We thus see that the result of the interpolation does not agree with the actual figure.

If the intervals between the values of the characteristic $y_0$, $y_1$, $y_2$, ... are not the same then we have the values of the series corresponding to the values of the characteristic $x_0$, $x_1$, $x_2$, ... but the differences between the consecutive values of variable $x$ are not all equal. In this case we base the interpolation formula on relative differences.

The first relative differences are the values

$$D_0^{(1)} = \frac{y_1 - y_0}{x_1 - x_0}, \quad D_1^{(1)} = \frac{y_2 - y_1}{x_2 - x_1}, \quad \ldots$$

The second relative differences are the values

$$D_0^{(2)} = \frac{D_1^{(1)} - D_0^{(1)}}{x_2 - x_0}, \quad D_1^{(2)} = \frac{D_2^{(1)} - D_1^{(1)}}{x_3 - x_1}, \quad \ldots$$

and, in general, the $k$th relative differences are the values

$$D_0^{(k)} = \frac{D_1^{(k-1)} - D_0^{(k-1)}}{x_k - x_0}, \quad D_1^{(k)} = \frac{D_2^{(k-1)} - D_1^{(k-1)}}{x_{k+1} - x_1}, \quad \ldots$$

The general interpolation formula is

$$y = y_0 + (x - x_0) D_0^{(1)} + (x - x_0)(x - x_1) D_0^{(2)} + (x - x_0)(x - x_1)(x - x_2)$$
$$D_0^{(3)} + \ldots + (x - x_0)(x - x_1)(x - x_2) \ldots (x - x_{k-1}) D_0^{(k)}. \tag{4}$$

The principles for using this formula are the same as for formula (1).

The population of Warsaw in 1860 was 158,000, in 1897—594,000, in 1910—781,000. We want to determine the population of Warsaw in 1880.

The consecutive relative differences are:

| $x$ | $x_{i+1} - x_i$ | $y$ | $y_{i+1} - y_i$ | $D^{(1)}$ | $D_{i+1}^{(1)} - D_i^{(1)}$ | $D^{(2)}$ |
|---|---|---|---|---|---|---|
| 1860 | | 158 | | | | |
| | 37 | | 436 | 11·8 | | |
| 1897 | | 594 | | | 2·6 | 0·052 |
| | 13 | | 187 | 14·4 | | |
| 1910 | | 781 | | | | |

By interpolation formula (2) we have

$$y = 158 + (x - 1860) \times 11·8 + (x - 1860) \times (x - 1897) \times 0·052. \tag{5}$$

Substituting $x = 1880$, we obtain

$$y = 376,000.$$

In fact, the population of Warsaw in 1880 was 383,000, and the interpolation gives a very good result.

In practice we resort to interpolation most often in using numerical tables. They are usually designed in such a way that in order to find intermediate values between two values in the table we can use linear interpolation. We can do this if the second differences of the consecutive values in the table are small. If they are very small we can obtain by interpolation values accurate not only to one more decimal place than appear in the table, but even to two more.

Suppose that we want to obtain the value of log 2663. Let us first try to interpolate between the values of log 2 and log 3. log 2 $= 0 \cdot 30103$ and log 3 $= 0 \cdot 47712$ and therefore log 2000 $= 3 \cdot 30103$ and log 3000 $= 3 \cdot 47712$. The difference between the last two logarithms is $0 \cdot 17600$. By linear interpolation we obtain here an approximate value.

$$\log 2663 = \log 2000 + \frac{663}{1000} (\log 3000 - \log 2000) = 3 \cdot 30103 + 0 \cdot 11675 = 3 \cdot 41778.$$

The difference of the logarithms of 4000 and 3000 is $0 \cdot 12494$ and is much smaller than the previous difference which was $0 \cdot 17609$. Thus the second difference is considerable and we cannot expect good results from linear interpolation.

Let us now try to interpolate the same value on the basis of the values of the logarithms of 266 and 267. log 266 $= 2 \cdot 42488$ and log 267 $= 2 \cdot 43651$, and therefore log 2660 $= 3 \cdot 42488$ and log 2670 $= 3 \cdot 42651$. The difference between these logarithms is log 2670 $-$ log 2660 $= 0 \cdot 00163$. Linear interpolation gives

$$\log 2663 = \log 2660 + \frac{3}{10}(\log 2670 - \log 2660) = 3 \cdot 42488 + 0 \cdot 00049 = 3 \cdot 42537.$$

The difference between the next two logarithms: log 2680 $-$ log 2670 $= 0 \cdot 00162$ is almost identical with the previous one. The second difference is very small and therefore we can expect the result of interpolation to be very good. Indeed, the five-figure table gives for log 2663 exactly the same value $3 \cdot 42537$ that we have obtained by interpolation.

In this case, in view of the very small value of the second difference we can also interpolate to two decimal places. Thus

$$\log 2663 \cdot 8 = \log 2660 + \frac{3 \cdot 8}{10} (\log 2670 - \log 2660) = 3 \cdot 42488 + 0 \cdot 00062 = 3 \cdot 42550.$$

This result also agrees with the value of log $2663 \cdot 8$ in the five-figure logarithmic tables.

Interpolation is also used in smoothing out life tables by Glover's method. This method requires less computation than other methods and the results of smoothing by this method are not any worse. The procedure is as follows. The data on the number of deaths and the number of survivors are combined into groups of 5 or 10 consecutive years of age. In this way we obtain sums of which we can say that they correspond to reality (see p. 619 on smoothing).

From these sums we calculate the average coefficients of deaths for 5 or 10 years, and then the corresponding probabilities of death. Then we apply Glover's formulae to these averages and smooth out each group by a fourth degree parabola, leaving their sums unchanged; every two consecutive paraboles have in common a point of tangency of the second order (which means that at this point both their first and second derivatives are equal). Interpolation of this kind, in which neighbouring parabolas have a second order point of tangency is called osculatory interpolation, as opposed to tangential interpolation ich which the tangency is of the first order.

Extrapolation is more risky and therefore more difficult than interpolation. It consists in determining on the basis of a series of data the values that come before or after all the values of this series. The procedure consists in extending forward and backward the line obtained by interpolation and introducing into its equation the corresponding values of the argument.

For instance, on the basis of the data on wireless sets in 1925, 1927, 1929 and 1931 we could estimate the number of sets in 1932 or in 1933, substituting in equation (3) based on these data, the value $x = 1932$ or $x = 1933$.

Similarly, on the basis of the number of births in Europe in 1821–30, 1841–30, 1861–70 we could estimate the number of births in 1881–90 by substituting in equation (2) the value $x = 1881$.

When extrapolation is very risky the results obtained may be quite fantastic in comparison with the changes in the dynamics of growth.

## C. OPERATIONS WITH APPROXIMATE NUMBERS

In statistics we often deal with approximate numbers. Numbers obtained by measuring can never be completely accurate because it is impossible to improve the accuracy of the instruments used for measuring beyond a certain limit. On the other hand, in statistical practice there is no need to have completely accurate data. For instance, it is sufficient to know that the output of coal in September 1949 was 6,295,000 tons. To use the exact figure to the last kilogramme would be akward and beside the point, not to mention a very high cost of obtaining such information.

Also when we obtain the data by adding up, they are not always accurate, particularly when large numbers are involved. For instance, according to the 1946 population census there were 23,929,757 people in Poland. This figure appears to be very accurate. However, it only appears so since there were undoubtedly people who were not included and others included in several places. Thus the last three or four digits, i.e. the units, the tens and the hundreds and perhaps even the thousands are not reliable.

We should distinguish between approximate numbers and false numbers with an error caused by bias. If we have a series of approximate numbers, say, on the output of coal in particular months then some of them are higher than the actual output in a given month and some are lower. False figures, on the other hand deviate from the actual level in one direction. For instance, very old persons are inclined to add years to their actual age.

Related to approximate numbers is the notion of significant figures or digits. The number 23,929,757 has eight significant digits, the number 23,929.8 has six significant digits, the number 23,930,000 has four significant digits. In the number 23,929,800 the hundreds are significant and in the number 23,930,000 the tens of thousands are significant.

Thus zeros appearing at the end of a number are usually not significant. If it happens that the last significant digit is a zero and we wish to indicate that fact, we put a short line above or below it. Thus 23,700 is significant to the nearest tens but not units. A zero after the decimal point is always significant. A zero between two other numbers is always significant.

In practice different methods of rounding off are used. The most appropriate method is to round off to the nearest digit with the required accuracy. For instance, if we want to round off to the nearest thousand the number of population recorded in 1946 then we write 23,930,000 since this number is closer to the original number 23,929,757 then the number 23,929,000.

However, sometimes we consistently round the figures down by crossing out a certain number of final digits. This sort of rounding off is used in giving the age in completed years. This method is not good since it creates difficulties in calculations with figures rounded off in this way.

There are certain commonly accepted ways of denoting the degree of accuracy of approximate numbers. We mentioned before that according to the 1946 population census there were 23,929,757 people in Poland. Rounding off this number to the nearest hundreds of persons we write 23,929,800. In rounding off to thousands we write 23,930,000, to tens of thousands we write 23,930,000. Another method is to write the number in the form of the product of a number by a power of 10: $1 \cdot 23 \times 10^{-5}$, or $5 \cdot 20 \times 10^9$. (In both cases three digits are significant).

We can determine the degree of the accuracy of an approximate number from the way it is written. The number written as 23,930,000 means that we have rounded it off to the tens of thousands and thus the original, accurate number is located between 23,925,000 and 23,935,000. Thus the largest possible difference between the accurate number and the approximate number in this case is 5000. This number is called the maximum absolute error. If we assume that the number 23,929,757 is accurate then the actual error is $23,929,757 - 23,930,000 = -243$ and the actual absolute error is 243. Usually we know only the maximum absolute error but we do not know the actual error.

Knowing the absolute error we can determine the relative error, i.e the ratio of the absolute error to the approximate number. In our example the actual relative error is

$$243/23,930,000 = 1/98,477 = 0 \cdot 001\%,$$

and the maximum relative error is

$$5000/23,930,000 = 1/4786 = 0 \cdot 02\%.$$

The relative error is usually given in the percentage form or as a fraction whose numerator equals one.

The maximum absolute error of an approximate number equals one half of the last significant digit. For 23,929,800 it is 50, for 23,930,000 it is 5000.

Above, we have determined the relative error on the basis of the absolute error. Often the procedure is reversed and the absolute error is determined on the basis of the relative error. For instance if the maximum relative error of the number 19,702 is $1/60$ then the maximum absolute error is

$$19 \cdot 702 \times 1/60 = 0 \cdot 357.$$

It follows that even the third digit of this number is not significant and therefore it should be given only with two significant figures as 20.

If we perform operations with approximate numbers then we always obtain an approximate result. Therefore, it is essential to determine the degree of accuracy of the result to avoid calculating it with an accuracy apparently greater than the data allow.

The result of adding and subtracting should be rounded off to the least number of the significant digits in the components. If possible we use one more significant digit in the given numbers than we expect in the answer.

The absolute error of the sum of approximate numbers is not greater than the sum of the absolute errors of the components. The relative error of the sum is not greater than the largest relative error of the components, but it may be much less since some components are rounded up, and some down, and therefore these deviations partially cancel out. The absolute error of the difference is also not greater than the sum of the errors of the given quantities, but the relative error of the difference may be much greater than the relative error of the given quantities.

Let us consider several examples.

The number of children of pre-school age on January 1, 1949 for various ages was as follows:

$$
\begin{array}{lcr}
3 \text{ years} & - & 381,000 \\
4 \text{ years} & - & 385,000 \\
5 \text{ years} & - & 380,000 \\
6 \text{ years} & - & 393,000 \\
\end{array}
$$

We want to establish the total number of children of pre-school age.

We do not know the exact number of children at each age. We know of 3-year-old children that their exact number is between 380,500 and 381,500; similarly, the number of 4-year olds is between 384,500 and 385,500, etc. Thus the total number of children aged 3–6 is between 1,537,000 and 1,541,000. We can see that the number thousands is not all reliable and only tens of thousands are significant.

Thus, in adding we have lost one significant digit. It is easy to check that in this case the relative errors of the components do not differ much from one another (the lowest is 1/786 and the highest 1/760) and that the relative error of the sum has a value close to 1/770.

Let us now suppose that we want to calculate how many repatriants and re-emigrants there were in Poland in 1945–1948. The data are as follows:

| | |
|---|---|
| 1945, January–June | 800,000 persons |
| 1945, July–December | 656,182 persons |
| 1946 | 536,644 persons |
| 1947 | 217,861 persons |
| 1948 | 55,773 persons |

In the first component only hundreds of thousands are significant and in the remaining components units are significant. Therefore the total must be rounded off to hundreds of thousands.

To obtain a value accurate to hundreds of thousands we use one more digit, i.e. tens of thousands. Thus we have the sum $800,000 + 660,000 + 540,000 + 220,000 + 60,000 = 2,280,000$.

This result we round off to hundreds of thousands, or 2,300,000.

We shall now show by an example that subtracting may give a result with a considerable relative error.

There were 381,000 3-year-old children and 385,000 4-year-old children. We want to determine how many more there were of 4-year-olds than 3-year-olds. The exact number of 3-year-old children is between 380,500 and 381,500 and the relative error is $500/381,000 = 0 \cdot 13$ per cent. The exact number of 4-year-old children is between 384,500 and 385,500 and the relative error is also $0 \cdot 13$ per cent. The difference of the approximate numbers is 4000 and the exact value of this difference is between $384,500 - 381,500 = 3000$, and $385,500 - 380,500 = 5000$. Thus the absolute error of this difference is 1000 and the relative error is $1000/4000 = 25$ per cent. It follows that even the first digit of this difference is not significant. The relative error of the difference is here almost 200 times as large as the relative error of the minuend and the relative error of the subtrahend.

In multiplication and division we round off the result according to the number of significant digits. Each of the approximate numbers used in multiplication or division must have at least as many significant digits as we want to have in the product or the quotient.

The relative error of the product and if the quotient is not greater than the sum of the relative errors of particular factors or of the dividend and the divisor. However, in the product, as in the sum, the errors may partially cancel out and consequently the relative error of the product may be smaller than the upper limit. The relative error of the $n$th power of an approximate number is $n$ times as large as the error in the number itself, but the relative error of the $m$th root is $m$ times the relative error of the number whose root is being extracted.

It follows that a sufficiently high power of an approximate number may have fewer significant digits than the number itself but when the power is not too high no significant digits are lost. A root of an approximate number has a many significant digits as the number itself. If we want to obtain a root of an approximate number with a definite number of significant digits we must take into consideration the same number of digits in the approximate number.

Let us consider several examples.

The yield of apples per fruit-bearing apple tree in 1948 was 37 kg and the number of fruit-bearing apple trees was 2,383,800. We want to calculate the total crop of apples on the basis of these data.

The number 37 has two significant digits and the number 2,383,800 has five significant digits. Therefore the result cannot have more than two significant digits. We round off 2,383,800 to three significant digits and hence obtain 2,380,000. We then have

$$37 \text{ kg} \times 2,380,000 = 88,060 \text{ tons.}$$

We round off this result to two significant digits and obtain 88,000 tons.

In 1948 the average monthly production of woolen fabrics was 1951 tons. We want to calculate annual production. The calculation consists in multiplying 1951 tons by 12 and in rounding off the result. The number 1951 has four significant digits and the number 12 is exact (we disregard the fact that the number of days in particular months varies). Therefore, we have to round off the result to four significant digits. We have

$$1951 \text{ tons} \times 12 = 23,412 \text{ tons,}$$

which after rounding off gives 23,410 tons.

The population of the county of Kraśnik in 1946 was 138,000 persons, and the area of this county was 1960 km². We want to determine the population density.

The number 138,000 has four significant digits, the same as the number 1960, and therefore the quotient will also have four significant digits. The result is

$$138,000/1960 = 70 \cdot 41 \text{ persons per km}^2.$$

The indices of passenger traffic carried by the Polish State Railways in 1947 and 1948 in relation to the preceding year were 135 and 117. We want to calculate the geometric mean of these indices.

The product of these indices will have three significant digits because each of them does

$$135 \times 117 = 15,795 = 158 \times 10^2.$$

The geometric mean will also have three significant digits

$$\sqrt{158 \times 10^2} = 12 \cdot 6 \times 10 = 126.$$

We have to calculate $(19 \cdot 5)^{10}$ and $19 \cdot 5$ is an approximate number. We have to determine the number of significant digits in the result of this calculation.

The absolute error of the number $19 \cdot 5$ is equal to one half—of the last decimal place and thus it is $0 \cdot 05$. It follows that the relative error is $0 \cdot 05 / 19 \cdot 5 = 1/390$.

The relative error of the tenth power of this number is 10 times as great and is $10/390 = 1/39 = 2 \cdot 6$ per cent. It follows that the result cannot have more than two significant digits; thus the number of significant digits has decreased.

Also the errors in functions of approximate numbers can be checked but the derivation of the appropriate formulae is very difficult.

However, from the rules for addition and multiplication certain suggestions can be derived concerning simple and composite indices calculated as aggregative indices. Indices are always expressed of ratios of numbers. The number of significant digits in these numbers should correspond to the number of significant digits that we want to have in the index. For instance, if we want to have a price index in full percentage points then its values will usually not deviate much from one hundred and therefore it will be a two- or three digit number; therefore, the prices included in this index should have at least three significant digits.

We mentioned before that some approximate numbers are greater and some less than the exact values and therefore when we add them the errors partially cancel out. Hence, we concluded that the error of the sum may be smaller than the errors of its components.

Since the relative error of the sum of approximate numbers is identical with the average error of the arithmetic mean of these numbers then the error of the arithmetic mean of approximate numbers may be smaller than the errors of the components.

Usually the more components there are the smaller the relative error of the arithmetic mean.

It can also be shown that the relative errors of the geometric mean and of the harmonic mean of approximate numbers decrease as the number of these numbers increases because the errors in the product of the factors and in the sum of the reciprocals of approximate numbers cancel out. The same applies to the standard deviation.

We also operate with approximate numbers in using logarithms since they are always given only to a certain number of decimal places. In can be shown that if we want to have results with a definite number of significant digits we should use logarithmic tables with the same number of decimal places. Thus to obtain results with three significant digits logarithmic tables with three decimal places will suffice.

A logarithmic slide rule of the most common length (25 cm) permits us to read off three significant digits (and at the beginning of the scale even four digits). Therefore, we can use it for performing operations with an accuracy to three significant digits.

## D. TABLES

Table 1 contains areas under the normal curve and gives the part of the area under the curve contained—if we use the notations of Fig. 18.5 on p. 515—between $A$ and $B$; in other words: the probability that under given conditions the actual value is not less than $-X/\sigma$ and not more than $+X/\sigma$.

Table 2 gives the areas under the curve for a small sample (Student's test) and the numbers denote the probability that the actual value is equal to or less than the last column of this table (p. 638) express in the same way the probability when the number of degrees of freedom is infinite. Accordingly, the figures shown in this column are complements to unity of the corresponding figures from Table 1. For instance, for $X/\sigma = 2 \cdot 5$ in Table 1 we have $0 \cdot 9876$ and in Table 2, $0 \cdot 0124$. The differences between the figures in the column for 20 degrees of freedom (the next to the last column on p. 638) and for an infinite number of degrees of freedom (the last column) give us an idea what risk we run when we use the methods for a large sample when the number of units drawn exceeds 20, but is not very large (see pp. 534–36).

In Table 3—for the $\chi^2$ test—the figures denote the probability that for a given value of $\chi^2$ and a given number of the degrees of freedom the distributions compared are consistent. If the figures are small this means that the hypothesis that the distributions are consistent should be rejected. On the other hand, large numbers (i.e. approaching unity) do not always prove that the distributions are consistent (see p. 536 et seq.).

The tables of random numbers (Table 4) are a partial reprint—with certain changes—of the tables prepared by Egon Vielrose and published by the Central Statistical Office (Warsaw, 1951). The author checked the tables and introduced certain changes which increase the scope of the in application. In the original publication the author warned that the numbers can be used in the horizontal direction, but it is not advisable to use them in the vertical direction since in this direction they have not been thoroughly checked. This reservation does not apply to the tables reprinted in this book. The method of using the tables is described in detail on pp. 561–3. As mentioned above, the part of the tables with four—digit numbers can be used if the sample is large, i.e. if at least several hundred units are to be drawn. For smaller samples the second part of the tables with two-digit numbers should be used.

Tables 5 and 6 are auxiliary tables to statistical computations. Table 5 contains seven-digit logarithms of factorials from $n = 1$ to $n = 100$. In the theory of probability it is easiest to calculate the values of the consecutive terms of a binomial distribution by using factorials. We give this small table because such tables are not easy to find in Polish literature although the reader of this book will not use it very often.

The calculation is very simple. According to formula XVIII.1 (p. 511) for $p=0 \cdot 5$ the value of the term in the $(r+1)$th place in a binomial distribution is calculated by the formula $\frac{n!}{r!(n-r)!}$. Let us make a calculation assuming that $n=10$, $r=5$.

In this way we calculate the middle terms of Pascal's triangle from the table on p. 510.

Substituting the figures to the formula we obtain

$$\frac{10!}{5!(10-5)} = \frac{10!}{5!\,5!}.$$

When we use logarithms we have to subtract from log $10! = 6 \cdot 5597630$ twice log $5! = 2 \cdot 0791812$ which gives $2 \cdot 4014006$. Corresponding to this logarithm is the number 252, exactly as in the table.

Let us suppose that we want to calculate the third term for $n=20$. Then $r=2$, $n-r=18$. We have to calculate the quotient

$$\frac{20!}{2!\,18!}$$

From log $20! = 18 \cdot 386246$ we have to subtract log $2! = 0 \cdot 3010300$ and log 18! $= 15 \cdot 8063410$. We obtain $2 \cdot 2787536$. The number 190 corresponds to this logarithm. Since the total number of possibilities for $n=20$ is 1,048,576 ($2^{20}$), the probability that the result will be the same as the third term in the expanded Newton's binomial is very small (the third term in the series for $n=20$ corresponds to the case that 20 coins will fall with 2 heads and 18 tails, or vice versa).

In the general case, when $p \neq 0 \cdot 5$ and the series is asymmetrical the result obtained by formula (XVIII.1) should be multiplied by $p^r q^{n-r}$ (see formula XVIII.2. p. 511).

Table 6 gives squares, square roots and the reciprocals of the numbers from 1 to 1000. This table is of great help in performing calculations. Remember that the reciprocals can be used to substitute multiplication for division when using the calculating machine. This saves time, especially when we have to divide many numbers by the same divisor (e.g. in calculating percentages with respect to one number).

## TABLE 1. AREA UNDER THE NORMAL CURVE

| $\dfrac{X}{\sigma}$ | $P$ | $\dfrac{X}{\sigma}$ | $P$ | $\dfrac{X}{\sigma}$ | $P$ | $\dfrac{X}{\sigma}$ | $P$ |
|---|---|---|---|---|---|---|---|
| 0·01 | 0·0080 | 0·51 | 0·3899 | 1·01 | 0·6875 | 1·51 | 0·8690 |
| 0·02 | 0160 | 0·52 | 3969 | 1·02 | 6923 | 1·52 | 8715 |
| 0·03 | 0239 | 0·53 | 4039 | 1·03 | 6970 | 1·53 | 8740 |
| 0·04 | 0319 | 0·54 | 4108 | 1·04 | 7017 | 1·54 | 8764 |
| 0·05 | 0399 | 0·55 | 4177 | 1·05 | 7063 | 1·55 | 8789 |
| 0·06 | 0478 | 0·56 | 4245 | 1·06 | 7109 | 1·56 | 8812 |
| 0·07 | 0558 | 0·57 | 4313 | 1·07 | 7154 | 1·57 | 8836 |
| 0·08 | 0638 | 0·58 | 4381 | 1·08 | 7199 | 1·58 | 8859 |
| 0·09 | 0717 | 0·59 | 4448 | 1·09 | 7243 | 1·59 | 8882 |
| 0·10 | 0797 | 0·60 | 4515 | 1·10 | 7287 | 1·60 | 8904 |
| 0·11 | 0876 | 0·61 | 4581 | 1·11 | 7330 | 1·61 | 8926 |
| 0·12 | 0955 | 0·62 | 4647 | 1·12 | 7373 | 1·62 | 8948 |
| 0·13 | 1034 | 0·63 | 4713 | 1·13 | 7415 | 1·63 | 8969 |
| 0·14 | 1113 | 0·64 | 4778 | 1·14 | 7457 | 1·64 | 8990 |
| 0·15 | 1192 | 0·65 | 4843 | 1·15 | 7499 | 1·65 | 9011 |
| 0·16 | 1271 | 0·66 | 4907 | 1·16 | 7540 | 1·66 | 9031 |
| 0·17 | 1350 | 0·67 | 4971 | 1·17 | 7580 | 1·67 | 9051 |
| 0·18 | 1428 | 0·68 | 5035 | 1·18 | 7620 | 1·68 | 9070 |
| 0·19 | 1507 | 0·69 | 5098 | 1·19 | 7660 | 1·69 | 9090 |
| 0·20 | 1585 | 0·70 | 5161 | 1·20 | 7699 | 1·70 | 9109 |
| 0·21 | 1663 | 0·71 | 5223 | 1·21 | 7737 | 1·71 | 9127 |
| 0·22 | 1741 | 0·72 | 5285 | 1·22 | 7775 | 1·72 | 9146 |
| 0·23 | 1819 | 0·73 | 5346 | 1·23 | 7813 | 1·73 | 9164 |
| 0·24 | 1897 | 0·74 | 5407 | 1·24 | 7850 | 1·74 | 9181 |
| 0·25 | 1974 | 0·75 | 5467 | 1·25 | 7887 | 1·75 | 9199 |
| 0·26 | 2051 | 0·76 | 5527 | 1·26 | 7923 | 1·76 | 9216 |
| 0·27 | 2128 | 0·77 | 5587 | 1·27 | 7959 | 1·77 | 9233 |
| 0·28 | 2205 | 0·78 | 5646 | 1·28 | 7995 | 1·78 | 9249 |
| 0·29 | 2282 | 0·79 | 5705 | 1·29 | 8029 | 1·79 | 9265 |
| 0·30 | 2358 | 0·80 | 5763 | 1·30 | 8064 | 1·80 | 9281 |
| 0·31 | 2434 | 0·81 | 5821 | 1·31 | 8098 | 1·81 | 9297 |
| 0·32 | 2510 | 0·82 | 5878 | 1·32 | 8132 | 1·82 | 9312 |
| 0·33 | 2586 | 0·83 | 5935 | 1·33 | 8165 | 1·83 | 9327 |
| 0·34 | 2661 | 0·84 | 5991 | 1·34 | 8198 | 1·84 | 9342 |
| 0·35 | 2737 | 0·85 | 6047 | 1·35 | 8230 | 1·85 | 9357 |
| 0·36 | 2812 | 0·86 | 6102 | 1·36 | 8262 | 1·86 | 9371 |
| 0·37 | 2886 | 0·87 | 6157 | 1·37 | 8293 | 1·87 | 9385 |
| 0·38 | 2961 | 0·88 | 6211 | 1·38 | 8324 | 1·88 | 9399 |
| 0·39 | 3035 | 0·89 | 6265 | 1·39 | 8355 | 1·89 | 9412 |
| 0·40 | 3108 | 0·90 | 6319 | 1·40 | 8385 | 1·90 | 9426 |
| 0·41 | 3182 | 0·91 | 6372 | 1·41 | 8415 | 1·91 | 9439 |
| 0·42 | 3255 | 0·92 | 6424 | 1·42 | 8444 | 1·92 | 9451 |
| 0·43 | 3328 | 0·93 | 6476 | 1·43 | 8473 | 1·93 | 9464 |
| 0·44 | 3401 | 0·94 | 6528 | 1·44 | 8501 | 1·94 | 9476 |
| 0·45 | 3473 | 0·95 | 6579 | 1·45 | 8529 | 1·95 | 9488 |
| 0·46 | 3545 | 0·96 | 6629 | 1·46 | 8557 | 1·96 | 9500 |
| 0·47 | 3616 | 0·97 | 6680 | 1·47 | 8584 | 1·97 | 9512 |
| 0·48 | 3688 | 0·98 | 6729 | 1·48 | 8611 | 1·98 | 9523 |
| 0·49 | 3759 | 0·99 | 6778 | 1·49 | 8638 | 1·99 | 9534 |
| 0·50 | 3829 | 1·00 | 6827 | 1·50 | 8664 | 2·00 | 9545 |

See comments on p. 633

TABLE 1. AREA UNDER THE NORMAL CURVE

| $\dfrac{X}{\sigma}$ | $P$ | $\dfrac{X}{\sigma}$ | $P$ | $\dfrac{X}{\sigma}$ | $P$ | $\dfrac{X}{\sigma}$ | $P$ |
|---|---|---|---|---|---|---|---|
| 2·01 | 0·9556 | 2·51 | 0·9879 | 3·01 | 0·99739 | 3·51 | 0·99955 |
| 2·02 | 9566 | 2·52 | 9883 | 3·02 | 99747 | 3·52 | 99957 |
| 2·03 | 9576 | 2·53 | 9886 | 3·03 | 99755 | 3·53 | 99958 |
| 2·04 | 9586 | 2·54 | 9889 | 3·04 | 99763 | 3·54 | 99960 |
| 2·05 | 9596 | 2·55 | 9892 | 3·05 | 99771 | 3·55 | 99961 |
| 2·06 | 9606 | 2·56 | 9895 | 3·06 | 99779 | 3·56 | 99963 |
| 2·07 | 9615 | 2·57 | 9898 | 3·07 | 99786 | 3·57 | 99964 |
| 2·08 | 9625 | 2·58 | 9901 | 3·08 | 99793 | 3·58 | 99966 |
| 2·09 | 9634 | 2·59 | 9904 | 3·09 | 99800 | 3·59 | 99967 |
| 2·10 | 9643 | 2·60 | 9907 | 3·10 | 99806 | 3·60 | 99968 |
| 2·11 | 9651 | 2·61 | 9909 | 3·11 | 99813 | 3·61 | 99969 |
| 2·12 | 9660 | 2·62 | 9912 | 3·12 | 99819 | 3·62 | 99971 |
| 2·13 | 9668 | 2·63 | 9915 | 3·13 | 99825 | 3·63 | 99972 |
| 2·14 | 9676 | 2·64 | 9917 | 3·14 | 99831 | 3·64 | 99973 |
| 2·15 | 9684 | 2·65 | 9920 | 3·15 | 99837 | 3·65 | 99974 |
| 2·16 | 9692 | 2·66 | 9922 | 3·16 | 99842 | 3·66 | 99975 |
| 2·17 | 9700 | 2·67 | 9924 | 3·17 | 99848 | 3·67 | 99976 |
| 2·18 | 9707 | 2·68 | 9926 | 3·18 | 99853 | 3·68 | 99977 |
| 2·19 | 9715 | 2·69 | 9929 | 3·19 | 99858 | 3·69 | 99978 |
| 2·20 | 9722 | 2·70 | 9931 | 3·20 | 99863 | 3·70 | 99978 |
| 2·21 | 9729 | 2·71 | 9933 | 3·21 | 99867 | 3·71 | 99979 |
| 2·22 | 9736 | 2·72 | 9935 | 3·22 | 99872 | 3·72 | 99980 |
| 2·23 | 9743 | 2·73 | 9937 | 3·23 | 99876 | 3·73 | 99981 |
| 2·24 | 9749 | 2·74 | 9939 | 3·24 | 99880 | 3·74 | 99982 |
| 2·25 | 9756 | 2·75 | 9940 | 3·25 | 99885 | 3·75 | 99982 |
| 2·26 | 9762 | 2·76 | 9942 | 3·26 | 99889 | 3·76 | 99983 |
| 2·27 | 9768 | 2·77 | 9944 | 3·27 | 99892 | 3·77 | 99984 |
| 2·28 | 9774 | 2·78 | 9946 | 3·28 | 99896 | 3·78 | 99984 |
| 2·29 | 9780 | 2·79 | 9947 | 3·29 | 99900 | 3·79 | 98985 |
| 2·30 | 9786 | 2·80 | 9949 | 3·30 | 99903 | 3·80 | 99986 |
| 2·31 | 9791 | 2·81 | 9950 | 3·31 | 99907 | 3·81 | 99986 |
| 2·32 | 9797 | 2·82 | 9952 | 3·32 | 99910 | 3·82 | 99987 |
| 2·33 | 9802 | 2·83 | 9953 | 3·33 | 99913 | 3·83 | 99987 |
| 2·34 | 9807 | 2·84 | 9955 | 3·34 | 99916 | 3·84 | 99988 |
| 2·35 | 9812 | 2·85 | 9956 | 3·35 | 99919 | 3·85 | 99988 |
| 2·36 | 9817 | 2·86 | 9958 | 3·36 | 99922 | 3·86 | 99989 |
| 2·37 | 9822 | 2·87 | 9959 | 3·37 | 99925 | 3·87 | 99989 |
| 2·38 | 9827 | 2·88 | 9960 | 3·38 | 99928 | 3·88 | 99990 |
| 2·39 | 9832 | 2·89 | 9961 | 3·39 | 99930 | 3·89 | 99990 |
| 2·40 | 9836 | 2·90 | 9963 | 3·40 | 99933 | 3·90 | 99990 |
| 2·41 | 9840 | 2·91 | 9964 | 3·41 | 99935 | 3·91 | 99991 |
| 2·42 | 9845 | 2·92 | 9965 | 3·42 | 99937 | 3·92 | 99991 |
| 2·43 | 9849 | 2·93 | 9966 | 3·43 | 99940 | 3·93 | 99991 |
| 2·44 | 9853 | 2·94 | 9967 | 3·44 | 99942 | 3·94 | 99992 |
| 2·45 | 9857 | 2·95 | 9968 | 3·45 | 99944 | 3·95 | 99992 |
| 2·46 | 9861 | 2·96 | 9969 | 3·46 | 99946 | 3·96 | 99992 |
| 2·47 | 9865 | 2·97 | 9970 | 3·47 | 99948 | 3·97 | 99993 |
| 2·48 | 9869 | 2·98 | 9971 | 3·48 | 99950 | 3·98 | 99993 |
| 2·49 | 9872 | 2·99 | 9972 | 3·49 | 99952 | 3·99 | 99993 |
| 2·50 | 9876 | 3·00 | 9973 | 3·50 | 99953 | 4·00 | 99994 |

## TABLE 2. AREA UNDER THE CURVE FOR SMALL SAMPLES

| $t = \dfrac{X}{s}$ | Number of degrees of freedom | | | | | | | | | |
|---|---|---|---|---|---|---|---|---|---|---|
| | 1 | 2 | 3 | 4 | 5 | 6 | 7 | 8 | 9 | 10 |
| 0·1 | 0·937 | 0·929 | 0·927 | 0·925 | 0·924 | 0·924 | 0·923 | 0·923 | 0·923 | 0·922 |
| 0·2 | 874 | 860 | 854 | 851 | 849 | 848 | 847 | 846 | 846 | 845 |
| 0·3 | 814 | 792 | 784 | 779 | 776 | 774 | 773 | 772 | 771 | 770 |
| 0·4 | 758 | 728 | 716 | 710 | 706 | 703 | 701 | 700 | 698 | 698 |
| 0·5 | 705 | 667 | 651 | 643 | 638 | 635 | 632 | 631 | 629 | 628 |
| 0·6 | 656 | 609 | 591 | 581 | 575 | 570 | 567 | 565 | 563 | 562 |
| 0·7 | 611 | 556 | 534 | 523 | 515 | 510 | 507 | 504 | 502 | 500 |
| 0·8 | 570 | 508 | 482 | 469 | 460 | 454 | 450 | 447 | 444 | 442 |
| 0·9 | 533 | 463 | 434 | 419 | 409 | 403 | 398 | 394 | 392 | 389 |
| 1·0 | 500 | 423 | 391 | 374 | 363 | 356 | 351 | 347 | 343 | 341 |
| 1·1 | 470 | 386 | 352 | 333 | 321 | 313 | 308 | 303 | 300 | 297 |
| 1·2 | 442 | 353 | 316 | 296 | 284 | 275 | 269 | 264 | 261 | 258 |
| 1·3 | 417 | 323 | 284 | 263 | 250 | 241 | 235 | 230 | 226 | 223 |
| 1·4 | 395 | 296 | 256 | 234 | 220 | 211 | 204 | 199 | 195 | 192 |
| 1·5 | 374 | 272 | 231 | 208 | 194 | 184 | 177 | 172 | 168 | 165 |
| 1·6 | 356 | 251 | 208 | 185 | 170 | 161 | 154 | 148 | 144 | 141 |
| 1·7 | 339 | 231 | 188 | 164 | 150 | 140 | 133 | 128 | 123 | 120 |
| 1·8 | 323 | 214 | 170 | 146 | 132 | 122 | 115 | 110 | 105 | 102 |
| 1·9 | 308 | 198 | 154 | 130 | 116 | 106 | 099 | 094 | 090 | 087 |
| 2·0 | 295 | 184 | 139 | 116 | 102 | 092 | 086 | 081 | 077 | 073 |
| 2·1 | 283 | 171 | 127 | 104 | 090 | 080 | 074 | 069 | 065 | 062 |
| 2·2 | 272 | 159 | 115 | 093 | 079 | 070 | 064 | 059 | 055 | 052 |
| 2·3 | 261 | 148 | 105 | 083 | 070 | 061 | 055 | 050 | 047 | 044 |
| 2·4 | 251 | 138 | 096 | 074 | 062 | 053 | 047 | 043 | 040 | 037 |
| 2·5 | 242 | 130 | 088 | 067 | 054 | 047 | 041 | 037 | 034 | 031 |
| 2·6 | 234 | 122 | 080 | 060 | 048 | 041 | 035 | 032 | 029 | 026 |
| 2·7 | 226 | 114 | 074 | 054 | 043 | 036 | 031 | 027 | 024 | 022 |
| 2·8 | 218 | 107 | 068 | 049 | 038 | 031 | 027 | 023 | 021 | 019 |
| 2·9 | 211 | 101 | 063 | 044 | 034 | 027 | 023 | 020 | 018 | 016 |
| 3·0 | 205 | 095 | 058 | 040 | 030 | 024 | 020 | 017 | 015 | 013 |
| 3·1 | 199 | 090 | 053 | 036 | 027 | 021 | 017 | 015 | 013 | 011 |
| 3·2 | 193 | 085 | 048 | 033 | 024 | 019 | 015 | 013 | 011 | 009 |
| 3·3 | 187 | 081 | 045 | 030 | 021 | 016 | 013 | 011 | 009 | 008 |
| 3·4 | 182 | 077 | 042 | 027 | 019 | 014 | 011 | 009 | 008 | 007 |
| 3·5 | 177 | 073 | 039 | 025 | 017 | 013 | 010 | 008 | 007 | 006 |
| 3·6 | 172 | 069 | 037 | 023 | 016 | 011 | 009 | 007 | 006 | 005 |
| 3·7 | 168 | 066 | 034 | 021 | 014 | 010 | 008 | 006 | 005 | 004 |
| 3·8 | 164 | 063 | 032 | 019 | 013 | 009 | 007 | 005 | 004 | 003 |
| 3·9 | 160 | 060 | 030 | 018 | 011 | 008 | 006 | 005 | 004 | 003 |
| 4·0 | 156 | 057 | 028 | 016 | 010 | 007 | 005 | 004 | 003 | 003 |
| 4·1 | 152 | 055 | 026 | 015 | 009 | 006 | 005 | 003 | 003 | 002 |
| 4·2 | 149 | 052 | 025 | 014 | 008 | 006 | 004 | 003 | 002 | 002 |
| 4·3 | 145 | 050 | 023 | 013 | 008 | 005 | 004 | 003 | 002 | 002 |
| 4·4 | 142 | 048 | 022 | 012 | 007 | 005 | 003 | 002 | 002 | 001 |
| 4·5 | 139 | 046 | 020 | 011 | 006 | 004 | 003 | 002 | 001 | 001 |
| 4·6 | 136 | 044 | 019 | 010 | 006 | 004 | 002 | 002 | 001 | 001 |
| 4·7 | 133 | 042 | 018 | 009 | 005 | 003 | 002 | 002 | 001 | 001 |
| 4·8 | 131 | 041 | 017 | 009 | 005 | 003 | 002 | 001 | 001 | 001 |
| 4·9 | 128 | 039 | 016 | 008 | 004 | 003 | 002 | 001 | 001 | 001 |
| 5·0 | 126 | 038 | 015 | 007 | 004 | 002 | 002 | 001 | 001 | 001 |

See comments on p. 633

APPENDIX

## TABLE 2. AREA UNDER THE CURVE FOR SMALL SAMPLES

| $t = \dfrac{X}{s}$ | \multicolumn{11}{c}{Number of degrees of freedom} |
|---|---|

| $t = \dfrac{X}{s}$ | 11 | 12 | 13 | 14 | 15 | 16 | 17 | 18 | 19 | 20 | ∞ |
|---|---|---|---|---|---|---|---|---|---|---|---|
| 0·1 | 0·922 | 0·922 | 0·922 | 0·922 | 0·922 | 0·922 | 0·922 | 0·921 | 0·921 | 0·921 | 0·9203 |
| 0·2 | 845 | 845 | 845 | 844 | 844 | 844 | 844 | 844 | 844 | 844 | 8415 |
| 0·3 | 770 | 769 | 769 | 769 | 768 | 768 | 768 | 768 | 767 | 767 | 7642 |
| 0·4 | 697 | 696 | 696 | 695 | 695 | 694 | 694 | 694 | 694 | 693 | 6892 |
| 0·5 | 627 | 626 | 625 | 625 | 624 | 624 | 623 | 623 | 623 | 623 | 6171 |
| 0·6 | 561 | 560 | 559 | 558 | 557 | 557 | 556 | 556 | 556 | 555 | 5485 |
| 0·7 | 498 | 497 | 496 | 495 | 495 | 494 | 493 | 493 | 492 | 492 | 4839 |
| 0·8 | 441 | 439 | 438 | 437 | 436 | 435 | 435 | 434 | 434 | 433 | 4237 |
| 0·9 | 387 | 386 | 384 | 383 | 382 | 381 | 381 | 380 | 379 | 379 | 3681 |
| 1·0 | 339 | 337 | 336 | 334 | 333 | 332 | 331 | 331 | 330 | 329 | 3173 |
| 1·1 | 295 | 293 | 291 | 290 | 289 | 288 | 287 | 286 | 285 | 284 | 2713 |
| 1·2 | 255 | 253 | 252 | 250 | 249 | 248 | 247 | 246 | 245 | 244 | 2301 |
| 1·3 | 220 | 218 | 216 | 215 | 213 | 212 | 211 | 210 | 209 | 208 | 1936 |
| 1·4 | 189 | 187 | 185 | 183 | 182 | 181 | 179 | 179 | 178 | 177 | 1615 |
| 1·5 | 162 | 159 | 158 | 156 | 154 | 153 | 152 | 151 | 150 | 149 | 1336 |
| 1·6 | 138 | 136 | 134 | 132 | 130 | 129 | 128 | 127 | 126 | 125 | 1096 |
| 1·7 | 117 | 115 | 113 | 111 | 110 | 108 | 107 | 106 | 105 | 105 | 0891 |
| 1·8 | 099 | 097 | 095 | 093 | 092 | 091 | 090 | 089 | 088 | 087 | 0719 |
| 1·9 | 084 | 082 | 080 | 078 | 077 | 076 | 075 | 074 | 073 | 072 | 0574 |
| 2·0 | 071 | 069 | 067 | 065 | 064 | 063 | 062 | 061 | 060 | 059 | 0455 |
| 2·1 | 060 | 058 | 056 | 054 | 053 | 052 | 051 | 050 | 049 | 049 | 0357 |
| 2·2 | 050 | 048 | 046 | 045 | 044 | 043 | 042 | 041 | 040 | 040 | 0278 |
| 2·3 | 042 | 040 | 039 | 037 | 036 | 035 | 034 | 034 | 033 | 032 | 0214 |
| 2·4 | 035 | 034 | 032 | 031 | 030 | 029 | 028 | 027 | 027 | 026 | 0164 |
| 2·5 | 030 | 028 | 027 | 025 | 024 | 024 | 023 | 022 | 022 | 021 | 0124 |
| 2·6 | 025 | 023 | 022 | 021 | 020 | 019 | 019 | 018 | 018 | 017 | 0093 |
| 2·7 | 021 | 019 | 018 | 017 | 016 | 016 | 015 | 015 | 014 | 014 | 0069 |
| 2·8 | 017 | 016 | 015 | 014 | 013 | 013 | 012 | 012 | 011 | 011 | 0051 |
| 2·9 | 014 | 013 | 012 | 012 | 011 | 010 | 010 | 010 | 009 | 009 | 0037 |
| 3·0 | 012 | 011 | 010 | 010 | 009 | 008 | 008 | 008 | 007 | 007 | 0027 |
| 3·1 | 010 | 009 | 008 | 008 | 007 | 007 | 006 | 006 | 006 | 005 | 0019 |
| 3·2 | 008 | 008 | 007 | 006 | 006 | 006 | 005 | 005 | 005 | 004 | 0014 |
| 3·3 | 007 | 006 | 006 | 005 | 005 | 005 | 004 | 004 | 004 | 004 | 0010 |
| 3·4 | 006 | 005 | 005 | 004 | 004 | 004 | 003 | 003 | 003 | 003 | 0007 |
| 3·5 | 005 | 004 | 004 | 004 | 003 | 003 | 003 | 003 | 002 | 002 | 0005 |
| 3·6 | 004 | 004 | 003 | 003 | 003 | 002 | 002 | 002 | 002 | 002 | 0003 |
| 3·7 | 004 | 003 | 003 | 002 | 002 | 002 | 002 | 002 | 002 | 001 | 0002 |
| 3·8 | 003 | 003 | 002 | 002 | 002 | 002 | 001 | 001 | 001 | 001 | 0001 |
| 3·9 | 002 | 002 | 002 | 002 | 001 | 001 | 001 | 001 | 001 | 001 | 0001 |
| 4·0 | 002 | 002 | 002 | 001 | 001 | 001 | 001 | 001 | 001 | 001 | 0001 |
| 4·1 | 002 | 001 | 001 | 001 | 001 | 001 | 001 | 001 | 001 | 001 | 0000 |
| 4·2 | 001 | 001 | 001 | 001 | 001 | 001 | 001 | 001 | 000 | 000 | |
| 4·3 | 001 | 001 | 001 | 001 | 001 | 001 | 000 | 000 | | | |
| 4·4 | 001 | 001 | 001 | 001 | 001 | 000 | | | | | |
| 4·5 | 001 | 001 | 001 | 000 | 000 | | | | | | |
| 4·6 | 001 | 001 | 000 | | | | | | | | |
| 4·7 | 001 | 001 | | | | | | | | | |
| 4·8 | 001 | 000 | | | | | | | | | |
| 4·9 | 000 | | | | | | | | | | |
| 5·0 | | | | | | | | | | | |

## TABLE 3. $\chi^2$ PROBABILITY TABLE

| | | | | | Number of degrees of freedem | | | | | |
|---|---|---|---|---|---|---|---|---|---|---|
| $\chi^2$ | 1 | 2 | 3 | 4 | 5 | 6 | 7 | 8 | 9 | 10 |
| 1 | 0·317 | 0·607 | 0·801 | 0·910 | 0·963 | 0·986 | 0·995 | 0·998 | 0·999 | 1·000 |
| 2 | 157 | 368 | 572 | 736 | 849 | 920 | 960 | 981 | 991 | 0·996 |
| 3 | 083 | 223 | 392 | 558 | 700 | 809 | 885 | 934 | 964 | 981 |
| 4 | 046 | 135 | 261 | 406 | 549 | 677 | 780 | 857 | 911 | 947 |
| 5 | 025 | 082 | 172 | 287 | 416 | 544 | 660 | 758 | 834 | 891 |
| 6 | 014 | 050 | 112 | 199 | 306 | 423 | 540 | 647 | 740 | 815 |
| 7 | 008 | 030 | 072 | 136 | 221 | 321 | 429 | 537 | 637 | 725 |
| 8 | 005 | 018 | 046 | 092 | 156 | 238 | 333 | 433 | 534 | 629 |
| 9 | 003 | 011 | 029 | 061 | 109 | 174 | 253 | 342 | 437 | 532 |
| 10 | 002 | 007 | 019 | 040 | 075 | 125 | 189 | 265 | 350 | 440 |
| 11 | 001 | 004 | 012 | 027 | 051 | 088 | 139 | 202 | 276 | 358 |
| 12 | 001 | 002 | 007 | 017 | 035 | 062 | 101 | 151 | 213 | 285 |
| 13 | 000 | 002 | 005 | 011 | 023 | 043 | 072 | 112 | 163 | 224 |
| 14 | 000 | 001 | 003 | 007 | 016 | 030 | 051 | 082 | 122 | 173 |
| 15 | 000 | 001 | 002 | 005 | 010 | 020 | 036 | 059 | 091 | 132 |
| 16 | 000 | 000 | 001 | 003 | 007 | 014 | 025 | 042 | 067 | 100 |
| 17 | 000 | 000 | 001 | 002 | 005 | 009 | 017 | 030 | 049 | 074 |
| 18 | 000 | 000 | 000 | 001 | 003 | 006 | 012 | 021 | 035 | 055 |
| 19 | 000 | 000 | 000 | 001 | 002 | 004 | 008 | 015 | 025 | 040 |
| 20 | 000 | 000 | 000 | 000 | 001 | 003 | 006 | 010 | 018 | 029 |
| 21 | 000 | 000 | 000 | 000 | 001 | 002 | 004 | 007 | 013 | 021 |
| 22 | 000 | 000 | 000 | 000 | 001 | 001 | 003 | 005 | 009 | 015 |
| 23 | 000 | 000 | 000 | 000 | 000 | 001 | 002 | 003 | 006 | 011 |
| 24 | 000 | 000 | 000 | 000 | 000 | 001 | 001 | 002 | 004 | 008 |
| 25 | 000 | 000 | 000 | 000 | 000 | 000 | 001 | 002 | 003 | 005 |
| 26 | 000 | 000 | 000 | 000 | 000 | 000 | 001 | 001 | 002 | 004 |
| 27 | 000 | 000 | 000 | 000 | 000 | 000 | 000 | 001 | 001 | 003 |
| 28 | 000 | 000 | 000 | 000 | 000 | 000 | 000 | 000 | 001 | 002 |
| 29 | 000 | 000 | 000 | 000 | 000 | 000 | 000 | 000 | 001 | 001 |
| 30 | 000 | 000 | 000 | 000 | 000 | 000 | 000 | 000 | 000 | 001 |

See comments on p. 633

APPENDIX

## TABLE 3. $\chi^2$ PROBABILITY TABLE

| | Number of degrees of freedom | | | | | | | | | |
|---|---|---|---|---|---|---|---|---|---|---|
| $\chi^2$ | 11 | 12 | 13 | 14 | 15 | 16 | 17 | 18 | 19 | 20 |
| 1 | 1·000 | 1·000 | 1·000 | 1·000 | 1·000 | 1·000 | 1·000 | 1·000 | 1·000 | 1·000 |
| 2 | 0·998 | 0·999 | 1·000 | 1·000 | 1·000 | 1·000 | 1·000 | 1·000 | 1·000 | 1·000 |
| 3 | 991 | 996 | 0·998 | 0·999 | 1·000 | 1·000 | 1·000 | 1·000 | 1·000 | 1·000 |
| 4 | 970 | 983 | 991 | 995 | 998 | 0·999 | 0·999 | 1·000 | 1·000 | 1·000 |
| 5 | 931 | 958 | 975 | 986 | 992 | 996 | 998 | 0,999 | 0·999 | 1·000 |
| 6 | 873 | 916 | 946 | 966 | 980 | 988 | 993 | 996 | 998 | 0,999 |
| 7 | 799 | 858 | 902 | 935 | 958 | 973 | 984 | 990 | 994 | 997 |
| 8 | 713 | 785 | 844 | 889 | 924 | 949 | 967 | 979 | 987 | 992 |
| 9 | 622 | 703 | 773 | 831 | 878 | 913 | 940 | 960 | 973 | 983 |
| 10 | 530 | 616 | 694 | 762 | 820 | 867 | 904 | 932 | 953 | 968 |
| 11 | 443 | 529 | 611 | 686 | 753 | 809 | 857 | 894 | 924 | 946 |
| 12 | 363 | 446 | 528 | 606 | 679 | 744 | 800 | 847 | 886 | 916 |
| 13 | 293 | 369 | 448 | 527 | 602 | 673 | 736 | 792 | 839 | 877 |
| 14 | 233 | 301 | 374 | 450 | 526 | 599 | 667 | 729 | 784 | 830 |
| 15 | 182 | 241 | 307 | 378 | 451 | 525 | 595 | 662 | 723 | 776 |
| 16 | 141 | 191 | 249 | 313 | 382 | 453 | 524 | 593 | 657 | 717 |
| 17 | 108 | 150 | 199 | 256 | 319 | 386 | 454 | 523 | 590 | 653 |
| 18 | 082 | 116 | 158 | 207 | 263 | 324 | 389 | 456 | 522 | 587 |
| 19 | 061 | 089 | 123 | 165 | 214 | 269 | 329 | 392 | 457 | 522 |
| 20 | 045 | 067 | 095 | 130 | 172 | 220 | 274 | 333 | 395 | 458 |
| 21 | 033 | 050 | 073 | 102 | 137 | 179 | 226 | 279 | 337 | 397 |
| 22 | 024 | 038 | 055 | 079 | 108 | 143 | 185 | 232 | 284 | 341 |
| 23 | 018 | 028 | 042 | 060 | 084 | 114 | 149 | 191 | 237 | 289 |
| 24 | 013 | 020 | 031 | 046 | 065 | 090 | 119 | 155 | 196 | 242 |
| 25 | 009 | 015 | 023 | 035 | 050 | 070 | 095 | 125 | 161 | 201 |
| 26 | 006 | 011 | 017 | 026 | 038 | 054 | 074 | 100 | 130 | 166 |
| 27 | 005 | 008 | 012 | 019 | 029 | 041 | 058 | 079 | 105 | 135 |
| 28 | 003 | 006 | 009 | 014 | 022 | 032 | 045 | 062 | 083 | 109 |
| 29 | 002 | 004 | 007 | 010 | 016 | 024 | 035 | 048 | 066 | 088 |
| 30 | 002 | 003 | 005 | 008 | 012 | 018 | 026 | 037 | 052 | 070 |

TABLE 3. $\chi^2$ PROBABILITY TABLE

### Number of degrees of freedom

| $\chi^2$ | 21 | 22 | 23 | 24 | 25 | 26 | 27 | 28 | 29 |
|---|---|---|---|---|---|---|---|---|---|
| 1 | 1·000 | 1·000 | 1·000 | 1·000 | 1·000 | 1·000 | 1·000 | 1·000 | 1·000 |
| 2 | 1·000 | 1·000 | 1·000 | 1·000 | 1·000 | 1·000 | 1·000 | 1·000 | 1·000 |
| 3 | 1·000 | 1·000 | 1·000 | 1·000 | 1·000 | 1·000 | 1·000 | 1·000 | 1·000 |
| 4 | 1·000 | 1·000 | 1·000 | 1·000 | 1·000 | 1·000 | 1·000 | 1·000 | 1·000 |
| 5 | 1·000 | 1·000 | 1·000 | 1·000 | 1·000 | 1·000 | 1·000 | 1·000 | 1·000 |
| 6 | 0·999 | 1·000 | 1·000 | 1·000 | 1·000 | 1·000 | 1·000 | 1·000 | 1·000 |
| 7 | 998 | 0·999 | 0·999 | 1·000 | 1·000 | 1·000 | 1·000 | 1·000 | 1·000 |
| 8 | 995 | 997 | 998 | 0·999 | 0·999 | 1·000 | 1·000 | 1·000 | 1·000 |
| 9 | 989 | 993 | 996 | 998 | 999 | 0·999 | 1·000 | 1·000 | 1·000 |
| 10 | 979 | 986 | 991 | 995 | 997 | 998 | 0·999 | 0·999 | 1·000 |
| 11 | 963 | 975 | 983 | 989 | 993 | 996 | 997 | 998 | 0·999 |
| 12 | 940 | 957 | 970 | 980 | 987 | 991 | 994 | 996 | 998 |
| 13 | 909 | 933 | 952 | 966 | 977 | 984 | 989 | 993 | 995 |
| 14 | 870 | 901 | 927 | 947 | 962 | 973 | 981 | 987 | 991 |
| 15 | 823 | 862 | 895 | 921 | 941 | 957 | 969 | 978 | 985 |
| 16 | 770 | 816 | 855 | 888 | 915 | 936 | 953 | 966 | 976 |
| 17 | 711 | 763 | 809 | 849 | 882 | 909 | 931 | 949 | 962 |
| 18 | 649 | 706 | 757 | 803 | 842 | 876 | 904 | 926 | 944 |
| 19 | 585 | 645 | 701 | 752 | 797 | 836 | 870 | 898 | 921 |
| 20 | 521 | 583 | 642 | 697 | 747 | 792 | 831 | 864 | 893 |
| 21 | 459 | 521 | 581 | 639 | 693 | 742 | 786 | 825 | 859 |
| 22 | 400 | 460 | 520 | 579 | 636 | 689 | 737 | 781 | 820 |
| 23 | 344 | 402 | 461 | 520 | 578 | 633 | 685 | 733 | 777 |
| 24 | 293 | 347 | 404 | 462 | 519 | 576 | 630 | 682 | 729 |
| 25 | 247 | 297 | 350 | 406 | 462 | 519 | 574 | 628 | 678 |
| 26 | 206 | 252 | 301 | 353 | 408 | 463 | 519 | 573 | 625 |
| 27 | 171 | 211 | 256 | 304 | 356 | 409 | 464 | 518 | 572 |
| 28 | 140 | 176 | 216 | 260 | 308 | 358 | 411 | 464 | 518 |
| 29 | 114 | 145 | 180 | 220 | 264 | 311 | 361 | 413 | 465 |
| 30 | 092 | 118 | 149 | 185 | 224 | 268 | 314 | 363 | 414 |

TABLE 4. RANDOM NUMBERS
Table 1

| 7875 | 8695 | 9718 | 9086 | 8600 | 0860 | 7715 | 1690 | 0793 | 2141 |
|------|------|------|------|------|------|------|------|------|------|
| 4693 | 2122 | 3861 | 2254 | 0368 | 9337 | 6227 | 4870 | 3616 | 5036 |
| 1650 | 0507 | 5455 | 3317 | 6935 | 3867 | 0748 | 9775 | 5501 | 5182 |
| 8818 | 4330 | 3702 | 8898 | 0822 | 8674 | 0493 | 5584 | 7101 | 7112 |
| 2493 | 0341 | 7572 | 3715 | 3217 | 7946 | 9657 | 5827 | 7758 | 5562 |
| 7588 | 8347 | 2277 | 8783 | 6490 | 8582 | 7684 | 4580 | 4727 | 7995 |
| 5622 | 4782 | 7836 | 4908 | 5827 | 6845 | 0379 | 5073 | 2679 | 0196 |
| 3021 | 3550 | 0903 | 9402 | 7315 | 2121 | 1404 | 8391 | 4292 | 0283 |
| 6384 | 8151 | 5778 | 1197 | 4351 | 8438 | 9283 | 0589 | 5816 | 7016 |
| 7000 | 1054 | 7899 | 7971 | 6700 | 0105 | 4789 | 1466 | 2742 | 2753 |
| 6949 | 1975 | 6871 | 9722 | 0424 | 4073 | 8256 | 3696 | 1063 | 2941 |
| 3732 | 1295 | 1633 | 4050 | 3291 | 3156 | 5929 | 1315 | 6063 | 6718 |
| 1083 | 6718 | 0857 | 2128 | 4424 | 7609 | 0592 | 3121 | 8024 | 7114 |
| 5308 | 7625 | 3463 | 4101 | 5797 | 2088 | 7876 | 8910 | 2629 | 1861 |
| 3310 | 9249 | 9369 | 7589 | 1211 | 0555 | 2865 | 7048 | 3916 | 3487 |
| 5048 | 9142 | 9119 | 1820 | 2231 | 2183 | 6384 | 8340 | 8024 | 7811 |
| 9743 | 5184 | 2918 | 4530 | 8763 | 8928 | 3031 | 5253 | 4167 | 0001 |
| 0536 | 7234 | 3249 | 1670 | 1579 | 4789 | 1872 | 0827 | 4227 | 5367 |
| 2656 | 8919 | 4919 | 1202 | 6719 | 7224 | 2076 | 1320 | 4243 | 1073 |
| 8256 | 3690 | 9411 | 9936 | 6106 | 3097 | 5373 | 2176 | 2301 | 4754 |
| 3789 | 2635 | 6945 | 5656 | 9710 | 1835 | 0480 | 9271 | 8849 | 3165 |
| 6713 | 9673 | 5626 | 7101 | 9356 | 2500 | 4647 | 5754 | 3789 | 2635 |
| 6429 | 9262 | 3894 | 5565 | 8856 | 3016 | 9748 | 3714 | 5982 | 5684 |
| 0939 | 1123 | 9320 | 1304 | 2874 | 5472 | 5485 | 8024 | 2587 | 4987 |
| 2478 | 9871 | 5428 | 7348 | 7145 | 7725 | 4146 | 8785 | 7423 | 2541 |
| 4687 | 5478 | 5742 | 3254 | 0869 | 5548 | 7537 | 7551 | 9054 | 2447 |
| 8523 | 1484 | 8754 | 5939 | 5175 | 3751 | 2321 | 4826 | 9387 | 4587 |
| 5411 | 0028 | 7095 | 1291 | 0465 | 6930 | 2114 | 8847 | 3958 | 7930 |
| 1649 | 0880 | 7931 | 3213 | 4896 | 1335 | 5820 | 6836 | 7399 | 9824 |
| 5158 | 7501 | 1937 | 1881 | 7319 | 2227 | 6104 | 7173 | 4440 | 3446 |
| 1757 | 7833 | 5067 | 0419 | 6811 | 9098 | 3769 | 4483 | 3765 | 8245 |
| 1587 | 5011 | 9726 | 2844 | 5023 | 5635 | 3768 | 4150 | 5080 | 6848 |
| 1574 | 0544 | 3573 | 3092 | 6776 | 0740 | 5380 | 4656 | 9181 | 6772 |
| 8159 | 7611 | 4615 | 9965 | 4160 | 6354 | 3050 | 5760 | 5081 | 4974 |
| 9800 | 6655 | 7666 | 1305 | 5163 | 0995 | 1116 | 8062 | 1538 | 0777 |
| 4023 | 4670 | 6758 | 0827 | 2351 | 0154 | 0610 | 7356 | 7130 | 8770 |
| 2891 | 2461 | 5676 | 8812 | 8191 | 2833 | 1815 | 1328 | 1281 | 8573 |
| 6702 | 1288 | 3648 | 2982 | 9727 | 5498 | 4796 | 9890 | 2571 | 8397 |
| 9862 | 2910 | 9612 | 8311 | 3041 | 3730 | 3578 | 3109 | 4862 | 1095 |
| 3052 | 0351 | 1715 | 5923 | 1860 | 9079 | 9685 | 2107 | 1784 | 7818 |
| 1300 | 5491 | 7035 | 1898 | 0323 | 0421 | 0714 | 4444 | 0097 | 9968 |
| 0746 | 6057 | 2182 | 9032 | 9516 | 0384 | 2786 | 5440 | 5520 | 8862 |
| 5011 | 1339 | 6206 | 1993 | 4300 | 8053 | 5097 | 6799 | 6627 | 6996 |
| 6224 | 6469 | 8162 | 8437 | 3573 | 3771 | 5139 | 3444 | 8565 | 3899 |
| 0155 | 3732 | 3029 | 9881 | 6356 | 4229 | 4587 | 1521 | 8705 | 1886 |
| 9552 | 6952 | 8124 | 7424 | 1237 | 9799 | 4351 | 5135 | 5929 | 1785 |
| 3860 | 9230 | 8392 | 4158 | 3979 | 5555 | 2113 | 6785 | 1170 | 8584 |
| 3979 | 6374 | 2776 | 8369 | 3933 | 1993 | 1739 | 9602 | 1333 | 3520 |
| 4675 | 3819 | 5948 | 7604 | 5956 | 3561 | 5385 | 7044 | 1092 | 1320 |
| 7674 | 3516 | 9633 | 4253 | 9551 | 2934 | 6394 | 1451 | 5754 | 1608 |

See comments on p. 633

## TABLE 4. RANDOM NUMBERS
### Table 1

| | | | | | | | | | |
|---|---|---|---|---|---|---|---|---|---|
| 4266 | 1833 | 1920 | 6140 | 9806 | 1980 | 2124 | 7160 | 2395 | 5496 |
| 9326 | 9451 | 7687 | 2194 | 2154 | 8626 | 5273 | 7401 | 5485 | 7006 |
| 3360 | 7336 | 6112 | 0067 | 4657 | 8891 | 0981 | 8172 | 3475 | 3668 |
| 7695 | 8271 | 3176 | 5233 | 1675 | 7959 | 0097 | 8138 | 6258 | 1316 |
| 0562 | 0265 | 3884 | 6613 | 7555 | 6072 | 4812 | 2508 | 5849 | 5606 |
| | | | | | | | | | |
| 3117 | 0579 | 1518 | 7745 | 6331 | 0055 | 6613 | 1165 | 0494 | 2737 |
| 3373 | 1201 | 1616 | 5253 | 7692 | 4582 | 1532 | 2434 | 7435 | 9308 |
| 4797 | 6115 | 5354 | 4885 | 1128 | 5845 | 7971 | 0776 | 9193 | 3186 |
| 7084 | 9440 | 0610 | 1333 | 1020 | 1553 | 6874 | 8111 | 8439 | 5171 |
| 2077 | 5204 | 0147 | 0275 | 7940 | 2005 | 4349 | 8211 | 5244 | 0556 |
| | | | | | | | | | |
| 8425 | 9790 | 2850 | 6893 | 1414 | 0923 | 3077 | 6358 | 4082 | 2604 |
| 5008 | 3587 | 7722 | 9855 | 9086 | 5121 | 1357 | 9237 | 3381 | 5194 |
| 5879 | 5136 | 7146 | 5498 | 9477 | 4934 | 4431 | 9456 | 0380 | 6048 |
| 4834 | 2688 | 0162 | 7590 | 7694 | 5176 | 6164 | 0819 | 4042 | 9638 |
| 6019 | 2653 | 9949 | 5183 | 5669 | 2379 | 9169 | 4388 | 8271 | 0897 |
| | | | | | | | | | |
| 4456 | 6666 | 7277 | 5740 | 3535 | 0520 | 7083 | 1958 | 7383 | 6050 |
| 1040 | 2938 | 7097 | 9417 | 6440 | 3701 | 9889 | 5292 | 8656 | 5716 |
| 5920 | 4839 | 7960 | 5010 | 1111 | 5227 | 6929 | 9205 | 4169 | 2155 |
| 3262 | 7698 | 2095 | 3504 | 3310 | 8842 | 7777 | 4681 | 8757 | 3288 |
| 3422 | 3163 | 2964 | 4839 | 2482 | 6342 | 5426 | 4491 | 3354 | 1550 |
| | | | | | | | | | |
| 5200 | 4662 | 1067 | 6596 | 5213 | 1391 | 9709 | 5764 | 1316 | 9836 |
| 4382 | 1950 | 5826 | 9658 | 3542 | 2147 | 7325 | 0145 | 7065 | 6088 |
| 3075 | 2963 | 6050 | 2543 | 3838 | 4683 | 9409 | 7941 | 5081 | 3349 |
| 6392 | 5109 | 8070 | 0504 | 3131 | 5151 | 3376 | 5783 | 7589 | 1719 |
| 2992 | 4830 | 8819 | 4907 | 6895 | 0626 | 7856 | 5908 | 5996 | 8176 |
| | | | | | | | | | |
| 1042 | 7968 | 9335 | 3676 | 7449 | 3535 | 3676 | 7265 | 5834 | 6632 |
| 8201 | 7552 | 7554 | 9778 | 9603 | 1056 | 2213 | 9888 | 7432 | 2107 |
| 0261 | 4793 | 0460 | 8583 | 3473 | 9666 | 1154 | 7775 | 6521 | 0894 |
| 5159 | 1827 | 8329 | 8481 | 0239 | 1432 | 6181 | 4440 | 6472 | 1297 |
| 7015 | 6589 | 2563 | 7734 | 2862 | 4953 | 4104 | 4659 | 3273 | 1617 |
| | | | | | | | | | |
| 9197 | 1648 | 3196 | 0991 | 1074 | 7536 | 9231 | 0151 | 5916 | 9033 |
| 8142 | 0953 | 1572 | 3523 | 9706 | 8005 | 3784 | 6377 | 0332 | 4213 |
| 1566 | 0563 | 8832 | 6191 | 4474 | 3894 | 7950 | 0685 | 0560 | 7206 |
| 0362 | 1316 | 3605 | 7469 | 0329 | 7130 | 8797 | 7144 | 3931 | 2641 |
| 9964 | 5760 | 8798 | 1697 | 6530 | 8280 | 8999 | 3769 | 2857 | 5019 |
| | | | | | | | | | |
| 6416 | 9596 | 0461 | 2575 | 0135 | 6928 | 3593 | 7940 | 8990 | 1739 |
| 0899 | 6489 | 8310 | 7109 | 9154 | 8480 | 4169 | 7637 | 9418 | 5246 |
| 7555 | 9860 | 1078 | 4041 | 3425 | 2124 | 6752 | 5298 | 8411 | 1997 |
| 6653 | 3931 | 9746 | 6681 | 8012 | 0968 | 3035 | 6846 | 6146 | 5465 |
| 9935 | 0705 | 8944 | 9359 | 2235 | 7204 | 5230 | 5966 | 0452 | 4021 |
| | | | | | | | | | |
| 1687 | 3483 | 5103 | 6616 | 2842 | 1067 | 3124 | 3811 | 2985 | 9131 |
| 4783 | 8325 | 8627 | 5214 | 6128 | 9435 | 8657 | 5672 | 0500 | 5619 |
| 7520 | 8697 | 1346 | 6143 | 1315 | 1950 | 6204 | 2744 | 9359 | 8887 |
| 4159 | 1822 | 5693 | 5637 | 7357 | 1645 | 7235 | 5106 | 8505 | 6879 |
| 8101 | 7398 | 1124 | 6379 | 4041 | 3597 | 4609 | 6473 | 2501 | 8428 |
| | | | | | | | | | |
| 8319 | 2390 | 7208 | 9256 | 5605 | 0133 | 7678 | 5968 | 3221 | 7832 |
| 0262 | 4960 | 9970 | 6806 | 0361 | 6979 | 6489 | 4185 | 2516 | 6810 |
| 7580 | 5913 | 3827 | 6089 | 2074 | 3785 | 8424 | 2566 | 7633 | 4165 |
| 4513 | 9696 | 2345 | 2464 | 0053 | 4291 | 5998 | 3204 | 0267 | 7998 |
| 3449 | 7980 | 8099 | 9859 | 0530 | 2946 | 2431 | 1721 | 0421 | 6499 |

TABLE 4. RANDOM NUMBERS
Table 1

| | | | | | | | | | |
|---|---|---|---|---|---|---|---|---|---|
| 1498 | 3222 | 5087 | 8199 | 3133 | 5466 | 8986 | 3423 | 9013 | 6476 |
| 3284 | 8491 | 2283 | 6283 | 4067 | 8115 | 1066 | 3240 | 0434 | 3676 |
| 2319 | 5745 | 7157 | 6134 | 8539 | 6823 | 9629 | 2583 | 5542 | 1733 |
| 4558 | 7615 | 5803 | 5606 | 1782 | 2253 | 6429 | 2254 | 4567 | 0048 |
| 0353 | 9402 | 0618 | 1422 | 7204 | 1603 | 1211 | 5023 | 3565 | 2630 |
| 9325 | 2501 | 4425 | 9689 | 1664 | 1315 | 2085 | 2706 | 8183 | 3488 |
| 7081 | 9685 | 3248 | 0217 | 3701 | 9438 | 8948 | 2579 | 8339 | 6179 |
| 5697 | 8746 | 1197 | 3790 | 5310 | 0660 | 2655 | 1334 | 7873 | 6188 |
| 9343 | 1663 | 8734 | 7155 | 0689 | 7940 | 2663 | 5468 | 0769 | 8329 |
| 9524 | 8034 | 3097 | 2245 | 8018 | 7608 | 8399 | 7604 | 7679 | 8792 |
| 6388 | 6095 | 5061 | 8152 | 4037 | 7122 | 3534 | 8501 | 5089 | 2005 |
| 9046 | 3693 | 8827 | 8293 | 5146 | 6018 | 2576 | 0043 | 7891 | 8157 |
| 9850 | 9317 | 1296 | 0131 | 7509 | 7989 | 1815 | 4378 | 5769 | 0601 |
| 8221 | 9691 | 6994 | 0354 | 0132 | 9968 | 9416 | 3726 | 4406 | 3550 |
| 3823 | 9921 | 1219 | 1149 | 2050 | 2682 | 7697 | 2895 | 3397 | 8988 |
| 1406 | 3241 | 8226 | 7541 | 4635 | 4184 | 9325 | 0726 | 0613 | 4372 |
| 1362 | 5191 | 6353 | 5093 | 7829 | 4786 | 5495 | 3445 | 0688 | 2419 |
| 8890 | 9912 | 3216 | 9937 | 0380 | 7370 | 9477 | 5374 | 5165 | 2034 |
| 2457 | 5948 | 6090 | 1974 | 8721 | 5114 | 7461 | 0662 | 2371 | 1970 |
| 2365 | 1584 | 5651 | 3397 | 5485 | 6489 | 9927 | 5053 | 9884 | 8116 |
| 4059 | 6410 | 0445 | 8247 | 5672 | 1923 | 7295 | 1864 | 9076 | 8760 |
| 4186 | 0562 | 0907 | 3927 | 7941 | 2051 | 8649 | 2750 | 5323 | 2169 |
| 9418 | 4936 | 8276 | 9904 | 6369 | 0199 | 3940 | 2622 | 0783 | 0405 |
| 9607 | 8736 | 2995 | 2771 | 2264 | 4014 | 0663 | 5351 | 6525 | 1585 |
| 9641 | 3636 | 4558 | 0182 | 8893 | 4348 | 0344 | 3534 | 8035 | 5033 |
| 2418 | 2937 | 8290 | 3424 | 0456 | 5170 | 0445 | 5166 | 3830 | 9735 |
| 0157 | 8239 | 9267 | 0478 | 6557 | 5963 | 3979 | 8247 | 3437 | 8734 |
| 7225 | 6089 | 2211 | 2541 | 4495 | 3448 | 6034 | 8556 | 7201 | 5748 |
| 0182 | 5760 | 0437 | 8218 | 1579 | 8509 | 3170 | 7960 | 1958 | 5629 |
| 1241 | 3183 | 6558 | 7963 | 6547 | 8982 | 6403 | 6536 | 9674 | 2473 |
| 7473 | 4318 | 2600 | 3361 | 1115 | 8786 | 9580 | 3061 | 4114 | 6556 |
| 8861 | 4062 | 6880 | 5364 | 0398 | 2258 | 1563 | 5620 | 2451 | 1916 |
| 1044 | 2323 | 8387 | 3170 | 3104 | 2694 | 6989 | 2686 | 6738 | 5414 |
| 1161 | 9330 | 7686 | 4403 | 2058 | 9463 | 3671 | 2737 | 2901 | 1598 |
| 6818 | 6236 | 6635 | 2662 | 3336 | 8732 | 1075 | 8420 | 0094 | 1162 |
| 1026 | 9026 | 1866 | 7839 | 4029 | 4710 | 4177 | 9630 | 2945 | 0001 |
| 7423 | 9379 | 4480 | 0147 | 5364 | 0273 | 5379 | 0568 | 9590 | 0965 |
| 5402 | 0221 | 3755 | 8076 | 6868 | 8318 | 7024 | 8918 | 7269 | 8131 |
| 4843 | 2906 | 0757 | 5291 | 1946 | 3095 | 9973 | 2298 | 6719 | 8046 |
| 0042 | 6664 | 7569 | 5233 | 2706 | 7533 | 8380 | 0837 | 0566 | 7497 |
| 3318 | 9319 | 9022 | 1162 | 7016 | 3836 | 2845 | 5818 | 1472 | 3125 |
| 8472 | 5480 | 6451 | 1563 | 3513 | 9867 | 5875 | 2993 | 2817 | 0615 |
| 2798 | 5993 | 7475 | 0921 | 7827 | 2337 | 1727 | 1215 | 7746 | 3526 |
| 7833 | 2035 | 3936 | 7884 | 3829 | 4691 | 1019 | 0421 | 6983 | 8468 |
| 5800 | 5970 | 4541 | 6587 | 4326 | 2057 | 4429 | 8476 | 5496 | 2296 |
| 4332 | 8805 | 3329 | 7242 | 9570 | 1082 | 7572 | 0874 | 3346 | 7333 |
| 8961 | 9445 | 3488 | 3457 | 0524 | 7940 | 1963 | 3188 | 3494 | 6728 |
| 8473 | 8813 | 1754 | 9561 | 1204 | 8769 | 2846 | 7521 | 5535 | 1665 |
| 9657 | 3058 | 1768 | 3224 | 1967 | 5430 | 5401 | 0827 | 5720 | 8743 |
| 3467 | 3338 | 9619 | 4453 | 4883 | 4570 | 5247 | 9401 | 9633 | 1883 |

## TABLE 4. RANDOM NUMBERS
### Table 1

| | | | | | | | | | |
|---|---|---|---|---|---|---|---|---|---|
| 2862 | 8184 | 4827 | 7758 | 5824 | 6854 | 9137 | 9199 | 0583 | 3278 · |
| 2826 | 6621 | 6000 | 5036 | 3136 | 2908 | 4942 | 2149 | 8929 | 0915 |
| 4271 | 2018 | 3717 | 0577 | 7803 | 1372 | 5855 | 2449 | 4718 | 8231 |
| 0701 | 8940 | 2009 | 7881 | 9540 | 7969 | 2931 | 2074 | 4829 | 4950 |
| 4176 | 4312 | 8228 | 2176 | 6265 | 3619 | 9522 | 2909 | 5564 | 1824 |
| 7716 | 5855 | 6169 | 6265 | 3619 | 9522 | 2909 | 5641 | 8277 | 1658 |
| 9322 | 1625 | 6459 | 3231 | 3935 | 0345 | 0928 | 4344 | 0118 | 2662 |
| 9319 | 8353 | 1750 | 7588 | 1531 | 5701 | 1223 | 2628 | 9410 | 5201 |
| 3487 | 4904 | 1343 | 5813 | 0409 | 0058 | 0879 | 3058 | 4930 | 9478 |
| 7133 | 2586 | 5258 | 6299 | 8427 | 7774 | 6818 | 7573 | 2883 | 4223 |
| 1632 | 9644 | 8392 | 4826 | 3425 | 5234 | 4913 | 3415 | 5052 | 0046 |
| 6210 | 6765 | 9652 | 1331 | 9197 | 0015 | 7684 | 5265 | 2271 | 9503 |
| 3383 | 2522 | 6051 | 5698 | 9459 | 0162 | 2894 | 5901 | 6228 | 9416 |
| 9768 | 6153 | 3661 | 9298 | 7353 | 7381 | 2022 | 0839 | 8932 | 0046 |
| 3351 | 3717 | 8265 | 2992 | 2609 | 2315 | 5485 | 5751 | 7417 | 0682 |
| 3919 | 9376 | 8517 | 1311 | 2923 | 7056 | 6752 | 6479 | 6687 | 8723 |
| 2619 | 9190 | 4808 | 1209 | 8216 | 5392 | 8594 | 0293 | 8709 | 7941 |
| 6440 | 3701 | 9889 | 5292 | 8656 | 5716 | 6920 | 4839 | 7960 | 5110 |
| 1111 | 5227 | 6929 | 9205 | 4169 | 2755 | 3262 | 7698 | 0953 | 5037 |
| 4380 | 6159 | 2678 | 2424 | 7975 | 4336 | 6730 | 6476 | 8293 | 6995 |
| 8738 | 3280 | 9965 | 8063 | 2550 | 0701 | 4787 | 7701 | 4849 | 7131 |
| 7779 | 3521 | 2794 | 6202 | 2079 | 0893 | 6746 | 1090 | 8494 | 0831 |
| 9763 | 7388 | 3909 | 6012 | 1420 | 4276 | 1301 | 7613 | 0173 | 6987 |
| 7164 | 1739 | 9100 | 3913 | 0080 | 7862 | 0707 | 0248 | 9190 | 1980 |
| 4667 | 8114 | 5366 | 6067 | 1232 | 8175 | 5772 | 6735 | 3505 | 3274 |
| 9851 | 1568 | 1120 | 9246 | 7883 | 2739 | 9362 | 6536 | 1995 | 2292 |
| 0955 | 6418 | 2477 | 1758 | 6240 | 4007 | 9428 | 8719 | 6316 | 4775 |
| 7308 | 5505 | 6705 | 1527 | 8360 | 6145 | 1312 | 6854 | 6492 | 8603 |
| 1925 | 9937 | 3872 | 3693 | 8318 | 7281 | 9504 | 4747 | 5926 | 7393 |
| 3501 | 0017 | 2542 | 9795 | 9785 | 3349 | 3799 | 7039 | 1814 | 8474 |
| 8318 | 4323 | 2853 | 5561 | 5119 | 0656 | 9034 | 7903 | 5329 | 2799 |
| 2579 | 5327 | 6471 | 9066 | 1594 | 7378 | 9921 | 3877 | 8862 | 4040 |
| 0794 | 2887 | 1963 | 1647 | 7573 | 0855 | 0567 | 0515 | 2783 | 6061 |
| 4513 | 0668 | 5464 | 9286 | 0319 | 0710 | 4304 | 7575 | 2657 | 1195 |
| 5384 | 3970 | 7138 | 2795 | 6810 | 9038 | 0923 | 6384 | 3588 | 8995 |
| 4151 | 9079 | 3713 | 1843 | 8107 | 1419 | 7105 | 2352 | 5630 | 9526 |
| 9862 | 9095 | 0760 | 9396 | 1108 | 7958 | 4277 | 6525 | 6125 | 1701 |
| 8230 | 2203 | 5837 | 0417 | 7069 | 8163 | 9603 | 1811 | 1961 | 0303 |
| 0616 | 0509 | 5012 | 0628 | 1394 | 0839 | 9048 | 1077 | 1015 | 5308 |
| 4997 | 1235 | 9125 | 2020 | 5946 | 4012 | 0727 | 9214 | 4668 | 4912 |
| 9902 | 9714 | 5639 | 0175 | 0031 | 3813 | 8081 | 3447 | 5790 | 6701 |
| 2332 | 2445 | 2910 | 8455 | 4960 | 5144 | 9530 | 0148 | 0204 | 1032 |
| 1584 | 7502 | 3695 | 5620 | 8915 | 5727 | 4102 | 1129 | 0066 | 8262 |
| 6011 | 8418 | 7873 | 2314 | 5269 | 0501 | 4804 | 1937 | 9458 | 4750 |
| 2369 | 5567 | 6389 | 4016 | 9442 | 0198 | 7866 | 8237 | 2911 | 8451 |
| 7732 | 0469 | 6070 | 6333 | 4843 | 3375 | 5277 | 6189 | 8485 | 9098 |
| 4945 | 1925 | 0184 | 6067 | 9699 | 0744 | 5000 | 7360 | 2563 | 9408 |
| 7677 | 9326 | 4269 | 4822 | 8871 | 5178 | 8829 | 0693 | 6160 | 7758 |
| 6834 | 7384 | 9379 | 9192 | 8085 | 2914 | 7460 | 3570 | 8508 | 4405 |
| 4302 | 0675 | 2388 | 1336 | 1212 | 3937 | 0174 | 9103 | 1802 | 1015 |

## TABLE 4. RANDOM NUMBERS
### Table 2

| | | | | | | | | | |
|---|---|---|---|---|---|---|---|---|---|
| 88 | 95 | 48 | 56 | 49 | 96 | 85 | 10 | 07 | 37 |
| 15 | 87 | 21 | 26 | 02 | 10 | 64 | 75 | 27 | 72 |
| 70 | 87 | 59 | 35 | 18 | 98 | 67 | 19 | 84 | 83 |
| 24 | 43 | 09 | 44 | 61 | 77 | 96 | 50 | 94 | 90 |
| 13 | 43 | 55 | 80 | 14 | 15 | 08 | 39 | 24 | 46 |
| 69 | 49 | 19 | 73 | 68 | 71 | 97 | 22 | 04 | 24 |
| 40 | 73 | 82 | 56 | 36 | 96 | 10 | 63 | 29 | 41 |
| 37 | 32 | 22 | 95 | 16 | 33 | 40 | 50 | 32 | 91 |
| 31 | 56 | 58 | 29 | 13 | 15 | 60 | 63 | 67 | 18 |
| 10 | 83 | 67 | 18 | 08 | 57 | 21 | 28 | 44 | 24 |
| 14 | 95 | 54 | 58 | 01 | 31 | 38 | 78 | 50 | 12 |
| 95 | 38 | 86 | 87 | 58 | 50 | 35 | 46 | 31 | 90 |
| 32 | 81 | 12 | 77 | 07 | 97 | 78 | 28 | 79 | 86 |
| 91 | 21 | 44 | 52 | 27 | 74 | 12 | 80 | 05 | 47 |
| 03 | 19 | 66 | 51 | 08 | 03 | 70 | 61 | 44 | 45 |
| 66 | 43 | 75 | 71 | 82 | 86 | 04 | 82 | 95 | 57 |
| 15 | 36 | 04 | 93 | 58 | 73 | 58 | 88 | 73 | 45 |
| 28 | 75 | 58 | 29 | 48 | 66 | 03 | 99 | 83 | 50 |
| 61 | 20 | 26 | 25 | 49 | 42 | 15 | 01 | 35 | 91 |
| 16 | 36 | 16 | 03 | 64 | 77 | 60 | 76 | 76 | 33 |
| 34 | 81 | 71 | 35 | 08 | 45 | 70 | 24 | 70 | 85 |
| 57 | 62 | 81 | 05 | 72 | 67 | 36 | 00 | 15 | 10 |
| 68 | 37 | 46 | 93 | 28 | 63 | 38 | 06 | 01 | 81 |
| 34 | 03 | 53 | 28 | 28 | 74 | 66 | 93 | 49 | 24 |
| 41 | 09 | 87 | 69 | 20 | 59 | 01 | 52 | 19 | 43 |
| 93 | 25 | 25 | 01 | 44 | 25 | 96 | 89 | 16 | 64 |
| 13 | 15 | 20 | 85 | 27 | 06 | 81 | 83 | 34 | 88 |
| 70 | 81 | 96 | 85 | 32 | 48 | 02 | 17 | 37 | 01 |
| 94 | 38 | 89 | 48 | 25 | 79 | 83 | 39 | 61 | 79 |
| 56 | 97 | 87 | 46 | 11 | 97 | 37 | 90 | 53 | 10 |
| 10 | 36 | 90 | 26 | 18 | 66 | 78 | 39 | 40 | 19 |
| 47 | 10 | 41 | 77 | 96 | 30 | 29 | 45 | 00 | 01 |
| 74 | 23 | 93 | 79 | 44 | 80 | 01 | 47 | 53 | 64 |
| 02 | 73 | 53 | 79 | 05 | 68 | 95 | 90 | 09 | 65 |
| 54 | 02 | 08 | 21 | 37 | 55 | 80 | 76 | 68 | 68 |
| 26 | 74 | 88 | 60 | 63 | 18 | 37 | 47 | 99 | 78 |
| 79 | 50 | 69 | 48 | 07 | 16 | 45 | 51 | 72 | 25 |
| 39 | 60 | 48 | 44 | 51 | 40 | 76 | 55 | 67 | 85 |
| 80 | 17 | 71 | 85 | 38 | 44 | 00 | 55 | 02 | 51 |
| 49 | 71 | 49 | 59 | 46 | 33 | 22 | 88 | 09 | 90 |
| 28 | 09 | 22 | 25 | 57 | 61 | 15 | 96 | 14 | 15 |
| 30 | 82 | 79 | 34 | 94 | 97 | 68 | 13 | 08 | 78 |
| 31 | 62 | 58 | 23 | 75 | 87 | 75 | 92 | 93 | 30 |
| 57 | 26 | 36 | 48 | 10 | 36 | 60 | 90 | 63 | 00 |
| 02 | 88 | 92 | 93 | 03 | 77 | 41 | 11 | 77 | 02 |
| 36 | 80 | 49 | 03 | 52 | 18 | 18 | 56 | 56 | 31 |
| 54 | 86 | 44 | 32 | 91 | 53 | 75 | 65 | 27 | 70 |
| 15 | 36 | 38 | 44 | 87 | 94 | 78 | 72 | 62 | 39 |
| 11 | 10 | 10 | 38 | 46 | 66 | 80 | 21 | 74 | 13 |
| 50 | 63 | 23 | 48 | 99 | 14 | 22 | 26 | 19 | 62 |

## TABLE 4. RANDOM NUMBERS
### Table 2

| | | | | | | | | | |
|---|---|---|---|---|---|---|---|---|---|
| 07 | 50 | 22 | 87 | 74 | 53 | 95 | 71 | 89 | 47 |
| 04 | 79 | 90 | 53 | 42 | 57 | 97 | 01 | 73 | 09 |
| 03 | 28 | 90 | 41 | 49 | 83 | 16 | 19 | 09 | 58 |
| 38 | 84 | 74 | 10 | 39 | 61 | 54 | 63 | 18 | 73 |
| 03 | 24 | 61 | 05 | 25 | 83 | 37 | 17 | 96 | 08 |
| 65 | 98 | 68 | 27 | 24 | 32 | 17 | 01 | 78 | 94 |
| 56 | 23 | 15 | 99 | 06 | 21 | 83 | 56 | 51 | 31 |
| 66 | 21 | 83 | 56 | 58 | 24 | 56 | 13 | 48 | 44 |
| 11 | 27 | 57 | 65 | 44 | 36 | 37 | 76 | 37 | 80 |
| 79 | 80 | 13 | 82 | 80 | 53 | 79 | 65 | 85 | 57 |
| 18 | 13 | 65 | 82 | 44 | 61 | 58 | 86 | 59 | 29 |
| 72 | 62 | 47 | 39 | 44 | 01 | 37 | 92 | 81 | 33 |
| 42 | 34 | 28 | 67 | 70 | 02 | 85 | 90 | 35 | 99 |
| 71 | 50 | 94 | 73 | 64 | 76 | 19 | 84 | 54 | 04 |
| 94 | 27 | 22 | 00 | 40 | 30 | 53 | 14 | 91 | 70 |
| 68 | 53 | 35 | 78 | 78 | 35 | 67 | 14 | 49 | 27 |
| 42 | 81 | 25 | 99 | 37 | 88 | 67 | 29 | 95 | 86 |
| 43 | 10 | 43 | 50 | 22 | 49 | 30 | 67 | 27 | 61 |
| 19 | 13 | 19 | 73 | 04 | 04 | 37 | 59 | 75 | 85 |
| 17 | 34 | 04 | 84 | 56 | 80 | 64 | 92 | 90 | 37 |
| 90 | 86 | 58 | 41 | 31 | 75 | 52 | 18 | 90 | 35 |
| 79 | 60 | 21 | 37 | 39 | 14 | 18 | 92 | 66 | 93 |
| 20 | 84 | 35 | 95 | 24 | 07 | 69 | 56 | 72 | 16 |
| 51 | 67 | 54 | 34 | 59 | 98 | 50 | 18 | 67 | 63 |
| 63 | 48 | 34 | 77 | 66 | 69 | 28 | 12 | 73 | 74 |
| 67 | 45 | 65 | 38 | 71 | 89 | 75 | 27 | 50 | 69 |
| 23 | 11 | 14 | 18 | 82 | 40 | 32 | 82 | 78 | 17 |
| 68 | 31 | 46 | 66 | 58 | 28 | 27 | 36 | 30 | 73 |
| 97 | 98 | 40 | 06 | 33 | 90 | 36 | 79 | 48 | 12 |
| 85 | 43 | 57 | 43 | 78 | 42 | 07 | 59 | 99 | 10 |
| 97 | 84 | 56 | 26 | 54 | 40 | 02 | 08 | 99 | 92 |
| 08 | 49 | 64 | 29 | 39 | 40 | 67 | 96 | 86 | 31 |
| 44 | 59 | 10 | 57 | 70 | 54 | 88 | 10 | 66 | 53 |
| 47 | 71 | 71 | 84 | 82 | 99 | 61 | 27 | 64 | 83 |
| 76 | 14 | 83 | 69 | 72 | 13 | 14 | 01 | 20 | 76 |
| 22 | 76 | 19 | 99 | 90 | 38 | 45 | 70 | 70 | 67 |
| 03 | 68 | 34 | 94 | 95 | 17 | 61 | 26 | 75 | 53 |
| 89 | 88 | 32 | 49 | 74 | 55 | 08 | 88 | 65 | 06 |
| 28 | 50 | 04 | 43 | 42 | 07 | 18 | 46 | 67 | 13 |
| 84 | 60 | 51 | 06 | 19 | 82 | 10 | 72 | 26 | 21 |
| 68 | 02 | 08 | 69 | 14 | 02 | 43 | 89 | 07 | 64 |
| 59 | 92 | 52 | 74 | 21 | 83 | 43 | 61 | 28 | 64 |
| 86 | 87 | 07 | 07 | 52 | 79 | 15 | 75 | 08 | 17 |
| 81 | 51 | 14 | 86 | 64 | 95 | 30 | 87 | 13 | 13 |
| 53 | 95 | 94 | 82 | 47 | 77 | 75 | 43 | 22 | 11 |
| 40 | 82 | 45 | 41 | 97 | 71 | 85 | 82 | 49 | 75 |
| 62 | 11 | 57 | 93 | 09 | 64 | 99 | 50 | 08 | 24 |
| 74 | 42 | 95 | 50 | 98 | 03 | 13 | 87 | 46 | 64 |
| 53 | 97 | 90 | 52 | 41 | 12 | 06 | 98 | 43 | 34 |
| 54 | 05 | 23 | 11 | 34 | 46 | 32 | 28 | 74 | 55 |

TABLE 4. RANDOM NUMBERS
Table 2

| | | | | | | | | | |
|---|---|---|---|---|---|---|---|---|---|
| 92 | 41 | 76 | 71 | 17 | 19 | 97 | 53 | 61 | 32 |
| 53 | 33 | 68 | 16 | 56 | 36 | 10 | 94 | 04 | 66 |
| 54 | 13 | 42 | 58 | 18 | 05 | 57 | 53 | 92 | 24 |
| 18 | 79 | 63 | 41 | 18 | 14 | 33 | 96 | 47 | 55 |
| 12 | 80 | 04 | 67 | 49 | 50 | 10 | 23 | 28 | 15 |
| 44 | 56 | 62 | 66 | 72 | 77 | 57 | 40 | 35 | 35 |
| 05 | 20 | 70 | 83 | 19 | 58 | 73 | 83 | 60 | 50 |
| 10 | 40 | 29 | 87 | 70 | 97 | 94 | 17 | 64 | 40 |
| 37 | 01 | 98 | 89 | 52 | 92 | 86 | 56 | 57 | 16 |
| 69 | 20 | 48 | 39 | 79 | 60 | 50 | 10 | 11 | 11 |
| 31 | 91 | 47 | 83 | 78 | 68 | 20 | 71 | 91 | 13 |
| 06 | 34 | 25 | 06 | 49 | 50 | 81 | 29 | 41 | 92 |
| 04 | 96 | 51 | 97 | 29 | 35 | 63 | 53 | 09 | 38 |
| 24 | 26 | 06 | 35 | 49 | 37 | 89 | 45 | 66 | 23 |
| 65 | 40 | 08 | 04 | 84 | 75 | 05 | 73 | 95 | 16 |
| 10 | 42 | 79 | 68 | 39 | 35 | 36 | 76 | 47 | 49 |
| 35 | 35 | 36 | 76 | 72 | 65 | 58 | 34 | 66 | 32 |
| 82 | 01 | 75 | 52 | 75 | 54 | 97 | 78 | 91 | 03 |
| 10 | 56 | 22 | 13 | 98 | 88 | 74 | 32 | 26 | 07 |
| 02 | 61 | 47 | 93 | 04 | 60 | 85 | 83 | 34 | 73 |
| 92 | 22 | 25 | 42 | 37 | 35 | 50 | 56 | 04 | 76 |
| 71 | 70 | 61 | 14 | 09 | 63 | 60 | 54 | 29 | 87 |
| 42 | 86 | 47 | 06 | 27 | 94 | 47 | 04 | 42 | 57 |
| 16 | 03 | 57 | 93 | 97 | 09 | 14 | 39 | 99 | 49 |
| 14 | 88 | 35 | 51 | 91 | 93 | 98 | 16 | 03 | 85 |
| 99 | 19 | 39 | 90 | 40 | 74 | 99 | 08 | 94 | 47 |
| 55 | 87 | 03 | 43 | 57 | 09 | 53 | 91 | 26 | 07 |
| 05 | 18 | 82 | 08 | 41 | 62 | 10 | 93 | 26 | 02 |
| 07 | 04 | 28 | 30 | 06 | 70 | 26 | 72 | 82 | 49 |
| 41 | 74 | 35 | 73 | 87 | 10 | 24 | 67 | 09 | 04 |
| 83 | 18 | 43 | 23 | 28 | 53 | 55 | 61 | 51 | 19 |
| 06 | 56 | 90 | 34 | 79 | 03 | 53 | 29 | 27 | 99 |
| 52 | 79 | 53 | 27 | 64 | 71 | 90 | 66 | 15 | 94 |
| 73 | 78 | 99 | 21 | 38 | 77 | 88 | 62 | 40 | 40 |
| 07 | 94 | 28 | 87 | 21 | 63 | 16 | 47 | 75 | 73 |
| 28 | 63 | 50 | 54 | 73 | 16 | 33 | 36 | 81 | 52 |
| 90 | 65 | 49 | 17 | 58 | 40 | 43 | 99 | 84 | 46 |
| 94 | 04 | 92 | 03 | 81 | 24 | 27 | 00 | 18 | 69 |
| 96 | 11 | 50 | 97 | 64 | 91 | 65 | 88 | 65 | 32 |
| 05 | 85 | 29 | 03 | 41 | 47 | 74 | 61 | 49 | 11 |
| 72 | 20 | 98 | 03 | 81 | 00 | 50 | 87 | 05 | 61 |
| 37 | 23 | 32 | 12 | 47 | 06 | 56 | 62 | 34 | 06 |
| 37 | 72 | 92 | 64 | 48 | 76 | 33 | 86 | 19 | 59 |
| 58 | 57 | 50 | 99 | 91 | 24 | 64 | 60 | 86 | 91 |
| 69 | 69 | 17 | 62 | 56 | 55 | 86 | 61 | 97 | 74 |
| 08 | 15 | 32 | 01 | 61 | 99 | 49 | 05 | 50 | 57 |
| 17 | 26 | 82 | 26 | 11 | 52 | 16 | 43 | 88 | 06 |
| 23 | 81 | 52 | 37 | 67 | 23 | 40 | 28 | 62 | 26 |
| 26 | 77 | 68 | 82 | 49 | 47 | 99 | 23 | 66 | 95 |
| 34 | 76 | 68 | 10 | 80 | 94 | 15 | 48 | 12 | 72 |

## TABLE 4. RANDOM NUMBERS
### Table 2

| | | | | | | | | | |
|---|---|---|---|---|---|---|---|---|---|
| 18 | 71 | 28 | 08 | 63 | 99 | 30 | 61 | 14 | 44 |
| 38 | 27 | 44 | 99 | 41 | 28 | 17 | 86 | 63 | 58 |
| 24 | 63 | 46 | 34 | 60 | 08 | 20 | 34 | 76 | 68 |
| 15 | 39 | 05 | 42 | 60 | 33 | 72 | 75 | 20 | 29 |
| 16 | 87 | 42 | 79 | 48 | 72 | 76 | 73 | 06 | 09 |
| 24 | 48 | 14 | 05 | 52 | 33 | 74 | 69 | 73 | 62 |
| 42 | 43 | 85 | 33 | 84 | 28 | 01 | 87 | 13 | 74 |
| 91 | 71 | 89 | 82 | 65 | 00 | 37 | 03 | 17 | 57 |
| 01 | 68 | 78 | 93 | 11 | 76 | 55 | 36 | 46 | 96 |
| 98 | 53 | 79 | 20 | 02 | 57 | 26 | 96 | 22 | 84 |
| 90 | 26 | 50 | 18 | 81 | 16 | 79 | 53 | 56 | 45 |
| 81 | 23 | 65 | 22 | 41 | 49 | 82 | 89 | 84 | 66 |
| 24 | 74 | 44 | 57 | 19 | 13 | 45 | 77 | 99 | 27 |
| 12 | 34 | 91 | 66 | 65 | 33 | 88 | 59 | 32 | 70 |
| 56 | 80 | 26 | 73 | 52 | 43 | 31 | 18 | 09 | 89 |
| 69 | 69 | 33 | 65 | 61 | 80 | 22 | 91 | 62 | 02 |
| 06 | 07 | 95 | 83 | 50 | 00 | 37 | 29 | 29 | 18 |
| 41 | 45 | 66 | 43 | 57 | 74 | 56 | 91 | 63 | 61 |
| 88 | 64 | 41 | 81 | 63 | 94 | 47 | 78 | 84 | 96 |
| 12 | 23 | 66 | 87 | 39 | 05 | 55 | 82 | 59 | 64 |
| 48 | 76 | 51 | 17 | 80 | 91 | 97 | 85 | 73 | 78 |
| 81 | 20 | 06 | 74 | 65 | 78 | 89 | 10 | 97 | 06 |
| 27 | 62 | 04 | 46 | 18 | 44 | 70 | 24 | 64 | 00 |
| 45 | 98 | 36 | 01 | 98 | 38 | 29 | 68 | 82 | 82 |
| 57 | 95 | 07 | 32 | 50 | 33 | 52 | 48 | 13 | 69 |
| 61 | 41 | 98 | 83 | 67 | 71 | 53 | 01 | 19 | 34 |
| 01 | 22 | 62 | 73 | 03 | 05 | 04 | 33 | 34 | 84 |
| 19 | 27 | 10 | 70 | 12 | 37 | 87 | 44 | 41 | 69 |
| 70 | 49 | 87 | 59 | 56 | 43 | 66 | 90 | 52 | 83 |
| 73 | 87 | 70 | 27 | 11 | 54 | 49 | 61 | 64 | 59 |
| 02 | 33 | 07 | 08 | 63 | 38 | 34 | 83 | 56 | 11 |
| 39 | 69 | 92 | 20 | 26 | 51 | 10 | 77 | 83 | 58 |
| 59 | 06 | 45 | 24 | 59 | 50 | 34 | 28 | 96 | 51 |
| 53 | 26 | 46 | 73 | 35 | 90 | 41 | 45 | 02 | 71 |
| 93 | 37 | 52 | 88 | 84 | 07 | 71 | 19 | 67 | 99 |
| 02 | 20 | 22 | 53 | 40 | 41 | 63 | 01 | 34 | 65 |
| 52 | 04 | 39 | 07 | 65 | 23 | 10 | 31 | 96 | 89 |
| 00 | 58 | 22 | 28 | 27 | 02 | 33 | 57 | 81 | 23 |
| 31 | 84 | 14 | 17 | 97 | 85 | 25 | 51 | 71 | 63 |
| 82 | 66 | 35 | 69 | 01 | 18 | 47 | 75 | 65 | 00 |
| 74 | 15 | 54 | 88 | 17 | 71 | 25 | 49 | 95 | 13 |
| 93 | 77 | 43 | 61 | 67 | 68 | 42 | 03 | 90 | 76 |
| 40 | 78 | 19 | 92 | 39 | 37 | 62 | 92 | 00 | 82 |
| 58 | 54 | 72 | 72 | 21 | 86 | 64 | 91 | 60 | 07 |
| 14 | 23 | 53 | 19 | 83 | 39 | 45 | 09 | 65 | 03 |
| 60 | 89 | 73 | 53 | 50 | 53 | 07 | 73 | 09 | 67 |
| 39 | 54 | 24 | 32 | 32 | 50 | 11 | 95 | 59 | 54 |
| 69 | 29 | 19 | 69 | 04 | 93 | 88 | 36 | 92 | 18 |
| 75 | 80 | 24 | 59 | 38 | 19 | 06 | 62 | 76 | 68 |
| 75 | 06 | 20 | 59 | 38 | 77 | 77 | 20 | 48 | 64 |

TABLE 5. LOGARITHMS OF FACTORIALS

| $n$ | log $n$! | $n$ | log $n$! |
|-----|----------|-----|----------|
| 1 | 0·000 0000 | 51 | 66·190 6450 |
| 2 | 0·301 0300 | 52 | 67·906 6484 |
| 3 | 0·778 1513 | 53 | 69·630 9243 |
| 4 | 1·380 2112 | 54 | 71·363 3180 |
| 5 | 2·079 1812 | 55 | 73·103 6807 |
| 6 | 2·857 3325 | 56 | 74·851 8687 |
| 7 | 3·702 4305 | 57 | 76·607 7436 |
| 8 | 4·605 5205 | 58 | 78·371 1716 |
| 9 | 5·559 7630 | 59 | 80·142 0236 |
| 10 | 6·559 7630 | 60 | 81·920 1748 |
| 11 | 7·601 1557 | 61 | 83·705 5047 |
| 12 | 8·680 3370 | 62 | 85·497 8964 |
| 13 | 9·794 2803 | 63 | 87 297 2369 |
| 14 | 10·940 4084 | 64 | 89·103 4169 |
| 15 | 12·116 4996 | 65 | 90·916 3303 |
| 16 | 13·320 6196 | 66 | 92·735 8742 |
| 17 | 14·551 0685 | 67 | 94 561 9490 |
| 18 | 15·806 3410 | 68 | 96·394 4579 |
| 19 | 17·085 0946 | 69 | 98·233 3070 |
| 20 | 18 386 1246 | 70 | 100·078 4050 |
| 21 | 19·708 3439 | 71 | 101·929 6634 |
| 22 | 21·050 7666 | 72 | 103·786 9959 |
| 23 | 22·412 4944 | 73 | 105·650 3187 |
| 24 | 23·792 7057 | 74 | 107·519 5505 |
| 25 | 25·190 6457 | 75 | 109 394 6117 |
| 26 | 26·605 6190 | 76 | 111·275 4253 |
| 27 | 28·036 9828 | 77 | 113·161 9160 |
| 28 | 29·484 1408 | 78 | 115·054 0106 |
| 29 | 30·946 5388 | 79 | 116·951 6377 |
| 30 | 32 423 6601 | 80 | 118·854 7277 |
| 31 | 33·915 0218 | 81 | 120·763 2127 |
| 32 | 35·420 1717 | 82 | 122·677 0266 |
| 33 | 36·938 6857 | 83 | 124·596 1047 |
| 34 | 38 470 1646 | 84 | 126·520 3840 |
| 35 | 40·014 2326 | 85 | 128·449 8029 |
| 36 | 41·570 5351 | 86 | 130·384 3013 |
| 37 | 43·138 7369 | 87 | 132·323 8206 |
| 38 | 44 718 5205 | 88 | 134·268 3033 |
| 39 | 46·309 5851 | 89 | 136 217 6933 |
| 40 | 47 911 6451 | 90 | 138·171 9358 |
| 41 | 49 524 4289 | 91 | 140·130 9772 |
| 42 | 51·147 6782 | 92 | 142·094 7650 |
| 43 | 52.781 1467 | 93 | 144·063 2480 |
| 44 | 54 424 5993 | 94 | 146·036 3758 |
| 45 | 56·077 8119 | 95 | 148·014 0994 |
| 46 | 57·740 5697 | 96 | 149·996 3707 |
| 47 | 59·412 6676 | 97 | 151·983 1424 |
| 48 | 61·093 9088 | 98 | 153·974 3685 |
| 49 | 62·784 1049 | 99 | 155·970 0037 |
| 50 | 64·483 0749 | 100 | 157·970 0037 |

See comments on p. 634

## TABLE 6. SQUARES, SQUARE ROOTS, RECIPROCALS

| $n$ | $n^2$ | $\sqrt{n}$ | $\dfrac{1}{n}$ | $n$ | $n^2$ | $\sqrt{n}$ | $\dfrac{1}{n}$ |
|---|---|---|---|---|---|---|---|
| 1 | 1 | 1 | 1 | 51 | 2601 | 7·1414 | 0·0196078 |
| 2 | 4 | 1·4142 | 0·5 | 52 | 2704 | 7·2111 | 0·0192308 |
| 3 | 9 | 1·7321 | 0·3333333 | 53 | 2809 | 7·2801 | 0·0188679 |
| 4 | 16 | 2 | 0·25 | 54 | 2916 | 7·3485 | 0·0185185 |
| 5 | 25 | 2·2361 | 0·2 | 55 | 3025 | 7·4162 | 0·0181818 |
| 6 | 36 | 2·4495 | 0·1666667 | 56 | 3136 | 7·4833 | 0·0178571 |
| 7 | 49 | 2·6458 | 0·1428571 | 57 | 3249 | 7·5498 | 0·0175439 |
| 8 | 64 | 2·8284 | 0·125 | 58 | 3364 | 7·6158 | 0·0172414 |
| 9 | 81 | 3 | 0·1111111 | 59 | 3481 | 7·6811 | 0·0169492 |
| 10 | 100 | 3·1623 | 0·1 | 60 | 3600 | 7·7460 | 0·0166667 |
| 11 | 121 | 3·3166 | 0·0909091 | 61 | 3721 | 7·8102 | 0·0163934 |
| 12 | 144 | 3·4641 | 0·0833333 | 62 | 3844 | 7·8740 | 0·0161290 |
| 13 | 169 | 3·6056 | 0·0769231 | 63 | 3969 | 7·9373 | 0·0158730 |
| 14 | 196 | 3·7417 | 0·0714286 | 64 | 4096 | 8 | 0·0156250 |
| 15 | 225 | 3·8730 | 0·0666667 | 65 | 4225 | 8·0623 | 0·0153846 |
| 16 | 256 | 4 | 0·0625 | 66 | 4356 | 8·1240 | 0·0151515 |
| 17 | 289 | 4·1231 | 0·0588235 | 67 | 4489 | 8·1854 | 0·0149254 |
| 18 | 324 | 4·2426 | 0·0555556 | 68 | 4624 | 8·2462 | 0·0147059 |
| 19 | 361 | 4·3589 | 0·0526316 | 69 | 4761 | 8·3066 | 0·0144928 |
| 20 | 400 | 4·4721 | 0·05 | 70 | 4900 | 8·3666 | 0·0142857 |
| 21 | 441 | 4·5826 | 0·0476190 | 71 | 5041 | 8·4261 | 0·0140845 |
| 22 | 484 | 4·6904 | 0·0454545 | 72 | 5184 | 8·4853 | 0·0138889 |
| 23 | 529 | 4·7958 | 0·0434783 | 73 | 5329 | 8·5440 | 0·0136986 |
| 24 | 576 | 4·8990 | 0·0416667 | 74 | 5476 | 8·6023 | 0·0135135 |
| 25 | 625 | 5 | 0·04 | 75 | 5625 | 8·6603 | 0·0133333 |
| 26 | 676 | 5·0990 | 0·0384615 | 76 | 5776 | 8·7178 | 0·0131579 |
| 27 | 729 | 5·1962 | 0·0370370 | 77 | 5929 | 8·7750 | 0·0129870 |
| 28 | 784 | 5·2915 | 0·0357143 | 78 | 6084 | 8·8318 | 0·0128205 |
| 29 | 841 | 5·3852 | 0·0344828 | 79 | 6241 | 8·8882 | 0·0126582 |
| 30 | 900 | 5·4772 | 0·0333333 | 80 | 6400 | 8·9443 | 0·0125 |
| 31 | 961 | 5·5678 | 0·0322581 | 81 | 6561 | 9 | 0·0123457 |
| 32 | 1024 | 5·6569 | 0·03125 | 82 | 6724 | 9·0554 | 0·0121951 |
| 33 | 1089 | 5·7446 | 0·0303030 | 83 | 6889 | 9·1104 | 0·0120482 |
| 34 | 1156 | 5·8310 | 0·0294118 | 84 | 7056 | 9·1652 | 0·0119048 |
| 35 | 1225 | 5·9161 | 0·0285714 | 85 | 7225 | 9·2195 | 0·0117647 |
| 36 | 1296 | 6 | 0·0277778 | 86 | 7396 | 9·2736 | 0·0116279 |
| 37 | 1369 | 6·0828 | 0·0270270 | 87 | 7569 | 9·3274 | 0·0114943 |
| 38 | 1444 | 6·1644 | 0·0263158 | 88 | 7744 | 9·3808 | 0·0113836 |
| 39 | 1521 | 6·2450 | 0·0256410 | 89 | 7921 | 9·4340 | 0·0112360 |
| 40 | 1600 | 6·3246 | 0·025 | 90 | 8100 | 9·4868 | 0·0111111 |
| 41 | 1681 | 6·4031 | 0·0243902 | 91 | 8281 | 9·5394 | 0·0109890 |
| 42 | 1764 | 6·4807 | 0·0238095 | 92 | 8464 | 9·5917 | 0·0108696 |
| 43 | 1849 | 6·5574 | 0·0232558 | 93 | 8649 | 9·6437 | 0·0107527 |
| 44 | 1936 | 6·6332 | 0·0227273 | 94 | 8836 | 9·6954 | 0·0106383 |
| 45 | 2025 | 6·7082 | 0·0222222 | 95 | 9025 | 9·7468 | 0·0105263 |
| 46 | 2116 | 6·7823 | 0·0217391 | 96 | 9216 | 9·7980 | 0·0104167 |
| 47 | 2209 | 6·8557 | 0·0212766 | 97 | 9409 | 9·8489 | 0·0103093 |
| 48 | 2304 | 6·9282 | 0·0208333 | 98 | 9604· | 9·8995 | 0·0102041 |
| 49 | 2401 | 7 | 0·0204082 | 99 | 9801 | 9·9499 | 0·0101010 |
| 50 | 2500 | 7·0711 | 0·02 | 100 | 10000 | 10 | 0·01 |

See comments on p. 634

### TABLE 6. SQUARES, SQUARE ROOTS, RECIPROCALS

| $n$ | $n^2$ | $\sqrt{n}$ | $\dfrac{1}{n}$ | $n$ | $n^2$ | $\sqrt{n}$ | $\dfrac{1}{n}$ |
|---|---|---|---|---|---|---|---|
| 101 | 10201 | 10·0499 | 0·0099010 | 151 | 22801 | 12·2882 | 0·0066225 |
| 102 | 10404 | 10·0995 | 0·0098039 | 152 | 23104 | 12·3288 | 0·0065789 |
| 103 | 10609 | 10·1489 | 0·0097087 | 153 | 23409 | 12·3693 | 0·0065359 |
| 104 | 10816 | 10·1980 | 0·0096154 | 154 | 23716 | 12·4097 | 0·0064935 |
| 105 | 11025 | 10·2470 | 0·0095238 | 155 | 24025 | 12·4499 | 0·0064516 |
| 106 | 11236 | 10·2956 | 0·0094340 | 156 | 24336 | 12·4900 | 0·0064103 |
| 107 | 11449 | 10·3441 | 0·0093458 | 157 | 24649 | 12·5300 | 0·0063694 |
| 108 | 11664 | 10·3923 | 0·0092593 | 158 | 24964 | 12·5698 | 0·0063291 |
| 109 | 11881 | 10·4403 | 0·0091743 | 159 | 25281 | 12·6095 | 0·0062893 |
| 110 | 12100 | 10·4881 | 0·0090909 | 160 | 25600 | 12·6491 | 0·0062500 |
| 111 | 12321 | 10·5357 | 0·0090090 | 161 | 25921 | 12·6886 | 0·0062112 |
| 112 | 12544 | 10·5830 | 0·0089286 | 162 | 26244 | 12·7279 | 0·0061728 |
| 113 | 12769 | 10·6301 | 0·0088496 | 163 | 26569 | 12·7671 | 0·0061350 |
| 114 | 12996 | 10·6771 | 0·0087719 | 164 | 26896 | 12·8062 | 0·0060976 |
| 115 | 13225 | 10·7238 | 0·0086957 | 165 | 27225 | 12·8452 | 0·0060606 |
| 116 | 13456 | 10·7703 | 0·0086207 | 166 | 27556 | 12·8841 | 0·0060241 |
| 117 | 13689 | 10·8167 | 0·0085470 | 167 | 27889 | 12·9228 | 0·0059880 |
| 118 | 13924 | 10·8628 | 0·0084746 | 168 | 28224 | 12·9615 | 0·0059524 |
| 119 | 14161 | 10·9087 | 0·0084034 | 169 | 28561 | 13 | 0·0059172 |
| 120 | 14400 | 10·9545 | 0·0083333 | 170 | 28900 | 13·0384 | 0·0058824 |
| 121 | 14641 | 11 | 0·0082645 | 171 | 29241 | 13·0767 | 0·0058480 |
| 122 | 14884 | 11·0454 | 0·0081967 | 172 | 29584 | 13·1149 | 0·0058140 |
| 123 | 15129 | 11·0905 | 0·0081301 | 173 | 29929 | 13·1529 | 0·0057803 |
| 124 | 15376 | 11·1355 | 0·0080645 | 174 | 30276 | 13·1909 | 0·0057471 |
| 125 | 15625 | 11·1803 | 0·008 | 175 | 30625 | 13·2288 | 0·0057143 |
| 126 | 15876 | 11·2250 | 0·0079365 | 176 | 30976 | 13·2665 | 0·0056818 |
| 127 | 16129 | 11·2694 | 0·0078740 | 177 | 31329 | 13·3041 | 0·0056497 |
| 128 | 16384 | 11·3137 | 0·0078125 | 178 | 31684 | 13·3417 | 0·0056180 |
| 129 | 16641 | 11·3578 | 0·0077519 | 179 | 32041 | 13·3791 | 0·0055866 |
| 130 | 16900 | 11·4018 | 0·0076923 | 180 | 32400 | 13·4164 | 0·0055556 |
| 131 | 17161 | 11·4455 | 0·0076336 | 181 | 32761 | 13·4536 | 0·0055249 |
| 132 | 17424 | 11·4891 | 0·0075758 | 182 | 33124 | 13·4907 | 0·0054945 |
| 133 | 17689 | 11·5326 | 0·0075188 | 183 | 33489 | 13·5277 | 0·0054645 |
| 134 | 17956 | 11·5758 | 0·0074627 | 184 | 33856 | 13·5647 | 0·0054348 |
| 135 | 18225 | 11·6190 | 0·0074074 | 185 | 34225 | 13·6015 | 0·0054054 |
| 136 | 18496 | 11·6619 | 0·0073529 | 186 | 34596 | 13·6382 | 0·0053763 |
| 137 | 18769 | 11·7047 | 0·0072993 | 187 | 34969 | 13·6748 | 0·0053476 |
| 138 | 19044 | 11·7473 | 0·0072464 | 188 | 35344 | 13·7113 | 0·0053191 |
| 139 | 19321 | 11·7898 | 0·0071942 | 189 | 35721 | 13·7477 | 0·0052910 |
| 140 | 19600 | 11·8322 | 0·0071429 | 190 | 36100 | 13·7840 | 0·0052632 |
| 141 | 19881 | 11·8743 | 0·0070922 | 191 | 36481 | 13·8203 | 0·0052356 |
| 142 | 20164 | 11·9164 | 0·0070423 | 192 | 36864 | 13·8564 | 0·0052083 |
| 143 | 20449 | 11·9583 | 0·0069930 | 193 | 37249 | 18·8924 | 0·0051813 |
| 144 | 30736 | 12 | 0·0069444 | 194 | 37636 | 13·9284 | 0·0051546 |
| 145 | 21025 | 12·0416 | 0·0068966 | 195 | 38025 | 13·9642 | 0·0051282 |
| 146 | 21316 | 12·0830 | 0·0068493 | 196 | 38416 | 14 | 0·0051020 |
| 147 | 21609 | 12·1244 | 0·0068027 | 197 | 38809 | 14·0357 | 0·0050761 |
| 148 | 21904 | 12·1655 | 0·0067568 | 198 | 39204 | 14·0712 | 0·0050505 |
| 149 | 22201 | 12·2066 | 0·0067114 | 199 | 39601 | 14·1067 | 0·0050251 |
| 150 | 22500 | 12·2474 | 0·0066667 | 200 | 40000 | 14·1421 | 0·005 |

TABLE 6. SQUARES, SQUARE ROOTS, RECIPROCALS

| $n$ | $n^2$ | $\sqrt{n}$ | $\dfrac{1}{n}$ | $n$ | $n^2$ | $\sqrt{n}$ | $\dfrac{1}{n}$ |
|---|---|---|---|---|---|---|---|
| 201 | 40401 | 14·1774 | 0·0049751 | 251 | 63001 | 15·8430 | 0·0039841 |
| 202 | 40804 | 14·2127 | 0·0049505 | 252 | 63504 | 15·8745 | 0·0039683 |
| 203 | 41209 | 14·2478 | 0·0049261 | 253 | 64009 | 15·9060 | 0·0039526 |
| 204 | 41616 | 14·2829 | 0·0049020 | 254 | 64516 | 15·9374 | 0·0039370 |
| 205 | 42025 | 14·3178 | 0·0048780 | 255 | 65025 | 15·9687 | 0·0039216 |
| 206 | 42436 | 14·3527 | 0·0048544 | 256 | 65536 | 16 | 0·0039063 |
| 207 | 42849 | 14·3875 | 0·0048309 | 257 | 66049 | 16·0312 | 0·0038911 |
| 208 | 43264 | 14·4222 | 0·0048077 | 258 | 66564 | 16·0624 | 0·0038760 |
| 209 | 43681 | 14·4568 | 0·0047847 | 259 | 67081 | 16·0935 | 0·0038610 |
| 210 | 44100 | 14·4914 | 0·0047619 | 260 | 67600 | 16·1245 | 0·0038462 |
| 211 | 44521 | 14·5258 | 0·0047393 | 261 | 68121 | 16·1555 | 0·0038314 |
| 212 | 44944 | 14·5602 | 0·0047170 | 262 | 68644 | 16·1864 | 0·0038168 |
| 213 | 45369 | 14·5945 | 0·0046948 | 263 | 69169 | 16·2173 | 0·0038023 |
| 214 | 45796 | 14·5287 | 0·0046729 | 264 | 69696 | 16·2481 | 0·0037879 |
| 215 | 46225 | 14·6629 | 0·0046512 | 265 | 70225 | 16·2788 | 0·0037736 |
| 216 | 46656 | 14·6969 | 0·0046296 | 266 | 70756 | 16·3095 | 0·0037594 |
| 217 | 47089 | 14·7309 | 0·0046083 | 267 | 71289 | 16·3401 | 0·0037453 |
| 218 | 47524 | 14·7648 | 0·0045872 | 268 | 71824 | 16·3707 | 0·0037313 |
| 219 | 47961 | 14·7986 | 0·0045662 | 269 | 72361 | 16·4012 | 0·0037175 |
| 220 | 48400 | 14·8324 | 0·0045455 | 270 | 72900 | 16·4317 | 0·0037037 |
| 221 | 48841 | 14·8661 | 0·0045249 | 271 | 73441 | 16·4621 | 0·0036900 |
| 222 | 49284 | 14·8997 | 0·0045045 | 272 | 73984 | 16·4924 | 0·0036765 |
| 223 | 49729 | 14·9332 | 0·0044843 | 273 | 74529 | 16·5227 | 0·0036630 |
| 224 | 50176 | 14·9666 | 0·0044643 | 274 | 75076 | 16·5529 | 0·0036496 |
| 225 | 50625 | 15 | 0·0044444 | 275 | 75625 | 16·5831 | 0·0036364 |
| 226 | 51076 | 15·0333 | 0·0044248 | 276 | 76176 | 16·6132 | 0·0036232 |
| 227 | 51529 | 15·0665 | 0·0044053 | 277 | 76729 | 16·6433 | 0·0036101 |
| 228 | 51984 | 15·0997 | 0·0043860 | 278 | 77284 | 16·6733 | 0·0035971 |
| 229 | 52441 | 15·1327 | 0·0043668 | 279 | 77841 | 16·7033 | 0·0035842 |
| 230 | 52900 | 15·1658 | 0·0043478 | 280 | 78400 | 16·7332 | 0·0035714 |
| 231 | 53361 | 15·1987 | 0·0043290 | 281 | 78961 | 16·7631 | 0·0035587 |
| 232 | 53824 | 15·2315 | 0·0043103 | 282 | 79524 | 16·7929 | 0·0035461 |
| 233 | 54289 | 15·2643 | 0·0042918 | 283 | 80089 | 16·8226 | 0·0035336 |
| 234 | 54756 | 15·2971 | 0·0042735 | 284 | 80656 | 16·8523 | 0·0035211 |
| 235 | 55225 | 15·3297 | 0·0042553 | 285 | 81225 | 16·8819 | 0·0035088 |
| 236 | 55696 | 15·3623 | 0·0042373 | 286 | 81796 | 16·9115 | 0·0034965 |
| 237 | 56169 | 15·3948 | 0·0042194 | 287 | 82369 | 16·9411 | 0·0034843 |
| 238 | 56644 | 15·4272 | 0·0042017 | 288 | 82944 | 16·9706 | 0·0034722 |
| 239 | 57121 | 15·4596 | 0·0041841 | 289 | 83521 | 17 | 0·0034602 |
| 240 | 57600 | 15·4919 | 0·0041667 | 290 | 84100 | 17·0294 | 0·0034483 |
| 241 | 58081 | 15·5242 | 0·0041494 | 291 | 84681 | 17·0587 | 0·0034364 |
| 242 | 58564 | 15·5563 | 0·0041322 | 292 | 85264 | 17·0880 | 0·0034247 |
| 243 | 59049 | 15·5885 | 0·0041152 | 293 | 85849 | 17·1172 | 0·0034130 |
| 244 | 59536 | 15·6205 | 0·0040984 | 294 | 86436 | 17·1464 | 0·0034014 |
| 245 | 60025 | 15·6525 | 0·0040816 | 295 | 87025 | 17·1756 | 0·0033898 |
| 246 | 60516 | 15·6844 | 0·0040650 | 296 | 87616 | 17·2047 | 0·0033784 |
| 247 | 61009 | 15·7162 | 0·0040486 | 297 | 88209 | 17·2337 | 0·0033670 |
| 248 | 61504 | 15·7480 | 0·0040323 | 298 | 88804 | 17·2627 | 0·0033557 |
| 249 | 62001 | 15·7797 | 0·0040161 | 299 | 89401 | 17·2916 | 0·0033445 |
| 250 | 62500 | 15·8114 | 0·004 | 300 | 90000 | 17·3205 | 0·0033333 |

## TABLE 6. SQUARES, SQUARE ROOTS, RECIPROCALS

| $n$ | $n^2$ | $\sqrt{n}$ | $\frac{1}{n}$ | $n$ | $n^2$ | $\sqrt{n}$ | $\frac{1}{n}$ |
|---|---|---|---|---|---|---|---|
| 301 | 90601 | 17·3494 | 0·0033223 | 351 | 123201 | 18·7350 | 0·0028490 |
| 302 | 91204 | 17·3781 | 0·0033113 | 352 | 123904 | 18·7617 | 0·0028409 |
| 303 | 91809 | 17·4069 | 0·0033003 | 353 | 124609 | 18·7883 | 0·0028329 |
| 304 | 92416 | 17·4356 | 0·0033895 | 354 | 125316 | 18·8149 | 0·0028249 |
| 305 | 93025 | 17·4622 | 0·0032787 | 355 | 126025 | 18·8414 | 0·0028169 |
| 306 | 93636 | 17·4929 | 0·0032680 | 356 | 126736 | 18·8680 | 0·0028090 |
| 307 | 94249 | 17·5214 | 0·0032573 | 357 | 127449 | 18·8944 | 0·0028011 |
| 308 | 94864 | 17·5499 | 0·0032468 | 358 | 128164 | 18·9209 | 0·0027933 |
| 309 | 95481 | 17·5784 | 0·0032362 | 359 | 128881 | 18·9473 | 0·0027855 |
| 310 | 96100 | 17·6068 | 0·0032258 | 360 | 129600 | 18·9737 | 0·0027778 |
| 311 | 96721 | 17·6352 | 0·0032154 | 361 | 130321 | 19 | 0·0027701 |
| 312 | 97344 | 17·6635 | 0·0032051 | 362 | 131044 | 19·0263 | 0·0027624 |
| 313 | 97969 | 17·6918 | 0·0031949 | 363 | 131769 | 19·0526 | 0·0027548 |
| 314 | 98596 | 17·7200 | 0·0031847 | 364 | 132496 | 19·0788 | 0·0027473 |
| 315 | 99225 | 17·7482 | 0·0031746 | 365 | 133225 | 19·1050 | 0·0027397 |
| 316 | 99856 | 17·7764 | 0·0031646 | 366 | 133956 | 19·1311 | 0·0027322 |
| 317 | 100489 | 17·8045 | 0·0031546 | 367 | 134689 | 19·1572 | 0·0027248 |
| 318 | 101124 | 17·8326 | 0·0031447 | 368 | 135424 | 19·1833 | 0·0027174 |
| 319 | 101761 | 17·8606 | 0·0031348 | 369 | 136161 | 19·2094 | 0·0027100 |
| 320 | 102400 | 17·8885 | 0·0031250 | 370 | 136900 | 19·2354 | 0·0027027 |
| 321 | 103041 | 17·9165 | 0·0031153 | 371 | 137641 | 19·2614 | 0·0026954 |
| 322 | 103684 | 17·9444 | 0·0031056 | 372 | 138384 | 19·2873 | 0·0026882 |
| 323 | 104329 | 17·9722 | 0·0030960 | 373 | 139129 | 19·3132 | 0·0026810 |
| 324 | 104976 | 18 | 0·0030864 | 374 | 139876 | 19·3391 | 0·0026738 |
| 325 | 105625 | 18·0278 | 0·0030769 | 375 | 140625 | 19·3649 | 0·0026667 |
| 326 | 106276 | 18·0555 | 0·0030675 | 376 | 141376 | 19·3907 | 0·0026596 |
| 327 | 106929 | 18·0831 | 0·0030581 | 377 | 142129 | 19·4165 | 0·0026525 |
| 328 | 107584 | 18·1108 | 0·0030488 | 378 | 142884 | 19·4422 | 0·0026455 |
| 329 | 108241 | 18·1384 | 0·0030395 | 379 | 143641 | 19·4679 | 0·0026385 |
| 330 | 108900 | 18·1659 | 0·0030303 | 380 | 144400 | 19·4936 | 0·0026316 |
| 331 | 109561 | 18·1934 | 0·0030211 | 381 | 145161 | 19·5192 | 0·0026247 |
| 332 | 110224 | 18·2209 | 0·0030120 | 382 | 145924 | 19·5448 | 0·0026178 |
| 333 | 110889 | 18·2483 | 0·0030030 | 383 | 146689 | 19·5704 | 0·0026110 |
| 334 | 111556 | 18·2757 | 0·0029940 | 384 | 147456 | 19·5959 | 0·0026042 |
| 335 | 112225 | 18·3030 | 0·0029851 | 385 | 148225 | 19·6214 | 0·0025974 |
| 336 | 112896 | 18·3303 | 0·0029762 | 386 | 148996 | 19·6469 | 0·0025907 |
| 337 | 113569 | 18·3576 | 0·0029674 | 387 | 149769 | 19·6723 | 0·0025840 |
| 338 | 114244 | 18·3848 | 0·0029586 | 388 | 150544 | 19·6977 | 0·0025773 |
| 339 | 114921 | 18·4120 | 0·0029499 | 389 | 151321 | 19·7231 | 0·0025707 |
| 340 | 115600 | 18·4391 | 0·0029412 | 390 | 152100 | 19·7484 | 0·0025641 |
| 341 | 116281 | 18·4662 | 0·0029326 | 391 | 152881 | 19·7737 | 0·0025575 |
| 342 | 116964 | 18·4932 | 0·0029240 | 392 | 153664 | 19·7990 | 0·0025510 |
| 343 | 117649 | 18·5203 | 0·0029155 | 393 | 154449 | 19·8242 | 0·0025445 |
| 344 | 118336 | 18·5472 | 0·0029070 | 394 | 155236 | 19·8494 | 0·0025381 |
| 345 | 119025 | 18·5742 | 0·0028986 | 395 | 156025 | 19·8746 | 0·0025316 |
| 346 | 119716 | 18·6011 | 0·0028902 | 396 | 156816 | 19·8997 | 0·0025253 |
| 347 | 120409 | 18·6279 | 0·0028818 | 397 | 157609 | 19·9249 | 0·0025189 |
| 348 | 121104 | 18·6548 | 0·0028736 | 398 | 158404 | 19·9499 | 0·0025126 |
| 349 | 121801 | 18·6815 | 0·0028653 | 399 | 159201 | 19·9750 | 0·0025063 |
| 350 | 122500 | 18·7083 | 0·0028571 | 400 | 160000 | 20 | 0·0025 |

## TABLE 6. SQUARES, SQUARE ROOTS, RECIPROCALS

| $n$ | $n^2$ | $\sqrt{n}$ | $\dfrac{1}{n}$ | $n$ | $n^2$ | $\sqrt{n}$ | $\dfrac{1}{n}$ |
|---|---|---|---|---|---|---|---|
| 401 | 160801 | 20·0250 | 0·0024938 | 451 | 203401 | 21·2368 | 0·0022173 |
| 402 | 161604 | 20·0499 | 0·0024876 | 452 | 204304 | 21·2603 | 0·0022124 |
| 403 | 162409 | 20·0749 | 0·0024814 | 453 | 205209 | 21·2838 | 0·0022075 |
| 404 | 163216 | 20·0998 | 0·0024752 | 454 | 206116 | 21·3073 | 0·0022026 |
| 405 | 164025 | 20·1246 | 0·0024691 | 455 | 207025 | 21·3307 | 0·0021978 |
| 406 | 164836 | 20·1494 | 0·0024631 | 456 | 207936 | 21·3542 | 0·0021930 |
| 407 | 165649 | 20·1742 | 0·0024570 | 457 | 208849 | 21·3776 | 0·0021882 |
| 408 | 166464 | 20·1990 | 0·0024510 | 458 | 209764 | 21·4009 | 0·0021834 |
| 409 | 167281 | 20·2237 | 0·0024450 | 459 | 210681 | 21·4243 | 0·0021786 |
| 410 | 168100 | 20·2485 | 0·0024390 | 460 | 211600 | 21·4476 | 0·0021739 |
| 411 | 168921 | 20·2731 | 0·0024331 | 461 | 212521 | 21·4709 | 0·0021692 |
| 412 | 169744 | 20·2978 | 0·0024272 | 462 | 213444 | 21·4942 | 0·0021645 |
| 413 | 170569 | 20·3224 | 0·0024213 | 463 | 214369 | 21·5174 | 0·0021598 |
| 414 | 171396 | 20·3470 | 0·0024155 | 464 | 215296 | 21·5407 | 0·0021552 |
| 415 | 172225 | 20·3715 | 0·0024096 | 465 | 216225 | 21·5639 | 0·0021505 |
| 416 | 173056 | 20·3961 | 0·0024038 | 466 | 217156 | 21·5870 | 0·0021459 |
| 417 | 173889 | 20·4206 | 0·0023981 | 467 | 218089 | 21·6102 | 0·0021413 |
| 418 | 174724 | 20·4450 | 0·0023923 | 468 | 219024 | 21·6333 | 0·0021368 |
| 419 | 175561 | 20·4695 | 0·0023866 | 469 | 219961 | 21·6564 | 0·0021322 |
| 420 | 176400 | 20·4939 | 0·0023810 | 470 | 220900 | 21·6795 | 0·0021277 |
| 421 | 177241 | 20·5183 | 0·0023753 | 471 | 221841 | 21·7025 | 0·0021231 |
| 422 | 178084 | 20·5426 | 0·0023697 | 472 | 222784 | 21·7256 | 0·0021186 |
| 423 | 178929 | 20·5670 | 0·0023641 | 473 | 223729 | 21·7486 | 0·0021142 |
| 424 | 179776 | 20·5913 | 0·0023585 | 474 | 224676 | 21·7715 | 0·0021097 |
| 425 | 180625 | 20·6155 | 0·0023529 | 475 | 225625 | 21·7945 | 0·0021053 |
| 426 | 181476 | 20·6398 | 0·0023474 | 476 | 226576 | 21·8174 | 0·0021008 |
| 427 | 182329 | 20·6640 | 0·0023419 | 477 | 227529 | 21·8403 | 0·0020964 |
| 428 | 183184 | 20·6882 | 0·0023364 | 478 | 228484 | 21·8632 | 0·0020921 |
| 429 | 184041 | 20·7123 | 0·0023310 | 479 | 229441 | 21·8861 | 0·0020877 |
| 430 | 184900 | 20·7364 | 0·0023256 | 480 | 230400 | 21·9089 | 0·0020833 |
| 431 | 185761 | 20·7605 | 0·0023202 | 481 | 231361 | 21·9317 | 0·0020790 |
| 432 | 186624 | 20·7846 | 0·0023148 | 482 | 232324 | 21·9545 | 0·0020747 |
| 433 | 187489 | 20·8087 | 0·0023095 | 483 | 233289 | 21·9773 | 0·0020704 |
| 434 | 188356 | 20·8327 | 0·0023041 | 484 | 234256 | 22 | 0·0020661 |
| 435 | 189225 | 20·8567 | 0·0022989 | 485 | 235225 | 22·0227 | 0·0020619 |
| 436 | 190096 | 20·8806 | 0·0022936 | 486 | 236196 | 22·0454 | 0·0020576 |
| 437 | 190969 | 20·9045 | 0·0022883 | 487 | 237169 | 22·0681 | 0·0020534 |
| 438 | 191844 | 20·9284 | 0·0022831 | 488 | 238144 | 22·0907 | 0·0020492 |
| 439 | 192721 | 20·9523 | 0·0022779 | 489 | 239121 | 22·1133 | 0·0020450 |
| 440 | 193600 | 20·9762 | 0·0022727 | 490 | 240100 | 22·1359 | 0·0020408 |
| 441 | 194481 | 21 | 0·0022676 | 491 | 241081 | 22·1585 | 0·0020367 |
| 442 | 195364 | 21·0238 | 0·0022624 | 492 | 242064 | 22·1811 | 0·0020325 |
| 443 | 196249 | 21·0476 | 0·0022573 | 493 | 243049 | 22·2036 | 0·0020284 |
| 444 | 197136 | 21·0713 | 0·0022523 | 494 | 244036 | 22·2261 | 0·0020243 |
| 445 | 198025 | 21·0950 | 0·0022472 | 495 | 245025 | 22·2486 | 0·0020202 |
| 446 | 198916 | 21·1187 | 0·0022422 | 496 | 246016 | 22·2711 | 0·0020161 |
| 447 | 199809 | 21·1424 | 0·0022371 | 497 | 247009 | 22·2935 | 0·0020121 |
| 448 | 200704 | 21·1660 | 0·0022321 | 498 | 248004 | 22·3159 | 0·0020080 |
| 449 | 201601 | 21·1896 | 0·0022272 | 499 | 249001 | 22·3383 | 0·0020040 |
| 450 | 202500 | 21·2132 | 0·0022222 | 500 | 250000 | 22·3607 | 0·002 |

42*

## TABLE 6. SQUARES, SQUARE ROOTS, RECIPROCALS

| $n$ | $n^2$ | $\sqrt{n}$ | $\dfrac{1}{n}$ | $n$ | $n^2$ | $\sqrt{n}$ | $\dfrac{1}{n}$ |
|---|---|---|---|---|---|---|---|
| 501 | 251001 | 22·3830 | 0·0019960 | 551 | 303601 | 23·4734 | 0·0018149 |
| 502 | 252004 | 22·4054 | 0·0019920 | 552 | 304704 | 23·4947 | 0·0018116 |
| 503 | 253009 | 22·4277 | 0·0019881 | 553 | 305809 | 23·5160 | 0·0018083 |
| 504 | 254016 | 22·4499 | 0·0019841 | 554 | 306916 | 23·5372 | 0·0018051 |
| 505 | 255025 | 22·4722 | 0·0019802 | 555 | 308025 | 23·5584 | 0·0018018 |
| 506 | 256036 | 22·4944 | 0·0019763 | 556 | 309136 | 23·5797 | 0·0017986 |
| 507 | 257049 | 22·5167 | 0·0019724 | 557 | 310249 | 23·6008 | 0·0017953 |
| 508 | 258064 | 22·5389 | 0·0019685 | 558 | 311364 | 23·6220 | 0·0017921 |
| 509 | 259081 | 22·5610 | 0·0019646 | 559 | 312481 | 23·6432 | 0·0017889 |
| 510 | 260100 | 22·5832 | 0·0019608 | 560 | 313600 | 23·6643 | 0·0017857 |
| 511 | 261121 | 22·6053 | 0·0019569 | 561 | 314721 | 23·6854 | 0·0017825 |
| 512 | 262144 | 22·6274 | 0·0019531 | 562 | 315844 | 23·7056 | 0·0017794 |
| 513 | 263169 | 22·6495 | 0·0019493 | 563 | 316969 | 23·7276 | 0·0017762 |
| 514 | 264196 | 22·6716 | 0·0019455 | 564 | 318096 | 23·7487 | 0·0017730 |
| 515 | 265225 | 22·6936 | 0·0019417 | 565 | 319225 | 23·7697 | 0·0017699 |
| 516 | 266256 | 22·7156 | 0·0019380 | 566 | 320356 | 23·7908 | 0·0017668 |
| 517 | 267289 | 22·7376 | 0·0019342 | 567 | 321489 | 23·8118 | 0·0017637 |
| 518 | 268324 | 22·7596 | 0·0019305 | 568 | 322624 | 23·8328 | 0·0017606 |
| 519 | 269361 | 22·7816 | 0·0019268 | 569 | 323761 | 23·8537 | 0·0017575 |
| 520 | 270400 | 22·8035 | 0·0019231 | 570 | 324900 | 23·8747 | 0·0017544 |
| 521 | 271441 | 22·8254 | 0·0019194 | 571 | 326041 | 23·8956 | 0·0017513 |
| 522 | 272484 | 22·8473 | 0·0019157 | 572 | 327184 | 23·9165 | 0·0017483 |
| 523 | 273529 | 22·8692 | 0·0019120 | 573 | 328329 | 23·9374 | 0·0017452 |
| 524 | 274576 | 22·8910 | 0·0019084 | 574 | 329476 | 23·9583 | 0·0017422 |
| 525 | 275625 | 22·9129 | 0·0019048 | 575 | 330625 | 23·9792 | 0·0017391 |
| 526 | 276676 | 22·9347 | 0·0019011 | 576 | 331776 | 24 | 0·0017361 |
| 527 | 277729 | 22·9565 | 0·0018975 | 577 | 332929 | 24·0208 | 0·0017331 |
| 528 | 278784 | 22·9783 | 0·0018939 | 578 | 334084 | 24·0416 | 0·0017301 |
| 529 | 279841 | 23 | 0·0018904 | 579 | 335241 | 24·0624 | 0·0017271 |
| 530 | 280900 | 23·0217 | 0·0018868 | 580 | 336400 | 24·0832 | 0·0017241 |
| 531 | 281961 | 23·0434 | 0·0018832 | 581 | 337561 | 24·1039 | 0·0017212 |
| 532 | 283024 | 23·0651 | 0·0018797 | 582 | 338724 | 24·1247 | 0·0017182 |
| 533 | 284089 | 23·0868 | 0·0018762 | 583 | 339889 | 24·1454 | 0·0017153 |
| 534 | 285156 | 23·1084 | 0·0018727 | 584 | 341056 | 24·1661 | 0·0017123 |
| 535 | 286225 | 23·1301 | 0·0018692 | 585 | 342225 | 24·1868 | 0·0017094 |
| 536 | 287296 | 23·1517 | 0·0018657 | 586 | 343396 | 24·2074 | 0·0017065 |
| 537 | 288369 | 23·1733 | 0·0018622 | 587 | 344569 | 24·2281 | 0·0017036 |
| 538 | 289444 | 23·1948 | 0·0018587 | 588 | 345744 | 24·2487 | 0·0017007 |
| 539 | 290521 | 22·2164 | 0·0018553 | 589 | 346921 | 24·2693 | 0·0016978 |
| 540 | 291600 | 23·2379 | 0·0018519 | 590 | 348100 | 24·2899 | 0·0016949 |
| 541 | 292681 | 23·2594 | 0·0018484 | 591 | 349281 | 24·3105 | 0·0016920 |
| 542 | 293764 | 23·2809 | 0·0018450 | 592 | 350464 | 24·3311 | 0·0016892 |
| 543 | 294849 | 23·3024 | 0·0018416 | 593 | 351649 | 24·3516 | 0·0016863 |
| 544 | 295936 | 23·3238 | 0·0018382 | 594 | 352836 | 24·3721 | 0·0016835 |
| 545 | 297025 | 23·3452 | 0·0018349 | 595 | 354025 | 24·3926 | 0·0016807 |
| 546 | 298116 | 23·3666 | 0·0018315 | 596 | 355216 | 24·4131 | 0·0016779 |
| 547 | 299209 | 23·3880 | 0·0018282 | 597 | 356409 | 24·4336 | 0·0016750 |
| 548 | 300304 | 23·4094 | 0·0018248 | 598 | 357604 | 24·4540 | 0·0016722 |
| 549 | 301401 | 23·4307 | 0·0018215 | 599 | 358801 | 24·4745 | 0·0016694 |
| 550 | 302500 | 23·4521 | 0·0018182 | 600 | 360000 | 24·4949 | 0·0016667 |

TABLE 6. SQUARES, SQUARE ROOTS, RECIPROCALS

| $n$ | $n^2$ | $\sqrt{n}$ | $\dfrac{1}{n}$ | $n$ | $n^2$ | $\sqrt{n}$ | $\dfrac{1}{n}$ |
|---|---|---|---|---|---|---|---|
| 601 | 361201 | 24·5153 | 0·0016639 | 651 | 423801 | 25·5147 | 0·0015361 |
| 602 | 362404 | 24·5357 | 0·0016621 | 652 | 425104 | 25·5343 | 0·0015337 |
| 603 | 363609 | 24·5561 | 0·0016584 | 653 | 426409 | 25·5539 | 0·0015314 |
| 604 | 364816 | 24·5764 | 0·0016556 | 654 | 427716 | 25·5734 | 0·0015291 |
| 605 | 366025 | 24·5967 | 0·0016529 | 655 | 429025 | 25·5930 | 0·0015267 |
| 606 | 367236 | 24·6171 | 0·0016502 | 656 | 430336 | 25·6125 | 0·0015244 |
| 607 | 368449 | 24·6374 | 0·0016474 | 657 | 431649 | 25·6320 | 0·0015221 |
| 608 | 369664 | 24·6577 | 0·0016447 | 658 | 432964 | 25·6515 | 0·0015198 |
| 609 | 370881 | 24·6779 | 0·0016420 | 659 | 434281 | 25·6710 | 0·0015175 |
| 610 | 372100 | 24·6982 | 0·0016393 | 660 | 435600 | 25·6905 | 0·0015152 |
| 611 | 373321 | 24·7184 | 0·0016367 | 661 | 436921 | 25·7099 | 0·0015129 |
| 612 | 374544 | 24·7386 | 0·0016340 | 662 | 438244 | 25·7294 | 0·0015106 |
| 613 | 375769 | 24·7588 | 0·0016313 | 663 | 439569 | 25·7488 | 0·0015083 |
| 614 | 376996 | 24·7790 | 0·0016287 | 664 | 440896 | 25·7682 | 0·0015060 |
| 615 | 378225 | 24·7992 | 0·0016260 | 665 | 442225 | 25·7876 | 0·0015038 |
| 616 | 379456 | 24·8193 | 0·0016234 | 666 | 443556 | 25·8070 | 0·0015015 |
| 617 | 380689 | 24·8305 | 0·0016207 | 667 | 444889 | 25·8263 | 0·0014993 |
| 618 | 381924 | 24·8596 | 0·0016181 | 668 | 446224 | 25·8457 | 0·0014970 |
| 619 | 383161 | 24·8797 | 0·0016155 | 669 | 447561 | 25·8650 | 0·0014948 |
| 620 | 384400 | 24·8998 | 0·0016129 | 670 | 448900 | 25·8844 | 0·0014925 |
| 621 | 385641 | 24·9199 | 0·0016103 | 671 | 450241 | 25·9037 | 0·0014903 |
| 622 | 386884 | 24·9399 | 0·0016077 | 672 | 451584 | 25·9230 | 0·0014881 |
| 623 | 388129 | 24·9600 | 0·0016051 | 673 | 452929 | 25·9422 | 0·0014859 |
| 624 | 389376 | 24·9800 | 0·0016026 | 674 | 454276 | 25·9615 | 0·0014837 |
| 625 | 390625 | 25 | 0·0016000 | 675 | 455625 | 25·9808 | 0·0014815 |
| 626 | 391876 | 25·0200 | 0·0015974 | 676 | 456976 | 26 | 0·0014793 |
| 627 | 393129 | 25·0400 | 0·0015949 | 677 | 458329 | 26·0192 | 0·0014771 |
| 628 | 394384 | 25·0599 | 0·0015924 | 678 | 459684 | 26·0384 | 0·0014749 |
| 629 | 395641 | 25·0799 | 0·0015898 | 679 | 461041 | 26·0576 | 0·0014728 |
| 630 | 396900 | 25·0998 | 0·0015873 | 680 | 462400 | 26·0768 | 0·0014706 |
| 631 | 398161 | 25·1197 | 0·0015848 | 681 | 463761 | 26·0960 | 0·0014684 |
| 632 | 399424 | 25·1396 | 0·0015823 | 682 | 465124 | 26·1151 | 0·0014663 |
| 633 | 400689 | 25·1595 | 0·0015798 | 683 | 466489 | 26·1343 | 0·0014641 |
| 634 | 401956 | 25·1794 | 0·0015773 | 684 | 467856 | 26·1534 | 0·0014620 |
| 635 | 403225 | 25·1992 | 0·0015748 | 685 | 469225 | 26·1725 | 0·0014599 |
| 636 | 404496 | 25·2190 | 0·0015723 | 686 | 470596 | 26·1916 | 0·0014577 |
| 637 | 405769 | 25·2389 | 0·0015699 | 687 | 471969 | 26·2107 | 0·0014556 |
| 638 | 407044 | 25·2587 | 0·0015674 | 688 | 473344 | 26·2298 | 0·0014535 |
| 639 | 408321 | 25·2784 | 0·0015649 | 689 | 474721 | 26·2488 | 0·0014514 |
| 640 | 409600 | 25·2982 | 0·0015625 | 690 | 476100 | 26·2679 | 0·0014493 |
| 641 | 410881 | 25·3180 | 0·0015601 | 691 | 477481 | 26·2869 | 0·0014472 |
| 642 | 412164 | 25·3377 | 0·0015576 | 692 | 478864 | 26·3059 | 0·0014451 |
| 643 | 413449 | 25·3574 | 0·0015552 | 693 | 480249 | 26·3249 | 0·0014430 |
| 644 | 414736 | 25·3772 | 0·0015528 | 694 | 481636 | 26·3439 | 0·0014409 |
| 645 | 416025 | 25·3969 | 0·0015504 | 695 | 483025 | 26·3629 | 0·0014388 |
| 646 | 417316 | 25·4165 | 0·0015480 | 696 | 484416 | 26·3818 | 0·0014368 |
| 647 | 418609 | 25·4362 | 0·0015456 | 697 | 485809 | 26·4008 | 0·0014347 |
| 648 | 419904 | 25·4558 | 0·0015432 | 698 | 487204 | 26·4197 | 0·0014327 |
| 649 | 421201 | 25·4755 | 0·0015408 | 699 | 488601 | 26·4386 | 0·0014306 |
| 650 | 422500 | 25·4951 | 0·0015385 | 700 | 490000 | 26·4575 | 0·0014286 |

## TABLE 6. SQUARES, SQUARE ROOTS, RECIPROCALS

| $n$ | $n^2$ | $\sqrt{n}$ | $\dfrac{1}{n}$ | $n$ | $n^2$ | $\sqrt{n}$ | $\dfrac{1}{n}$ |
|---|---|---|---|---|---|---|---|
| 701 | 491401 | 26·4764 | 0·0014265 | 751 | 564001 | 27·4044 | 0·0013316 |
| 702 | 492804 | 26·4953 | 0·0014245 | 752 | 565504 | 27·4226 | 0·0013298 |
| 703 | 494209 | 26·5141 | 0·0014225 | 753 | 567009 | 27·4408 | 0·0013280 |
| 704 | 495616 | 26·5330 | 0·0014205 | 754 | 568516 | 27·4591 | 0·0013263 |
| 705 | 497025 | 26·5518 | 0·0014184 | 755 | 570025 | 27·4773 | 0·0013245 |
| 706 | 498436 | 26·5707 | 0·0014164 | 756 | 571536 | 27·4955 | 0·0013228 |
| 707 | 499849 | 26·5895 | 0·0014144 | 757 | 573049 | 27·5136 | 0·0013210 |
| 708 | 501264 | 26·6083 | 0·0014124 | 758 | 574564 | 27·5318 | 0·0013193 |
| 709 | 502681 | 26·6271 | 0·0014104 | 759 | 576081 | 27·5500 | 0·0013175 |
| 710 | 504100 | 26·6458 | 0·0014085 | 760 | 577600 | 27·5681 | 0·0013158 |
| 711 | 505521 | 26·6646 | 0·0014065 | 761 | 579121 | 27·5862 | 0·0013141 |
| 712 | 506944 | 26·6833 | 0·0014045 | 762 | 580644 | 27·6043 | 0·0013123 |
| 713 | 508369 | 26·7021 | 0·0014025 | 763 | 582169 | 27·6225 | 0·0013106 |
| 714 | 509796 | 26·7208 | 0·0014006 | 764 | 583696 | 27·6405 | 0·0013089 |
| 715 | 511225 | 26·7395 | 0·0013986 | 765 | 585225 | 27·6586 | 0·0013072 |
| 716 | 512656 | 26·7582 | 0·0013966 | 766 | 586756 | 27·6767 | 0·0013055 |
| 717 | 514089 | 26·7769 | 0·0013947 | 767 | 588289 | 27·6948 | 0·0013038 |
| 718 | 515524 | 26·7955 | 0·0013928 | 768 | 589824 | 27·7128 | 0·0013021 |
| 719 | 516961 | 26·8142 | 0·0013908 | 769 | 591361 | 27·7308 | 0·0013004 |
| 720 | 518400 | 26·8328 | 0·0013889 | 770 | 592900 | 27·7489 | 0·0012987 |
| 721 | 519841 | 26·8514 | 0·0013870 | 771 | 594441 | 27·7669 | 0·0012970 |
| 722 | 521284 | 26·8701 | 0·0013850 | 772 | 595984 | 27·7849 | 0·0012953 |
| 723 | 522729 | 26·8887 | 0·0013831 | 773 | 597529 | 27·8029 | 0·0012937 |
| 724 | 524176 | 26·9072 | 0·0013812 | 774 | 599076 | 27·8209 | 0·0012920 |
| 725 | 525625 | 26·9258 | 0·0013793 | 775 | 600625 | 27·8388 | 0·0012903 |
| 726 | 527076 | 26·9444 | 0·0013774 | 776 | 602176 | 27·8568 | 0·0012887 |
| 727 | 528529 | 26·9629 | 0·0013755 | 777 | 603729 | 27·8747 | 0·0012870 |
| 728 | 529984 | 26·9815 | 0·0013736 | 778 | 605284 | 27·8927 | 0·0012853 |
| 729 | 531441 | 27 | 0·0013717 | 779 | 606841 | 27·9106 | 0·0012837 |
| 730 | 532900 | 27·0185 | 0·0013699 | 780 | 608400 | 27·9285 | 0·0012821 |
| 731 | 534361 | 27·0370 | 0·0013680 | 781 | 609961 | 27·9464 | 0·0012804 |
| 732 | 535824 | 27·0555 | 0·0013661 | 782 | 611524 | 27·9643 | 0·0012788 |
| 733 | 537289 | 27·0740 | 0·0013643 | 783 | 613089 | 27·9821 | 0·0012771 |
| 734 | 538756 | 27·0924 | 0·0013624 | 784 | 614656 | 28 | 0·0012755 |
| 735 | 540225 | 27·1109 | 0·0013605 | 785 | 616225 | 28·0179 | 0·0012739 |
| 736 | 541696 | 27·1293 | 0·0013587 | 786 | 617796 | 28·0357 | 0·0012723 |
| 737 | 543169 | 27·1477 | 0·0013569 | 787 | 619369 | 28·0535 | 0·0012706 |
| 738 | 544644 | 27·1662 | 0·0013550 | 788 | 620944 | 28·0713 | 0·0012690 |
| 739 | 546121 | 27·1846 | 0·0013532 | 789 | 622521 | 28·0891 | 0·0012674 |
| 740 | 547600 | 27·2029 | 0·0013514 | 790 | 624100 | 28·1069 | 0·0012658 |
| 741 | 549081 | 27·2213 | 0·0013495 | 791 | 625681 | 28·1247 | 0·0012642 |
| 742 | 550564 | 27·2397 | 0·0013477 | 792 | 627264 | 28·1425 | 0·0012626 |
| 743 | 552049 | 27·2580 | 0·0013459 | 793 | 628849 | 28·1603 | 0·0012610 |
| 744 | 553536 | 27·2764 | 0·0013441 | 794 | 630436 | 28·1780 | 0·0012594 |
| 745 | 555025 | 27·2947 | 0·0013423 | 795 | 632025 | 28·1957 | 0·0012579 |
| 746 | 556516 | 27·3130 | 0·0013405 | 796 | 633616 | 28·2135 | 0·0012563 |
| 747 | 558009 | 27·3313 | 0·0013387 | 797 | 635209 | 28·2312 | 0·0012547 |
| 748 | 559504 | 27·3496 | 0·0013369 | 798 | 636804 | 28·2489 | 0·0012531 |
| 749 | 561001 | 27·3679 | 0·0013351 | 799 | 638401 | 28·2666 | 0·0012516 |
| 750 | 562500 | 27·3861 | 0·0013333 | 800 | 640000 | 28·2843 | 0·00125 |

TABLE 6. SQUARE, SQUARE ROOTS, RECIPROCALS

| $n$ | $n^2$ | $\sqrt{n}$ | $\dfrac{1}{n}$ | $n$ | $n^2$ | $\sqrt{n}$ | $\dfrac{1}{n}$ |
|---|---|---|---|---|---|---|---|
| 801 | 641601 | 28·3019 | 0·0012484 | 851 | 724201 | 29·1719 | 0·0011751 |
| 802 | 643204 | 28·3196 | 0·0012469 | 852 | 725904 | 29·1890 | 0·0011737 |
| 803 | 644809 | 29·3373 | 0·0012453 | 853 | 727609 | 29·2062 | 0·0011723 |
| 804 | 646416 | 28·3549 | 0·0012438 | 854 | 729316 | 29·2233 | 0·0011710 |
| 805 | 648025 | 28·3725 | 0·0012422 | 855 | 731025 | 29·2404 | 0·0011696 |
| 806 | 649636 | 28·3901 | 0·0012407 | 856 | 732736 | 29·2575 | 0·0011682 |
| 807 | 651249 | 28·4077 | 0·0012392 | 857 | 734449 | 29·2746 | 0·0011669 |
| 808 | 652864 | 28·4253 | 0·0012376 | 858 | 736164 | 29·2916 | 0·0011655 |
| 809 | 654481 | 29·4429 | 0·0012361 | 859 | 737881 | 29·3087 | 0·0011641 |
| 810 | 656100 | 28·4605 | 0·0012346 | 860 | 739600 | 29·3258 | 0·0011628 |
| 811 | 657721 | 28·4781 | 0·0012330 | 861 | 741321 | 29·3428 | 0·0011614 |
| 812 | 659344 | 28·4956 | 0·0012315 | 862 | 743044 | 29·3598 | 0·0011601 |
| 813 | 660969 | 28·5132 | 0·0012300 | 863 | 744769 | 29·3769 | 0·0011587 |
| 814 | 662596 | 28·5307 | 0·0012285 | 864 | 746496 | 29·3939 | 0·0011574 |
| 815 | 664225 | 28·5482 | 0·0012270 | 865 | 748225 | 29·4109 | 0·0011561 |
| 816 | 665856 | 28·5657 | 0·0012255 | 866 | 749956 | 29·4279 | 0·0011547 |
| 817 | 667489 | 28·5832 | 0·0012240 | 867 | 751689 | 29·4449 | 0·0011534 |
| 818 | 669124 | 28·6007 | 0·0012225 | 868 | 753424 | 29·4618 | 0·0011521 |
| 819 | 670761 | 28·6182 | 0·0012210 | 869 | 755161 | 29·4788 | 0·0011507 |
| 820 | 672400 | 28·6356 | 0·0012195 | 870 | 756900 | 29·4958 | 0·0011494 |
| 821 | 674041 | 28·6531 | 0·0012180 | 871 | 758641 | 29·5127 | 0·0011481 |
| 822 | 675684 | 28·6705 | 0·0012165 | 872 | 760384 | 29·5296 | 0·0011468 |
| 823 | 677329 | 28·6880 | 0·0012151 | 873 | 762129 | 29·5466 | 0·0011455 |
| 924 | 678976 | 28·7054 | 0·0012136 | 874 | 763876 | 29·5635 | 0·0011442 |
| 825 | 680625 | 28·7228 | 0·0012121 | 875 | 765625 | 29·5804 | 0·0011429 |
| 826 | 682276 | 28·7402 | 0·0012107 | 876 | 767376 | 29·5973 | 0·0011416 |
| 827 | 683929 | 28·7576 | 0·0012092 | 877 | 769129 | 29·6142 | 0·0011403 |
| 828 | 685584 | 28·7750 | 0·0012077 | 878 | 770884 | 29·6311 | 0·0011390 |
| 829 | 687241 | 28·7924 | 0·0012063 | 879 | 772641 | 29·6479 | 0·0011377 |
| 830 | 688900 | 28·8097 | 0·0012048 | 880 | 774400 | 29·6648 | 0·0011364 |
| 831 | 690561 | 28·8271 | 0·0012034 | 881 | 776161 | 29·6816 | 0·0011351 |
| 832 | 692224 | 28·8444 | 0·0012019 | 882 | 777924 | 29·6985 | 0·0011338 |
| 833 | 693889 | 28·8617 | 0·0012005 | 883 | 779689 | 29·7153 | 0·0011325 |
| 834 | 695556 | 28·8791 | 0·0011990 | 884 | 781456 | 29·7321 | 0·0011312 |
| 835 | 697225 | 28·8964 | 0·0011976 | 885 | 783225 | 29·7489 | 0·0011299 |
| 836 | 698896 | 28·9137 | 0·0011962 | 886 | 784996 | 29·7658 | 0·0011287 |
| 837 | 700569 | 28·9310 | 0·0011947 | 887 | 786769 | 29·7825 | 0·0011274 |
| 838 | 702244 | 29·9482 | 0·0011933 | 888 | 788544 | 29·7993 | 0·0011261 |
| 839 | 703921 | 28·9655 | 0·0011919 | 889 | 790321 | 29·8161 | 0·0011249 |
| 840 | 705600 | 28·9828 | 0·0011905 | 890 | 792100 | 29·8329 | 0·0011236 |
| 841 | 707281 | 29 | 0·0011891 | 891 | 793881 | 29·8496 | 0·0011223 |
| 842 | 708964 | 29·0172 | 0·0011876 | 892 | 795664 | 29·8664 | 0·0011211 |
| 843 | 710649 | 29·0345 | 0·0011862 | 893 | 797449 | 29·8831 | 0·0011198 |
| 844 | 712336 | 29·0517 | 0·0011848 | 894 | 799236 | 29·8998 | 0·0011186 |
| 845 | 714025 | 29·0689 | 0·0011834 | 895 | 801025 | 29·9166 | 0·0011173 |
| 846 | 715716 | 29·0861 | 0·0011820 | 896 | 802816 | 29·9333 | 0·0011161 |
| 847 | 717409 | 29·1033 | 0·0011806 | 897 | 804609 | 29·9500 | 0·0011148 |
| 848 | 719104 | 29·1204 | 0·0011792 | 898 | 806404 | 29·9666 | 0·0011136 |
| 849 | 720801 | 29·1376 | 0·0011779 | 899 | 808201 | 29·9833 | 0·0011123 |
| 850 | 722500 | 29·1548 | 0·0011765 | 900 | 810000 | 30· | 0·0011111 |

### TABLE 6. SQUARES, SQUARE ROOTS, RECIPROCALS

| $n$ | $n^2$ | $\sqrt{n}$ | $\dfrac{1}{n}$ | $n$ | $n^2$ | $\sqrt{n}$ | $\dfrac{1}{n}$ |
|---|---|---|---|---|---|---|---|
| 901 | 811801 | 30·0167 | 0·0011099 | 951 | 904401 | 30·8383 | 0·0010515 |
| 902 | 813604 | 30·0333 | 0·0011086 | 952 | 906304 | 30·8545 | 0·0010504 |
| 903 | 815409 | 30·0500 | 0·0011074 | 953 | 908209 | 30·8707 | 0·0010493 |
| 904 | 817216 | 30·0666 | 0·0011062 | 954 | 910116 | 30·8869 | 0·0010482 |
| 905 | 819025 | 30·0832 | 0·0011050 | 955 | 912025 | 30·9031 | 0·0010471 |
| 906 | 820836 | 30·0998 | 0·0011038 | 956 | 913936 | 30·9192 | 0·0010460 |
| 907 | 822649 | 30·1164 | 0·0011025 | 957 | 915849 | 30·9354 | 0·0010449 |
| 908 | 824464 | 30·1330 | 0·0011013 | 958 | 917764 | 30·9516 | 0·0010438 |
| 909 | 826281 | 30·1496 | 0·0011001 | 959 | 919681 | 30·9677 | 0·0010428 |
| 910 | 228100 | 30·1662 | 0·0010989 | 960 | 921600 | 30·9839 | 0·0010417 |
| 911 | 829921 | 30·1828 | 0·0010977 | 961 | 923521 | 31 | 0·0010406 |
| 912 | 831744 | 30·1993 | 0·0010965 | 962 | 925444 | 31·0161 | 0·0010395 |
| 913 | 833569 | 30·2159 | 0·0010953 | 963 | 927369 | 31·0322 | 0·0010384 |
| 914 | 835396 | 30·2324 | 0·0010941 | 964 | 929296 | 31·0483 | 0·0010373 |
| 915 | 837225 | 30·2490 | 0·0010929 | 965 | 931225 | 31·0644 | 0·0010363 |
| 916 | 839056 | 30·2655 | 0·0010917 | 966 | 933156 | 31·0805 | 0·0010352 |
| 917 | 840889 | 30·2820 | 0·0010905 | 967 | 935089 | 31·0966 | 0·0010341 |
| 918 | 842724 | 30·2985 | 0·0010893 | 968 | 937024 | 31·1127 | 0·0010331 |
| 919 | 844561 | 30·3150 | 0·0010881 | 969 | 938961 | 31·1288 | 0·0010320 |
| 920 | 846400 | 30·3315 | 0·0010870 | 970 | 940900 | 31·1448 | 0·0010309 |
| 921 | 848241 | 30·3480 | 0·0010858 | 971 | 942841 | 31·1609 | 0·0010299 |
| 922 | 850084 | 30·3645 | 0·0010846 | 972 | 944784 | 31·1769 | 0·0010288 |
| 923 | 851929 | 30·3809 | 0·0010834 | 973 | 946729 | 31·1929 | 0·0010277 |
| 924 | 853776 | 30·3974 | 0·0010823 | 974 | 948676 | 31·2090 | 0·0010267 |
| 925 | 855625 | 30·4138 | 0·0010811 | 975 | 950625 | 31·2250 | 0·0010256 |
| 926 | 857476 | 30·4302 | 0·0010799 | 976 | 952576 | 31·2410 | 0·0010246 |
| 927 | 859329 | 30·4467 | 0·0010787 | 977 | 954529 | 31·2570 | 0·0010235 |
| 928 | 861184 | 30·4631 | 0·0010776 | 978 | 956484 | 31·2730 | 0·0010225 |
| 929 | 863041 | 30·4795 | 0·0010764 | 979 | 958441 | 31·2890 | 0·0010215 |
| 930 | 864900 | 30·4959 | 0·0010753 | 980 | 960400 | 31·3050 | 0·0010204 |
| 931 | 866761 | 30·5123 | 0·0010741 | 981 | 962361 | 31·3209 | 0·0010194 |
| 932 | 868624 | 30·5287 | 0·0010730 | 982 | 964324 | 31·3369 | 0·0010183 |
| 933 | 870489 | 30·5450 | 0·0010718 | 983 | 966289 | 31·3528 | 0·0010173 |
| 934 | 872356 | 30·5614 | 0·0010707 | 984 | 968256 | 31·3688 | 0·0010163 |
| 935 | 874225 | 30·5778 | 0·0010695 | 985 | 970225 | 31·3847 | 0·0010152 |
| 936 | 876096 | 30·5941 | 0·0010684 | 986 | 972196 | 31·4006 | 0·0010142 |
| 937 | 877969 | 30·6105 | 0·0010672 | 987 | 974169 | 31·4166 | 0·0010132 |
| 938 | 879844 | 30·6268 | 0·0010661 | 988 | 976144 | 31·4325 | 0·0010121 |
| 939 | 881721 | 30·6431 | 0·0010650 | 989 | 978121 | 31·4484 | 0·0010111 |
| 940 | 883600 | 30·6594 | 0·0010638 | 990 | 980100 | 31·4643 | 0·0010101 |
| 941 | 885481 | 30·6757 | 0·0010627 | 991 | 982081 | 31·4802 | 0·0010091 |
| 942 | 887364 | 30·6920 | 0·0010616 | 992 | 984064 | 31·4960 | 0·0010081 |
| 943 | 889249 | 30·7083 | 0·0010604 | 993 | 986049 | 31·5119 | 0·0010070 |
| 944 | 891136 | 30·7246 | 0·0010593 | 994 | 988036 | 31·5278 | 0·0010060 |
| 945 | 893025 | 30·7409 | 0·0010582 | 995 | 990025 | 31·5436 | 0·0010050 |
| 946 | 894916 | 30·7571 | 0·0010571 | 996 | 992016 | 31·5595 | 0·0010040 |
| 947 | 896809 | 30·7734 | 0·0010560 | 997 | 994009 | 31·5753 | 0·0010030 |
| 948 | 898704 | 30·7896 | 0·0010549 | 998 | 996004 | 31·5911 | 0·0010020 |
| 949 | 900601 | 30·8058 | 0·0010537 | 999 | 998001 | 31·6070 | 0·0010010 |
| 950 | 902500 | 30·8221 | 0·0010526 | 1000 | 1000000 | 31·6228 | 0·001 |

# NAME INDEX

# SUBJECT INDEX